The
Wiltshire
FLORA

The *Wiltshire* *FLORA*

Edited by Beatrice Gillam

Pisces
PUBLICATIONS

Pisces Publications is the imprint of The Nature Conservation Bureau Limited

First published by Pisces Publications 1993. Pisces Publications is the imprint of The Nature Conservation Bureau Limited.

British Library-in-Publication Data.
A catalogue record for this book is available from the British Library.

ISBN 0 9508245 8 5

Designed and produced by The Nature Conservation Bureau Limited, 36 Kingfisher Court, Hambridge Road, Newbury, Berkshire RG14 5SJ.

Printed by Information Press, Oxford.

Cover photograph: Burnt orchid *Orchis ustulata* © Bob Gibbons, Natural Image.

CONTENTS

PART TWO – SPECIES MONOGRAPHS

PART THREE – THE FLORA

FOREWORD

Franklyn Perring

'O bold majestic downs, fair and lovely;

O still solitude, only matched in the skies.'

Robert Bridges' lines remind me vividly of my first wonderful days botanising in Wiltshire, around Salisbury, in the early 1950s when I stayed at what I shall for ever call the 'Cold Comfort Research Station'. On the contrary I developed a real warmth for the Wiltshire landscape and its chalk grassland.

This warm feeling for the county was intensified a few years later when, seeking records for vice-counties 7 and 8 for the Distribution Maps Scheme, we discovered that Wiltshire was already 'done'. Detailed records, as complete as could be hoped for from any other part of the British Isles, already existed and, in due course, master-cards for over 50 10km squares were received from that shy, efficient, master-of-the-cards, Donald Grose, coordinator of the magnificent *Flora of Wiltshire 1957*.

My only sadness at such thoroughness was that I then had no excuse to return to Wiltshire during the Maps Scheme and had to be content with the 'underdone' squares of Rotherham, Ross or Roscommon.

Happily, in the early 1970s, after my move to the Biological Records Centre (BRC), I was able to return, for, once again, Wiltshire was leading the way by seeing the need to set up a Natural History Forum and its own local BRC. It is encouraging to see how that led eventually to the creation of the Wiltshire Flora Mapping Project (WFMP) which, after a decade of dedication, imagination and sheer hard work has produced this important new flora.

Most of the work for Grose's flora was done in the 1940s and early 1950s and his book summarises knowledge of the county's plants before the agricultural revolution which so devastated our landscape in the 1960s and 1970s. But now, in the face of surpluses of grain, beef and butter, land is being taken out of production and put to other uses which may be more sympathetic to wild flowers and we must hope that many species which were driven to the verge of extinction can be restored to their former abundance.

Now, the work of the WFMP gives us a snapshot of the county at precisely the right time – at the moment of change – and the importance of *The Wiltshire Flora* will increase over the years as it comes to be used as a reference point for a dramatic period in the history of the Wiltshire landscape.

The value of the work does not rest only within the county. It contributes to the assessment of change in the flora of the British Isles as a whole. Just as Grose's flora anticipated the *Atlas of the British Flora*, so the new Wiltshire flora has anticipated the work recently begun by the Botanical Society of the British Isles and the BRC at Monks Wood to produce a new atlas before the end of the century.

Wiltshire can be justifiably proud of this flora and of the foresight of those who have produced it at this time.

ORGANISERS OF THE WILTSHIRE FLORA MAPPING PROJECT 1984-92

STEERING GROUP

Ted Culling *Chairman*
Beatrice Gillam
David Green *VC Recorder N.Wilts.*
José Hall 1987-90
Ann Hutchison *VC Recorder S.Wilts.*
Stewart Lane 1984-91
John Lovell 1987-89
Joy Newton
Jack Oliver from 1988
John Rayner *Treasurer from 1986*
Audrey Summers
Joan Woodgate *Minutes Secretary 1988-90*
Patricia Woodruffe from 1990

Advisers
Norman Baldock, Damian Hughes, Peter Phillipson
and Ann Skinner (WTNC Conservation Officers)

PROJECT COODINATORS

Assistant Curator (Natural Sciences) The Museum,
   Devizes
Susan Cross 1984-85
Sarah Nash 1986-89
Andrew Tucker from 1990

SCIENCE GROUP

David Green
Ann Hutchison
Patricia Woodruffe
Sally Scott-White (Biological Recorder)
   The Museum, Devizes

PUBLICATION WORKING PARTY

John Rayner *Chairman*
Beatrice Gillam *Editor*
Sylvia Chandler *Minutes Secretary*
Michael Balfe
David Green
Ann Hutchison
Vera Scott
Roy Fussell co-opted 1992

Advisers
John Chandler – technical
Valerie Headland – artistic

RECORDERS

The names of coordinators for each 10 km square are shown in heavy type.

Mrs J Acornley
Mrs I E Adgie
Mrs K Adye
D J Adye
Miss B Allen
Sir C Andrewes
Mrs J E Andrews
Mrs Arengo-Jones
Miss S Bailey
Miss H Baker
Mrs J Baker
Mrs L Balfe
Mrs S Barnett
G T Baskerville
S Baynes
Mrs A Benford
H F Bennett
Mrs E Biles
D Blackford
Mrs J V Blackstaffe
Miss C Boughey
Miss J Bowker
Mrs A Bradley
Miss E Brandwood
E H Bromley
Mrs A Brown
Mrs J D Buchanan
N Buick
Mrs P Bunce
Mrs C Burnard
Mrs M Burnard
T Burnard
Mrs L Burrows

Mrs P Burton
Miss L Burville-Holmes
Miss M Butt
Dr A Byfield
Miss L Cady
Mrs H Camp
Mrs E Cannicott
Mrs P Carter
Mrs J Cass
Mrs B K Chadwick
N L Chadwick
R Chadwick
Mrs S Chandler
Mrs S Chaplin
Mrs P Chave
Mrs J Chinnery
Mrs S Clague
Miss E M W Clarke
P Cleverly
Mrs A Clifton
M Coker
M Collister
Mrs B Conway
Mrs D Cooper
N Cope
M Cragg-Barber
Mrs J Cragg-Barber
S Crockett
Mrs V Croker
Miss S A Cross
E W Culling
Mrs E Curtis
P Darby

Miss R Dauncey
Mrs E Diment
Dr C W Dodd
Mrs B Easterbrook
Mrs M Eastwood
Mrs J E Edmunds
Mrs J E Edwards
Mrs P Farey
Mrs S O Farr
Miss D Forbes
G Foxwell
Mrs M Foxwell
J Fraser
Mrs P M W Froud
R Fussell
W H Gardner
S Gent
Mrs K Gifford
P Gifford
Miss B Gillam
Miss L Giovanelli
Mrs V Gleed
Mrs C Goodchild
J Goodrich
Lady M Gray
Miss A Grayson
D Green
Miss C Greenwell
Mrs D Griffiths
J Grose
Mrs R Grose
Mrs D Graiff
Dr J Hall

M Hambidge
Mrs J Hammond
Mrs J Handford
M Hardstaff
Mrs I Hargrave
Rev B G Harris
B Harvey
Mrs S Harvey
G Hatch
Miss V Headland
Mrs S Henly
Mrs D Herrod-Taylor
Mrs E Hewett
Mrs P W Hewett
Miss B Higgens
Mrs A Hill
Mrs P Hill
J Hindley
Mrs S Hirst
Mrs D Hodgson
Mrs C Hole
Mrs V Hopkinson
J Howitt
Mrs K Howitt
Prof C J Hughes
Mrs D L Hughes
Miss V Hunt
Miss A M Hutchison
Mrs C Jackson
Mrs J Jackson
Mrs A James
Mrs J Jefferies
K Jefferies

Mrs J Jenkin
Mrs J Jenkyns
Mrs A Jepson
J Jepson
Miss C Johnson
Mrs S Johnson
Lady M Jones
Mrs M Jones
Mrs B Karn
Mrs Kent
Mrs S Kirkman
Mrs C Kitchen
M A R Kitchen
P Lake
Mrs M Lambert
Mrs B Last
R H Last
Mrs C Laysell
Mrs J Lippitt
Mrs B Little
J Lovell
T Machin
Miss E Mackinlay
Lady J Maitland
Mrs M Marsden
K Marsh
Mrs R Marshall
Mrs M May
Mrs C McQuitty
P R Merritt
Mrs M Metters
J Miller
Mrs M Mobsby
P Mobsby
A Money-Kyrle
Mrs E Moorsom
Mrs M More
Miss S E Nash

G Newbery
Mrs M Newbery
Mrs J Newton
Mrs K Nicol
Mrs E M Oakey
Mrs M Ogbourne
Dr J E Oliver
J Ounsted
R F Packham
S M Palmer
Mrs J Papé
Mrs D Payne
K Payne
C J Perraton
Mrs O M Perraton
B Phillips
L G Phillips
Mrs P Phillips
D W Pickering
J Pile
A Pitcher
Mrs K Pitcher
Mrs M Ponting
H Porter
J Presland
Mrs F Price
S Price
D Puttock
J Rawlings
Mrs J Rawlings
J N Rayner
Mrs M Rayner
P Rayner
D Read
M Reed
Mrs L Reid
Mrs M Robertson
Mrs J M Robertson

Mrs E Rollo
Mrs J Roseaman
Mrs G Rycroft
Dr J Rycroft
Mrs J Sajo
Mrs J Salisbury
Mrs R Sanders
Mrs A Sawyer
Mrs V Scott
Mrs J Shallcross
Mrs O Simmonds
D Simpson-Green
Miss L Smith
M H Smith
Mrs S Smith
Miss U Snell
Mrs P Sneyd
Mrs J Stewart
Mrs S Stiles
Dr M W Storey
Mrs A Sturt
Mrs A Summers
Mrs J Sykes
Mrs H Tanner
A Taylor
Mrs J Taylor
Mrs M Tempest
Mrs M D Thomas
Mrs E Thomson
M Tickner
Mrs J Timmins
Miss H D Tonge
Mrs J Toomer
Mrs J Tozer
D Tullis
Mrs J Tullis
M Tyte

Mrs L Vaughan
Mrs D Verney
Dr D H Wall
Mrs J Wall
Mrs D Walters
Mrs B Warren-Smith
Mrs M Wheeler
L White
Mrs W White
Cmdr P Whitehead
S Whitworth
Mrs L Wild
R Wild
Mrs J Wilder
J Williams
T M Williams
Mrs V Williams
Mrs C Williamson
Dr P Wilson
Mrs A Wise
K Wise
Mrs S Wolfe-Barry
D J Wood
Mrs W Wood
Mrs E Woods
R Woods
Mrs J Woodgate
Dr P M Woodruffe
Miss E G Woolford
Mrs H Wright
A Wycherley
Mrs J Yeadon
W Yeadon
Mrs G C Yerrington
Dr S Young

ACKNOWLEDGEMENTS

This work celebrates the dedicated fieldwork of Wiltshire naturalists who systematically searched the county for its plants during the 1980s. This was only possible thanks to the generous cooperation of hundreds of farmers and landowners who allowed access to their land.

The project was indebted to the Governors and Principal of Lackham College for their support and encouragement and in particular, to the Vice-Principal, Ted Culling, whose enthusiasm did so much to sustain the 'flora mappers' during the eight years. Under his chairmanship, a small group of people steered the project and, through their determination to ensure that the flora would be published, funds to finance it were raised from donations, loans and grants.

Without the support of the Wiltshire Biological Records Centre (WBRC) (funded by Wiltshire County Council and housed at Devizes Museum) with its array of computers in the capable hands of Sally Scott-White and her assistants, the 250,000 field records collected could not have been collated and sorted and the distribution maps drawn. The time-consuming work involved in the production of these maps was undertaken at the WBRC by volunteers Katie Hill, Christopher Perraton, Maureen Ponting, Michael Ponting and Jean Wall.

From the computed data David Green and Ann Hutchison, VC7 and VC8 recorders, carried out the daunting task of writing comments for each of the county's 1,200 plants for The Flora, the main section of the book. In the later stages they were greatly assisted by Roy Fussell and Patricia Woodruffe. The arrangement of this text into taxonomic order was carried out under

contract by Carol Head, Principal of Conkers Desktop Publishing Services.

The importance and interest of this publication has been enhanced by the contributions of botanists, many from outside Wiltshire, who kindly accepted invitations to write articles on individual species or groups of plants with which they have been closely associated either as professionals or amateurs. We hope that publication of these articles will bring them satisfaction and reward. Our thanks are also extended to those who contributed articles which describe various aspects of the county and to the many people who provided information for inclusion. Gilbert Green's geology map, with its key and description of soil types, is a valuable addition.

All those involved in the production of The Wiltshire Flora hope that it will be a welcome addition to many book-shelves and that its attractive cover will become a familiar sight to botanists far and wide. Valerie Headland gave invaluable professional advice on many aspects of the art work. The colour plates, chosen from 500 slides collected from project members and other people, were sorted into categories by Joan and Charles Woodgate to simplify the final selection. Acknowledgement to individual photographers is given in the caption to each plate.

The compilation of the species list, complicated by a late decision to adopt Stace and Kent's revised order and nomenclature was carried out, without computer assistance, by Basil Harris and checked by Jack Oliver. Supporting jobs of many kinds included minute-taking, proof reading and auditing of accounts which were undertaken by volunteers from all parts of the county. We received valuable technical guidance on publishing a book of this kind from John Chandler.

The help given so readily by all those named and unnamed generous people epitomises the spirit of the Wiltshire Flora Mapping Project from its inception to the production of The Wiltshire Flora.

Appreciation is also due to the staff of the Nature Conservation Bureau and especially to Peter Creed who accepted our material in batches as and when our volunteers were able to produce it. His expertise in handling this material has resulted in the publication of a book of a very high standard. With the advantage of his business experience, John Rayner has been an invaluable link between Peter and the editor ensuring full understanding and ease of negotiation at all times. In addition he arranged for the proof-reading to be carried out by volunteers to whom he personally delivered the manuscripts.

Finally, as editor, I would like to express my personal gratitude to Michael Balfe, Roy Fussell, Bill Griffiths, Judith Roseaman and Jean Wall who so patiently entered the text on to discs for me to edit and re-edit until it was correct; to Katie Hill who computerised the scientific names in taxonomic order for The Flora and Christopher Perraton for rearranging them alphabetically for the index; to Roy Fussell, Vera Scott and Patricia Woodruffe for invaluable assistance in checking the accuracy of the text and to members of the Publication Working Party for their support at every stage.

Beatrice Gillam
Editor
Devizes 1993

I am privileged to acknowledge the major role so ably accomplished by the editor Beatrice Gillam and to put on record the appreciation of those who have been associated with the publication. Her knowledge of the county in which she has lived for over 40 years – she knew Donald Grose – and the fact that during the course of the project she herself recorded 64 tetrads, made her uniquely qualified for this position. She carried out her duties, complicated as they were, with a firm tenacity and a patience which has been appreciated by everyone. All the users of the publication are greatly in her debt.

John Rayner
Chairman, Publication Working Party
Collingbourne Ducis 1993

FINANCIAL ASSISTANCE

This publication has been grant-aided by **English Nature**.

The **Royal Society** provided an interest-free loan.

The **Charles Walker Memorial Trust** at Lackham College made a donation.

The **Wiltshire Trust for Nature Conservation** contributed towards the cost of the colour plates.

The **Wild Flower Society** expressed the wish that its donation should support the cost of the illustration on the front cover.

The **Botanical Society of the British Isles** promised a donation from the Welch Bequest when publication was imminent.

Donations were received from the **Forte Community Chest Scheme**, the **Salisbury and District Natural History Society** and **Thames Water**.

The Wiltshire Natural History Forum is very grateful to the above organisations and to the individuals named below who assisted with loans or donations. Without their generous support this publication would not have been possible.

Mrs L Balfe	Lady M Jones
H F Bennett	Mrs S Kirkman
Mrs A Bradley	Mrs B C Last
Mrs J D Buchanan	Mrs J C McQuitty
Mrs B K Chadwick	Lady J M Maitland
Miss E M Clarke	A R More
Mrs D G Cooper	Mrs J M Newton
A C Dale	S M Palmer
Mr and Mrs S Durnell	C Perraton
Miss D L Forbes	S Price
Mrs P M Froud	J Rayner
R Fussell	Mrs M Robertson
Miss B Gillam	Mrs E A Rollo
D Green	Mrs J Roseaman
Mr and Mrs J E H Grose	Mrs V Scott
Miss M J Harrington	Mrs A Summers
Mrs D Hodgson	Mrs W E White
J W Howitt	Mr and Mrs R L Williams
Prof C H Hughes	Dr P M Woodruffe
Miss A Hutchison	Miss J Yates

A CHAIRMAN'S VIEW

Since coming to Wiltshire to teach at Lackham College of Agriculture more than 30 years ago, I have always been astounded at the ability of the student to acquire knowledge and skill. I suppose, therefore, that I should also not be surprised at the accomplishments of the many contributors to this book, some of whom were beginners in that jealously exact science of botany, when the idea of a project aimed at compiling a new flora was first aired.

I believe, and have always sought to emphasise, that although the aim throughout the project has been to produce a record, the educational experiences of all who have played a part in its production have been of major importance.

The Steering Group, of which I have had the privilege to act as Chairman, is conscious of the profound generosity of all who worked as a team towards the culmination of the production of this Flora.

There seems to me to be a certain irony in the fact that the rarities for which we have searched so assiduously have been made so rare, to some extent, by the efforts of those like my students, who have carried out the intensive farming methods in faithful fashion over the past 50 years, and yet the great botanical wealth of the chalk downland owes its very evolution to agricultural practices, albeit those of a past age. The busy cropping of the sheep, the effect of their so-called golden hooves and the gentle nourishing of the soil by their manure, were largely responsible for the development of the varied beauty of chalk grassland.

Some of us can still remember the abundance of wild flowers which graced our lowland meadows. We could pick them with guiltless pleasure and, seemingly, not threaten their profusion. Today, those flowery meadows have become a forgotten feature and those common beauties have become precious survivors. In this book we seek to remind everyone that the need to ensure their survival continues.

The amount of work needed to collect and verify the many thousands of records required is almost beyond measure. Such effort is sometimes difficult to sustain, but we will all have experienced the urge to share with others a discovery we deem to be exciting and important. Perhaps it was this which prompted us to continued endeavour?

And so the study has reached its goal and, it is hoped, will provide a fitting reward to the many whose love of Wiltshire and its plants encouraged them to contribute.

Ted Culling
Vice-Principal, Lackham College.

PART ONE

The Background

THE WILTSHIRE FLORA MAPPING PROJECT

Joy Newton

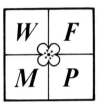

This account tells the story of how an idea, lit by a spark in 1982, led to many Wiltshire people deriving great enjoyment and becoming good botanists while recording the county's flora.

The Project (WFMP) was initiated by the Wiltshire Natural History Forum (WNHF). This body was founded in 1974 with the object of improving liaison and cooperation amongst voluntary and statutory organisations concerned with natural history and conservation in the county.

On the agenda of its first meeting was the proposed appointment of an Assistant Curator for Natural History at the Wiltshire Archaeological and Natural History Society's (WANHS) museum at Devizes. This post was eventually filled seven years later. At its next meeting Dr Franklyn Perring, the Director of the Biological Records Centre (BRC) of the Institute of Terrestrial Ecology, was invited to speak on the proposed county BRC.

In 1975, Richard Sandell, who was a close friend of the eminent Wiltshire botanist Donald Grose and Honorary Librarian at the WANHS Museum, agreed to establish a Wiltshire BRC there. This he set up and guided, with assistance from those employed under the Manpower Services Commission (MSC) job creation programme, from 1977 until his sudden death in 1978. The MSC workers continued for another year, supervised by museum staff.

The Forum continued to press for the appointment of a natural history curator. In 1981, Susan Cross was appointed by WANHS for a period of two years to reorganise and display the

natural history material in its museum. At this time the WBRC entered a dormant period and was only partially revived by a worker on the Community Programme 1983/4. In the meantime, individual members of Forum organisations from many parts of the county were collecting botanical records but many did not send them to the WBRC.

In 1982, the chairman of the Forum presented a paper on biological recording to the Forum for discussion. This suggested that it should organise the fieldwork necessary for the publication of a flora of the county which would include distribution maps. This would update *The Flora of Wiltshire* by Donald Grose published in 1957, and its supplement published in 1975. The decision was made to attempt a pilot road verge survey in 1983 to find out whether there would be enough botanists willing to sustain a project that might run for seven or eight years.

A public meeting at Lackham College attracted 60 enthusiasts who gave the Forum the encouragement to launch the WFMP, using the road verge survey to test the recording system and organisation of volunteers.

Then, with her contract extended and funded jointly by the Area Museums Service (South West), WANHS and WCC, Susan Cross was able to include the coordination of the WFMP in her duties.

In 1985, Claire Appleby was appointed full-time Wiltshire Biological Recorder by Wiltshire County Council (WCC) and WANHS, but computer equipment was not acquired until two years later.

Project Organisation

A steering group was required to run the project. Its members, drawn from both voluntary and statutory organisations, elected Ted Culling, Vice-Principal of Lackham College and chairman of the Forum from 1984-88, as its chairman. Scientific matters were referred to a small group guided by David Green and Ann Hutchison, Botanical Society of the British Isles (BSBI) recorders for North and South Wiltshire respectively. The organisation of field and indoor activities was handled by another small sub-group.

Recording Method

The scientific group established that the recording unit would be the 10 km square, each square being sub-divided into 25 2x2 km squares (tetrads). All land within the present county boundary and also the Watsonian vice-counties 7 and 8 was to be included, covering 27 complete and 25 partial 10 km

squares, a total of 948 tetrads. For recording purposes, species were divided into three frequency categories: A common, B intermediate, C rare. Selection was made by the BSBI recorders. The 235 A species were numbered, listed alphabetically by their Latin names followed by the English name and printed on yellow A4 cards. The 343 B species were listed similarly, each being followed by a box divided into quarters to represent the four 1 km squares in a tetrad, and printed on green cards. Each tetrad was allocated a set of A and B cards. The recording requirement for an A species was that it grew somewhere within the tetrad. B species required a search in each of the four 1 km squares in order to show their more limited distribution. Species not named on either A or B cards were deemed to be C species, which required a six-figure grid reference and notes on habitat and frequency. These were entered on A5 cards, one for each species within a 10 km square. The production of all the recording cards was sponsored by the Royal Society for Nature Conservation and the Nature Conservancy Council (NCC). Their design is shown in Figure 1.

Figure 1. Recording cards used in the Mapping Project.

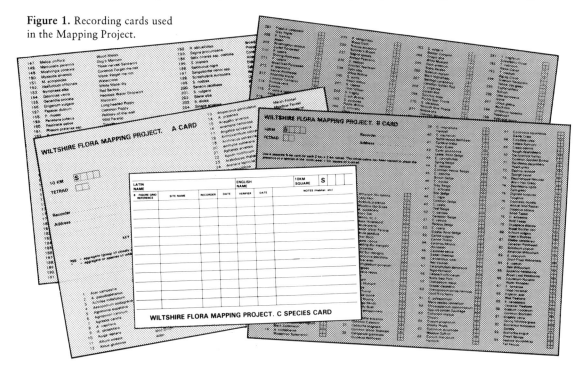

4

As in a similar, successful project in Shropshire, one person was appointed as coordinator for each 10 km square. Having found a team of recorders for the pilot road verge scheme, these coordinators were ready to put the FMP proper into action in 1984. They collected cards and instructions from the project coordinator at Devizes Museum in March, allocated tetrads to their recorders and supplied them with sets of cards. They collected the cards from their recorders in October and returned them to the museum. Recording, which lasted for eight years, involved 260 people, many of whom worked throughout that period. In practice there were some tetrads with no coverage for several years and others with a minimal workforce. These were worked on in later years by those who had finished their original areas. 'Tetrad bashing' field meetings, also held in these areas, gave a morale boost to the coordinators and enabled recorders to experience new habitats.

In 1987, the WNHF financed leaflets which explained the aims of the fieldwork. Recorders were encouraged to give these to landowners when asking for permission to record the flora on their land. Almost without exception access was gladly given and many farming families were keen to know what had been found. Without their generous cooperation the project would not have been completed and their contribution is gratefully acknowledged.

Help with identification was offered to recorders by professional botanists and experienced amateurs at field meetings and at indoor winter meetings when the Grose herbarium was made available at Devizes Museum. Some coordinators held informal meetings in their homes to help with problems of identification and the coverage of tetrads.

David Green and Ann Hutchison became aware that, even after several years, some recorders were loath to believe that a tetrad was 'finished'. Therefore, the cards of those tetrads deemed to be sufficiently complete were not returned after 1988 and recorders were encouraged to move to pastures new to help cover a very large county.

For the first two years an annual evening meeting was held at Lackham College for all recorders. From 1986 this became an all-day Saturday event in early March. Each year approximately 100 recorders from all over the county attended this mainly informal get-together at which cards were returned to coordinators in readiness for the coming season's fieldwork. The steering group arranged displays on botanical themes and maps to show the progress of recording and a wide range of botanical books was on sale. In later years, a computer display showed the progress of recording as dots spread over the county map. Plans were discussed and an illustrated talk given by an invited speaker ended the day. Our grateful thanks for entertaining and informing us go to Dr John Dony, Sue Everett, David Green, Philip Horton, Dr Franklyn Perring and Dr Francis Rose.

These events were much enjoyed and had great value in advancing the social side of the project as recorders from all over the county met and compared experiences. We became a cohesive body with an aim – to record the flora of Wiltshire.

Data Storage

By October 1987, the WBRC was ready to enter the 1984-87 A and B records into the computer and it became necessary to mark the record cards with a different symbol in each of the following years to facilitate computer entry. Sally Scott-White was appointed to the WBRC in 1989 and, with the help of a team of MSC and Employment Training personnel, had entered all the A, B and C records from 1984-89 into the computer by March 1990. The 1990-91 records were entered by March 1992 and all computer records are now stored in the WBRC database. The data was, in the first instance, to be used to plot the distribution maps in this publication but will be available thereafter for consultation by those wishing to carry out scientific studies of species' distribution and the identification of important sites for conservation.

During the winter months throughout the project the BSBI recorders carried out the laborious task of assessing which tetrads were 'finished' using slips listing nine different habitats, which had been completed by the recorders. They checked every C species entry, requesting a specimen for verification where necessary and identified hundreds of specimens sent to them. They also forwarded many specimens to the BSBI referees for identification or verification. These checks were very necessary because many recorders had more enthusiasm than knowledge in the early years. Every effort was made throughout the project to achieve accurate identification.

Land used for training by all three armed services occupies nearly one-ninth of the county. Much of this was not accessible to botanists during the years prior to the publication of Donald Grose's *The Flora of Wiltshire*. In 1973, the Ministry of Defence appointed its first Conservation Officer who encouraged the establishment of voluntary Conservation Groups throughout the United Kingdom. In Wiltshire, groups were set up at Porton Down, West Dean, Boscombe Down, Chilmark and three on Salisbury Plain Training Area (SPTA). Some of these groups had experienced botanists among their members ready and eager to carry out flora mapping. With the exception of two danger areas, the whole of the SPTA was systematically recorded for the first time.

Between 1985 and 1990 the NCC employed botanists to survey most of the chalk downland in the county including that on Salisbury Plain. Their records and those resulting from BSBI field meetings in 1987 were also incorporated into the mapping project. By the end of 1991 all 948 tetrads covering the county had been recorded.

The Future

As work on the publication of *The Wiltshire Flora* progressed, the steering group discussed the need for the formation of a new organisation that would continue the botanical interest and enthusiasm which had been such a feature of the eight years of the WFMP. At the annual meeting held at Lackham in 1992 recorders were asked if they would be interested in joining a Wiltshire Botanical Society. Sixty people expressed an interest and, in April 1992, at a meeting held in Devizes, a committee was formed which adopted a constitution and the Wiltshire Botanical Society became a reality.

The years of learning and recording have not only resulted in the publication of this volume but also in a legacy of enthusiastic botanists keen to continue the study of the county's flora into the 21st century.

Recorders on the steps of Lackham House at the Wiltshire Flora Mapping Project annual meeting in March 1991.

THE COUNTY OF WILTSHIRE

John Chandler

The image of Wiltshire, to those who live elsewhere, may well be of chalk downland studded with antiquities, a place to be passed through on the way to the west country or the south coast. But closer acquaintance reveals a county of great variety, with landscapes as diverse as the upper Thames valley at Cricklade, the fringes of the New Forest around Downton, the southern Cotswolds and Cranborne Chase.

Wiltshire is the largest inland county in southern England. Its outline is a ragged oblong, extending some 84 km from north to south and 59 km from east to west, enclosing an area of 348,070 ha. Its boundaries march with seven 'modern' English counties but, unlike all its neighbours, Wiltshire was left unscathed by county restructuring in 1974. In fact, the external boundary has altered little since it was first defined in the Saxon period. It extends southwards to within 24 km of the English Channel at Christchurch Bay and westwards to within 43 km of the Bristol Channel at Weston-super-Mare. London lies 100 km east of the Wiltshire border near Ramsbury.

Although there is little variation in mean temperature between one part of Wiltshire and another, or between Wiltshire and its neighbours, average rainfall is slightly higher in the south-west corner than elsewhere and lowest in the Highworth and Amesbury areas of north-east and south-east Wiltshire respectively.

Three river systems drain virtually the whole county. With two minor exceptions, all south Wiltshire rivers flow into the River Avon (dubbed variously the Salisbury, Hampshire or Christchurch Avon) whose main tributaries,

Wylye, Nadder, Ebble and Bourne, join it near Salisbury to flow south to the English Channel. West Wiltshire is drained by another Avon river system, the Bristol Avon, derived from two headwaters which meet at Malmesbury, which takes a circuitous route through and between the towns of West Wiltshire and leaves the county near Bath. North-east Wiltshire is served by streams flowing into the River Kennet, a tributary of the Thames, and by the infant Thames itself.

The watershed between these three river systems occurs on the Marlborough Downs above Bishop's Cannings, close to the geographical centre of the county. Nearby, the domed chalk hilltops of Tan Hill and Milk Hill, at about 295 m above sea level, are Wiltshire's highest points. The Bristol Avon, where it leaves the county under the Dundas Aqueduct, is only about 24 m above sea level. This aqueduct carries the Kennet and Avon Canal which, by lying east-west across its centre, bisects the county into north and south. It marks the boundary between the two Watsonian vice-counties (7 and 8) of North and South Wiltshire.

'Chalk-and-cheese' is often used as a shorthand to describe the two geological regions into which much of the county falls. 'Chalk' denotes the three areas of rolling downland – Cranborne Chase, Salisbury Plain and the Marlborough Downs – which together constitute more than half Wiltshire's land mass and dominate its southern, eastern and central parts. Chalk stream valleys interrupt the downs and the underlying greensand and older rocks are exposed in two larger valleys, the Vales of Wardour and Pewsey, which separate the downland blocks. 'Cheese' refers to the flatter pasture lands

Figure 2. Topographical map of Wiltshire showing locations most frequently referred to in the text. NNR = National Nature Reserve, SPTA = Salisbury Plain Training Area.

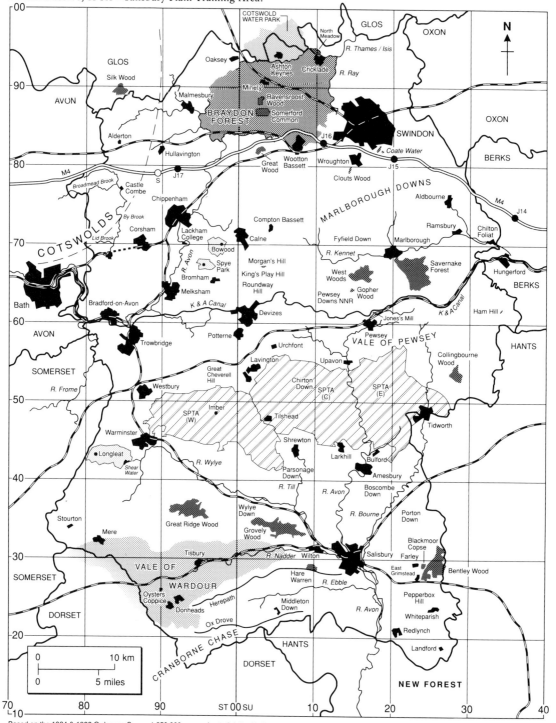

Based on the 1984 & 1988 Ordnance Survey 1:250 000 maps, sheets 8 & 9, with the permission of the Controller of Her Majesty's Stationery Office. © Crown Copyright.

of north-west Wiltshire, which consist of beds of Oxford and Kellaways clay separated by a ridge of Corallian limestone. Other geological formations impinge on the county's borderlands, most notably the Oolitic limestones of the Cotswolds along the north-western edge and the tertiary deposits of the Hampshire Basin in the south-eastern corner.

The 'chalk-and-cheese' distinction pervades other facets of Wiltshire life including ecology, settlement and culture. The pattern of settlement on the chalklands consists typically of beads of villages strung along river valleys, each tending a block of territory which extends from the river up the hillside and on to the high downland. A mixed farming regime known as sheep-and-corn husbandry was, until nineteenth century changes, the dominant agriculture. Paucity of good building stone has resulted in picturesque cottages built either of flint, or of flint and blocks of chalk, or of chalk cob, and roofed with thatch. There are few towns in south and east Wiltshire apart from Salisbury (with a population of about 40,000) near the great confluence of the Avon tributaries, and Marlborough (about 7,000) at an important crossing of the Kennet.

The clayland, by contrast, is a region of small towns, dispersed farms, and heterogeneous villages. By 1700 timber-framing for houses was giving way to bricks made from local clay. Stone was also used, brought from nearby limestone quarries in the Box-Corsham area and at Okus near Swindon. Alongside dairying, especially for cheese-making, a vigorous textile industry developed in west Wiltshire during the later middle ages and continued into the nineteenth century. Its legacy is the solid Bath stone domestic and industrial buildings to be seen in the county town of Trowbridge (28,000 population) and in Chippenham (26,000), Devizes, Melksham, Warminster, Westbury and, pre-eminently, Bradford-on-Avon.

With nearly 200,000 people, the Swindon conurbation in the north-east corner of Wiltshire accounts for more than one-third of the county's 566,000 population and stands in sharp contrast to its predominantly rural character elsewhere. Swindon, until 1840 a small hilltop market town,

is now shaking off the shabby railway town image it acquired from the Victorians and making its name as a centre for business, commerce and modern technology. Its rapid expansion was stimulated after 1952 by London overspill housing and, in 1971, by the completion of the M4 motorway which has brought much of north Wiltshire within the bounds of the London commuter.

The built-up areas of Wiltshire account for some 8% of its area. Apart from the predominant arable farming of the chalklands and the pastoral clays and greensand, a large area of the county (some 11%) is devoted to military uses. The majority of this is to be found within the Salisbury Plain Training Area (SPTA) which has, since 1897, been purchased piecemeal in large blocks for military training. Part of this training area is let to tenant farmers and has been kept under arable cultivation or as grazing land, but the wilder tracts are used exclusively for manoeuvres and firing. Another area, the Porton ranges, is reserved for chemical experiments. Other extensive military establishments in Wiltshire include air force bases at Lyneham, Boscombe Down, Upavon and Hullavington.

Place-names and forest perambulations suggest that, during the middle ages and earlier, large areas of Wiltshire were heavily wooded. Woodland was not restricted to a single geological region, but extended in a great arc from the south-western tip at Zeals, which derives its name from Selwood Forest, up the western edge of the county to the Melksham and Chippenham areas and across north Wiltshire as far as Purton. This northern portion, the forest of Braydon, remains largely unpopulated, although most of its ancient woodland has been lost to agriculture. A second corresponding tract of woodland ran up the eastern side of Wiltshire, from Bentley Wood and Melchet Forest in the south-eastern corner, through Clarendon and Chute to Savernake Forest, between Marlborough and Hungerford.

Several former woodland areas, especially on the greensand, were converted to gentleman's parks surrounding their mansion houses, of which three – Stourhead, Longleat and Bowood – have become major tourist attractions. Other leisure activities are

9

catered for by the series of flooded gravel extraction sites along the upper Thames valley bordering Wiltshire and Gloucestershire. This area, designated the Cotswold Water Park, is used for various water sports as well as being of considerable ecological importance. The abiding landscapes of antiquity, the Great Ridgeway and Wansdyke, Avebury and Stonehenge, continue to bring their dimension of timelessness to the multifarious county of Wiltshire.

References

Barron, R S (1976). *The Geology of Wiltshire. A Field Guide.* Moonraker Press, Bradford-on-Avon.

Crittall, Elizabeth (ed) (1959). *A History of Wiltshire,* Vol. 4. Victoria History of the Counties of England. Oxford University Press, Oxford.

Jennings, R A U (1957). The climate of Wiltshire. In D Grose (ed) *The Flora of Wiltshire.* Wiltshire Archaeological and Natural History Society, Devizes.

Slocombe, P M (1988). *Wiltshire Farmhouses and Cottages, 1500-1850.* Devizes Books Press, Devizes.

Wiltshire County Council (1990). *Population Estimates for Towns and Parishes, 1990.* Wiltshire County Council, Trowbridge.

GEOLOGY
AND SOILS

Gilbert W Green

The geological map (Figure 3, page 12) is based on the British Geological Survey's (BGS) published 1:250,000 scale maps which depict the solid bedrock (solid geology). In many places the bedrock is obscured by unconsolidated deposits (drift) that are the products of the erosion of the solid rocks and may profoundly affect the nature of the overlying soil. The larger patches of drift shown have been reduced from the BGS 1:50,000 and 1-inch to 1-mile scale maps and superimposed on the solid geology of the map. All the main valleys are floored by flood deposits or alluvia but only the widest spreads could be shown. The older BGS maps do not depict Head deposits (see key) and, for the sake of consistency, these have been omitted. For the same reason the important landslips fronting the Lower Greensand/Corallian escarpment between Melksham and Chippenham have also been omitted. Drift deposits less than about 1 metre in thickness are, in general, not mapped by BGS but may also give rise to significant soil differences. Such differences are picked out on the soil maps of the Soil Survey of England and Wales when these are based on large scale mapping (1:10,000 and 1:25,000) but unfortunately only a small part of Wiltshire is covered by such maps. An 'overview' of the soils of England and Wales is provided by the Soil Survey's 1:250,000 scale maps (see Sheet 5, 1983 for Wiltshire) and accompanying descriptive text. Although the publications of the Soil Survey are written from the standpoint of agricultural use and employ a sophisticated nomenclature based on a very large number of soil series they, nevertheless, form a very valuable source of reference. The soil types used in the map key refer to the major groups and subgroups recognised by the Survey.

Soil Formation

Soils are formed by the modification of the parent rock material by the processes of weathering combined with the activities of colonising living organisms. From the point of view of plant ecology the most important soil/subsoil characteristics refer to their acidity or alkalinity (measured as pH) and to their water-retaining capacity. Rain gradually alters the soil by leaching and lessivage, both processes that increase soil acidity. The former is the removal of soluble compounds, most importantly lime, and the latter is the washing downwards of the finer mineral particles. These substances are redeposited in the lowest part of the subsoil unless they are completely removed by excessive drainage. Soils thus bereft of clay and silt are known as *sol lessivé*. Decaying vegetation in base-rich soil, which contains an abundant micro-fauna and numerous earthworms, is incorporated into the soil as humus and this in turn impedes the processes of leaching and lessivage. Where the soil is very acid, such as occurs in sandy soils under heathland or conifers, the micro-fauna is impoverished and there are no earthworms. The slow decay of the vegetation generates humic acids which leads to extreme leaching. Waterlogging has the effect of severely depleting the oxygen content of a soil. The soil micro-organisms continue to live by gaining energy from the conversion (reduction) of the red and

11

Figure 3. Geological map of Wiltshire (modified from British Geological Survey 1:250,000 Series for Solid rocks and 1:50,000 and 1:63,360 Series for Drift deposits). The reader is referred to Figure 2, page 8 for topographical details.

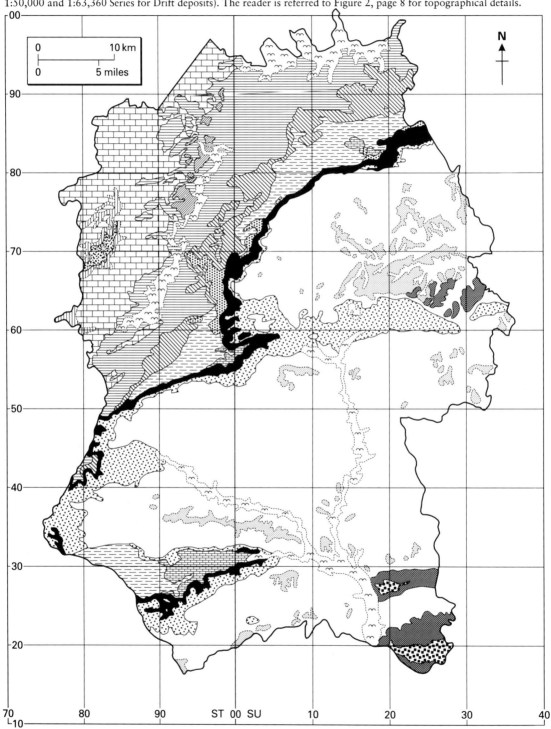

Key to Geological Map.

	Geological nomenclature	Main soil-forming rocks	Soil types
DRIFT or SUPERFICIAL DEPOSITS	Landslip	Great Oolite limestone masses and rubble overlying Fuller's Earth clays.	Calcareous brown earth, gleyed in boggy patches due to Fuller's Earth clays.
	River alluvia and river terrace gravels	Modern, silty alluvium adjacent to rivers. Terrace gravel spreads farther away. Gravels, flinty in chalk areas, limestone elsewhere.	Ground water gley (modern alluvium). Calcareous brown earth, gleyed in part (gravels). Surface water gley (older silty alluvium overlying gravel).
	Clay-with-flint and plateau flint gravels	Confined to chalk. Sandy and silty clays with variable flint content.	Brown earth, sometimes gleyed (sol lessivé).
	Head and hill downwash	Downwash debris that varies in composition according to the nature of the upslope parent material.	Most importantly, calcareous loamy and clayey deposits below the chalk escarpments. Sandy material below the greensands.
Not shown on map			
SOLID ROCKS	Bagshot Beds	Sands with variable interbedded clays.	Gleyed podzols and surface water gleys.
	London Clay and Reading Beds	Clay, sandy clay and sand.	Brown earth. Gleyed brown earth. Sol lessivé (sandy beds). Surface-water gley (clays).
	Chalk	Includes rubbly hillslope drift.	Rendzina.
	Upper Greensand	Silty sand and sandstone with chert important in south-west.	Brown earth, glauconitic. Often calcareous at depth. Sol lessivé.
	Gault	Heavy non-calcareous clay, much obscured by downwash from Chalk and Upper Greensand.	Surface water gley.
	Lower Greensand	Sands and silty sands, local ironstones.	Brown earth - sol lessivé. Tendency to podzolization under conifers.
	Purbeck Portland	Variable group of silty/sandy clays, limestones, sands and sandstones. Purbeck with more clay, Portland with more limestone.	Brown earth/surface water gley (clays). Brown earth - sol lessivé (sandy beds). Calcareous brown earth (limestones).
	Kimmeridge Clay	Heavy calcareous clay.	Surface water gley, calcareous at depth.
	Corallian Beds	Very variable group of limestones, sands, sandstones, sandy/silty clay, and, locally, ironstones.	Calcareous brown earth and brown earth (limestones). Brown earth - gleyed over clays, sol lessivé over sands.
	Oxford Clay Kellaways Sand	As for Kimmeridge but northwards from Chippenham includes silty sands near the base (Kellaways Sand).	Surface water gley, calcareous at depth. The sands may give rise to gleyed brown earth.
	Great Oolite Group	Cornbrash (limestone). Forest Marble (middle and upper) calcareous clay with variable sandstones and limestones. Great Oolite and Forest Marble (lower) thick limestones. Fuller's Earth-calcareous clays (see under LANDSLIP).	Calcareous brown earth (limestones) with rendzinas on steepest slopes (Avon valley system). Gleyed calcareous brown earth over clays and brown earth over sandy beds.
	Inferior Oolite	Limestone similar to Great Oolite but thinner.	Calcareous brown earth with transition to rendzina on steepest slopes.
	Lias	Midford Sand - yellow silty sands.	Brown earth, variable gleying.

brown ferric compounds of the subsoil into grey ferrous compounds – a change known as gleying. Soils which are seasonally waterlogged are recognised by their grey and orange mottling due to the incomplete oxidation or reduction of their iron content. The zone of mottling corresponds to the limits of the up and down seasonal water movement. Plants such as bracken *Pteridium aquilinum* and dog's mercury *Mercurialis perennis* are unable to survive the lack of oxygen and/or the toxicity of the ferrous ions. This directly affects the nature of the vegetation (Rackham 1980).

Soil Types

Rendzinas are thin, very dark, grey-brown, humus-rich soils directly overlying mechanically weathered limestone. They are highly calcareous, free-draining and are developed over chalk, pure chalk rubble and steep, scree-type slopes over Great Oolite. **Calcareous brown earths** are dark brown, humus-rich soils overlying reddish-brown, blocky-structured subsoils which rest on mechanically weathered limestone. Types with very stony subsoils are transitional to rendzinas. They are calcareous, free-draining and are developed over thick, relatively pure limestones such as the Inferior and Great Oolites and over Cornbrash, the thicker limestones present in the Forest Marble, Corallian and Portland and, more locally, over limestone gravels (drift). With progressive leaching these soils grade into brown earths. Similar, but deeper and gleyed, soils are derived from calcareous clays especially where these are associated with limestone bands, as in the Forest Marble. **Brown earths** are slightly acidic, well-drained, or moderately well-drained, brown soils. They are the usual 'end product' of long-continued soil formation in temperate areas of moderate rainfall with a deciduous tree cover, as in southern Britain under climax vegetation. As a result of the soils being well aerated and the organic matter quickly oxidised, lessivage is not in evidence except over the freer-draining sands or the oldest drift deposits such as the Clay-with-flints. Brown earths are developed over a wide variety of pervious substrates and gleying may occur over the finer grained strata. The cherts in the Upper Greensand south-westwards from Warminster may become excessively leached on plateau surfaces and give rise to podzols.

Gley soils are those in which gleying occurs in the upper 400 mm or so due to seasonal water-logging. They are either calcareous or non-calcareous. These are subdivided into surface-water gleys due to poor surface water drainage and ground-water gleys due to the up and down movement of an underlying permanent water table, such as occurs under river flood plains.

Gley podzols are confined to parts of the Bagshot Beds outcrop on Landford and Whaddon commons. They have the characteristic podzolic upper bleached and lower, dark, humus/iron/alumina-enriched subsoil horizons, but with a greyish mottled horizon directly beneath the lower horizon due to seasonal water-logging consequent on the presence of interbedded clay bands.

References

British Geological Survey. 1:250,000 map series. Bristol Channel (1988), Chilterns (1991), Portland (1983) and Wight (1976) sheets (Solid editions).

Rackham, O (1980). *Ancient Woodland, Its History, Vegetation and Uses in England*. Edward Arnold, London.

Soil Survey of England and Wales (1983). *1:250,000 Soil Map of England and Wales* with legend and brief explanation of the constituent soil associations. Sheet 5. South West England.

THE HABITATS OF WILTSHIRE

Beatrice Gillam and Patricia Woodruffe

During the years 1942-1954, when Donald Grose was recording the county's flora in preparation for the publication of his Wiltshire flora in 1957, he listed plants in 26 habitats. These fell naturally into four main sections: woodland, grassland, watery places and disturbed places. In order to ensure that stands were evenly distributed over the county he made 30 lists in each 5 kilometre square.

During the eight years of the Wiltshire Flora Mapping Project (WFMP), recorders were asked to indicate on specially designed 'habitat slips' the presence or absence of nine habitat types within a tetrad. The main purpose of this request was to help the Botanical Society of the British Isles recorders to assess the completeness of the recording within the tetrad and the possibility of misidentification of some species. For example, in a tetrad without a wetland habitat no water plants would be found. Information on the percentage cover by a habitat within the tetrad was also requested.

Although, from the available data, no exact comparison can be made between the area covered by a habitat prior to 1957 with that in the 1980s, changes can be detected particularly those resulting from more-intensive farming practices, increased urbanisation, mineral extraction and road building. The purchase and subsequent management of woodland and unimproved grassland by statutory and voluntary conservation bodies mark a significant change.

In this article habitats identified during the WFMP are described and some of the changes that have taken place since the 1950s and their effects on the Wiltshire flora are discussed.

Woodland

Wiltshire is not renowned for the extent of its woodlands, but their diversity is considerable. It is doubtful whether the county has any woods recorded as primary woodland, that is, those derived directly from natural 'wildwood'. All are considered to be secondary, but many have developed on semi-natural ancient woodland sites which are known to have existed for more than 300 years. The more important sites were identified during surveys carried out by the Wiltshire Trust for Nature Conservation (WTNC) 1984-85 and the Nature Conservancy Council (now English Nature) in 1981. Ancient woodlands of over 2 hectares account for only 3.7% of the woodland land-area of the county and by reference to the map on page 16 and the geology map on page 12 the reader can relate the distribution of ancient woodland to geological formations. It is evident that few occur on chalky soils although some notable ones, Grovely Wood, Great Ridge Wood and Savernake Forest, do occur where Clay-with-flints overlies the chalk and, in the west, Colerne Wood and Inwood are on Oolitic Limestone. Others are found on greensand (Stourton and Longleat), on London Clay (part of Bentley Wood and those close to the New Forest) and on Oxford Clay (parts of Braydon Forest).

A few woodlands, particularly those now owned by the conservation bodies WTNC and the Woodland Trust, are still managed in a traditional fashion as coppice with standards. The standards are mixed and may consist of pedunculate oak *Quercus robur*, ash *Fraxinus*

Figure 4. The recorded occurrence of *Tilia cordata* and *Sorbus torminalis* during the period 1984-1991 in relation to the distribution of Roman forests (R B Grundy) and ancient woodland listed in the NCC's Ancient Woodland Inventory 1987.

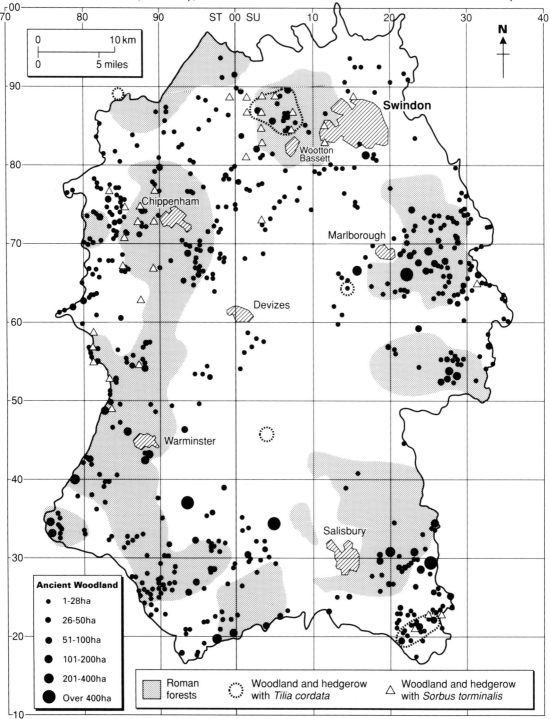

Based on the 1984 & 1988 Ordnance Survey 1:250 000 maps, sheets 8 & 9, with the permission of the Controller of Her Majesty's Stationery Office. © Crown Copyright.

excelsior, field maple *Acer campestre* and silver birch *Betula pendula.* The coppice is usually hazel *Corylus avellana* which, over a long period, has been cut on a 7-10 year cycle by spar and hurdle makers. Such crafts are practised only infrequently today and there are many stands which have not been coppiced for 40 or more years. Many of these woods are carpeted in spring with bluebells *Hyacinthoides non-scripta* and support wood anemone *Anemone nemorosa,* dog's mercury *Mercurialis perennis* and solomon's-seal *Polygonatum multiflorum* and, in some, the more unusual plants, lily-of-the-valley *Convallaria majalis,* early-purple orchid *Orchis mascula* and herb-Paris *Paris quadrifolia.*

There are remnants of several Royal Hunting Forests at Buckholt, Chute, Grovely and Savernake. The term 'forest' did not originally indicate a wooded area but was used to describe an area in which deer were protected by special laws. Some of the woods within such areas were frequently managed as pasture-woodlands. Traditionally, animals were allowed to graze under pollarded trees which were cut to a height of 2-3 m above the ground to protect the new growth from browsing. The practice of pollarding provided a source of wood and allowed more light to reach the forest floor, which stimulated plant growth. Local people often had rights of common over these areas and could take firewood and graze their stock. Such woods exist at Somerford and Whiteparish although today few, if any, practising commoners remain and, in the case of Whiteparish Common, the trees are no longer pollarded and the understorey grows unchecked.

Braydon Forest, another ancient Royal Forest, has given its name to a project which is operated by the WTNC. The aims of the management of the Braydon Forest Project are to improve the natural history of the woodland and to encourage the marketing of forest products while improving the amenity value of the area. Through consultation with landowners and Councils the project seeks to improve the wildlife potential not only of nature reserves in the area but of woodland, flower-rich meadows and the countryside as a whole. This Forest area in the north of the county between Malmesbury, Cricklade and Wootton Bassett was once extensively wooded, but now only relatively small fragments remain. One of these, Ravensroost Wood, owned by the WTNC, is being actively managed to bring derelict coppice back into rotation. It is an excellent example of coppice with standards management. Evidence of the antiquity of this wood can be gained from the presence of midland hawthorn *Crataegus laevigata,* wild service-tree *Sorbus torminalis* and small-leaved lime *Tilia cordata,* all of which are regarded as indicator species of ancient woodland.

Woods to the south-west of the county, for example those close to Stourton, provide an interesting contrast. The springs which emerge from the junction of Gault Clay and Upper Greensand provide a much wetter habitat where wood club-rush *Scirpus sylvaticus,* wood horsetail *Equisetum sylvaticum,* opposite-leaved golden-saxifrage *Chrysosplenium oppositifolium* and a variety of ferns can be found. Much of the drier part of the area has been used to grow conifers, some of which are now quite old. Whereas the ground flora is restricted, the bryophyte and lichen flora are well-developed (Rose 1985).

Colerne Wood, an ancient woodland on the steep slopes of the By Brook valley in the north-west, lies on Oolitic Limestone. Here, *Fraxinus excelsior* forms the climax tree vegetation together with extensive areas of wych elm *Ulmus glabra,* which is regenerating after severe reduction in the 1970s caused by Dutch elm disease. The dominant ground flora varies with the water table, *Mercurialis perennis* occurring above the water line and ramsons *Allium ursinum* below. The wood is well known for its highly localised colonies of *Convallaria majalis,* angular solomon's-seal *Polygonatum odoratum,* green hellebore *Helleborus viridis* and fingered sedge *Carex digitata.* Inwood, which lies on level ground adjacent to the Avon valley, also lies on Oolitic Limestone, but here *Quercus robur* grows with *Fraxinus excelsior* to form the canopy and *Corylus avellana* is the main understorey shrub. The ground flora includes a number of unusual plants. There are large populations of meadow saffron *Colchicum autumnale* which grow in the more open glades and spiked star-of-Bethlehem *Ornithogalum pyrenaicum,* a speciality of Wiltshire which is discussed in detail elsewhere in this publication.

During the past 70 years, the Forestry Commission has acquired significant areas of woodland or has entered into management agreements with owners for the planting of commercial timber crops. Some of these plantations, for example at Bentley Wood, Grovely Wood and Savernake Forest, stand on ancient woodland sites which retain much of their former interest. Planting took place mainly in the 1950s and 1960s and the wide rides associated with timber extraction maintain a varied flora. In the early 1980s, Government policy of selling non-productive woodland has allowed Bentley Wood, an area of 665 hectares which has been designated a Site of Special Scientific Interest (SSSI) primarily for its lepidoptera, to be acquired by a Charitable Trust. The aims of management combine conservation and amenity with timber production and in time it is hoped that some of the former glory of the wood, which was once part of the Royal Forest of Buckholt, will be restored.

Human intervention in the natural cycle of tree growth for the purpose of harvesting a crop is frequently resented by people who use woodlands for amenity, a fact which those who aim to develop a multiple-use approach to management need to understand. Decisions over tree-felling or coppicing can present dilemmas for conservation organisations which may face criticism from the public who support them. In recent years the matter has to some extent been taken out of the hands of woodland owners and managers by storms, hurricanes and Dutch elm disease which have caused considerable damage to woodlands. In October 1987 storms brought down many old deciduous trees in the south of the county which, because they were still in leaf, were particularly vulnerable. Another storm in January 1990 hit the centre of the county, including Salisbury Plain and Savernake Forest. Many elderly beeches *Fagus sylvatica* growing on the shallow chalk soils were unable to withstand the force of the gusting winds and were blown over. Many of these trees, some more than 200 years old, were growing in the hangers which are characteristic features of the high points of many downs. These hangers are small stands of trees closely planted 150-200 years ago which now cast a great deal of shade and support an interesting, but limited, ground flora. The saprophyte bird's-nest orchid *Neottia nidus-avis* grows in these dark conditions where it is able to survive because it does not depend upon photosynthesis for its supply of organic nutrients. Following the storms the increased light falling on the woodland floor and the disturbance associated with clearance have upset the delicate balance and permitted nettles *Urtica dioica* and cleavers *Galium aparine* to invade. In time, these opportunists will be superseded by other less-invasive species more typical of the habitat. Tree seedlings will germinate, develop and gradually close the canopy again, thus limiting the ground flora species to those specialist plants which are well-adapted to such conditions.

In the January 1990 storm conifers too suffered very badly, many snapping like matchsticks. Mini whirlwinds flattened areas as effectively as a clear-fell, leaving owners to clear up and decide on replanting programmes. Until recently, Government grants encouraged the production of conifers, but this is no longer the case. The Forestry Commission's Woodland Grant Scheme currently offers greater incentives to plant broadleaved trees and from April 1992 management of wildlife habitats, including scrub and open space in woodlands, will qualify for grant-aid.

Disease has resulted in the premature death of some species of broad-leaved trees including beech, but the most dramatic event has been the loss of the county's elms to Dutch elm disease. The massive trees of English elm *Ulmus procera*, planted at the time of the enclosures in the early nineteenth century, which once lined so many roads, lanes and hedgerows on the lowland clays of Wiltshire gave the impression to travellers in the Vale of Pewsey and the Bristol Avon valley of approaching a forest but never in fact reaching it.

The disease which devastated the native elm population is carried by two species of elm bark beetle *Scolytus scolytus* and *Scolytus multistriatus,* but caused by a fungus *Ceratocystis ulmi,* which restricts the flow sap, first to individual branches and finally to the whole of the host tree. Death follows swiftly. At the height of the epidemic it appeared that autumn had arrived early because of the premature turning of leaf-colour in woodlands and hedgerows.

Pollen analysis suggests that Dutch elm disease ravaged the elm population some 3,000 years ago but it was first recognised as a serious problem during an outbreak in the 1930s. At that time, infected unbarked logs were sent to North America. An importation from America in the 1960s carried a more virulent form of the disease and resulted in catastrophic damage to the elm population in Britain.

The disease spread from London and the Thames ports in Kent and along the Severn Valley from Bristol, but Wiltshire's elms remained largely unscathed during the early years. However, during the 1970s, they succumbed with increasing frequency. Between 1971 and 1976 the Forestry Commission annually counted standard elms having a trunk diameter of 150 mm at 1.5 m above ground level. Results indicate that there were well over 900,000 elms in Wiltshire during the 1970s in the following proportions:

English Elm	*Ulmus procera*	59%
Wych Elm	*Ulmus glabra*	28%
Small-leaved Elm	*Ulmus minor*	13%

It was found that 60% of these occurred in rural habitats such as roadside hedges and field boundaries, 34% in woodlands and 6% in urban areas. The survey, which tracked the escalation in elm casualties over six years, found that the figures rose from 8,000 dead trees in 1971 to 459,000 five years later. By this time about half the elms in the county were dead. A final count in 1978 showed that, of the 724,000 elms left standing, 683,000 were dead.

In 1984, at the start of the Wiltshire Flora Mapping Project, there was hardly a living standard elm to be recorded. *Ulmus procera* was the first to become infected, followed some 18 months later by *Ulmus glabra. Ulmus minor,* the only other elm in substantial numbers in the county, was less affected and some standards remain healthy to this day.

An attempt was made to halt the spread of the disease by felling and burning affected trees, but the chainsaw could not keep pace with the infection and, for years, cutting, felling and burning were commonplace across the lowlands of England. Dead elms, with their skeletal crowns and bleached trunks, became part of the landscape and the disappearance of the most common Wiltshire farmland tree led to a bareness, especially since it accelerated the loss of hedgerows as farmers sought ever more agricultural productivity.

The elm survived in hedgerows and woodlands in the form of bushes which regenerated from sucker growth and were too young to form bark which would attract the elm bark beetle. In recent years *Ulmus procera* and *Ulmus glabra* have gained in size without falling prey to the disease and thousands of young standards at least 5 m in height can be seen across the county. Should they too be struck down, there will be an entire generation who will never see a landscape of mature standard elms in full glory.

There appears to be some recognition by the Government of the value of woodlands not only as sources of timber but also as wildlife habitats and places for recreation. With careful management, conflict between these uses can be minimised and it is to be hoped that, as we approach the twenty-first century, the future of semi-natural woodland in Britain will be more secure than it has been throughout this century.

Unimproved Grassland

Awareness of the vulnerability of all unimproved grassland remaining in Wiltshire and the growing knowledge by conservation organisations of their whereabouts and content, should help to increase the chance of their protection by enabling their owners to take advantage of government schemes as they become available.

In 1991, the Government invited the Countryside Commission to develop a new initiative to conserve, manage and re-create some of Britain's most valued landscapes. As a result, the Countryside Stewardship Scheme was developed, in cooperation with English Nature and English Heritage, and proved popular with land-owners. They are able to take advantage of the scheme by entering into a 10-year management agreement in return for a payment of £50 per hectare per annum. The scheme is open throughout England to land-owners of five distinct landscapes, chalk and limestone grassland, lowland heath, waterside landscapes, coastal areas and uplands.

In contrast, the Environmentally Sensitive Areas (ESA) scheme allows all land-owners within a designated area to participate. ESAs are determined by the Ministry of Agriculture, Fisheries and Food. In 1992, ten were operating in England with a further 12 to be designated during 1992-3. The proposed North Dorset-South Wiltshire Downs ESA will be the first within Wiltshire. Farmers whose land has been accepted for such schemes receive incentive payments for conserving and enhancing it through a series of specific measures. In the case of downland it is necessary to practise livestock farming on permanent pasture and to restrict the application of fertilisers, pesticides and herbicides.

Through both of these incentives the value of traditional farming and the role of the farmer as a custodian of the landscape is being recognised and, where there is a high level of participation in a scheme within an area, the impact upon the landscape, wildlife and flora could be appreciable.

Chalk Downland

Downland, whether intensively cultivated or used extensively by grazing animals, produces an open landscape which typifies much of the southern part of the county and the Marlborough Downs in the north. Nationally, many of the grassland sites which support a 'good flora' occur on steep slopes where agricultural improvements have been difficult to accomplish but, in Wiltshire, the presence of the Ministry of Defence (MOD) on the

Salisbury Plain Training Area (SPTA) has been instrumental in protecting extensive areas of less-steep ground from the plough. Species-rich chalk grassland develops very slowly and may require several hundred years of suitable management before a typical flora is established. Therefore, damage created by a few hours' ploughing cannot be reversed in the short-term. The agricultural practices associated with arable crop production can be almost as damaging as the plough itself. High levels of fertiliser, pesticide and herbicide application can affect downland through run-off or spray drift. Improved techniques of application, particularly the use of low-flying aircraft, have made it possible to spray steep slopes to 'improve' the grassland with the resulting loss of species diversity.

MOD-owned downlands on the SPTA and elsewhere comprise almost 50% of the land which has been designated by Wiltshire County Council as sites of High Ecological Value (WCC 1981). Of the remaining area, a substantial number of sites are also prime downland areas such as the Pewsey Down and Fyfield Down National Nature Reserves (NNR), the Ebble Chalk Ridge and 'The Deverills' south of Warminster. The significance of this habitat at a county and national level can be appreciated when it is realised that all three Areas of Outstanding Natural Beauty (AONB) in Wiltshire and five out of six NNRs are so designated because of the quality of their chalk grassland. McSweeney (1991) calculated that there were 16,165 hectares of calcareous grassland in Wiltshire, including that within MOD areas, and that this amount accounted for 55% of that remaining in England.

Reference to the map of the geology of Wiltshire (page 12) will show the extent of chalk and limestone in the county. Present-day downlands lie on these strata, their flora being determined by a range of factors which include the depth and nature of the overlying deposits, aspect, slope, climate and past and present management. Plants growing in such situations need to be tolerant of high pH, high winds and very good drainage as well as grazing and trampling. The extent to which these factors operate at any one site differs and thus a range of plant associations have developed, each reflecting local conditions.

The typical short turf, described by Defoe (1724) and Cobbett (1830), has been deflected from the succession from grassland into woodland to produce a relatively stable plagioclimax maintained by grazing animals. Without the influence of grazing, plant succession continues through a scrub stage to woodland. Hawthorn *Crataegus monogyna* is commonly one of the first invaders, with buckthorn *Rhamnus cathartica*, blackthorn *Prunus spinosa*, wild privet *Ligustrum vulgare*, spindle *Euonymus europaeus*, common whitebeam *Sorbus aria* and wayfaring-tree *Viburnum lantana* all occurring in well-developed scrub, together with scramblers such as dog-rose *Rosa canina*, bramble *Rubus fruticosus* agg. and traveller's-joy *Clematis vitalba*. Less frequently, juniper *Juniperus communis* is found. It colonises exposed slopes with thin soils, as found on the Porton Ranges and at Pepperbox Hill, near Salisbury. However, at the present time, its reduced level of regeneration at many sites gives cause for concern. Contributing factors appear to be the Eriophyid mite *Trisetacus quadrisetus*, the juniper seed chalcid *Megastigmus bipunctatus* and a fungal disease which causes die-back of the growing apices. These factors, coupled with the loss of downland and the plant's intolerance of shade as scrub develops into woodland, cast doubt over its long-term future on our downlands.

In some localities, notably along the Dean Hill scarp, scrub has developed into yew *Taxus baccata* woodland. Few other plants are able to survive in these situations, the most probable being *Sorbus aria* and *Juniperus communis*, which represent relics of previous scrub.

The vegetation of grazed grassland appears as expanses of very short, tight and springy turf with individual plants of small stature. The variety of species can be great: thirty or more in a square metre and, characteristically, none is dominant. Such a community has been described as a *Festuca ovina - Helictotrichon pratense* grassland (Rodwell 1992) and indicates that sheep's-fescue *Festuca ovina* and meadow oat-grass *Helictotrichon*

pratense are two of the most characteristic species. Other 'constants' include quaking-grass *Briza media*, glaucous sedge *Carex flacca*, mouse-ear hawkweed *Pilosella officinarum*, crested hair-grass *Koeleria macrantha* and rough hawkbit *Leontodon hispidus*. National rarities, such as dwarf sedge *Carex humilis*, chalk milkwort *Polygala calcarea*, autumn lady's-tresses *Spiranthes spiralis*, field fleawort *Tephroseris integrifolia*, bastard-toadflax *Thesium humifusum* and a number of orchid species, may be found in turf of this quality. Excellent examples can be found on Parsonage Down NNR, Porton Ranges, areas of Cranborne Chase, Middleton Down and Great Cheverell Down.

Anthills are a significant feature of such grasslands. The meadow ant *Lasius flavus*, in creating the mounds, helps to aerate the soil and produce a warm and sheltered microclimate. Certain plants, such as wild thyme *Thymus polytrichus* and common rock-rose *Helianthemum nummularium*, thrive under these conditions and can also withstand the continued soil disturbance during the building of the anthills. Rabbits too can influence the flora, their grazing not only helping to keep the turf short but aiding the selection of less palatable, woody species. The role of the rabbit in maintaining a short turf was not fully appreciated until after the advent of the disease myxomatosis in 1954 which brought about their demise. In the absence of their grazing, coarse grasses became dominant on many downlands and many scrub species survived. Rabbit populations have fluctuated since their dramatic decline in the 1950s but, in the early 1990s, are building-up to approach their former high levels. The build-up of the rabbit population is probably due to the increased levels of their resistance to the myxoma virus and the predominance of less-virulent strains of the disease. In some areas, notably on MOD lands, over-grazing by rabbits is changing the plant communities in favour of those species which they will not eat. Large patches of ground-ivy *Glechoma hederacea* occur where open downland is adjacent to scrub or woodland while plants such as *Helianthemum nummularium* and horseshoe vetch *Hippocrepis comosa* spread and dominate areas. The disturbance associated with rabbit warrens also permits plants such as deadly nightshade *Atropa belladonna* and hound's-tongue *Cynoglossum officinale* to thrive.

Such changes in grazing pressure can lead to the development of *Bromopsis erecta* grassland (Rodwell 1992). The term is applied to all swards where upright brome *Bromopsis erecta* comprises more than 10% of the vegetation. The nature of the associated plants depends on the frequency of this grass and whether or not it forms dense tussocks. Where there is little *Bromopsis erecta* the general flora may be similar to that of the *Festuca ovina-Helictotrichon pratense* grassland, but where it develops greater density those plants with low, mat-like formations such as *Thymus polytrichus* and *Helianthemum nummularia* are greatly reduced or absent. The survivors include salad burnet *Sanguisorba minor*, *Carex flacca*, dwarf thistle *Cirsium acaule* and common bird's-foot-trefoil *Lotus corniculatus*, plants which are able to grow through the bulky grass. In such instances, *Festuca ovina* tends to be replaced by red fescue *Festuca rubra*. Many of the rare species associated with a low-growing turf cannot survive in this situation but others, such as round-headed rampion *Phyteuma orbiculare*, grow very well. Taller species of orchid, for example pyramidal orchid *Anacamptis pyramidalis* and fragrant orchid *Gymnadenia conopsea*, also thrive and are often more common and more robust under such conditions than in shorter turf, especially if the litter produced by the coarse grass is not excessive.

Bromopsis erecta - dominated grassland occurs where there is little or no grazing. The grass is palatable to sheep, cattle and rabbits which do much to keep it in check. Examples of this type of plant community can be seen on Porton Ranges, on National Trust properties at Winn Green and Pepperbox Hill and in N. Wiltshire, at Morgan's Hill and Pewsey Downs NNR.

These two examples of plant associations on the chalk represent two extremes. More extensive coverage of the subject can be found in the National

Vegetation Classification (Rodwell 1992). Two surveys of Wiltshire's chalk grasslands have been carried out in recent years, one dealing with Salisbury Plain (Porley 1989) and the other with grasslands outside MOD areas (McSweeney 1991). Marked contrasts in the nature of the grasslands have been revealed with much more *Bromopsis erecta* grassland on the SPTA. These differences have been attributed to a lack of grazing livestock on the SPTA compared with the more intensively farmed areas outside. McSweeney found that in non-MOD areas 75% of the grassland resource fell into the categories *Festuca ovina-Helictotrichon pubescens* grasslands or *Bromopsis erecta* grasslands and 20% was classified as the mesotrophic grassland *Centaurea nigra-Cynosurus cristatus* type. Data collected by Porley indicated less than 1% *Festuca ovina-Helictotrichon pubescens* type, 83% *Bromopsis erecta*, no *Centaurea nigra-Cynosurus cristatus* but 14% *Arrhenatherum elatius-A. elatioris* grassland.

The survey conducted by McSweeney (1991) also revealed differences in the distribution of calcareous grassland types between the north and south of the county. The total amount of calcareous grassland in the south (the Districts of West Wiltshire and Salisbury) amounted to 2,014 hectares. and in the north of the county (the Districts of Kennet, North Wiltshire and Thamesdown) 1,223 hectares. In 1966 a 5% larger area of chalk grassland was identified by Blackwood and Tubbs in the north. Analysis of the grassland types and of their sub-communities showed broadly similar relative proportions of sub-community coverage. However, in the northern sector of the *Festuca ovina-Helictotrichon* grasslands, the *Holcus lanatus-Trifolium repens* sub-community was the most common and the *Cirsium acaule-Asperula cynanchica* sub-community was the least common. In contrast, in the south the *Succisa pratensis-Leucanthemum vulgare* sub-community was by far the most widespread, making up 44% of the total. The reasons for these differences are believed to be related to topography and related lack of opportunity for agricultural improvements. The steep scarps running along the river valleys west of Salisbury have made it impractical for farmers to manage the grassland other than by grazing in a traditional fashion. Some of these sites have probably remained unchanged for hundreds of years and are of the highest botanical standard, many enjoying SSSI status.

Unimproved downland in the county has undoubtedly declined in area over the last 40 years due to intensive farming. The effects of aerial spraying, which took place in the 1960s and 1970s, can clearly be seen on the Marlborough Downs. The grasses responded to the additional fertiliser and thrived to the detriment of the herbs, which were unable to cope with the extra competition. This change in species composition has produced a new sward which cannot survive trampling as well as the original sward mixture. This factor, together with an increasing tendency for farmers to graze downland with cattle rather than sheep, is creating major problems of erosion on some steep slopes. The role of downland within the working of a modern farm is being demonstrated in the county by English Nature. In 1980 the NCC acquired 276 hectares of farmland on Salisbury Plain in order to continue the traditional way of farming the land. Parsonage Down is now designated a National Nature Reserve. The long-term success of projects such as this is essential if farmers and politicians are to be persuaded that less-intensive methods of agriculture are beneficial to all.

Limestone Downland

In the north-west of the county the eroding action of water on Oolitic limestone has formed the steep-sided valleys of the By Brook and Bristol Avon atypical of the rest of Wiltshire but characteristic of the southern Cotswolds. Despite this contrasting landscape, where areas of downland are comparatively small and many are sheltered by a woodland fringe, the conditions which prevail are similar to those found on many areas of chalk. The soils are alkaline, shallow and well-drained and support many of the plants found on chalk downland including the calcicolous herbs. Tor-grass *Brachypodium pinnatum* is perhaps one of the better examples of a plant which colonises limestone more readily than chalk grassland. One of the best remaining areas is West Yatton Down, a reserve managed by the WTNC. Grazing by both sheep and cattle allows a wide range of plants to survive including yellow-wort *Blackstonia perfoliata* and green-winged orchid *Orchis morio*, which are far more common on the limestone than on the chalk in the county.

Neutral Lowland Meadows

In 1975, Wells and King *(Supplement to the Flora of Wiltshire)* identified four main groups of neutral grassland in Wiltshire according to soil type and water regime. They described in detail the plant communities of each and commented that only a small number of herb-rich hay meadows remained in north Wiltshire at that time, expressing the hope that their article would lead to a wider ecological interest in neutral grasslands. Their hope has been fulfilled to some extent.

In the 1970s, the NCC assessed the botanical interest of the meadows along the five river valleys in south Wiltshire, and in the 1980s teams of botanists, employed by the Manpower Services Commission and directed by the WTNC, surveyed unimproved meadows in north Wiltshire, principally in the upper Thames valley. With the launch of the Braydon Forest Project in 1990 there were further opportunities to locate meadows in the north of the county and by the early 1990s three of these, with a total area of 31 hectares, had been purchased by the WTNC. Traditional management was being carried out on others but many were in danger, partly due to change of ownership but mainly due to economic pressure which was forcing the farmers to increase the productivity of their meadows by the application of artificial fertilisers. Others had been drained, ploughed and reseeded. Many of these meadows lie on clays and silts, deposited by countless winter floods, which cover well-drained river gravel, a valuable mineral resource which has been extensively extracted since the 1950s with the loss of whole communities of meadow flora and fauna.

The remaining unimproved meadows are inheritors of many years of simple farming practices which had been developed to sustain herds of dairy cows. A hay crop was taken in June or July, according to the season's weather, after which the cows were turned out to graze the aftermath but were taken off again before the land became so wet that their trampling would damage the sward to the detriment of the following year's crop. The cows were housed during the winter and fed on hay and other fodder crops (probably turnips and kale) until grass on the farm's drier land was ready for grazing in the spring. This grass would have received straw and dung manure from the wintering sheds in the previous year. By this system of management, the only fertiliser that the hay meadows would have received was that produced by the grazing cows in late summer and autumn. Many of the meadows were probably ploughed for the first time in the Middle Ages by a team of oxen pulling asymmetrical mouldboards which automatically produced a ridge-and-furrow profile. On sloping land, ploughing was usually carried out up and down the slope to facilitate drainage.

Today's flora of these unimproved meadows owes its character and composition to these practices and to the neutral to slightly acid soil. On sloping ridge-and-furrow land, as in the WTNC's meadows at Emmett Hill and Distillery Farm near Minety, the two different communities of the drier ridges and damper furrows can be seen at a glance. Cuckooflower *Cardamine pratensis,* several rare *Carex* species, adder's-tongue *Ophioglossum vulgatum* and great burnet *Sanguisorba officinalis* are examples of species in the furrows, the lines of which are marked by hard rush *Juncus inflexus* throughout the year. The list of species on the ridges is long. *Orchis morio,* cowslip *Primula veris,* saw-wort *Serratula tinctoria* and devils'-bit scabious *Succisa pratensis* are just a personal selection but the reader is referred to the full list given by Wells and King.

North Meadow, the 44-hectare NNR at Cricklade, is Wiltshire's outstanding example of an alluvial hay meadow where today the hay is cut in June or July with the use of mechanically driven cutters instead of scythes wielded by a team of men. Another change from the past is the collection of seed by vacuum harvester from about eight hectares before the hay is mown. The seed is sold to meet the growing interest in re-creating similar grassland elsewhere. The meadow, which lies between the rivers Thames and Churn, regularly floods in winter and this contributes to variations in soil water-levels, creating local conditions which favour different species of plant. Marsh-marigold *Caltha palustris,* slender tufted-sedge *Carex acuta* and early marsh-orchid *Dactylorhiza incarnata* are among those growing in the damper hollows. Following the show of fritillaries *Fritillaria meleagris* in April (see page 95), meadowsweet *Filipendula ulmaria,* lady's bedstraw *Galium verum* and common meadow-rue *Thalictrum flavum* are just three of the broad-leaved species which combine with the meadow's 28 grass species to make a unique spectacle in mid-June.

Pike Corner, a meadow designated as an SSSI, lies on well-drained, highly impoverished calcareous loam adjacent to the Wiltshire/ Gloucestershire border. The water-table is high and, combined with the undulating ground, a subtle variety of habitats occur, each with its own distinct plant community. In the drier areas, where anthills are found, flat-sedge *Blysmus compressus, Bromopsis erecta,* meadow thistle *Cirsium dissectum,* southern marsh-orchid *Dactylorhiza praetermissa,* parsley water-dropwort *Oenanthe lachenalii* and spiny restharrow *Ononis spinosa* occur. In the more acidic areas bog pimpernel *Anagallis tenella,* common yellow-sedge *Carex viridula* ssp. *oedocarpa,* tawny sedge *Carex hostiana,* common sedge *Carex nigra,* few-flowered spike-rush *Eleocharis quinqueflora,* slender spike-rush *Eleocharis uniglumis* and marsh pennywort *Hydrocotyle vulgaris* are found.

Additional small hay meadows are known to be tucked away behind old hedges in the undulating countryside of north Wiltshire waiting for the next team of botanists to find and survey. *Orchis morio* is one of the plants which reveals a history of unimproved grassland and will be sought.

A few unimproved neutral meadows and green lanes still remain in an area surrounding Melksham Forest between Devizes and Chippenham. These were probably unknown to Grose (1957); the first record for corky-fruited water-dropwort *Oenanthe pimpinelloides* in north Wiltshire was of a single plant found in 1958. In a different location but in this previously unrecorded area, Green found it in abundance in 1989. Other species discovered were *Ononis spinosa*, pepper-saxifrage *Silaum silaus*, betony *Stachys officinalis* and strawberry clover *Trifolium fragiferum*.

In south Wiltshire, neutral soils are limited to Kimmeridge Clay in part of the Wardour Vale around East Knoyle in the south-west and to Reading Beds and London Clay at Whiteparish and Cowsfield in the extreme south-east corner. In both areas, small hay meadows have been identified by WTNC botanists in recent years. Many cover fewer than two hectares and many are no longer part of a working farm but belong to the occupier of an adjacent house.

Although fewer species occur here than in the larger neutral meadows of north Wiltshire, totals of 100 have been counted. These grassland species include 16 grasses, 5 rushes, 8 sedges and, among the herbs, sneezewort *Achillea ptarmica*, heath spotted-orchid *Dactylorhiza maculata*, dyer's greenweed *Genista tinctoria*, *Orchis morio*, *Silaum silaus* and marsh woundwort *Stachys palustris*.

The future of these meadows may be threatened, not necessarily by modern agricultural techniques, but through change of ownership or due to neglect if the owner, through advancing years or financial difficulties, is no longer able to provide the grazing or cutting necessary to maintain the floristic interest.

Water-meadows

Wet meadows lying on valley gravels adjacent to the rivers are the fourth type of unimproved grassland to be found in Wiltshire. Working water-meadows were developed mainly in the seventeenth century although there is some evidence of much earlier ones (Atwood 1963). An elaborate system of 'carriages' distributed water across the meadows from a weir upstream and into channels from which it was returned to the river further downstream. This method enabled irrigation of the meadows to be controlled and was usually carried out during the winter. In view of man's impact upon the landscape today, it is perhaps worth reflecting on the degree of disturbance which the construction of ridges and furrows, drainage channels, carriers and hatches had on the river valleys and their wildlife and the extent to which the system depended on good maintenance. The meadows became part of a farming system in the chalk country in which sheep were essential fertility builders of the arable land. The animals were grazed on the downland by day and folded on fodder crops such as rape or turnips in the fields at night. The role of the water-meadow was to provide additional early grazing and nutritious keep for ewes prior to lambing and before the downland grass was ready for grazing.

This farming system survives at Britford in the Salisbury Avon valley but elsewhere the water-meadows have fallen into neglect. Most have been drained and ploughed, others planted with poplars or the grass has been agriculturally improved.

The flora of the worked water-meadows was never species-rich because smaller herbs could not compete with the luxuriant grass. In the late 1880s, following the cessation of annual drowning of the meadows, the water gradually became stagnant and, as the land reverted to marsh, the flora changed and became more varied, although the extent of this variation is dependent upon subsequent management. Some sites, such as Smallbrook Meadows on the river Were at Warminster, have become nature reserves. Here a variety of plants including purple-loosestrife *Lythrum salicaria*, yellow iris *Iris pseudacorus*, water avens *Geum rivale*, ragged-Robin *Lychnis flos-cuculi* and *Caltha palustris* can be found which have become uncommon due to land drainage and intensive modern agriculture. The remnants of the ridge-and-furrow system, together with the drains and carriers, provide a range of habitats from open water to damp grassland which can accommodate many species. In the vale of

Pewsey, at Jones's Mill, also a nature reserve, neglected water-meadows have developed into fenland, a rare habitat in Wiltshire. Here, wet peat is flushed by alkaline water. The vegetation includes a wide range of sedges, grasses and herbs including bogbean *Menyanthes trifoliata*, *Dactylorhiza praetermissa*, marsh valerian *Valeriana dioica* and common valerian *V. officinalis*. At this site there are also tree and shrub species dominated by alder *Alnus glutinosa* and crack willow *Salix fragilis*.

Rivers and Wetlands

The area around Salisbury is noted for its river systems and associated wet meadows. The fast-flowing rivers support few plants although species of water-crowfoot can make a spectacular sight in May. Smaller streams, with clear chalk water and slower flow rates, support a greater range of species, particularly if there is a gradual shelving of the banks. The tall grasses, common reed *Phragmites australis*, reed canary-grass *Phalaris arundinacea* and reed sweet-grass *Glyceria maxima* are found in such situations, their roots helping to trap silt and produce conditions suitable for the growth of other plants. Access to many river banks is restricted for various reasons but where the River Avon flows adjacent to the central car park in Salisbury it is possible to see gipsywort *Lycopus europaeus*, *Lythrum salicaria* and *Stachys palustris* and rarer species such as *Thalictrum flavum*. Further upstream near the cattle market, flowering-rush *Butomus umbellatus* and arrowhead *Sagittaria sagittifolia* occur.

In Grose's day, the largest areas of standing water in the north of the county were Coate Water and Braydon Pond. Since then the extraction of gravel to the north of the Swillbrook and eastward along the Thames valley has led to the formation of the Cotswold Water Park. The area is outstanding botanically because so many different habitats have been formed and modified within very short time periods. Gravel pits with fluctuating water tables, often eutrophic and dangerously steep-sided, produce habitats grading from pure fresh gravel to willow carr climax. The whole area is incredibly dynamic, human intervention producing enormous ecological diversity. Specialities of the area are numerous and include flat-sedge *Blysmus compressus*, needle spike-rush *Eleocharis acicularis* which is induced to flower when the water level falls, lesser pondweed *Potamogeton pusillus*, brookweed *Samolus valerandi* and grey club-rush *Schoenoplectus tabernaemontani*.

To the north of Devizes lies an area of free-draining Lower Greensand, part of which is known as Spye Park. The area has been little modified by agricultural activities and lime-rich water emerges from the Corallian as wet flushes in three steep-sided valleys. A complex interaction of pH and water level produce very unusual soil conditions creating the only area in the north for alternate-leaved golden-saxifrage *Chrysosplenium alternifolium*. Although the area is poor for orchids, violet helleborine *Epipactis purpurata* can be found here. Lush bracken *Pteridium aquilinum*, which dominates the valley sides, flourishes under the deep shade of climax *Alnus glutinosa* woodland. Growing in the clear area around the basic flushes are *Anagallis tenella*, *Samolus valerandi* and marsh violet *Viola palustris*.

At Landford, in the extreme south-east of the county, one small acid bog remains. *Cirsium dissectum*, round-leaved sundew *Drosera rotundifolia*, bog asphodel *Narthecium ossifragum*, white beak-sedge *Rhynchospora alba* and a range of sphagnum moss species can be found together with less specialised marsh plants including *Menyanthes trifoliata*. This site, which until recently had remained ungrazed for many years, provides a sharp contrast to nearby New Forest wetlands where grazing has been unrelenting.

Cultivated Land

It is generally accepted by botanists and others interested in natural history that farming has changed dramatically since the 1950s. However, the many and varied underlying reasons for these changes and their impact on the flora are not so widely understood. As with any financial enterprise, they arise from the need to produce enough to satisfy the market and create a profit for the producer.

The production of food for human consumption is achieved either directly from the growing of cereals (arable farming) or indirectly from growing grass and other crops for feeding stock (livestock farming). In Wiltshire, the former is mainly carried out on the chalk in the south of the county and the pastoral farming on the wet claylands in the north-west.

Arable Farming

The Agriculture Act of 1947 and, later, the Common Agricultural Policy (CAP) of the European Community (EC), have encouraged cereal growing in preference to all other arable crops. Before the 1980s, wheat was the only cereal successfully sown in winter. Most barleys and oats were spring sown, an important factor in securing good quality malting barley. In the 1980s, plant breeding researchers developed many successful varieties of winter barley. This led to a significant change in seasonal cultivation. Following harvest, it was possible to sow the next year's crop in September and so, in order to prepare the seed bed by this early date and to control fungi, the straw and stubble were burnt in the common practice of 'stubble burning'. In the mid-1980s it became compulsory to incorporate the ash within 24 hours of burning and, from 1993, burning was prohibited.

Cereal fields are large monoculture systems repeated, in some cases, for ten years or more without a break. In order to achieve maximum production, competition from weeds is checked by the application of herbicides, but problems with black-grass *Alopecurus myosuroides* and pineappleweed *Matricaria discoidea* persist. The regimented tramlines punctuating the visually homogenous and dull arable fields have been developed as a technique for chemical spray accuracy. From the 1960s onwards there were cases in which continuous cereal systems were not completely successful because yield suffered as the result of fungal infection. This led to research to find break crops – maize, beans, turnips, fodder beet, mustard and linseed (supported by CAP subsidy) have been used, but oilseed rape has undoubtedly been the most popular, its brilliant yellow colour making a visual impact on the countryside. Although these crops provide a more favourable habitat for fauna, there is little advantage to the native flora which remains confined to steep banks, field margins and gateways.

In the late 1980s, cereal production became too successful and alternative uses of a proportion of the arable land were sought in order to reduce grain surpluses. Government grants were offered to farmers prepared to set aside a minimum of 20% of their land on which certain arable crops had been grown in the base year 1987/88 and not to produce a profitable crop for a period of 1-5 years according to the chosen scheme. This had a marked impact on the flora; counts of over 100 species were made on several farms in 1991 and poppies *Papaver* sp. were a spectacular sight in the first year after cultivation ceased. Conservation organisations, the Wiltshire Farming and Wildlife Advisory Group (FWAG) in particular, are monitoring the effect of this scheme on the wildlife and are also encouraging alternative management of arable field margins for the benefit of wildlife. These include the establishment of perennial grass strips and adjustment of machinery to avoid herbicides drifting on to field edges.

Livestock Farming

Grassland is the main provider of food for livestock and the objective of its management is to produce grass and clover of high nutritional quality and in large quantity. Varieties have been bred to meet these requirements but, to attain their full potential, they demand high levels of applied potash, phosphate and, particularly, nitrogenous fertilisers. Intensive grazing can therefore be achieved without damage to the 'improved' grasses and the sward composition is confined to a few 'productive' species, chemical sprays preventing the ingress of 'wild' herb species.

Silage making, using early grasses and vigorous species of clover, now largely replaces haymaking as a more efficient method of conserving nutrients for livestock but at the expense of sward variety in botanical composition. [The hay meadow habitat is referred to under the sub-heading Neutral Lowland Meadows.]

Simple grass and clover seed mixtures consist of one to four species, usually with varieties of each, and are maintained by the use of a wide range of herbicides developed to assist weed control in the same way as for growing cereals. Ley farming techniques, developed in the 1940s and 1950s following the work of Sir George Stapledon at Aberystwyth, involve the ploughing up of old permanent pastures and putting them down to cash crops for a few years before reseeding to a short-term ley instead of permanent grass. Just as arable farming techniques have tended to cause changes in the notorious weed species, so have the techniques applied to pasture. Common chickweed *Stellaria media*, knotweeds *Polygonum* species, tall fescue *Festuca arundinacea* and creeping bent *Agrostis stolonifera* have become problems.

The older breeds of both dairy and beef cattle, which convert grass and clover into milk and meat respectively, have been replaced by alternative breeds since the 1950s. Shorthorns have been superseded by Friesians, which produce more milk per cow but, it is said, by having to be fed more expensive concentrates. Hereford and Angus beef cattle have made way for the heavier continental breeds, Charolais, Limousin and Simmental, which produce more meat.

Improvement in ventilation, insulation and the general design of animal houses has permitted a greater number of stock to be kept indoors in winter and consequently has created the necessity for the development of new methods of manure management. Manure is now in the form of slurry rather than being straw-based and is stored in lagoons or dispersed by spreaders from large tankers over arable land, or by 'dirty water' systems over grass. This leads to concentrations of animal waste and the danger of pollution to watercourses and ground-water. This infringement

of the law is vigorously pursued and legal action taken by the National Rivers Authority. In some areas the effect of pollution on aquatic and waterside plants has been dramatic. Instead of a mixture of species which included flowering-rush *Butomus umbellatus* and stream water-crowfoot *Ranunculus penicillatus*, the surviving species are reduced to *Phragmites australis* and common duckweed *Lemna minor*.

Other agricultural practices that have affected wildlife habitats are the changes in the management of hedges and wetland, mechanisation having increasingly replaced labour-intensive methods. A living hedge is no longer the only device available for confining livestock and most of those that have been retained are cut with mechanical trimmers instead of being laid by hand. A barbed wire, or electric, fence will do the job equally well and, where these have replaced a broad hedgerow, all the native flora will have been lost. Interest in hedgelaying has increased in recent years, but a laid hedge in Wiltshire is a rare sight.

Drainage ditches are becoming unnecessary since the advent of underdraining using plastic or clay pipes introduced into the soil by large, specialised machinery. The flora of easily drained wet meadows is therefore severely diminished.

Organic Farming

During the period since the 1950s, this so-called second revolution of agriculture, an alternative to intensive production, has been gaining ground. Begun by the Soil Association, organic farming and horticulture is now a significant movement claiming to be a sustainable form of production while simultaneously being more friendly to the environment and the natural habitat. The use of fertilisers and chemical control methods are replaced by natural growth stimulation and management – harnessing nature instead of attempting to control it. The method is rather more extreme than those recommended by the Game Conservancy, FWAG and other advisory bodies, but it now has a powerful lobby. Some benefits to the wild flora are readily observed by the layman.

Market Gardens and Horticultural Nurseries

Market gardening in Wiltshire is restricted to areas having sandy soil, the most extensive being at Bromham, north of Devizes, where the Lower Greensand is exploited. This light soil is very favourable for the germination of seeds of both cultivated and wild plants and the open nature of the 'gardens' permits easy dispersal of wind-blown seeds such as those of groundsel *Senecio vulgaris* and prickly sow-thistle *Sonchus asper*. At Bromham, the soil is derived from Lower Greensand which contains ironstone. It is light, dry and hungry with a pH of 6.5-7.0. Its fertility is maintained by regular and heavy applications of organic manure mainly obtained from local pig and poultry rearing enterprises.

Unlike arable and dairy farming, in which the land is only used for a single crop during the growing season, several short-duration crops, those used for salads for example, may be grown in any one year on the same ground. Between harvesting one crop and the sowing of its successor, the soil is rotovated and wild seeds that have survived these operations, such as those of dove's-foot crane's-bill *Geranium molle,* red dead-nettle *Lamium purpureum* and common field-speedwell *Veronica persica,* are scattered into a ready-made seed bed. This was probably true of most market gardens in the 1950s and 1960s when individual holdings consisted of a few acres and when a wide range of crops, including 'dirty' crops such as peas which encouraged the growth of 'weeds', were all raised from seed. The land was criss-crossed by access paths between the holdings which provided havens for wild plants. All drilling, hoeing and harvesting was carried out by hand and there was no chemical weed control.

By the 1990s, many of the smallholdings had been amalgamated and run by only two or three main growers, their crops no longer being raised from seed but plants 'bought-in' from specialist growers and planted by machine. Many of the access paths had been ploughed out in order to allow for larger areas in which fewer crops were grown and for easy movement of large machinery. Pre-emergent herbicides, which remain effective for up to six weeks, are now sprayed on the soil to prevent competition until the crop canopy totally covers the ground and shades out any remaining weeds. The use of machinery requires wide, unplanted headlands and here, bugloss *Anchusa arvensis,* mugwort *Artemisia vulgaris* and field pansy *Viola arvensis* are some of the wild plants that have survived.

These changes have also altered the distribution pattern of the wild flora from being an even spread throughout the area to more concentrated 'avenues' or 'cells' of plants confined to the headlands, the remaining access paths and the areas around irrigation tanks. Careful application of expensive herbicides now ensures that the crops are virtually free from wild competitors on the intensively managed sites. However, a few smaller enterprises still survive where management is less intensive, and here some of Wiltshire's least common annuals can be found, namely loose silky-bent *Apera spica-venti,* corn marigold *Chrysanthemum segetum,* small-flowered crane's-bill *Geranium pusillum,* cut-leaved dead-nettle *Lamium hybridum,* lesser snapdragon *Misopates orontium* and green field-speedwell *Veronica agrestis,* though their long-term future is uncertain.

Tree nurseries and garden centres increased during the 1970s and 1980s, partly due to a greater demand from farmers and other land owners who wished to take advantage of a range of woodland grant schemes and partly to an increased interest in private gardening with the all-year planting capability afforded by the development of container-grown plants. In Wiltshire, most are located on the lighter soils. In the north-west, between Atworth and Malmesbury, they are on limestone and cornbrash; at Bowood, Devizes and Market Lavington in the centre of the county and at Chapmanslade in the south-west they are on greensand and at Landford, in the south, on Bagshot Sand.

As in market gardens, management is usually rigorous and 'weeds' are generally not tolerated, but among a few unusual species that have been found in such situations are *Anchusa arvensis,* slender parsley-piert *Aphanes inexspectata,* treacle mustard *Erysimum cheiranthoides* and bird's-foot *Ornithopus perpusillus*. The spread of hairy bitter-cress *Cardamine hirsuta*, which has reached plague proportions in many gardens, can be attributed to the prolific production of its seeds which are translocated with nursery-grown containerised plants.

Man-made Habitats

Urban Development

The ability of plants to adapt to new or changing environments can best be illustrated by reference to the urban area of Swindon where the rapid rate of expansion is set to continue. Urban development is inevitably accompanied by losses or extinctions. For example, at Moredon, an estate has recently been built on a 'good wet meadow' which supported an abundance of *Silaum silaus* and many other species. In contrast, and not infrequently, disturbance can increase diversity, at least in the short term. Horse-radish *Armoracia rusticana*, black horehound *Ballota nigra*, hemlock *Conium maculatum*, goat's-rue *Galega officinalis*, cotton thistle *Onopordon acanthium*, field penny-cress *Thlaspi arvense* and dark mullein *Verbascum nigrum* all appeared on a wide verge near Elborough Bridge after it had been used as a bulldozer park. It is likely that the seeds of some of these opportunist species can be transported in mud picked up by vehicles and carried for many miles.

Building sites, car parks and derelict areas all provide good hunting ground for the botanist. In Ramsbury, a builder's yard supports narrow-leaved pepperwort *Lepidium ruderale* (also recorded in Devizes in 1991), and in Marlborough, bristly hawk's-beard *Crepis setosa* was found growing on a building site. Abandoned buildings, broken tarmac and concrete favour some species including biting stonecrop *Sedum acre,* which can cover large areas and colonise walls and roofs, blue fleabane *Erigeron acer* and sticky groundsel *Senecio viscosus*. Other species recorded in similar situations include caraway *Carum carvi,* common hawkweed *Hieracium vulgatum* and eastern rocket

Sisymbrium orientale. The vicinity of old railway sheds in Swindon and Salisbury has proved to be a good habitat for many of the plants listed above. In Salisbury, where the site is stony and well drained, there are records for *Pteridium aquilinum,* a plant which is rare in this area because of high alkalinity, *Orchis morio* (two plants in 1985), and more common species of bare, disturbed ground such as butterfly-bush *Buddleja davidii,* colt's-foot *Tussilago farfara* and great mullein *Verbascum thapsus*. Poorly tended footpaths, cycle tracks and disused railway lines also have yielded many interesting plants including stone parsley *Sison amomum,* broad-leaved everlasting-pea *Lathyrus latifolius,* grass vetchling *Lathyrus nissola,* red valerian *Centranthus ruber* and perennial wall-rocket *Diplotaxis tenuifolia*. Cracks in paving may support two unusual plants, shaggy soldier *Galinsoga quadriradiata* and fern-grass *Catapodium rigidum*. Common stork's-bill *Erodium cicutarium* has been recorded from the edges of frequently mown roundabouts in Salisbury, where the soil is scraped and eroded. Prickly lettuce *Lactuca serriola,* a plant introduced to the county and noted elsewhere in this publication, is becoming frequent not only in towns but also on expanses of bare ground, such as set-aside farmland. Although there are relatively few records from allotments these must, like gardens, be refuges for many plants in towns and cities. One such record is that of *Misopates orontium* in Salisbury.

Rubbish Tips

In this tale of nature's ability to camouflage some of the worst of man's blots on the landscape are the plants which colonise rubbish tips. At Froxfield, where top soil has been dumped on waste for several years, long-stalked crane's-bill *Geranium columbinum,* annual mercury *Mercurialis annua,* common broomrape *Orobanche minor,* *Polygonatum multiflorum* and small nettle *Urtica urens* have been recorded. There have been many earlier records of exotics and casuals from The Butts in Salisbury although these have diminished in recent years as dumping has been reduced. They include small melilot *Melilotus indicus,* which was abundant in the early part of the 1980s but only recorded in one year since 1984, common ramping-fumitory *Fumaria muralis*, of which there is a large colony on dumped soil, fennel *Foeniculum vulgare* (one plant survived for a few years) spotted medick *Medicago arabica*, which forms part of a sward of closely mown turf, and an unusual form of groundsel with ligulate ray florets *Senecio vulgaris* var *radiatus*.

Walls

Old walls provide another man-made habitat for plants which can survive in small pockets of soil. In the market town of Malmesbury, the extensive use of limestone as a building material has allowed the walls to become a significant site for calcium-loving plants. The ferns, wall-rue *Asplenium ruta-muraria*, maidenhair spleenwort *A. trichomanes* and rustyback *Ceterach officinarum* grow best on shaded, north-facing surfaces. *Sedum acre* thrives both on walls and exposed roofs here and in other towns including Salisbury. Pellitory-of-the-wall *Parietaria judaica*, another plant that colonises stone walls, can be found on the high wall supporting Potterne churchyard. Of the plants well-adapted to survive and reproduce in these dry conditions, ivy-leaved toadflax *Cymbalaria muralis* is unusual. Its seeds, believed to contain an oil attractive to ants perhaps as a source of food for later use, are carried by these insects into crevices and are unwittingly placed in excellent situations for germination.

Road Verges

Road verges which form important corridors of semi-natural vegetation have increased in significance in recent years as the intensity of modern farming has reduced the wealth of wildlife in hayfields and pasture land.

Newly-formed roadside verges can be rewarding hunting grounds – superb stands of common poppy *Papaver rhoeas* grew along the Steeple Langford bypass for a few years after its completion. Such plants rely on soil disturbance which allows light to trigger the germination of their seeds, but their displays diminish as each season passes unless further soil is turned over.

In the *Flora of Wiltshire* (1957), Grose described the verges of that period and in 1972 Horton, in an article in *The Supplement to the Flora of Wiltshire*, updated Grose's finding and also considered verge management. By comparing this earlier information with that supplied by Wiltshire County Council (WCC) in 1992, it is possible to evaluate the changes that have taken place. Between 1957 and 1972, the total length of roads maintained by WCC changed little – from 3,784 to 3,888 km – the construction of the M4 motorway being the most significant addition. In 1991, the total reached 5,064 km, the expansion of a number of towns, in particular Swindon and Melksham, playing an important part. Methods of management have also changed during this period. In 1957, Grose described a single late summer mowing regime while in 1972 Horton reported that many roads may have been cut four times a year. On rural roads WCC now operates a policy of cutting a single swathe from the edge of the carriageway. This is normally done twice a year but may vary according to the rate of growth. Spraying with herbicides has never been popular in the county, due mainly to the results of research to determine its effects on the vegetation, which Grose carried out in 1962. In the early 1990s, WCC recommends minimum use of chemical sprays, accepting that their use may be necessary to control growth at the edge of carriageways, on kerbs and central reservations and around sign posts. Whilst the local authority has become more aware of the conservation value of roadside verges in recent times, it would be of considerable interest to continue to monitor the effects of management. This is impractical over the county as a whole but efforts are being made, by local naturalists in conjunction with WCC, to do so on 49 protected verges which vary in length from about 1.5 km to just a few metres. Twenty-three of the sites are designated because of the general quality of the flora and, on two, there is reference to butterfly species. Eighteen sites are for the protection of a single rare species of plant and in a further eight, reference is made to two or more species of significance. In order to illustrate the variety of protected verges, three examples are described below.

At Redlynch, near Salisbury, asarabacca *Asarum europaeum* which grows on 100 m of verge, was first recorded in 1820 by F Popham. It is the only known site in the county where the plant occurs naturally and sets viable seed. At Ballard's Ash, Wootton Bassett, 1.5 km is now protected and the plants of interest have increased over the years. Druce recorded soapwort *Saponaria officinalis* there in 1889 and crown vetch *Securigera varia,* which was regarded by Grose as a casual which rarely persists for more than a few seasons, has been known at this site for 20 years. This is one of the few sites in Wiltshire where knapweed broomrape *Orobanche elatior* grows on non-chalk soils. In addition, one section of this verge is designated not for an individual species but for the herb-rich nature of the sward.

The steep, south-facing bank of the cutting through the chalk, beside a 650 m stretch of the A303 near Wylye, is now managed to protect the plants that quickly colonised the bare soil. These include kidney vetch *Anthyllis vulneraria* and *Hippocrepis comosa* which support strong populations of small and adonis blue butterflies respectively. There are many other road verges of equal interest and value but the importance of all verges as refuges for species such as *Primula veris* must be recognised. Such well-known plants may not merit specific protection but most certainly they are appreciated by a general public which is becoming increasingly aware of the infrequency with which they are seen.

Miscellaneous Man-made Habitats

No review of habitats can be complete without reference to ponds, quarries and chalk pits, created by the removal of material for industrial processes. They are a few of the many examples of potentially good wildlife habitats which can be created if management is sympathetic to these aims. The significance of churchyards, with relatively undisturbed grassland which in many cases has not been treated with herbicides, is being increasingly recognised. Steps are now being taken to increase the awareness of Parochial Church Councils of their value and appropriate methods of management.

Human disturbance of the land does much to increase the diversity of plants to be found in a given location. A 'good' building site will provide the habitat for many opportunist plants which more stable habitats cannot support. Some of these plants are not necessarily common. When the footings of new buildings are dug at Odstock Hospital, near Salisbury, a display of pheasant's - eye *Adonis annua* frequently ensues.

The Future

Wiltshire is predominantly a rural and agricultural county. This article has attempted to show that, as a result, it boasts a wide range of plant associations, many of which for various reasons now look likely to be well-understood and, consequently, nurtured for the benefit of all in future years. It is perhaps important to point out that three agencies are bringing considerable influence to bear upon this outcome, namely the groups interested in natural history – both amateur and official – the conservation arm of the MOD and forward-thinking farmers and landowners.

The inclusion of site names in this article does not imply that there is public access.

Colour Plates

During the last two years of fieldwork for the WFMP, recorders were invited to take colour slides suitable for reproduction in this publication. The subjects sought were Wiltshire's main habitats, preferably showing examples of their typical flora, and close-ups of species including those for which articles were to be written. Sixty were selected from which the final choice was made. A few of these did not meet the standard required for reproduction, the gaps being filled by the publisher.

Where the species in some of the habitat shots was not identified by the author at the time of taking the photograph, the genus name only is given. Acknowledgement to each author is implied by the appearance of their name in the caption.

Plate 1. Woodland.
TOP LEFT. Ravensroost Wood in the Braydon Forest area of N. Wilts. An oak/hazel coppice wood on Oxford Clay (Ann Skinner). TOP RIGHT. Spiked star-of-Bethlehem *Ornithogalum pyrenaicum* in Slittem's Wood on the Wilts/Avon county boundary. A mixed broadleaved wood on limestone (Beatrice Gillam). See article, page 99. BOTTOM LEFT. Leaves and flower-buds of small-leaved lime *Tilia cordata* (Patricia Woodruffe). See article, page 71. BOTTOM RIGHT. Leaves and flowers of the wild service-tree *Sorbus torminalis* (Patricia Woodruffe). See article, page 77.

Plate 2. Chalk Downland.

TOP LEFT. Knap Hill, Pewsey Downs National Nature Reserve (NNR), N. Wilts (Basil Harris). TOP RIGHT. Wylye Down NNR. Anthills on grazed downland (Barbara Last). CENTRE LEFT. Bastard-toadflax *Thesium humifusum*, found on many closely-grazed downlands in N. and S. Wilts (Bob Gibbons). See article, page 79. CENTRE RIGHT. Round-headed rampion *Phyteuma orbiculare,* almost entirely restricted to high downland north of the Vale of Pewsey (Peter Creed). See article, page 81. BOTTOM LEFT. Dwarf sedge *Carex humilis* on the Salisbury Plain Training Area (Stephen Palmer). See article, page 92. BOTTOM RIGHT. A group of musk orchids *Herminium monorchis* growing on steep downland (Richard Laurence).

Plate 3. Chalk Dowland.
TOP LEFT. Middleton Down, a Wiltshire Wildlife Trust reserve in S. Wilts. Early-purple orchids *Orchis mascula* and cowslips *Primula veris* (Richard Laurence). TOP RIGHT. Gorse Down adjacent to Middleton Down. Downland invaded by hawthorn *Crataegus monogyna* and gorse *Ulex europaeus* scrub (Barbara Last). BOTTOM LEFT. Downland herbs and grasses at Ham Hill in mid-July. Pyramidal orchid *Anacamptis pyramidalis*, burnt orchid *Orchis ustulata* (Barbara Last). BOTTOM RIGHT. Field fleawort *Tephroseris integrifolia*, a nationally scarce plant recorded in eighteen 10 km² in Wiltshire in the 1980s (Jeremy Fraser).

Plate 4. The Salisbury Plain Training Area (SPTA) and tuberous thistle *Cirsium tuberosum*.
TOP LEFT. A small area of the 19,690 hectares of unimproved chalk grassland on the SPTA designated a Site of Special Scientific Interest in 1993 (Beatrice Gillam). TOP RIGHT. A colony of tuberous thistles at Ladywell near Imber on the SPTA(W) (Valerie Headland). CENTRE LEFT. Dwarf thistle *Cirsium acaule* (Peter Creed). BOTTOM LEFT. The hybrid thistle *Cirsium tuberosum* x *C. acaule* which is deceptively close to *C. tuberosum* (Sue Everett). BOTTOM RIGHT. Tuberous thistle. Note the rounded and almost globular shape of both the flower and receptacle (Valerie Headland). See article, page 83.

Plate 5. Wetland – rivers and meadows.
TOP. River Wylye at Great Wishford. A typical stretch of a fast-flowing chalk river (Patricia Woodruffe). BOTTOM LEFT: Riverside vegetation including teasel *Dipsacus fullonum* and figwort *Scrophularia* sp. on the banks of the Bristol Avon (Stan Price). CENTRE RIGHT. Southern marsh-orchid *Dactylorhiza praetermissa* and ragged-Robin *Lychnis flos-cuculi* in an unimproved wet meadow adjacent to the R. Till (Barbara Last). BOTTOM RIGHT. North Meadow National Nature Reserve, Cricklade in early May. Fritillaries *Fritillaria meleagris* and common dandelions *Taraxacum officinale* (Peter Wakely/English Nature). See article, page 95.

Plate 6. Wetland – static water.
TOP LEFT. One of the oldest of the excavated gravel pits in the Cotswold Water Park. The black-poplar *Populus nigra* on the distant bank has survived the disturbance (Beatrice Gillam). TOP RIGHT. A stretch of the Kennet and Avon Canal west of Devizes completely covered with least duckweed *Lemna minuta* October 1991 (Valerie Headland). See article, page 57. BOTTOM LEFT. Common fleabane *Pulicaria dysenterica* and marsh thistle *Cirsium palustre* among the vegetation on a pond bank in the Braydon Forest area (Beatrice Gillam). BOTTOM RIGHT. Summer snowflake *Leucojum aestivum* in the valley of R. Kennet, near Ramsbury (Stan Price). See article, page 101.

Plate 7. Weeds of arable land and man-made structures.
TOP LEFT. Pheasant's-eye *Adonis annua* in a field of barley near Salisbury (Philip Wilson). See article, page 43. TOP RIGHT. Scarlet pimpernel *Anagallis arvensis* ssp. *arvensis* and blue pimpernel *A. arvensis* ssp. *caerula* on set-aside land after herbicides had been used to control weeds following a barley crop (Eunice Overend). BOTTOM LEFT. Poppy *Papaver* sp. and fool's parsley *Aethusa cynapium* growing on the edge of a rape crop near Bradford-on-Avon (John Presland). BOTTOM RIGHT. Perennial rye-grass *Lolium perenne* and biting stonecrop *Sedum acre* colonising the cement of an old brick wall (Beatrice Gillam).

Plate 8. Road verges and natural stone.
TOP LEFT. Colonisation of bare chalk by horseshoe vetch *Hippocrepis comosa* on a bank of the A303 dual carriageway near Wylye (Barbara Last). CENTRE LEFT. Colonisation of Upper Greensand by poppies *Papaver* sp. and beaked hawk's-beard *Crepis vesicaria* near Westbury (Valerie Headland). TOP RIGHT. Reflexed stonecrop *Sedum rupestre*, an introduced plant, on a dry limestone wall near Bradford-on-Avon (John Presland). BOTTOM. Wall-rue *Asplenium ruta-muraria*, maidenhair spleenwort *A. trichomanes* and rustyback *Ceterach officinarum* growing in the mortar of a dressed limestone wall near Bradford-on-Avon (John Presland). See article, page 107.

Acknowledgements

The authors gratefully acknowledge contributions included in the text from E W Culling, D Green, B Gregg, P Mobsby, J Newton, R Packham, L Ward and S Whitworth.

References and Sources of Additional Information

Atwood, G (1963). A study of the Wiltshire water meadows. *Wiltshire Archaeological and Natural History Society Magazine*, 58: 403-413.

Cobbett, (1967). *Rural Rides*. Penguin English Library, Penguin, Harmondsworth. First published 1830.

Defoe, (1982). *A Tour Through the Whole Island of Great Britain*. Everyman's Library. First published 1724.

Grose, D (1957). *The Flora of Wiltshire*. Wiltshire Archaeological and Natural History Society, Devizes.

Grose, D (1962). The treatment of roadside verges in Wiltshire. *Wiltshire Archaeological and Natural History Magazine*, 58: 274-291.

Harde, K W (1981). *Field Guide to Beetles*. Octopus, London.

Horton, P J (1978). Some notes on the vegetation of Wiltshire roadside verges. In L F Stearn (ed) *Supplement to the Flora of Wiltshire*. Wiltshire Archaeological and Natural History Society, Devizes.

McDonic, G F (1978). *Dutch Elm Disease in Wiltshire*. Wiltshire County Council.

McSweeney, P (1991). Botanical Survey and Assessment of Chalk Grassland in Wiltshire Outside the MOD Areas (1980-90). England Field Unit Project No. 102. English Nature (unpublished).

NCC publications: North Meadow, Cricklade National Nature Reserve Guide. Parsonage Down National Nature Reserve Guide. Nature Conservancy Council, Peterborough.

Porley, R (1989). A Botanical Survey and Assessment of the Chalk Grasslands of Salisbury Plain, Wiltshire (1985-86). Nature Conservancy Council (unpublished).

Rackham, O (1986). *The History of the Countryside*. Dent, London.

Ratcliffe, D A (ed) (1977). *A Nature Conservation Review,* Vol. 2. Cambridge University Press, Cambridge.

Rodwell, J S (ed) (1992). *British Plant Communities, Vol. 3: Grasslands and Montane Communities*. Cambridge University Press, Cambridge.

Tubbs, C R (1986). *The New Forest*. New Naturalist Series, Collins, London.

Wells, D A and King, N (1975). The flora of neutral grassland in Wiltshire. In L F Stearn (ed) *Supplement to the Flora of Wiltshire*. Wiltshire Archaeological and Natural History Society, Devizes.

Wiltshire County Council (1981). *Landscape Subject Plan – Survey Material*. Wiltshire County Council.

Wiltshire County Council (1992). *WCC Transport Policies and Programme 1992-93*. Wiltshire County Council.

Wiltshire Trust for Nature Conservation Reserve Guides: Great Cheverell (1988), Jones's Mill (1987), Middleton Down (1990), Smallbrook Meadows (1990), West Yatton Down (1989). Wiltshire Trust for Nature Conservation, Devizes.

Wiltshire Trust for Nature Conservation (1989). *Traditional Meadows in Wiltshire – Their History, Ecology and Management*. Wiltshire Trust for Nature Conservation, Devizes.

WILTSHIRE'S
ARABLE WEED FLORA

Philip Wilson

Britain has seen a revolution in arable farming methods during the last 50 years. Herbicides have largely replaced traditional methods of weed control, high yielding and nitrogen-responsive crop varieties have been developed and crop rotations have changed to include many more autumn-sown crops. In addition to these major developments, autumn-sown crops now tend to be sown earlier, stubbles are rarely left into the autumn and fields often bear the same crop year after year. Changes in farming methods have affected Wiltshire in the same way as they have the rest of the country, although it has been spared the full impact of the intensive cereal growing regimes practised in the east of England.

All these changes in farming methods have affected populations of arable weeds. The decline in the abundance and diversity of Wiltshire's arable weed flora was noted as long ago as 1954 (Grose 1957) and has accelerated in subsequent years. Many once common species have become much rarer or have even disappeared from the county. These declines are of course not exclusive to Wiltshire but have affected the whole country (Smith 1986).

Britain's arable weeds originate mainly in the annual flora of a variety of natural habitats in Europe and the Middle East. A substantial proportion of the species can no longer be found in semi-natural plant communities and may represent relics of the flora of disturbed, dry habitats that have either disappeared beneath arable farmland or which have been replaced by successional processes. These species include cornflower *Centaurea cyanus* and corn buttercup

Ranunculus arvensis which have become very rare, and others which are still common, such as black-grass *Alopecurus myosuroides* and field pansy *Viola arvensis*. Some species still occur in other habitats; for example, red hemp-nettle *Galeopsis angustifolia* may be found on coastal shingle and corn parsley *Petroselinum segetum* in dry coastal grasslands. Barren brome *Anisantha sterilis* and cleavers *Galium aparine,* which have become modern cereal pests, have invaded arable fields from surrounding habitats. A species which has become a recent addition to Wiltshire's weed flora is common field-speedwell *Veronica persica*, which was first recorded in 1859. By 1957 it was abundant in Wiltshire and still retains that status. Pineappleweed *Matricaria discoidea* has spread even more rapidly, being first recorded from Wiltshire in 1925 (Grose 1957).

The Ecology of Arable Weeds

Before the status of Wiltshire's arable weeds can be examined, some of the unusual features of arable weed biology and those constraints on plant growth that are peculiar to the arable environment must be considered.

Arable fields are ploughed either every year or in rotation with short periods of sown grass 'leys'. Efficient ploughing destroys all the vegetation above ground level and wild plants are able to survive such conditions in one of three ways. The plant can produce seed which mimics the crop seed in size and shape so that, in the days before the development of efficient seed-cleaning machinery, the seeds of many species would have been harvested, threshed, stored and resown with the crop (Salisbury 1963). Corncockle *Agrostemma githago* was once an abundant species in Britain and was a serious contaminant of cereal grain. Following improvements in seed-cleaning techniques, its decline was rapid, and it is now virtually extinct as a wild plant in Britain (Firbank 1988). The only recent Wiltshire records are for plants of dubious origin.

Perennial weed species such as field bindweed *Convolvulus arvensis*, couch *Elytrigia repens* and perennial sow-thistle *Sonchus arvensis* can regenerate from fragments of buried root or stem remaining in the soil after cultivation. Few of these have become rarer in recent years. The third way in which arable weeds can withstand periods of adverse conditions is by producing seeds that possess some degree of dormancy in the soil. This is a feature shared by most of Britain's arable weeds. Those which have declined most rapidly, such as *Agrostemma githago* and shepherd's-needle *Scandix pecten-veneris*, and those which have increased most rapidly in recent years, for example *Anisantha sterilis* and *Galium aparine*, seem to have seed which exhibits little dormancy. This seems contradictory, but in fact it means that both groups of species are highly sensitive to changes in farming conditions which can either be to their advantage or to their disadvantage. Poppies, *Papaver* spp. and charlock *Sinapis arvensis* are examples of plants which can persist for many years and are still widely distributed, although in many areas their abundance has declined recently.

The seeds of many species germinate at characteristic restricted times of the year, which means that their life cycles may be closely synchronised with favourable climatic conditions and farming practices. The more restricted the germination period of a plant, the more sensitive it is to the time at which cultivation takes place. Hence a species such as corn marigold *Chrysanthemum segetum,* whose seeds germinate mainly in the spring, are found almost entirely in spring-sown crops, while *Ranunculus arvensis*,

with seeds that germinate in early winter, is restricted to crops sown in the autumn. The seeds of common poppy *Papaver rhoeas* germinate in both spring and autumn, and plants may therefore be found in both spring and autumn-sown crops.

In addition to being able to survive periods of adverse conditions and to germinate when conditions become suitable, weeds must be able to grow and produce sufficient seed to ensure the persistence of the weed population from one year to the next. Two of the species which have declined to the greatest extent are *Ranunculus arvensis* and *Scandix pecten-veneris* which produce few seeds, even under optimum conditions. Many of the more adaptable species such as *Papaver rhoeas* and *Viola arvensis* can produce huge numbers, especially when competition from the crop is low.

No single feature of the biology of individual weed species, and no single change in farming practice, is responsible for the recent transformation of Wiltshire's weed communities. Those which have become more successful in recent years tend to be those which are difficult to control with herbicides, are highly responsive to nitrogenous fertilisers and are favoured by the early drilling of autumn sown cereals. Those which have suffered most tend to be poor competitors, produce few seeds, are sensitive to many herbicides and are poorly adapted to growing in crops that are now sown earlier than they were in the past.

The Distribution of Weed Species and Communities in Wiltshire

The underlying pattern of the distribution of arable weeds is a consequence of traditional patterns of land-use, climate and soil characteristics. It must be borne in mind when considering weed distributions that all these factors are intimately related.

As might be expected, there are considerable differences between the weed flora of different parts of Wiltshire. A number of species, including *Papaver rhoeas* and *Viola arvensis*, have been more or less ubiquitous for many years, while others such as *Anisantha sterilis, Galium aparine* and *Veronica persica* have become so recently. Garlic mustard *Alliaria petiolata* and hogweed *Heracleum sphondylium* are among those which occur as occasional immigrants from the vegetation of the field boundary. The distribution of abundant species shows little relationship to environmental factors and they owe their present frequency to current agricultural practices.

The distribution of most other weed species within Wiltshire is very strongly influenced by environmental factors, the chief of which is the complex of soil characteristics closely associated with geology.

Arable farming is restricted to the soils that permit cultivation and, until recently, wet soils, very stony soils and very acidic and infertile soils had escaped the plough. Even in the 1990s substantial areas of Wiltshire are still pastoral, but in the past, the division of the county into largely arable and pastoral regions was even more marked. Arable cultivation was, and still is, most widely practised on the calcareous, loamy soils overlying the less steep parts of the chalk and limestone regions which, in Wiltshire, may have been farmed for up to 5,000 years. An association has been demonstrated between the numbers of rare weed species present at a site and the length of time that arable farming has been practised (Wilson 1990). For this reason alone, it is not surprising that the majority of records for the rarer arable weeds are from these chalk and limestone areas.

The growing of individual crops is also associated with different soils, which can make it difficult to determine whether particular weeds are favoured by the soil type or the cropping system. Where the same types of crop have been grown for long periods, the weed communities present tend to become adapted to the growing cycle of the crop. For example, market gardening and spring vegetable growing are most extensive on easily cultivated light, sandy soils. Areas of these soils are noteworthy for the presence of a number of spring-germinating weeds which are otherwise very rare in Wiltshire. The crop rotations

traditionally practised over much of the chalk area were, and to a large extent still are, mixed, and the weed flora of the chalk tends to consist both of autumn and spring-germinating species. On the other hand, heavy clay soils tend to be better suited to wheat growing, are cultivated most easily in the autumn and tend to support mostly autumn-germinating species. It is highly likely, however, that the pH, calcium carbonate content and soil texture (whether sandy, loamy or clayey) also have a profound influence over the performance of individual species and the composition of weed communities.

The progressive impoverishment of arable weed communities has been least on calcareous soils and in areas with relatively high summer temperatures, both in Britain (Wilson 1990) and Europe (Holzner 1979). In comparison with much of the rest of the country, daily levels of sunshine and mean air temperatures in the southernmost part of Wiltshire are high during the summer months (White and Smith 1982). This is reflected in the slightly earlier dates on which cereal harvesting tends to start. The distribution of many of the rarer weeds is concentrated on the chalk around Salisbury.

Although much of Wiltshire overlies calcareous rocks, freely-draining acidic soils are also present. In the extreme south-east of the county these bear a rich variety of common weeds and a range of species which are otherwise very rare in Wiltshire, although many of them are common on similar soils in Hampshire and Dorset. These are largely spring-germinating and well-suited to the spring-sown crops that are the major arable produce of this area. *Chrysanthemum segetum* still persists between Whiteparish and Redlynch and bugloss *Anchusa arvensis*, many-seeded goosefoot *Chenopodium polyspermum*, stork's-bill *Erodium cicutarium*, small-flowered crane's-bill *Geranium pusillum* and lesser snapdragon *Misopates orontium* occur in a few places. The last species may also be found on alluvial soils in allotment gardens around Salisbury. Wild radish *Raphanus raphanistrum* and corn spurrey *Spergula arvensis* are also frequent. The small-flowered catchfly *Silene gallica*, thought to be extinct, was refound at Sandy Lane in 1988.

The Upper Greensand forms a narrow fringe to the north and west of the chalk but has relatively little influence over the arable flora, although *Anchusa arvensis, Chrysanthemum segetum*, cut-leaved dead-nettle *Lamium hybridum, Raphanus raphanistrum* and *Spergula arvensis* are all present in sandy fields along the northern edge of Salisbury Plain. *Ranunculus arvensis* persists in at least one locality near Shalbourne where the greensand is overlain by heavy clay, and the number of recent records of *Centaurea cyanus* from this area give some hope for its future in Wiltshire. These two species are now extremely rare in Britain.

The rich, light soils around Bromham are derived from the Lower Greensand and support market gardening. Many of the less common species found on the sands of the south-east, such as *Anchusa arvensis, Chrysanthemum segetum* and *Misopates orontium* all occur, with the addition of *Lamium hybridum*. This area is also rich in aliens which include fiddleneck *Amsinckia micrantha*, shaggy soldier *Galinsoga quadriradiata*, and green nightshade *Solanum sarachoides*. Loose silky-bent *Apera spica-venti* is increasing on sandy soils in this area and may have originated in contaminated seed supplies.

The clay and alluvial soils of the north of the county are poorly suited to arable farming and, although some areas have been ploughed in recent years, the traditional pattern of land-use is predominantly pastoral. The arable weed flora of this area is generally poor and few of the less common species have been recorded. The distribution maps for the otherwise widely distributed species *Anisantha sterilis, Papaver rhoeas*, scentless mayweed *Tripleurospermum inodorum* and *Viola arvensis* show a distinct absence of records from this area. The recent discovery of a well-established population of field cow-wheat *Melampyrum arvense* near Wootton Bassett is therefore very surprising, especially as most records for it from the rest of the country are from chalk areas. It is extremely rare in Britain.

The variations between the weed flora of the different areas of Wiltshire underlain by calcareous rocks are probably due to differences in soil types

between the Jurassic limestones of the north-west which give rise to less freely-draining soils than the more easily weathered chalk, differences between the climate of the north of the county, which experiences relatively cooler and less sunny summers than the more southerly chalklands, and different regional patterns of historical land-use.

The weed communities of fields over the Jurassic limestones can be rich in species, although with fewer of those that are less common on the chalk. Stinking chamomile *Anthemis cotula*, dwarf spurge *Euphorbia exigua*, both fluellens *Kickxia* spp., Venus's-looking-glass *Legousia hybrida*, field gromwell *Lithospermum arvense* and field madder *Sherardia arvensis* are widely distributed. There are also isolated occurrences of dense-flowered fumitory *Fumaria densiflora, Petroselinum segetum* and field woundwort *Stachys arvensis*. Pheasant's-eye *Adonis annua, Centaurea cyanus, Ranunculus arvensis* and *Scandix pecten-veneris* were reported in 1971 from the construction site of the M4 motorway near Leigh Delamere (Horton *et al.* 1972) but they have not persisted at this locality. One species which appears to be more common on the oolite than elsewhere is yellow-juiced poppy *Papaver dubium* ssp. *lecoqii*. Outside Wiltshire, it seems to be most frequent on clay-rich oolitic soils.

Wiltshire's chalky soils are highly calcareous and of varying depth, and are suited to growing a wide range of crops. Some of this area, especially in the south of the county, has been under arable cultivation for many years, maybe since 3000 BC.

Few of the less common species have been recorded from the Marlborough Downs or Salisbury Plain. *Euphorbia exigua* and *Lithospermum arvense* are, however, widely distributed in both areas and *Kickxia spuria, Legousia hybrida* and *Sherardia arvensis* are relatively frequent on Salisbury Plain. Spreading hedge-parsley, *Torilis arvensis* is still to be found on a roadside verge near Bratton.

In contrast to the areas described above, the weed communities of the chalk to the north and south of Salisbury are among the richest in Britain. *Anthemis cotula, Euphorbia exigua, Fumaria densiflora, Kickxia spuria, Legousia hybrida,*

Sherardia arvensis, and narrow-fruited cornsalad *Valerianella dentata* are frequent. In Wiltshire, rough poppy *Papaver hybridum* occurs only in this region where it is common in some localities. Its present distribution differs little from that recorded by Grose (1957). Prickly poppy *Papaver argemone* and night-flowering catchfly *Silene noctiflora* are both still present in a few fields but have become much rarer since the 1950s. Long-stalked crane's-bill *Geranium columbinum* and *Petroselinum segetum* may both be found in a few fields, as well as in disturbed chalky hedge-bottoms and are unusual in that they seem to be favoured by the recent practice of sowing crops earlier in the autumn. One species which appears to have become much rarer since 1957 is *Galeopsis angustifolia*, recorded by Grose (1957) as common to frequent on the chalk. It is now extremely uncommon, which reflects its decline over the whole of the country. Some of the most interesting sites for these species are between Downton and Salisbury and to the north of Salisbury, between Porton and Amesbury.

Adonis annua is now known from only about 15 sites in Britain, and it is probably more frequent within a 15 km radius of Salisbury than anywhere else. Earlier in this century, Sir Edward Salisbury studied the ecology of this species on the Longford Estate (Salisbury 1963) where it is still present in at least two fields. In 1987, it was found in a newly-constructed car park next to Odstock Hospital and many plants appeared on set-aside arable nearby during 1990 and 1991. It has also been reported from a garden to the north of Salisbury and large quantities have been found recently in two fields between Porton and Great Durnford. It still occurs in a few places immediately to the north of Bulford. In most of these localities, *Adonis annua* is accompanied by other uncommon species, in particular, *Papaver hybridum* and *Petroselinum segetum*. Three other fields where the species occurs are within the former county boundary near Damerham. They are also noteworthy for the presence of broad-leaved spurge *Euphorbia platyphyllos*, a species only recently recorded in Wiltshire from two other sites.

Conclusion

Since the publication of Grose's flora in 1957, both the distribution and abundance of many arable weed species have decreased in Wiltshire. Some species such as *Scandix pecten-veneris* have become extinct, while the status of others, in particular *Centaurea cyanus*, *Galeopsis angustifolia*, *Ranunculus arvensis* and *Silene gallica* is precarious. A number of species have, however, retained a foothold in the county, especially in the south-east, where rich calcareous soils coincide with warm and sunny summers. The rich communities of thermophilous, calcicole weeds in this area represent the westernmost part of the distribution of a number of uncommon species such as *Fumaria densiflora*, *Papaver hybridum*, *Silene noctiflora* and *Valerianella dentata* which extend over the chalk of south-east England although they are rarely as frequent as they are around Salisbury. Their distribution is strongly associated with those areas of Britain which experience the warmest and sunniest summer climates. This fact may help to explain their relative scarcity on the chalk of north Wiltshire. *Adonis annua* also shows this type of distribution, the area around Salisbury being of national importance.

The weed communities of other Wiltshire soil types are also of interest despite the small area that they cover. Species-rich communities occur on sandy soils near Bromham and around Whiteparish and Hamptworth, although most of the species concerned, such as *Anchusa arvensis*, *Chrysanthemum segetum* and *Misopates orontium* are still relatively frequent on similar soils in Dorset and Hampshire. Greensand soils around Shalbourne have at least one good population of *Ranunculus arvensis*, and *Centaurea cyanus* has also been recorded from this area. Both of these are now extremely rare in Britain. The population of *Melampyrum arvense* is one of only five in Britain. This species is now protected under Schedule 8 of the Wildlife and Countryside Act (1981).

Wiltshire still supports a number of weed species that are very rare in the rest of the country, and has many sites that are of great importance for their conservation. It is, of course, impossible to forecast the changes that might occur to the arable weed flora in future years but, with the greater interest that is being shown in their conservation and with less intensive methods of arable farming, it may mean that their future will be a little brighter than their recent past. It is to be hoped that the next 35 years will not see a decline of similar magnitude to that which has occurred during the last 35.

Colour plates, page 39.

References

Firbank, L G (1988). Biological flora of the British Isles, *Agrostemma githago* L. *Journal of Ecology,* 76: 1232-1246.

Grose, D (1957). *The Flora of Wiltshire.* Wiltshire Archaeological and Natural History Society, Devizes.

Holzner, W (1979). Weed species and weed communities. *Vegetation,* 38: 13-20.

Horton, P, Swanborough, J and Tyler, S (1972). Botanical interest created by the construction of the M4 motorway in Wiltshire. *Wiltshire Archaeological and Natural History Magazine,* 67a: 7-11.

Salisbury, E (1963). *Weeds and Aliens.* New Naturalist Series, Collins, London.

Smith, A (1986). *Endangered Species of Disturbed Habitats.* Nature Conservancy Council, Peterborough.

White, E J and Smith, R I (1982). Climatological maps of Great Britain. Institute of Terrestrial Ecology, Cambridge.

Wilson, P J (1990). The ecology and conservation of rare arable weed species and weed communities. Unpublished PhD thesis, University of Southampton.

WILTSHIRE'S
NON-NATIVE PLANTS

Jack Oliver

More than 626 non-native species of higher plants have become persistent in Britain (Crawley 1989). Hodgson (1989) predicts that with the increase of modern artificial habitats, the best adapted species, including many aliens, will continue to increase in number and variety at the expense of some of the more vulnerable native plant species. Hybridisation between taxa to form polyploids may be an effective mechanism for rapid adaptation to changing ecological conditions.

This article is essentially concerned with introductions (deliberate or not) by man and his domesticated animals. However, too much rigidity is inappropriate, as non-natives include a small proportion of species which may have invaded by natural means since Neolithic times, and there are inevitably varying degrees of historical uncertainty about numbers of these. Some plants native to Britain do not occur naturally within the county of Wiltshire according to Grose (1957). These are discussed in the text where there have been spectacular invasions (prickly lettuce *Lactuca serriola*), or widespread expansions into the wild (snowdrop *Galanthus nivalis*), but they are not listed within Tables 1 or 2.

Regret is often expressed in Wiltshire and elsewhere at the decline of the cornfield weeds such as corncockle *Agrostemma githago*, stinking chamomile *Anthemis cotula*, corn marigold *Chrysanthemum segetum*, shepherd's-needle *Scandix pecten-veneris*, corn chamomile *Anthemis arvensis*, thorow-wax *Bupleurum rotundifolium*, cornflower *Centaurea cyanus* and corn buttercup *Ranunculus arvensis*. However, the first four came with the Iron Age farmers, the last four with the

Romans and all eight were introductions dependent on the activities of man. Other species such as wild radish *Raphanus raphanistrum*, white campion *Silene latifolia* and charlock *Sinapis arvensis*, all of which arrived with the Iron Age farmers, have also survived, adapted and multiplied in a variety of habitats until today (Greig 1988). These, and the later invaders, rape *Brassica napus*, beaked hawk's-beard *Crepis vesicaria*, ivy-leaved toadflax *Cymbalaria muralis*, slender speedwell *Veronica filiformis* and common field-speedwell *V. persica* all continue to depend mainly on man but are vigorous and adaptable. As currently successful species, these latter eight are no less beautiful or interesting than the afore-mentioned eight which are fading from the landscape.

The Wiltshire Flora Mapping Project (WFMP) field recorders' returns, per species, depend ultimately on how these checklists were prepared and used. Expertise, conscientiousness and, most of all, attitudes were crucial, but some non-natives were peculiarly vulnerable to under-recording, simply because the checklists omitted them. Examples include the three trees, Lawson's cypress *Chamaecyparis lawsoniana*, Douglas fir *Pseudotsuga menziesii* and western red-cedar *Thuja plicata*, which were consequently hardly represented. However, in Wiltshire these trees produce seedlings and saplings more readily than walnut *Juglans regia*, European larch *Larix decidua* and Norway spruce *Picea abies*, yet hundreds of records were returned for the latter three listed species. The same argument applies to the county-wide but unlisted and therefore hardly-recorded bulb Spanish daffodil *Narcissus pseudonarcissus* ssp. *major*. The other important point is that a certain psychological 'set' in some recorders ignores recently invasive non-natives as unworthy or unimportant. One little transient *Ranunculus arvensis* could be hailed as a 'good find' because of sentimental associations with long-past agricultural practices dating from its ancient Roman origins, yet masses of stately North American Michaelmas-daisies could either be ignored or unhesitatingly dismissed without thought as garden throw-outs, even if clumps covered a quarter of a hectare and had been expanding and forming distant satellite colonies 'since before the last war'!

In general, therefore, the ensuing commentaries on special groups of non-natives largely relate to representatives from the 50 most common non-native taxa occurring in Wiltshire according to the WFMP records as listed in Table 1, but include some other species or groups when important considerations apply.

Non-native Asteraceae

Table 2 indicates dispersal and colonisation strategies of the ten most common non-native Asteraceae in Wiltshire. Eight employ aerial dispersal mechanisms by means of seed pappus, but probably only *Aster*, *Conyza*, *Crepis*, *Hieracium*, *Senecio* and *Solidago* spread to any great extent by seeding. *Lactuca serriola* is not native to Wiltshire (Grose 1957) although it is to Britain, and for this reason is not included in the two tables. Its range has expanded very rapidly in Wiltshire from 1988 onwards, being recorded from 112 1 km squares. However, Canadian fleabane *Conyza canadensis*, *Crepis vesicaria*, *Lactuca serriola*, and Oxford ragwort *Senecio squalidus* are all becoming common on waysides, pavements, building sites and waste land. *Senecio squalidus* is now three times as common as indicated by Grose.

Pineappleweed *Matricaria discoidea* and feverfew *Tanacetum parthenium* disperse vigorously by seed. The seeds are not airborne but stick to feet and tyres to be distributed in mud and dust. Both species resist trampling, the former

prospering in churned, barren and muddy farm and field gateways. Both these plants are very common in Wiltshire; indeed, *Matricaria discoidea* which originated from north-east Asia is now the most abundantly distributed of all non-natives in the county.

Of the habitats associated with man, roadside and railway verges are amongst the most likely to accommodate non-native invaders. Even here, infiltration of existing native species can be an immense challenge, Hodgson (1989) describes common nettle *Urtica dioica* as a 'monopolistic' native plant because of its ability to exclude other species. It is the most ubiquitous and commonly recorded of all plants in Wiltshire, but even it can suffer competition from some non-native invaders, despite forming dense clumps upon its almost solid network of roots. Examples of such invaders are Michaelmas-daisy *Aster novi-belgii* (and/or its hybrid *Aster* x *salignus*), common blue-sow-thistle *Cicerbita macrophylla* from the Caucasus, Canadian goldenrod *Solidago canadensis*, early goldenrod *Solidago gigantea* and *Solidago* hybrids. These alien perennial Asteraceae can compete successfully with nettlebeds in high summer and autumn. They can form independent clumps, varying from 3 to 30 metres across in numerous other habitats such as dumps, tracks, pavements, woodland edges, grassy verges, old or derelict hospital grounds, wetlands, downland hollows, roadsides, fieldsides, ditches and, most commonly, railway and motorway embankments. In Wiltshire, non-native asters and goldenrods are predominantly found in dry habitats contrasting in this respect with Sheffield and the Don valley (Gilbert 1992) where they can become the dominant riverside vegetation on 'made ground' which often includes cinders. In London also, wet habitats are favoured, but on heavy clays. Spread is usually vegetative, by rooting and rhizomes, but satellite colonies are sometimes due to self-seeding, particularly for asters and goldenrods. Some of the biggest expanses of these invasive and beautiful plants can be seen in and around Swindon, Trowbridge, Wroughton and Marlborough, along the verges of the M4, A345 and the old and current railway networks.

Table 1. The 50 commonest non-natives in Wiltshire, comparing early records, designations by Grose (1957) and current frequencies by tetrads∗ or 1 km².

	Place of origin	First records Britain	Wilts	1957 Status designations	Tetrad∗ or 1 km² in 1991
Matricaria discoidea	NE Asia	1871	1915	Colonist	662∗
Acer pseudoplatanus	Europe	15thC.	1862	Denizen	647∗
Aesculus hippocastanum	Balkans	1616	Pre 1950	Alien	620
Veronica persica	Persia	1825	1857	Colonist	590∗
Aegopodium podagraria	Eurasia	Medieval	1839	Denizen	502∗
Avena fatua	S Europe	Medieval	1694	Casual or Colonist	434∗
Larix decidua	C Europe	1620	Pre 1950	Alien	372
Armoracia rusticana	SE Europe	Medieval	Pre 1950	Alien	355
Melilotus altissimus	Europe	16thC	1811	Denizen	327
Symphoricarpos albus	N America (W)	1817	Pre 1950	Alien	308
Melilotus officinalis	Eurasia	16thC	1871	Casual or Colonist	280
Crepis vesicaria	NW Africa	1713	1888	Denizen	257∗
Cymbalaria muralis	S Europe	1640	1817	Denizen	243∗
Prunus domestica agg.	Caucasus	Roman	1889	Denizen	232
Lolium multiflorum	Italy	18thC	1877	Colonist	230
Veronica filiformis	Caucasus	1927	1951	Colonist	208∗
Castanea sativa	SW Asia	Roman	Pre 1950	Alien	189
Brassica napus	European hybrid	18thC	1860	Casual	183
Ligustrum ovalifolium	Japan	1885	Pre 1850	Alien	183
Picea abies	N Europe	1500	None		176
Tanacetum parthenium	SE Europe & SW Asia	16thC	1891	Alien	174
Epilobium ciliatum	N America	1891	1941	Denizen	164
Populus x canescens	Holland	Pre 1600	1904	Denizen	137
Rhododendron ponticum	Iberia, Turkey	18thC	Pre 1950	Alien	135
Syringa vulgaris	SE Europe	16thC	Pre 1940	Alien	118
Senecio squalidus	Italy, S Europe	1794	1863	Colonist	111
Buddleja davidii	China	1890	Pre 1950	Alien	110
Papaver somniferum	C&W Mediterranean	Medieval	1870	Casual	108
Pseudofumaria lutea	C&E Alps	Pre 1802	1908	Alien	103
Malus domestica	Asian/E Europe hybrid	Roman	1888	Alien	100
Erucastrum gallicum	C&W Europe	Pre 1873	1925	Alien	100
Chenopodium bonus-henricus	Europe, W Asia	15thC	1845	Denizen	99
Impatiens glandulifera	Himalayas	1839	1931	Alien	95
Fallopia japonica	Japan	1825	Pre 1950	Alien	92
Prunus laurocerasus	Balkans, SW Asia	1580	Pre 1950	Alien	83
Juglans regia	SE Europe, Asia to China	Roman	Pre 1950	Alien	82
Linaria purpurea	Italy, Sicily	1648	1888	Casual	80
Centranthus ruber	Mediterranean, W Asia	15thC	1839	Alien	79
Acer platanoides	Europe, Turkey, W Asia	Pre 1683	None		79
Elodea canadensis	N America	1834	1859	Denizen	79
Trifolium hybridum	Europe	18thC	Pre 1950	Alien or relic	79
Pentaglottis sempervirens	Iberia	Medieval	1888	Denizen	72
Vinca major	C&S Europe, N Africa	Pre 14thC	1843	Alien	71
Solidago canadensis	N America	1648	Pre 1950	Casual	70
Hesperis matronalis	Eurasia	Medieval	1839	Alien	69
Mentha spicata	Europe	Pre 1690	1782	Denizen	64
Calystegia silvatica	SE Europe, N Africa	1867	1948	Denizen	64
Mimulus guttatus	N America (W)	1826	1830	Denizen	63
Sinapis alba	Mediterranean & Nr. East	Roman	1834	Colonist or relic	53
Aster novi-belgii (incl. A. x salignus)	N American	1710	1890	Alien	52

Table 2. The ten most common non-native Asteraceae in Wiltshire, showing special features contributing to their survival and spread. Life cycles are indicated by letters: A Annual, B Biennial, P Perennial.

	Place of origin	Life cycle	Stem types	Roots	Seed dispersal	Frequency and main habitats
Matricaria discoidea	NE Asia	A	Vertical stems survive trampling in mud and dust.		Carried by feet and tyres.	662 tetrads. Farmland especially muddy gateways. Waysides.
Crepis vesicaria	NW Africa	B	Medium to tall vertical stems.	Storage tap root.	Aerial dispersal. Beaked pappus, simple hairs.	257 tetrads. Waysides and rough ground.
Tanacetum parthenium	SE Europe SW Asia	P	Vertical stems survive trampling on stone and hard ground.	Tough root stock.	Seedings on walls and pavements.	174 1 km². Waysides, walls, pavements.
Senecio squalidus	Italy and S Europe	A,B			Aerial dispersal by simple pappus hairs.	111 1 km². Walls, pavements and stony ground.
Solidago canadensis	N America	P	1. Tall, dense, occlusive clumps. 2. Rhizomes.	Dense occlusive networks.	Aerial dispersal. Ciliate pappus hairs.	91 1 km². Roadsides, grassy embankments, especially near motorways and railway lines.
Aster novi-belgii and hybrids	N America	P	Tall, dense, occlusive clumps.	Dense, woody, rapidly expanding occlusive networks.	Aerial dispersal. Ciliate pappus hairs.	52 1 km². Roadsides, grassy embankments, especially near motorways and railway lines.
Conyza canadensis	N America	A	Small to tall vertical stems.		Aerial dispersal. Simple pappus hairs.	43 1 km². Waysides and waste ground. Bare railway ballast.
Petasites fragrans	Italy and Sardinia	P	Rhizomes.		No seed in Britain.	32 1 km². Waste areas.
Cicerbita macrophylla	Caucasus	P	1. Tall, dense, occlusive clumps. 2. Rhizomes.	Occlusive networks.	Seldom? Simple pappus hairs.	25 1 km². Ditches and nettlebeds.
Pilosella aurantiaca	N&C Europe	P	Epigeal and hypogeal stolons. Matted sward formation.	Rooting rapidly in short or rough-cut grass.	Aerial dispersal. Simple pappus hairs.	21 1 km². Edges with rough-cut grass.

They all attract bees, butterflies, moths and other pollinators in large numbers in autumn, especially the Michaelmas-daisy clumps. Outside the Asteraceae, Rose-of-Sharon *Hypericum calycinum* is the other non-native rhizomatous perennial which competes to some extent with nettles and can form very large patches, but it does not span the range of habitats or compete with tall, natural vegetation to the extent of the large asters and goldenrods from North America.

All the non-native Asteraceae species listed in Table 2 have markedly increased in frequency and distribution since the time of Grose's (1957) flora. The perennial *Cicerbita*, *Solidago* and *Aster* species and hybrids are tall, vigorous and monopolistic (Hodgson 1989), each with formidably invasive vegetative capabilities. Several of these non-natives are now an established part of the flora of Wiltshire and seem set to expand still further.

Non-native Trees

There are ten tree species in the top 50 non-native plants listed in Table 1. Some of these, including sycamore *Acer pseudoplatanus*, horse-chestnut *Aesculus hippocastanum*, wild plum *Prunus domestica* agg. and cherry laurel *Prunus laurocerasus* can obviously seed themselves without assistance from man and have been increasing since the time of Grose. *Acer pseudoplatanus* is the second most common non-native plant in Wiltshire which naturalises itself in both urban and rural woodlands as well as numerous other natural, semi-natural and man-made habitats by means of its winged fruits. *Aesculus hippocastanum* conkers can be found germinating in almost as many situations, abundantly self-sown and with a proportion of seedlings surviving to become saplings and large trees. Norway maple *Acer platanoides*, which was not mentioned by Grose (1957), self-sows like sycamore and has also increased over the last 30 years and is now found in 79 1 km squares. Turkey oak *Quercus cerris*, whose acorns are dispersed and planted by jays and squirrels, is also becoming commoner and has so far been recorded in 22 Wiltshire 1 km squares. The knopper gall wasp *Andricus quercuscalicis* lays its eggs in the male flower buds of this species to give rise to its alternate (sexual) generation in the catkins. Because of the extra susceptibility of the acorns of the native pedunculate oak *Quercus robur* to the agamic wasp generation which causes knopper gall (Jukes 1984), *Quercus cerris*, which also grows faster than the native oaks, is likely to have an advantage in the future. There is one railway embankment near Warminster where its seedlings and saplings have spread for half a kilometre in the last few years, in strong association with expanses of *Hypericum calycinum* which grows under oak in its native habitats.

Vigorously suckering non-native tree species which are gaining ground in Wiltshire include *Prunus domestica* (232 1 km squares) and grey poplar *Populus* x *canescens* (137 1 km squares). Suckers of the latter and of white poplar *Populus alba* often form roadside patches up to 30 metres long, sometimes extending into other habitats. From the non-native *Prunus domestica* the fertile hybrid *P.* x *fruticans* (= *P. spinosa* x *P. domestica*) has evolved to become a commonly spreading Wiltshire taxon. Its suckers can form dense thickets of shrubby trees with damson-like fruits and formidable thorns up to 70mm long which are far tougher than those of blackthorn *Prunus spinosa*. Such thorns can puncture the tyres of bicycles, cars and even lorries.

Some trees may not deserve their high placing as naturally regenerating species in Table 1. For instance, *Larix decidua*, *Picea abies* and *Juglans regia* are widespread in Wiltshire, the two former often growing in plantations, but they seldom regenerate without human help. By contrast, I have seen naturally occurring seedlings and saplings of *Chamaecyparis lawsoniana*, *Pseudotsuga menziesii*, *Quercus cerris* and *Thuja plicata* in drives, churchyards, hospital grounds, weed-killed areas, parkland, roadsides, woodland, embankments and plantations. Apple *Malus domestica* (100 1 km squares) is another non-native tree which self-seeds and is frequent in Wiltshire by roadsides, in hedges and on old railway embankments and tracks, especially south of Swindon. Stace (1991) describes it as '...much commoner than the native crab-apple *Malus sylvestris*', but the two are interfertile.

Non-native Veronica Species

Veronica persica and *Veronica filiformis*, originating from Iran and the Caucasus respectively, continue to spread in a variety of habitats. The former is ubiquitous in Wiltshire, especially as a garden and cornfield weed. *V. filiformis* can be found in open woodland tracks, by water and on farmland, but is mainly a weed of short cut grass. The spread of this plant by suburban man and his mower is neither more nor less natural that the introduction of *Centaurea cyanus* by the Neolithic farmer and its subsequent decline and fall as a consequence of modern farming methods. In both cases the introduction was unintentional, the habitat was unnatural and the fate of the flower was a by-product of the subtle interplay of human and natural factors.

Non-native Grasses

Wild-oat *Avena fatua* originated from southern Europe, and can be a serious agricultural weed. Some farmers still employ 'roguers' to hand-weed it from their wheat and barley crops. It is also common on field verges, by waysides and around villages. The next most commonly recorded non-native grass is Italian rye-grass *Lolium multiflorum*, which occurs throughout Wiltshire farmland, field borders, waste ground and waysides. Its hybrid with native perennial rye-grass, *L. x boucheanum*, is widely planted for pasture but was not distinguished from its parents in the WFMP records. It can be found as a frequent and increasing relic of cultivation and is more persistent and invasive than other non-native crop escapes such as two-rowed barley *Hordeum distichon* and wheat *Triticum aestivum*.

Other alien grasses are not conspicuous in Wiltshire, but French oat-grass *Gaudinia fragilis* was first recorded near Melksham in 1957 and is now established in 21 1 km squares. California brome *Ceratochloa carinata* was first recorded by Grose near Salisbury in 1949. It had only been recorded at two sites up to the time of the present survey, but is now known in 12 1 km squares. Loose silky-bent *Apera spica-venti*, once confined to a few sandy fields in East Anglia as a native, has recently been spreading as an arable weed both in the north and south of the county, having been found in eight locations. Other examples include canary-grass *Phalaris canariensis*, a distinctive annual originating from the Canary Islands. Typically a birdseed alien, it can also spread to building sites together with

common millet *Panicum miliaceum* and bristle-grasses *Setaria* species from Asia. Awned canary-grass *Phalaris paradoxa* from south-west Europe, is an arable weed in Wiltshire. A perennial member of the genus, bulbous canary-grass *Phalaris aquatica*, from south Europe spreads vegetatively and also self-sows in isolated rural sites, particularly near old pheasantrys and in new plantations on the chalk hills.

Non-native Species with Bulbs or Corms

Except for the native bluebell *Hyacinthoides non-scripta*, *Galanthus nivalis* is the commonest bulbous monocotyledon found in Wiltshire. Grose (1957) termed it a 'denizen' with fewer than 40 sites noted since its first Wiltshire record in 1845. It may possibly be native to Britain and is therefore not listed in Table 1. It has since been recorded in 421 1 km squares, often in masses in woodlands and by roadsides, which make it more common than the Wiltshire natives, ramsons *Allium ursinum* and wild onion *Allium vineale*. There are dense masses of wild daffodil *Narcissus pseudonarcissus* ssp. *pseudonarcissus* in a few localities in Wiltshire, especially in West Woods south-west of Marlborough, but the non-native *N. pseudonarcissus* ssp. *major* is more widespread. Its distribution matches that of the snowdrop, especially in woodlands, ditchbanks and on grassy places by roadsides, but it has been much under-recorded. The same may apply to hybrids between the two *N. pseudonarcissus* subspecies. Forms of nonesuch daffodil *N. x incomparabilis* are also spreading naturally. They are derived from *N. pseudonarcissus* varieties crossed and backcrossed with pheasant's-eye daffodil *N. poeticus*.

The only other non-native monocotyledonous bulb or corm plants with more than ten 1 km square records in natural sites in Wiltshire are montbretia *Crocosmia* x *crocosmiiflora* and Spanish bluebell *Hyacinthoides hispanica*. The former is increasing very slowly and the latter, which may include hybrids with *H. non-scripta*, had not been recorded before 1984.

Non-native Water Plants

There are not many watery habitats in Wiltshire, but most have been subjected to dramatic invasions by non-natives. Canadian waterweed *Elodea canadensis* is now found in 79 1 km squares but is considered to be widespread rather than abundant, as it was in the early 1900s. Water fern *Azolla filiculoides* from tropical America has at times been abundant on the Kennet and Avon Canal since 1939 (see page 58) and can be invasive, but is now only recorded from 14 1 km squares. From 1981 onwards Nuttall's waterweed *Elodea nuttallii*, from North America, has increased in abundance in the Kennet and Avon Canal, largely displacing *Elodea canadensis* and becoming the dominant sub-aquatic plant by 1986. It was recorded in 1979 and 1982 in the extensive lakes of the Cotswold Water Park and, by December 1991, had dominated all the other submerged aquatics in the Thames/Isis river in north Wiltshire. It occurs in 34 1 km squares in the county.

The most dramatic non-native invader of all has been least duckweed *Lemna minuta*, from N and S America, which, like *Elodea nuttallii*, seems to be totally frost-resistant in Wiltshire. Before 1991 it had been recorded from two or three ponds in north Wiltshire but in 1991 had densely and completely covered many kilometres of the surface of the Kennet and Avon Canal. Like other *Lemna* species it usually thrives best in slow-moving and stagnant water. Nevertheless, at Salisbury and in stretches of the rivers Wylye and Thames/Isis it occurs in fast-flowing water in swirls and eddies amongst emergent aquatics, and is now recorded in 39 1 km squares.

Conclusion

Some non-natives are under-represented in WFMP records, but there is already sufficient evidence to demonstrate a huge increase in interesting invaders since the time of Grose (1957). The loss of arable weeds described by Wilson (1993) (see page 43) should be compared with increasing species diversity in urban, suburban and village settings; along roadsides, waysides, railway and motorway embankments; on dumps, tracks, tips, building sites, depots and waste ground and within churchyards, hospital grounds, parks, ponds and canals. Much of this diversity is due to the spread of non-native plants. Hodgson's sobering predictions (see introduction) are borne out for Wiltshire, indicating that introductions should be monitored for every county. Non-natives with firm footholds which may be spreading, vigorous or invasive, or which are long established, become ecologically important. Such invading aliens have as much interest to offer as established natives (Wurzell 1991).

Acknowledgement

The author wishes to thank Brian Wurzell for advice and for fine-tuning the text in completion of this article.

References

Crawley, M J (1989). Invaders. *Plants Today*, **2**(5): 152-158.

Gilbert, O L (1992). The ecology of an urban river. *British Wildlife*, **3**(3): 129-136.

Greig, J (1988). Traditional cornfield weeds – where are they now? *Plants Today*, **1**(6): 183-191.

Grose, D (1957). *The Flora of Wiltshire*. Wiltshire Archeological and Natural History Society, Devizes.

Hodgson, J G (1989). What is happening to the British flora? An investigation of commonness and rarity. *Plants Today*, **2**(1): 26-32.

Jukes, H R (1984). *The Knopper Gall*. Department of Environment Service. 55/84/ENT Arboricultural and Information.

Stace, C (1991). *New Flora of the British Isles*. Cambridge University Press, Cambridge.

Wurzell, B (1991). Return of the aliens and adventives. *BSBI News*, **57**: 31-36.

AQUATIC PLANTS OF THE KENNET AND AVON CANAL

Jack Oliver

In 1810, when the link between the Rivers Kennet and Bristol Avon was established, the Kennet and Avon Canal Company was formed. The canal stretches from Bristol to Reading, a distance of 98 miles. The main section, which crosses Wiltshire from Limpley Stoke in the west to Froxfield in the east, passes through 71 1 km map squares.

The opening of the railway line between Bristol and London marked a decline in the fortunes of the Canal Company and the canal was closed for traffic soon after the last through passage was made in 1947. In 1962 the Kennet and Avon Canal Trust was formed with the objective of reopening the canal for pleasure traffic. This was accomplished in 1991.

The fortunes of the higher vascular plants in the canal since Donald Grose wrote of the decades preceding 1957 is the main subject of this article. Grose stated that the canal's submerged and floating aquatics were more varied than those of the Wiltshire rivers. The main genera listed by him as being plentiful were pondweeds *Potamogeton*, duckweeds *Lemna*, water fern *Azolla*, water-milfoil *Myriophyllum* and hornwort *Ceratophyllum*.

Since 1957 the Kennet and Avon Canal has undergone major changes, any one of which might be considered by the botanist to be catastrophic. Firstly, neglect caused stretches to dry out, locks and pumps to be abandoned, reversion to dry land with a few muddy remnants, dumping and pollution. Secondly, restoration for historical, recreational and sentimental reasons put boats and fishermen equal first, with wildlife following as an also-ran. Thirdly, eutrophication caused by run-off of nitrates and phosphates from farm fertilisers led to overgrowths of algae, especially blanket-weed or 'cott' *Cladophora*, which aroused the ire of boaters who demanded its drastic chemical control to prevent the propellers of their boats being fouled. Finally, British Waterways (BW) uses cutting and dredging machines, in addition to regular herbicide application, to keep the canal viable.

There is much variation in adjacent stretches of the canal. There can be muddy water, with dead-looking floating debris, in lengths much used by boaters. Elsewhere, the water is frequently covered by a green mass of what appears to be a luxuriantly overgrown monoculture of a single higher vascular plant, sometimes accompanied by a slimy mass of the alga *Cladophora*. In the canal this alga can be in the form of freely drifting small patches, large masses several metres across, as a smothering under-water epiphyte or in all of these growth forms. Newly dredged segments of the canal may have the appearance of being denuded of higher vascular plants altogether, and sometimes there can be a temporary overgrowth of higher complex algae, the stoneworts *Chara* or *Nitella*. All this can give the general effect of the canal being barren or with only a scant diversity of higher vascular plants actually in the water. This impression is incorrect, for many submerged and floating species seldom flower but are present under or within the apparent monoculture canopy. Others are hidden in the muddy recesses or survive as broken, but viable, segments drifting slowly in opaque, brown water.

The classification of aquatic plants into submerged or sub-aquatic, floating and emergent used in the text and in the Tables is that of Spencer-Jones and Wade (1986). It is fairly easy to apply although some species, such as arrowhead *Sagittaria sagittifolia,* can fall into all three groups. For instance, during a period of two or three years the emergent form of *S. sagittifolia* may not be seen on the canal, yet the plant persists as submerged or floating green ribbons. However, the discrimination between emergents (aquatics) and riparian or marshy plants (non-aquatics) requires arbitrary decisions and for this reason the accepted Nature Conservancy Council's (NCC) lists of emergents in Table 5 (Palmer and Newbold 1983), have been followed.

Many aquatics have extraordinarily varied leaf-forms depending either on whether they are submerged, floating or emergent, or on their genetic variants (Spencer-Jones and Wade 1986). Examples include New Zealand pigmyweed *Crassula helmsii,* Nuttall's water-weed *Elodea nuttallii,* yellow water-lily *Nuphar lutea,* amphibious bistort *Persicaria amphibia,* arrowhead *Sagittaria sagittifolia* and common club-rush *Schoenoplectus lacustris.* This variability, especially in the submerged forms, combined with the general absence of flowers, makes identification very difficult. In spite of this problem the Kennet and Avon Canal flora in 1990 proved to be richer than Grose found it prior to the 1950s. From the following account it appears to be approaching the diversity of that richest of all British waterways, the Basingstoke Canal, which supports 102 aquatic species (Byfield 1990).

The following sections illustrate the diversity of the higher vascular plants and start with the most conspicuously prevalent.

Abundant Submerged or Floating Species

These are defined as aquatics which, at some time in the year, dominate all higher vascular plants for 100 metres or more, forming a dense submerged canopy *(Elodea)* or a deeper tangle *(Myriophyllum)* in the canal.

By the summer of 1986, *Elodea nuttallii* dominated at least eight miles of the central stretches of the canal, largely supplanting Canadian waterweed *E. canadensis.* Reasons for this relate mainly to the speed of growth of the stem, the root formation and the growth of the axillary shoot (Simpson 1990). Elongating, bright green shoots of this plant, visible in the refracted sunlight under the ice in February 1986, gave it an early advantage over all other aquatics apparent by the middle of the year.

Common duckweed *Lemna minor,* unlike *Elodea,* is conspicuous only in midsummer and autumn. The common form can dominate the water surface as a green carpet but sometimes it is overtaken by the small-frond variant (Rich & Rich 1988). *L. minor* is abundant and widely distributed both on stretches of the canal and elsewhere in the county.

Least duckweed *Lemna minuta* had not been seen on the canal before August 1990. By October 1990 it had become the dominant surface aquatic, especially on the Long Pound between Devizes and Pewsey, forming a lighter green carpet than *L. minor,* which it had almost occluded. Within three months this tiny plant, previously Wiltshire's rarest aquatic, became the most abundant on the Kennet and Avon Canal (Last 1990; Oliver 1991). It persists as a carpet at the time of writing, December 1991, and seems to be the most frost-resistant of the Lemnaceae because it survived and multiplied during the winter of 1990-91.

Greater duckweed *Spirodela polyrhiza* can largely squeeze out *L. minor* from most of the surface of some canal stretches, particularly in warm summers, except where *L. minor* survives in gaps between the larger fronds. In late summer 1990, *S. polyrhiza* survived competition with *L. minuta* somewhat better than *L. minor* (Last 1990; Oliver 1991). See Figure 5.

Spiked water-milfoil *Myriophyllum spicatum* was not widely recorded as a canal species in the 1980s except in some shallow, rather stagnant and muddy stretches, especially near Devizes where it was abundant.

Water fern *Azolla filiculoides* was intermittently abundant until 1990 over large areas of the canal in the west around Bradford-on-Avon and in the Long

Pound, east of Devizes. In 1939 evacuated Londoners solemnly informed newcomers that this surface weed, which made the canal look like a red asphalt road, was a government device to hoodwink German aerial reconnaissance!

Commonly Distributed Submerged or Floating Species

Certain species were widely dispersed along the canal in the 1980s. Each of the following submerged or floating species were found in more than one-quarter of the canal's length within Wiltshire.

Dicotyledons. Common water-starwort *Callitriche stagnalis*, rigid hornwort *Ceratophyllum demersum*, yellow water-lily *Nuphar lutea* and amphibious bistort *Persicaria amphibia*.

Monocotyledons. Common duckweed *Lemna minor*, ivy-leaved duckweed *Lemna trisulca*, fennel pondweed *Potamogeton pectinatus*, unbranched bur-reed *Sparganium emersum*, greater duckweed *Spirodela polyrhiza* and, from the edges, floating sweet-grass *Glyceria fluitans* and floating forms

of creeping bent *Agrostis stolonifera*. Records in 1990 of abundant and common species of submerged and floating canal aquatics referred to above, show that they were more numerous and varied than those for all the years preceding 1957 (Grose). In recent years *Elodea nuttallii* (1980) and *Lemna minuta* (1990) have been added to the flora of Wiltshire and have become conspicuous and abundant.

Submerged and Floating Species

Table 3 lists all the submerged and floating aquatics (except pondweeds) recorded on the Wiltshire stretch of the canal during the period 1984-1990 and indicates their comparative growth forms.

The commonest submerged aquatic in Wiltshire is stream water-crowfoot *Ranunculus penicillatus* but it has not been confirmed as surviving in the Kennet and Avon Canal. In contrast, the distribution of fan-leaved water-crowfoot *R. circinatus* shows that this species depends on the canal for half the county's records.

Figure 5. The three duckweeds showing the comparative size of their fronds and the number of veins. Drawings by Valerie Headland.

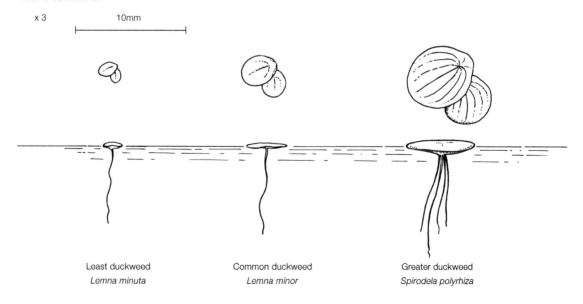

| Least duckweed | Common duckweed | Greater duckweed |
| *Lemna minuta* | *Lemna minor* | *Spirodela polyrhiza* |

Table 3. Growth forms of native and introduced submerged and/or floating canal aquatics, excluding pondweeds.
S submerged, F floating, E emergent, L land. Brackets indicate a form unusual for the species.
✳ Not confirmed as a persisting canal species, but in adjacent ponds, streams and canal feeders.

Native Species

✳ *Ranunculus aquatilis* Common water-crowfoot	SF
✳ *R. penicillatus* Stream water-crowfoot	S(F)
R. circinatus Fan-leaved water-crowfoot	S
Nymphaea alba White water-lily	S
Nuphar lutea Yellow water-lily	SF
Ceratophyllum demersum Rigid hornwort	S
Myriophyllum spicatum Spiked water-milfoil	S
Callitriche stagnalis Common water-starwort	SF(L)
Sagittaria sagittifolia Arrowhead	SFE
Zannichellia palustris Horned pondweed	S
Lemna minor Common duckweed	F
Lemna gibba Fat duckweed	F
Spirodela polyrhiza Greater duckweed	F
Lemna trisulca Ivy-leaved duckweed	S(F)
Sparganium erectum Branched bur-reed	(F)E(L)
Sparganium emersum Unbranched bur-reed	(S)F(E)
Schoenoplectus lacustris Common club-rush	SFE
Glyceria fluitans Floating sweet-grass	F(E)L
Glyceria notata Plicate sweet-grass	F(E)L
Agrostis stolonifera Creeping bent	F(E)L

Introduced Species and Date of Introduction to Wiltshire
✳ Probable but unconfirmed

Azolla filiculoides Water fern, 1939	F
✳ *Myriophyllum aquaticum* Parrot's-feather (1989?) 1991	S
Elodea canadensis Canadian waterweed, 1859	S
Elodea callitrichoides South American waterweed, 1956	S
Elodea nuttallii Nuttall's waterweed, 1979	S
Lagarosiphon major Curly waterweed, 1967	S
Lemna minuta Least duckweed, 1987	F

Table 4. The frequency of the Kennet and Avon Canal pondweeds according to the percentage of the total 71 1 km squares for the canal in which each was found.
✳ Not found elsewhere in Wiltshire.

Potamogeton pectinatus Fennel pondweed	29.5
P. natans Broad-leaved pondweed	22.5
P. crispus Curled pondweed	11.0
P. berchtoldii Small pondweed	7.0
P. perfoliatus Perfoliate pondweed	5.5
Groenlandia densa Opposite-leaved pondweed	1.5
Potamogeton lucens Shining pondweed	1.5
✳ *P. obtusifolius* Blunt-leaved pondweed	1.5
✳ *P. friesii* Flat-stalked pondweed	1.5
P. trichoides Hairlike pondweed	1.5

Tables 3 and 4 show the importance of the canal for several other submerged and floating aquatics, a few of which are only found in the canal habitat. Table 4 shows the frequency of the canal pondweeds, *Potamogeton* and *Groenlandia*. From these two genera 13 species, excluding hybrids, were recorded in Wiltshire in the 1980s. Ten of these were found in the canal.

Emergent and Waterside Plants

There are some species well-adapted to diverse habitats. For example, great willowherb *Epilobium hirsutum* can be an emergent, riparian or a dry land species. This plant, which occurs on canal banks in all 35 canal tetrads in Wiltshire, is often a canal emergent and is described as a streamside plant in local and standard floras (Grose 1957; Clapham, Tutin and Moore 1989). According to Grose, it was the most common river, canal and poolside plant in Wiltshire in 1957 and is now the most ubiquitous canalside and towpath species in the county, where it often dominates the vegetation.

There are six dominant or co-dominant fringing emergent species along many stretches of the canal in central Wiltshire. In approximate order of abundance they are reed canary-grass *Phalaris arundinacea*, yellow iris *Iris pseudacorus*, branched bur-reed *Sparganium erectum*, reed sweet-grass *Glyceria maxima*, greater pond-sedge *Carex riparia* and lesser pond-sedge *Carex acutiformis*. Bulrush *Typha latifolia* also forms dominant stands in shallow, muddy edges and backwaters where conditions are relatively anoxic.

There are, however, further common canalside species, all of which can be emergents in the canal but are not listed by the NCC and are therefore omitted from Table 5. The six most common of these are hairy sedge *Carex hirta*, false fox-sedge *Carex otrubae*, pendulous sedge *Carex pendula*, jointed rush *Juncus articulatus*, hard rush *Juncus inflexus*, and water figwort *Scrophularia auriculata*. Less common species are gipsywort *Lycopus europaeus*, purple-loosestrife *Lythrum salicaria*, skullcap *Scutellaria galericulata*, and marsh woundwort *Stachys palustris*.

The most interesting aquatic was bittersweet *Solanum dulcamara*, which is very commonly seen as an undeniable emergent in the canal and other aqueous habitats, even deeply rooted well away from the edges at low water levels.

Canal management tends to discourage waterside shrubs and trees, particularly on the towpath side, but there are numerous backwaters, low-lying wet areas, supply streams, water-meadows and marshes associated with the canal, as well as wild areas where trees grow, rooting in or at the edge of water. The commonest in order of descending frequency are crack willow *Salix fragilis*, alder *Alnus glutinosa*, grey willow *Salix cinerea*, goat willow *Salix caprea*, white willow *Salix alba* and osier *Salix viminalis*. Herbs occurring in these fringe habitats are ragged-Robin *Lychnis flos-cuculi* and species from the genera *Carex, Galium, Geum, Juncus, Stachys* and *Stellaria*. There are others, including common comfrey *Symphytum officinale*, hemp-agrimony *Eupatorium cannabinum* and great horsetail *Equisetum telmateia*, which can occasionally be emergents.

Table 5. Emergent plants of the Kennet and Avon Canal as defined by the NCC (Palmer and Newbold 1983), in descending order of distribution frequency.
T denotes percentage frequency by tetrads. K denotes percentage frequency of 1 km squares. (A) denotes occasional formation of dense, abundant stands. ✳ Denotes a plant that may occur in marshy edges rather than as an emergent from the main canal.

✳ *Juncus effusus* Soft-rush	89T
Phalaris arundinacea Reed canary-grass	83K(A)
Myosotis scorpioides Water forget-me-not	80T
Iris pseudacorus Yellow iris	77K(A)
Sparganium erectum Branched bur-reed	76K(A)
Mentha aquatica Water mint	73K
Glyceria maxima Reed sweet-grass	72K(A)
✳ *Veronica beccabunga* Brooklime	71T
Apium nodiflorum Fool's water-cress	69T
Oenanthe crocata Hemlock water-dropwort	69T
Rorippa nasturtium-aquaticum agg. Watercress	66T
Solanum dulcamara Bittersweet	57T
✳ *Caltha palustris* Marsh-marigold	54T
Alisma plantaga-aquatica Water-plantain	51K
Ranunculus sceleratus Celery-leaved buttercup	41K
Typha latifolia Bulrush	41K(A)
Carex riparia Greater pond-sedge	38K(A)
Persicaria hydropiper Water-pepper	37T
Carex acutiformis Lesser pond-sedge	35K(A)
✳ *Equisetum palustre* Marsh horsetail	34T
Rumex hydrolapathum Water dock	31K
Myosoton aquaticum Water chickweed	30K
Galium palustre Common marsh-bedstraw	28K
Equisetum fluviatile Water horsetail	25K
Phragmites australis Common reed	25K(A)
Eleocharis palustris Common spike-rush	23T
Berula erecta Lesser water-parsnip	21K
Veronica anagallis-aquatica Blue water-speedwell	17K
Sagittaria sagittifolia Arrowhead	17K
Myosotis laxa Tufted forget-me-not	14K
Carex paniculata Greater tussock-sedge	14K
Carex nigra Common sedge	11K
Oenanthe fistulosa Tubular water-dropwort	6K
Schoenoplectus lacustris Common club-rush	6K
✳ *Ranunculus flammula* Lesser spearwort	3K
Butomus umbellatus Flowering-rush	2K
Acorus calamus Sweet-flag	2K
Alisma lanceolatum Narrow-leaved water-plantain	2K
Rorippa amphibia Great yellow-cress	2K

Non-vascular Aquatic Plants

Charophyta and other algae, especially *Cladophora* and *Spirogyra*, aquatic mosses and liverworts also occur in the Kennet and Avon Canal but were not included in the WFMP survey.

Canal Management

British Waterways control waterweed by periodic application of a Diquat preparation which favours submerged vascular species such as some potamogetons. Alternate sections of approximately 500 metres are treated, usually in May each year. Weedcutters are sometimes used in high summer to take out heavy overgrowths in certain sections, as the need arises. Dredging is also carried out occasionally to reduce silt and encroaching reeds. Recreational boating influences the flora and there is evidence that a low level of slow boat traffic is beneficial in promoting floral diversity (Hanbury 1986, 1990).

Conclusion

The total of at least 72 higher vascular aquatic plants found between 1985 and 1990 is the greatest ever recorded in the Kennet and Avon Canal, putting this waterway in a high league for diversity amongst aquatic habitats. This would appear to justify current management policies.

Colour plate page 38.

References

Byfield, A (October 1990). The Basingstoke Canal – Britain's richest waterway under threat. *British Wildlife,* 2(2).

Clapham, A R, Tutin, T G and Moore, D M (1989). *Flora of the British Isles,* 3rd edition. Cambridge University Press, Cambridge.

Grose, D (1957). *The Flora of Wiltshire.* Wiltshire Archaeological and Natural History Society, Devizes.

Hanbury, R G (1986). Conservation on canals: a review of the present status and management of British navigable canals with particular reference to aquatic plants. *Proceedings EWRS/ AAB International 7th Symposium on Aquatic Weeds.*

Last, B (1990). *Lemna minuscula* in Wiltshire. *BSBI News,* 56: 9-10.

Oliver, J D (1991). *Lemna minuscula* in Wiltshire. *BSBI News,* 58: 10.

Palmer, M and Newbold, C (1983). *Wetland and Riparian Plants in Great Britain.* Nature Conservancy Council, Peterborough.

Rich, T C G and Rich, N D B (1988). *Plant Crib.* Botanical Society of the British Isles, London.

Simpson, D A (1990). Displacement of *Elodea canadensis* Michx by *Elodea nuttallii* (Planch.) H. St. John in the British Isles. *Watsonia,* 18: 173-177.

Spencer-Jones, D and Wade, M (1986). *Aquatic Plants – a Guide to Recognition.* ICI Professional Products, Farnham.

SIX WILTSHIRE BOTANISTS

Ann Hutchison

Joseph Donald Grose 1900-1973
Ivy May Grose 1903-1990

The death of May Grose in a Swindon nursing home in December 1990 focused thought on a remarkably able botanical partnership of 40 years. May outlived Donald by an unbelievable 17 years.

The memories of them both are good; very good at field meetings, which they led mostly for members of the Natural History Section of the Wiltshire Archaeological and Natural History Society (WANHS). Remembered are the green Rover, the greetings, the informality, the giving out of long slips of paper listing the site's previous records. These were in Latin only, helping us to learn names and their correct spellings without effort. May was in charge of the master list, as well as observing and checking species with Donald.

Donald was not seen to make notes; our records just appeared in a subsequent number of *Wiltshire Plant Notes*. Occasionally a plant was worthy of further investigation but, by present-day standards, the specimen collected was always small, a leaf or a flower which was placed in his mini-vasculum, a battered metal spectacle case. How we wished to have these diagnostic features at instant recall. The identification came in a letter, hand-written or in mini-typeface, within the week. Interestingly, the meetings remembered best were in woodland, at Collingbourne, Whitsbury and West Woods.

There were specialised field meetings too. A transect in Houndwood in the 1950s and, with the Salisbury and District Natural History Society, surveys of Blackmoor Copse and Pepperbox Hill/ West Dean Hill, both mapped on a large scale, in the 1960s. Frequencies, using four ratings, were discussed in comfort at lunchtime. The next stage was Dick Sandell's typing of the species lists.

The sheer size of Wiltshire (348,070 ha), covering two vice-counties, for which he was recorder, should be remembered. In addition to their involvement at field meetings there were other visits, some connected with records received, including journeys to the far south-west for *Juncus* species. Donald knew and botanised with Patrick Hall, JE Lousley and Barbara Welch but his constant companion was May. This was reflected in the high standard of her paper-work.

Between 1942 and 1954, habitat species lists were made in 5,000 locations across the county in preparation for Part II The Vegetation of Wiltshire of their flora. Indoors there were letter-writing – there were no fewer than 44 specialist helpers involved in *The Flora of Wiltshire* – the writing of articles (1944-1967), receipt and despatch of specimens and work on the herbarium. For 17 years, from 1938, Donald compiled Wiltshire Plant Notes in the WANHS Magazine and continued for a further 12 years after the publication of *The Flora of Wiltshire*.

If the county's size is large, 84 km from north to south, the time available was not. There was the family jeweller's shop in Swindon to run until Donald's retirement in 1967. It is amazing that somehow nearly all fieldwork was accomplished on Wednesday afternoons, in the evenings and on Sundays (with an early start home for chapel). Their home at Liddington provided the ideal work place with herbarium and record cards, both now housed in WANHS's museum, and library always available.

The Flora of Wiltshire (1957) was the culmination of 20 years of historical research in addition to field work. It is also testimony to hard, efficient work behind which there was much thought. Above all was the gift of being innovative, *The Flora of Wiltshire* being the first of the county floras to include an ecological section. Indeed, Part II is even better than the traditional Part I, and one would wish to have discovered it sooner! After 30 years *The Flora of Wiltshire* improves with use and is a certain source of interest. Without it there could not have been a Wiltshire Flora Mapping Project or, to be more accurate, it would have been different, difficult and taken longer to complete. The 26 year gap on which it was built was probably right.

May's contribution, including tending the shop, should not be under-estimated, especially that to *The Flora of Wiltshire* in the preparation of the habitat lists and in the general revision of the text. In 1939 she spent 3 days searching before refinding *Cirsium tuberosum* in its original site after a gap of 50 years. Thirty-five years on, and complying with modern practice, it is likely that *The Flora of Wiltshire* would have had a dual authorship.

One tends to think, incorrectly, that the Groses did not move out of Wiltshire. Their pre-war honeymoon was spent on Sark, where an island flower guide was bought and used, and there were visits to Alderney and to the Isles of Scilly in 1939 and 1952, their records being included in JE Lousley's *Flora of the Isles of Scilly* (1971). Later they spent a week in Devon each year.

Above all, Donald and May were interested listeners. They had the gift of enjoying plants with that of a non-botanical country-lover. Their outstanding legacy to botany was *The Flora of Wiltshire*. February 1973 saw the passing of Donald Grose, a fine, unassuming botanist.

Richard Emery Sandell 1911-1978

Richard Sandell, known as Dick, was born and died in the same house in Potterne, near Devizes. He obtained a degree in history and served in the Royal Air Force in World War II. On leaving the RAF he joined the Royal Auxiliary Air Force and ran the family wine business in Devizes.

In many ways, life began for Dick after he sold the business and then had time to develop his many hobbies, of which botany was just one. He was a bell-ringer and served on the Advisory Board of Redundant Churches Committee. His interest in the arts came from his mother who had been a calligrapher with the Kelmscott Press.

He joined the WANHS and eventually became its Honorary Librarian to which post he gave much time on regular days each week. Later, he assisted the archivist, Miss P Stewart, at Wren Hall in The Close, Salisbury where he was probably in his element. Other societies to which he belonged were the Botanical Society of the British Isles (BSBI) and the British Ecological Society, whose meetings he attended and to which he introduced others. He developed an exceptional interest in the flora of the Irish bogs and, through the BSBI, helped in under-recorded squares in County Cavan for the *Atlas of the British Flora* (1962). In 1958, he was elected a Fellow of the Linnaean Society.

Dick supported and helped Donald Grose in many ways. They worked together to collect data for *The Flora of Wiltshire* and he played a very large part in its preparation and production, not only as secretary of the Flora Committee but by writing miscellaneous notes, helping with its general revision and providing financial backing. Without his assistance production of the flora would certainly have been delayed. His role in the publication of *The Supplement to the Flora of Wiltshire* (1975), which was dedicated to Donald, was as chairman of the committee responsible for its production. He was the obvious choice for the post which he carried out with ability and with matters very much under his guidance and control.

Dick's first Wiltshire plant records appeared in 1950 with many more to follow in subsequent years from many areas including the south-east and south-west of the county. He regularly searched for *Carex*, a genus of special interest to him. He also botanised extensively in

Gloucestershire as a member of the Cotteswold Field Club on whose committee he served.

He was kind, thoughtful and generous and it is good to think of him planning shrub-planting for his large garden in what were to be his last years. He made a substantial bequest to the WAHNS.

Winifred Marjorie Stevenson
1912-1977

Winifred Stevenson, known to friends and colleagues as Steve, was born in Plumstead and studied at University College, London. She taught botany and zoology at Gosport Grammar School before coming to Wiltshire in the early 1940s to teach at Chippenham Grammar School. She held the position of senior mistress for several years before moving to Devizes Grammar School in the 1960s where she remained until retiring when the school became comprehensive in 1969. Her diligence and patience as a teacher enabled many of her pupils to follow careers in biological sciences.

For many years she was a member of the WANHS and its Natural History Section (NHS), regularly attending the Section's field meetings and helping members with plant identification. Shortly before moving to Devizes she learnt to drive and abandoned her bicycle. Her new mobility enabled her to take a full part as a committee member of the NHS and to botanise in pastures new in south Wiltshire where she fell in love with the downland flora. She had a particular interest in mosses and liverworts and had her own moss herbarium.

During these years, Steve became a close friend of Donald and May Grose and compiled *Wiltshire Plant Notes* for 1969 and 1970. Her first record was published in 1962. In 1973, the year of Donald's death, she succeeded him as BSBI recorder for N Wilts (VC7).

When the NHS decided to publish the *Wiltshire Plant Notes* for the years 1957-1972 as the *Supplement to the Flora of Wiltshire*, Steve was an obvious choice to serve as a member of the committee responsible for doing so. She worked

in the WANHS's museum with Richard Sandell checking records and rehousing the herbarium sheets in new plastic bags. Sadly, her health began to deteriorate soon after the Supplement was completed and the anticipated pursuit of her interest in botany in the relaxation of retirement was not to be.

Steve was a very good friend, kind and generous with her time, energy and worldly goods.

Joan Swanborough

Joan Swanborough was born in West Kington near Chippenham. She lived in Wiltshire all her life, dying in 1981 in her early sixties. She joined the Wild Flower Society (WFS) rather late in life and the Botanical Society of the British Isles even later and was the WFS's first member to become a vice-county recorder for Wiltshire. She inherited this position from Winifred Stevenson in 1978 and compiled *Wiltshire Plant Notes* for 1972-1980 inclusive. She was not a contributor to Donald Grose's *The Flora of Wiltshire*, her first record appearing in the Plant Notes for 1965. Two of her most notable records were the rediscovery of fingered sedge *Carex digitata* on a road verge near Colerne while pushing her bicycle uphill and finding spreading hedge-parsley *Torilis arvensis* on a roadside bank at Bratton in 1972.

One of her important contributions was to encourage the young to take an interest in botany and natural history generally. She was involved in several projects with local schools, helping the County Education Department to set up a schools' nature trail in woodland near Chipppenham for European Conservation Year and developing a small nature reserve in the grounds of Hardenhuish School. At one time she was simultaneously secretary to three WFS junior branches. Among those she encouraged at a more professional level were Philip Horton and Stephanie Tyler, with whom she surveyed the disturbed banks of the M4 Motorway during its construction. Their results appear in a paper published by the WANHS in 1972. The late Adrian Grenfell, a national authority on plant aliens, was also one of her protégés. Botanists from all over the country came to stay with Joan to be shown the Wiltshire flora by her.

She involved herself in the activities of the Box Archaeological and Natural History Society from its formation in 1969, sharing 'her' plants with its members, particularly during the society's field meetings which she was always delighted to lead.

Her botanical experience was not restricted to Wiltshire. She and her husband, Ron, spent holidays cycling in Great Britain and Europe in search of plants native to the countries they visited. Ron was an ideal companion and an accomplished plant photographer specialising in orchids. His collection of photographs was accepted by the British Museum after his death.

Joan created an amazing garden filled with as many alien as 'official' garden plants. Its care could have been a full-time job for anyone without her tremendous energy and enthusiasm. 'Plants and tea at Pew Hill', her visitors usually leaving with a number of potted-up plants, continued to be a great event even during her long and difficult terminal illness. Her friendliness rewarded her to the end.

Joan Swanborough
A personal tribute from Philip Horton

The prospect of a day's botanising with Joan Swanborough was always an occasion to relish. Her enthusiasm for all things botanical was infectious and her knowledge of the Wiltshire flora extensive. However, her great love was for the countryside to the west of Chippenham with its rich limestone flora. It was a district she knew intimately from her childhood and which she continued to explore almost daily on her trusty bike.

Despite her many commitments she would always find time to share her knowledge with interested visitors, provided of course she felt they could be trusted with it. My own interest in the flora of Wiltshire was both personal and, as the Nature Conservancy Council's Assistant Regional Officer for Wiltshire from 1969 to 1977,

professional. In several cases I considered the localities she showed me to be important enough for notification as Sites of Special Scientific Interest including Little Grubbin's Meadow, now a Wiltshire Wildlife Trust reserve. These remain today and form a fitting tribute to her memory.

Barbara Welch 1903-1986

Barbara Welch (*née* Gullick) was born in Salisbury where her father started a horticultural nursery just off Mill Road, very near the cathedral. Having trained as a horticulturist at Kew, he probably fostered an early interest in plants in his daughter. Gullick's Nurseries and the shop in Fisherton Street, which they opened in 1906, were certainly well-known in Salisbury for many years, the business being passed from father to son.

After obtaining a BSc degree in geology from Bristol University, Barbara became an assistant curator at Salisbury and South Wiltshire Museum with responsibility for archaeology. In 1921 she joined the Wild Flower Society and recorded to a high standard, winning the southern prize for the 'five-mile radius competition' in 1933 with a record 631 Wiltshire species. In 1928 she joined the Botanical Society of the British Isles.

She benefited from the encouragement of two local botanists, the Hon. Mrs G Campbell of Wilton Vicarage, with whom she jointly wrote her first botanical paper 'Notes on the flora of the Salisbury district' in 1932, and HJ Goddard, a graminologist retired from Dunn's Farm Seeds Ltd. Other botanical contacts were Major JRG Watkin and E Marsden-Jones, both of Potterne near Devizes. Although Wiltshire remained the chief county for her botanical studies, she knew Patrick Hall, one of the leading amateur botanists of the period, and botanised with him in Hampshire. She also joined the Sandwiths on visits to the Bristol dock areas to record their rich flora.

In 1936 she presented a series of her drawings to the Salisbury and South Wiltshire Museum and published in the Salisbury Times an account of a number of Roman coin-hoards located in

S Wiltshire. In 1940, the year following Barbara's marriage to a professional geologist, Dr FBA Welch, she moved with him to Richmond, Surrey. In spite of this, she continued to visit Wiltshire regularly and led meetings for the WANHS including those held at Landford and Plaitford Commons in 1949 and in the Wardour Castle area in 1950. From the number of her records from these two commons and her papers relating to three London commons, one wonders if this habitat was of particular interest to her. The way she walked the Army Ranges in the area now known as the Salisbury Plain Training Area (East) and High Post Golf Course searching for purple milk-vetch *Astragalus danicus* is an example of her energy. A first county record of hers was slender rush *Juncus tenuis* in 1936. She contributed many records to *Wiltshire Plant Notes* of which she was co-author with JD Grose in 1942. The geological section and two biographies in his *Flora of Wiltshire* of 1957 are by her.

In addition to all her Wiltshire input she made substantial contributions to the following counties and their floras especially from the early 1940s to the mid-1950s – Middlesex, Surrey, Gloucestershire (1948), the London Area (1951-52), Monmouthshire (1970), Essex (1974) and to *Flowering Plants of Wales* (1983). Barbara held more than one post with the BSBI, including that of an Assistant Secretary to help with conservation. She also became a voluntary worker in the Department of Botany, British Museum (Natural History) assisting Dr A Melderis several days a week in the national collection. All these activities ceased on her husband's retirement in 1963 when they moved to Cheltenham where she died 23 years later.

Having given so much of her time and energy to the BSBI, often in the company of her fellow members, Barbara left the society a large bequest, from which a generous sum was donated to the Wiltshire Flora Mapping Project towards the publication of this book (see Financial Assistance on page ix).

It is a reflection that these six botanists were lost to the county in various ways between 1973 and 1990. They have been followed by another generation who continue recording with a similar objective but in a different way.

References

Horton, P, Swanborough, J and Tyler, S (1972). Botanical interest created by the construction of the M4 Motorway in Wiltshire. *Wiltshire Archaeological and Natural History Magazine*, **67A**: 7-11.

Notes on the flora of the Salisbury district 1932. *Wiltshire Archaeological and Natural History Magazine*, **46**: 58-63.

PART TWO
Species Monographs

TILIA CORDATA Miller
Small-leaved Lime

Jonathan Spencer

Until recently, the native small-leaved lime *Tilia cordata* Miller was one of the least familiar trees in England. However, over the last ten years or so, there has been a great rise in interest in woodland history and ecology and the tree has become something of a totem amongst ecologists and botanists across the country. The reasons for the extraordinary rise in interest in this otherwise rather readily overlooked tree must surely lie in the potent mix of ancient history and natural history implicit in its presence in ancient woodland or hedgerow. This mix both excites the imagination and appeals to our strong sense of continuity in an otherwise rapidly changing landscape. An understanding of the distribution and behaviour of this tree in any region demands an understanding of history, ecology, plant physiology and climate, along with some inkling of the ways in which past land-use and present woodland character are interrelated. A study of native lime leads one along many interesting avenues of investigation.

Most of the native small-leaved lime in England is confined to ancient woodland sites, the species being only occasionally found in old churchyards and parkland (where it has almost certainly been planted) or in old hedgerows where, if present in abundance, it invariably marks the ghost boundaries of former woodland. Very occasionally it may be found on old commons. While its association with ancient woodland is very close, both coppice stools of native lime and occasional maiden stems may be found in old secondary woodland adjacent to or in the vicinity of ancient woods containing lime (Rackham 1980). At least one example of old coppice stools occurring on ancient ridge and furrow is known from Northamptonshire.

Tilia cordata is a species whose presence and distribution is peculiarly meaningful amongst British trees. Its former abundance in the pollen record suggests it was once a major component of our native woodland across much of England and parts of Wales. Its present relict status is the culmination of a long and continuous decline over the last 5,000 years. Its past importance and present rarity has attracted the attention of many botanists and palynologists, notably C D Pigott of the Botanic Garden, Cambridge. Donald Pigott's careful ecological studies, pursued over the last 20 years, have provided sufficient insight into the plant's behaviour under different climatic conditions for us to understand why this species has declined in abundance so dramatically and why it should be so closely associated with ancient woodland. Our understanding of the ecological history of small-leaved lime is perhaps better than for any other woodland plant (Pigott 1991).

Tilia cordata is essentially a continental species favouring a climate with long, hot summers. Studies of the reproductive biology of lime at the extremes of its native range in Cumbria and Lancashire (Pigott & Huntley 1981) have shown that it depends on a long period of hot sunny summer weather with the temperature rising to 20°C and above for several consecutive days in June or July, or July and August at the northern reaches of its range, for the pollen tube to grow sufficiently vigorously to reach the unfertilised ovule within the ovary. Such climatic conditions have not been prevalent in Great Britain since the onset of the

Atlantic period some 8,000 years ago (see Coleborne 1983 for a concise summary of past climatic change) when the climate became noticeably colder, with average summer temperatures falling by about 2°C and the weather becoming cooler and wetter in the summer and cold and wet in winter, a familiar pattern that has persisted, more or less, to the present day! Under these conditions lime is rarely able to produce much in the way of viable seed. Years in which seed production has been possible have become markedly infrequent in recent centuries, especially in the north and west of its range, though suitable conditions may perhaps have been present in northern England in the Middle Ages (Pigott 1989a). However, such climatic conditions do occasionally prevail in southern England today, and regeneration from seed can sometimes be found in woods of the right structure where trees have been allowed to mature in open sunlit conditions. The fruits are wind dispersed, with the close proximity of most seedlings and young maiden stems to parent trees suggesting that even when the plant does produce viable seed it is not readily or widely dispersed.

The seedlings are very prone to predation by bank voles *Clethrionomys glareolus* and other small mammals (Pigott 1985) and the ecology of these species in woodland of various types is almost certainly a critical factor in the successful recruitment of lime from seed. The relationship between lime, climate, voles and man is indeed a complex one.

While having limited capacity to reproduce by seed under prevailing climatic conditions, small-leaved lime nevertheless possesses remarkable powers of vegetative growth, being able to grow from coppice stools, broken roots, buried branches and fallen trees. It is one of the most vigorously persistent of native trees, being both shade tolerant and itself casting a dense shade, and hence a strong competitor with other tree and shrub species. It is, however, very palatable, both as fresh coppice regrowth and as a young seedling, and is consequently very vulnerable to the presence of grazing and browsing animals. It is generally absent from woods with a history of past grazing. Its

virtual absence from former Royal Forests, other wood-pastures or commons and from areas such as the Weald, where extensive grazing by the cattle and sheep of Saxon and earlier settlers took place, is very telling (Baker *et al.* 1984). The poor ability of *Tilia cordata* to make up lost ground by natural regeneration, coupled with its vulnerability to grazing, are key features in determining the present distribution of this otherwise very widespread and formerly successful species in Britain.

The pattern of lime distribution across England and South Wales is now remarkably discontinuous. Its once extensive cover has been fragmented into a complex pattern of groups of woods containing lime within wide tracts of countryside, often rich in ancient woodland, devoid of native lime stands. It is widely, if patchily, distributed from South Lakeland to Devon and from the west coast of Wales to Kent, with notable concentrations in Lincolnshire, East Anglia, the northern end of Rockingham Forest in Northamptonshire, the Derbyshire Dales, the Mendips in Somerset and the lower Wye Valley in Wales. Southern England possesses scattered pockets of lime woodland with patches occurring in ancient woodland near Shaftesbury in Dorset, in Hampshire, both in the west at Boulsbury Wood and on the Greensand hangars near Selborne, and in a few isolated stands in West Berkshire. Large stands of small-leaved lime are almost entirely absent from the home counties, Surrey, Sussex and Kent in spite of a wealth of ancient woodland, hedgerow and forest, though there are a fair number of scattered isolated stools, or groups of stools, especially on the Surrey/Sussex borders of the Weald.

The national pattern of distribution of lime is accurately mirrored in Wiltshire. It is absent from virtually the whole county except for two groups of woods, one north of Wootton Bassett, the second far to the south on the edge of the New Forest in a narrow belt from Loosehangar Copse, near Downton to Whiteparish Common. In both these closely circumscribed areas, lime occurs as quite extensive stands (as in Webb's Wood, Loosehangar Copse and Langley Wood) surrounded by woods containing smaller areas of lime stools or individual trees, both within ancient woodland or as hedgerow trees. Beyond these two 'lime zones' there are only two other authenticated localities presently known, one a line of limes in a hedgerow along an ancient lane running south-west from Orcheston near Shrewton, the other an isolated and very small, but otherwise very convincing stand of lime coppice stools at Gopher Wood, an ancient wood on the ridge of the downs north of Pewsey.

Small-leaved lime is a catholic tree, being found on a wide variety of soil types from limestone scarps to acidic sandstone slopes. In the present-day landscape it shows a marked preference for lowland clay soils, though this observed correlation is almost certainly greatly influenced by past patterns of land use. The pollen record suggests an abundant presence in a much wider range of situations. In Wiltshire, stands of native lime are almost entirely confined to the heavy and fairly acid clays that prevail within its two primary areas of distribution. At Webb's Wood and its satellites it is found on heavy Oxford Clay, while in the south between Redlynch and Whiteparish it occupies a narrow belt of London Clay fringing the more acidic and gravelly soils of the New Forest. The small stand at Gopher Wood is situated on similar, though geologically much more recent, superficial Clay-with-flints. The persistence of lime on these heavy clays, where it has occasionally persisted in sizeable stands, does seem to be a reflection of the past performance of lime in recruitment from either regrowth or regeneration into the developing woodland following past felling or disturbance. At Loosehangar Copse in the south of the county, the ancient woodland containing the lime straddles the geological boundary between the London Clay and the more free draining and acidic gravels of the Barton and Bracklesham Beds. The lime is largely absent from the latter, occurring only as occasional giant coppice stools or as coppice in the hedges on the ancient boundary banks of the wood. There is little evidence on the ground, however, to suggest that these areas, within the boundaries of the same coppices, were treated markedly differently in the past.

As with limewoods elsewhere in southern Britain, those in Wiltshire are most often on level ground with evidence of poor drainage and gleying. The soils are generally brown earth mull soils, acidic in character and tending towards the development of mor humus in places where the stands are long undisturbed, but with active earthworm activity readily incorporating the fallen leaves into the soil. That lime has a profound effect on the character and development of the underlying soil, promoting the development of woodland brown earth soils with a mull humus, has been demonstrated (Pigott 1989b), while Rackham (1980) has shown that in East Anglia the soils of limewoods are characteristically rich in loess, perhaps reflecting their probable descent from original uncleared woodland rather than from open grazed or cultivated land in the distant past. Similar studies of the soils under lime woodland in Wiltshire have yet to be undertaken.

The concentration of present-day lime stands in Wiltshire on the heavy Oxford and London clays rather restricts the range of woodland plant communities with which lime is now associated in the county. All of the more extensive stands known to the author are of the *Quercus robur-Pteridium aquilinum-Rubus fruticosus* woodland recognised by the National Vegetation Classification (NVC type W10; Rodwell 1991), a very widespread type of lowland oakwood found on the heavier, slightly acid clay soils and characteristically dominated by oak *Quercus robur* in the canopy, hazel *Corylus avellana* in the understorey and extensive stands of bracken *Pteridium aquilinum*, bramble *Rubus fruticosus* and bluebell *Hyacinthoides non-scripta* on the woodland floor. The impermeable nature of the clay soils within these woods, coupled with their rather flat topography, encourages the retention of surface water, which in turn encourages the spring-flowering wood anemone *Anemone nemorosa*, another characteristic and conspicuous component of this woodland type in Wiltshire. The stands of lime, though of considerable historical and ecological significance, do not change the floristic character of these woods sufficiently for them to be recognised as a separate entity under this particular classification, though the dense shade can suppress the abundance and vigour of many otherwise characteristic components of the community. Indeed, some of the more light-demanding species may be absent altogether in the most dense and darkest stands. The lime and hazel dominated stands of this type of woodland are best regarded as variants of the NVC W10 woodland type. In all the Wiltshire limewoods they occur together as a mosaic within tracts of extensive and more typical oak-bracken-bramble *Quercus robur-Pteridium aquilinum-Rubus fruticosus* woodland.

While most of the evidence for the extensive abundance of lime in the past comes from elsewhere in lowland England, it would seem likely that large areas of Wiltshire would have had lime present in prehistory, either in extensive stands or as a constituent of other less lime dominated types of woodland. Archaeological evidence of the preserved woodland soils under such ancient earthworks as Silbury Hill and other ancient Neolithic monuments suggests that even the extensive Salisbury Plain was lightly wooded in the past (Dimbleby 1984), while our knowledge of present-day woodland ecology would suggest that the original woodland here would have contained stands of lime as a constituent of woodland made up predominantly of ash and hazel. The paucity of ancient preserved deposits across the county precludes anything more than informed speculation on the exact nature of the original woodland in the area. What is likely, though, is that the forest soils of Salisbury Plain in the distant past would have been markedly different from those found today, with extensive stripping of the mantle of loess and lighter boulder clays following the clearance of woodland from the plain. The significance of the surviving fragment of lime woodland on superficial boulder clays at Gopher Wood becomes apparent here.

The recording of *Tilia cordata* in Wiltshire is far from complete. An exact distribution of the species within woods and hedgerows has not yet been compiled at a detailed level. Recording its presence and abundance within individual hedgerows and woods would give a picture of considerable historical and ecological value. It also seems likely that there may be further outliers of native lime awaiting discovery in the heavily wooded and comparatively poorly explored north and west of the county. As the Orcheston record suggests, native lime can crop up in the most unexpected locations! There has also been some considerable confusion in the past between the native *Tilia cordata* and the widely planted hybrid lime *Tilia* x *vulgaris*. In a recent survey of one wood (Clouts Wood near Swindon) the occurrence of two large 'coppice stools' of *Tilia* x *vulgaris*, resulting from the felling of two large ornamental trees planted into an undoubted ancient coppice woodland, was taken as sufficient evidence for these trees to be regarded as the native *Tilia cordata*! This is an interesting reversal of the more usual practice of using plant species as indicators of ancient woodland. The trees are readily distinguished with a little practice, the examination of known native populations being recommended for those uncertain of their ground.

The future of *Tilia cordata* in Wiltshire looks encouraging at present. Many of the sites are now nature reserves or designated as Sites of Special Scientific Interest, while the most extensive stands in the county, at Webb's Wood, are in the care of the Forestry Commission, who now manage their ancient woodland with considerably more sympathy than they have done in the past. The most vulnerable sites would appear to be those in hedgerows or ghost woodland boundaries for which there still remains no effective protection. Information on the location and extent of these sites would at least allow for their consideration for Tree Preservation Orders or for the recently proposed Hedgerow Orders, and would go some way to preventing further loss through ignorance.

Colour plate, page 33.

References

Baker, C A, Moxey, P A and Oxford, P M (1978). Woodland continuity and change in Epping Forest. *Field Studies*, 4: 645-669.

Coleborne, P (1983). *Hampshire's Countryside Heritage 2. Ancient Woodland.* Hampshire County Council.

Dimbleby, G W (1984). Anthropogenic changes from neolithic through medieval times. *New Phytology,* 98: 57-72.

Pigott, C D (1985). Selective damage to tree seedlings by bank voles *Clethrionomys glareolus. Oecologia (Berlin),* 67: 367-371.

Pigott, C D (1989a). Factors controlling the distribution of *Tilia cordata* Mill at the northern limits of its geographical range IV. Estimated ages of trees. *New Phytologist,* 112: 117-121.

Pigott, C D (1989b). The growth of Lime *Tilia cordata* in an experimental plantation and its influence on soil development and vegetation. *Quarterly Journal of Forestry,* LXXXIII, 1: 14-24.

Pigott, C D (1991). Biological flora of the British Isles, *Tilia cordata. Journal of Ecology,* 79, 4: 1147-1207.

Pigott, C D and Huntley, J P (1981). Factors controlling the distribution of *Tilia cordata* at the northern limits of its geographical range. III. Nature and causes of seed sterility. *New Phytologist,* 87: 817-839.

Rackham, O (1980). *Ancient Woodland: Its History, Vegetation and Uses in England.* Edward Arnold, London.

Rodwell, J (1991). *British Plant Communities, Vol. 1: Woodlands and Scrub.* Cambridge University Press, Cambridge.

SORBUS TORMINALIS (L.) Crantz
Wild Service-tree

David Rice

Wild service-tree *Sorbus torminalis* (L.) Crantz is native in the British Isles. It has been recorded in at least 53 vice-counties in Great Britain from Cumbria and Lincolnshire southwards, but not in Ireland.

The following quotation from John Aubrey's *Natural History of Wiltshire* 1685, is the first documented record for Wiltshire. 'Service-trees grow naturally in Grettwood, in the parish of Gretenham, belonging to George Ayliffe, Esq. In the park of Kington St Michel is onely one. At the foot of Hedington Hill, and also at the bottome of the hill at Whitesheet, which is the same range of hill, doe growe at least twenty cervise-trees.' No current records exist for Heddington and White Sheet Hill. It may be that the latter refers to a hill elsewhere which is no longer known by this name. Preston, in *Flowering Plants of Wilts* 1888, lists two confirmed sites. Three locations are named by Flower in *The Flora of Wiltshire* 1857-1874. Grose, in *The Flora of Wiltshire* 1957, lists 15 sites and Stearn, in the *Supplement to the Flora of Wiltshire* 1975, lists four additional locations not all of which were confirmed by the author.

In the 16 years since 1975, many more sites have been located. The majority result from the Wiltshire Trust for Nature Conservation's survey of ancient woodland sites. The remainder were discovered by Nature Conservancy Council (NCC) surveyors and individual botanists. The total number of reliable locations is now 47, 19 of which I have personally confirmed. Ten are in hedgerows, six are confined to woodland boundaries and 27 are within woods. The likelihood of more specimens being discovered in woodland is low, but I am sure

further trees in hedgerows remain to be found. Today, by far the best stand in the county is at Great Wood, Grittenham.

All the documented locations are shown on Map 202 (page 203). Most are on privately owned land, though some are adjacent to rights of way, therefore prior permission should be sought before searching them out. In the last 15 years a number of trees have been planted throughout the county but none of these are included on the map.

The wild service-tree is frequently overlooked or mistaken for a species of maple *Acer* sp. It can grow to 22 m with a tall-domed, spreading crown in open situations, but in woodland is frequently hemmed in by more dominant species. In such situations it is most noticeable in the autumn when the leaves turn from deep red to purple. In winter, the buds are distinctly glossy green and globular. The leaves are ovate, 80-100 mm long, 3-5 lobed, all finely and usually doubly serrate, borne alternately on shoots that are shiny, dark purplish-brown above and olive-brown beneath. They are hard, shiny, rather deep green on both sides with a yellow-green petiole 20-50 mm long. No other species of *Sorbus* has a similar leaf. Maple leaves are similar but borne opposite.

The flowers, which appear in May-June, are white, 10-20 mm across with yellow anthers in loose, green, densely pubescent heads 100-120 mm wide, similar to most *Sorbus* species. The fruit is obovoid, 10 mm in diameter, slightly ribbed, brown and speckled rusty.

Regeneration is by root suckers that often appear at some distance from the parent tree. Viable seed is produced but germination requires freezing and thawing, conditions that rarely occur naturally in this tree's British range. Furthermore, many seeds are destroyed by the parasitic wasp *Torymus druparum*, by fungi and by the predation of mammals and birds.

It has been speculated that there is a relationship between *Sorbus torminalis* and ancient woodland. Peterken states that *S. torminalis* has a strong affinity with ancient woods, showing little or no ability to colonise secondary woodland and rarely found in other habitats. Rackham (1980) confirms this statement and its distribution in Wiltshire appears to provide further supporting evidence. On the map (Figure 4, page 16) the present locations have been superimposed on the woodland cover at the end of the Roman period, according to Grundy. These boundaries are not claimed to be entirely accurate. Nevertheless, the greater proportion of the sites fall within, or close to, these ancient woodlands. Grundy makes no mention of the New Forest but it is supposed that his references to localities in the south-east of the county would have been in that area. The major clusters of ancient woodlands, as identified in the NCC's Ancient Woodland Inventory 1987, are also shown. It can be seen that there is a correlation between ancient woodland and the occurrence of *S. torminalis*.

The Forestry Commission has produced a map showing ten soil groups relevant to tree growth potential which indicates that *S. torminalis* is confined to only two soil groups, rendzinas over chalk and limestone and surface-water gleys and other clayey soils. All the locations within the former are on rendzinas over limestone. There are none on rendzinas over chalk.

The Future

Current forestry and nature conservation policies recognise the value of ancient, semi-natural woodland. It is important that the implementers of such policies are able to identify *S. torminalis* and recognise its historical and nature conservation value so that management plans give due regard to its continued existence. Ancient hedgerow specimens can only be protected by the voluntary agreement of the owner or by Tree Preservation Orders.

There is no evidence to suggest that *S. torminalis* was planted prior to the mid-1970s. Future surveyors must be aware of planted specimens dating from that time.

Conclusion

In Wiltshire *S. torminalis* is confined to limestone and clay soils. Its distribution shows a strong correlation with areas forested in the Roman period and the main areas of ancient woodland and hedgerows of ancient origin that exist today.

Colour plate, page 33.

References

Aubrey, J (1847). *Memoires of Naturall Remarques* in the County of Wiltshire MS. J Britton (ed). First published 1685.

Aubrey, J (1862). *Topographical Collection, 1659-70* MS. J E Jackson (ed).

Bowsher, P (1987). *Wiltshire Inventory of Ancient Woodlands* Provisional. Nature Conservancy Council, Peterborough.

Grose, D (1957). *The Flora of Wiltshire*. Wiltshire Archaeological and Natural History Society, Devizes.

Grundy, G B (1939). *The Ancient Woodland of Wiltshire*. Wiltshire Archaeological and Natural History Society, Devizes.

Peterken, G F (1981). *Woodland Conservation and Management*. Chapman and Hall, London.

Preston, Rev T A (1888). *The Flowering Plants of Wiltshire*. Wiltshire Archaeological and Natural History Society, Devizes.

Rackham, O (1976). *Trees and Woodland in the British Landscape*. Dent, London.

Rackham, O (1980). *Ancient Woodland*. Edward Arnold, London.

Stearn, L F (ed) (1975). *Supplement to the Flora of Wiltshire*. Wiltshire Archaeological and Natural History Society, Devizes.

THESIUM HUMIFUSUM DC.
Bastard-toadflax

Beatrice Gillam

I was introduced to this humble plant in 1964 at Barnsley Warren, Gloucestershire during a Cotswold Grassland Ecology Course at Cirencester Agriculture College. The investigation being carried out was not primarily concerned with the plant but with a cydnid bug *Sehirus dubius*, which feeds solely on bastard-toadflax *Thesium humifusum* DC. Having been 'bitten by the bug', it was a natural step to find out more about the distribution and ecology of its food plant.

Thesium humifusum is the only representative of Santalaceae in Great Britain where it is native. Its distribution is restricted to chalk and limestone soils. It is found on the North Downs in Surrey, the South Downs, in Hampshire, Dorset, Wiltshire, Gloucestershire, East Anglia and Lincolnshire. This distribution represents 67 10 km squares. It occurs widely on chalk downland in both north and south Wiltshire but is rare on Oolitic limestone in the north-west of the county. It was recorded in 18 10 km squares during the period 1984-1991. Wiltshire has more unimproved chalk grassland than any other county and probably supports the largest number of colonies of *Thesium*. Its distribution is shown on Map 248 (page 220).

Both the Latin and English names describe some aspect of the plant: *Thesium* after the legend that it formed part of the wreath that the Athenian hero, Thesus, gave to the Cretan princess Ariadne; *humifusum* derived from the Latin *humus* = on the ground and *fusus* = prostrate or stretched out. 'Bastard-toadflax' probably refers to the slight resemblance of its leaves to those of the legitimate toadflax, *Linaria*. Donald Grose quotes the early Latin name *Linaria adulterina* which would have been a direct translation of its English name.

Thesium humifusum is a slender, perennial hemi-parasite, hairless and yellow-green. Its haustoria are attached to the roots of herbs, including grasses, growing adjacent to it in the surrounding sward. It frequently occurs where sheep's-fescue *Festuca ovina* is the only host plant within reach. Other hosts known to me include quaking-grass *Briza media*, glaucous sedge *Carex flacca*, mouse-ear hawkweed *Pilosella officinarum*, and salad burnet *Sanguisorba minor*. Its parasitic habit is probably one of the reasons why it does not colonise bare ground including that of active ant-hills. It has not been found on any of the thousands of ant-hills on Parsonage Down National Nature Reserve where it is well-distributed in the surrounding vegetation. The rootstock and the lower part of the stem are woody. The stems, which have four minutely rough raised lines, are spreading or prostrate in very short grassland but grow vertically up to 300 mm long and forming dense clumps in areas where the grass is ungrazed, as on parts of the Salisbury Plain Training Area (SPTA).

The alternate leaves are linear, one-veined and average 15 mm in length and 2.5 mm in width. The flowers, which are arranged alternately along few-branching stems and arise from short stout pedicels; each have three narrow pointed bracteoles, one long and two short. These persist in the autumn after the fruits have fallen, giving the fading plant a unique appearance. The five off-white spreading petals and their supporting triangular sepals are like tiny stars, no more than 3-4 mm across.

The ovary is 3 mm long, ribbed and, at first, the same yellow-green as the rest of the plant but, as the seeds develop, the ovary and the fleshy pedicel swell and change to light orange and are crowned by the persistent inrolled pericarp.

Flowers can be found from June to late October, the youngest being at the tops of the stems. From mid-July, buds, open flowers and developed ovaries are present together.

In spite of its trailing habit, the spreading flower petals and the whole plant's yellow-green colour make it conspicuous among the darker green foliage of most of its associate plants, though it may be less obvious where it grows among the similarly coloured dwarf sedge *Carex humilis*.

Thesium humifusum is known to be the sole host food plant of two insects: the cydnid bug *Sehirus dubius*, already referred to, and a tiny moth *Epermenia insecurella* (Staint.).

Sehirus dubius, like all true bugs, has sucking mouth parts which enable it to feed on the sap of its host plant. The bug feeds exclusively on the swollen pedicel and probably on the epidermis of the ovary. In their early stage, the striking red and black nymphs sometimes cluster together on the food plant but, as they grow, they scatter and, like the larger iridescent black adults become more difficult to find. The range of this insect is necessarily limited by the distribution of *Thesium*. It was first found in Gloucestershire in 1964 and, from 1967, I have found it on most sites in Wiltshire where *Thesium* grows strongly and produces plenty of fruit to sustain the colony. Its long period of flowering and fruit production coincides with the time when the nymphs are feeding.

Epermenia insecurella is a small moth whose tiny larvae feed on more than one part of the plant. The first generation start by mining the leaves but, as they grow, they feed on them externally. In July, the second generation feed on the flowers and unripe seeds. This moth has probably been overlooked by entomologists in Wiltshire for many years. It was recorded in 1889 at Granham Hill near Marlborough, a locality where *Thesium* no longer occurs, and was next identified on Salisbury Plain in 1990.

The survival of *Thesium humifusum* in Wiltshire should be secure on chalk grassland that is not artificially fertilised because, as a prostrate perennial, it is tolerant of grazing and drought and has the ability to persist in very small colonies. On the SPTA it survives in grassland cut for hay, in small pockets on tumuli, other man-made banks and on the flat target ranges at Bulford. By the autumn of 1990, it was almost the only species not to have wilted on steep, south-facing slopes after a summer of almost tropical heat.

Colour plate, page 34.

References

Emmet, A M (ed) (1988). *A Field Guide to the Smaller British Lepidoptera*. British Entomological and Natural History Society, London.

Garrard, I and Streeter, D (1983). *The Wild Flowers of the British Isles*. Macmillan, London.

Grose, D (1957). *The Flora of Wiltshire*. Wiltshire Archaeological and Natural History Society, Devizes.

Handlist of the Microlepidoptera of the Marlborough District (10 mile radius) (1938). Cambridge University Press, Cambridge.

Lewis, C T (1975). *Elementary Latin Dictionary*. Oxford University Press, Oxford.

Macleod, R D (1952). *Key to the Names of British Plants*. Pitman Press, Bath.

Perring, F H and Walters, S M (eds) (1977). *Atlas of the British Flora*. Botanical Society of the British Isles. EP Publishing Ltd., Wakefield.

PHYTEUMA ORBICULARE L.
Round-headed Rampion

Beatrice Gillam and David Green

The genus *Phyteuma*, which is a member of the Campanulaceae family, is represented by two species in Great Britain of which only round-headed rampion *Phyteuma orbiculare* L. occurs in Wiltshire. A perennial native of chalk grassland, it is confined to central Europe and southern English counties from Dorset to Kent. *The Atlas of the British Flora* (1976) showed that it was present in 33 10 km squares, five of which were in Wiltshire, and that it was most abundant on the South Downs.

It has a strange distribution in Wiltshire. In S. Wilts (VC8), which lies mainly on the chalk (Map 388, page 274), it is found in only three localities, one being the scrubby bank of a lane at East Winterslow. In N. Wilts (VC7) it stretches along 12 km at the south-west end of the Marlborough Downs from Oliver's Castle near Devizes eastwards to Walker's Hill. The most northerly colony in the county, and therefore in Great Britain, is on the artificial earthen banks of the stone circle at Avebury. Colonies in many of these downland localities are scattered and scarce but on Oliver's Castle and Beacon Hill they are extensive with an estimated 5,000 plants.

The first documented evidence of *Phyteuma* in Wiltshire was by T Johnson in 1634 who observed it 'Between Selbury and Beacon Hill in the way to Bath'. It can still be found along the banked verges of the old London to Bath road not far from the historic milestone on Beacon Hill. In the 1980s it was found on all the downs in N. Wilts named by D Grose in *The Flora of Wiltshire* (1957).

Most of the unimproved chalk downland on which this plant grows lies between 137 m and 275 m and is steep or very steep, a good example of this type of geomorphology being the terracette banks of King's Play Hill. Like most perennials adapted to growing on the chalk, *Phyteuma* can tolerate grazing. Under its pressure, it produces short-stemmed, leafy, open rosettes of basal leaves. By contrast, where it survives in ungrazed *Brachypodium pinnatum-Bromopsis erecta* grassland, the basal leaves are reduced in number and have long petioles and narrower blades in response to shading by the long grass.

The height of the flowering period is late July and throughout August, but the basal leaves are identifiable from May onwards. They arise from deeply-buried, spindle-shaped roots. The shape of the blade is variable as already indicated, but is commonly lanceolate, narrowing at the base. Its main and secondary veins are pale, due to the latex within them, deeply sunk on the top surface and correspondingly prominent on the under surface of the blade. Each secondary vein runs from the mid-rib to the blade edge where it ends in a crenature tipped with a tiny, pointed pale swelling which is a useful diagnostic vegetative feature visible without the use of a lens. The blade edge is minutely rough but hairless. The slender petiole is somewhat wiry and grooved on the top side.

Stem leaves are alternate, linear-lanceolate and decreasing in size towards the flower head. The lower have short petioles but the upper are sessile and those at the top clasp the stem. All may be sparsely hairy along the edges only but, like the basal leaf blades, they always have the characteristic pale spot at each crenature.

The purple-blue flowers of *Phyteuma* might be confused at first sight with those of devils'-bit scabious *Succisa pratensis* with which it grows and which flowers at the same time of year. Both have numerous small flowers arranged in a globular fashion but *Phyteuma* has only a single flower head on each stem in contrast to several on that of *Succisa*.

The bracts are roughly triangular, irregularly hairy and small. The buds are inwardly curved, as are the five long and very narrow petals which are united at first to form a tube. As they develop, they remain joined at the top enclosing the long, thin purple style. Eventually the stigma breaks through, the petals become free and soon begin to wither, leaving an entanglement of dying petals, free styles and partly-free petals all curving inwards thus maintaining the globular shape of the flower head.

It would be speculative to suggest reasons for the present-day almost complete absence of *Phyteuma* from south Wiltshire without knowledge of its previous history. In the north, it occurs only on Middle and Upper Chalk and mainly on downland that is either too steep to plough or is a designated National Nature Reserve or Site of Special Scientific Interest. However, all these conditions also prevail in the south, which suggests that some other factors relate to its absence. It is encouraging that its distribution on the north Wiltshire downs has apparently not changed in the last 50 years, though its abundance has not been determined.

Colour plate, page 34.

References

Clapham, A R, Tutin, T G and Warburg, E F (1962). *Flora of the British Isles.* Cambridge University Press, Cambridge.

Grose, D (1957). *The Flora of Wiltshire.* Wiltshire Archaeological and Natural History Society, Devizes.

CIRSIUM TUBEROSUM (L.) All.
Tuberous Thistle

Sue Everett

The first written reference to tuberous thistle *Cirsium tuberosum* (L.) All. in Great Britain was that of Lambert, who recorded it at Great Ridge, Wiltshire in 1812. Grose (1957) compiled all the available records dating from Lambert's time to the mid-1950s and became familiar with most of the localities. However, the precise locations of many of these are undocumented. In 1985, I was employed by the Nature Conservancy Council (NCC) to assess the distribution and status of vascular plants listed in the British Red Data Book (Perring and Farrell 1983). With the help of a number of Wiltshire botanists and the chalk grassland survey team of the NCC, almost complete coverage of known sites for *C. tuberosum* and its hybrid with dwarf thistle *Cirsium acaule* Scop. was achieved in 1986. Most of the data cited below was collected during the 1986 survey.

Until 1992 *Cirsium tuberosum* was known from only eight sites in Britain, seven of which were in Wiltshire. Two of these sites were well-separated localities within the Salisbury Plain Training Area (SPTA). The locality outside Wiltshire is a small clifftop meadow in south Wales. *C. tuberosum* was also known from Eversden in Cambridgeshire, from where it disappeared in 1973 as a result of the destruction of its grassland habitat by intensive agriculture. Living material from the latter site survives in the Cambridge Botanic Garden. Shortly before going to press, Jack Pile reported finding *C. tuberosum* and the hybrid thistle in four additional locations on the Imber Ranges of the SPTA.

In Wiltshire, *C. tuberosum* and the hybrid thistle are found on semi-natural, agriculturally

unimproved grassland mainly on the Upper Chalk, with a few localities over the Middle and Lower Chalk (pers. comm. Gilbert Green 1991). Drift is not thought to be present on most of the sites but at least one may lie over material containing a large amount of flint. Its name, 'Stony Hill', would appear to confirm this. The plant's 10 km square distribution in Wiltshire is shown in Figure 6.

Figure 6. Distribution of *C. tuberosum* in Wiltshire. Pale grey 10 km square = hybrid only, dark grey 10 km squares = tuberous thistle, E = extinct (none of these localities appear to have been good well-established ones, except at Rowde ST 96).

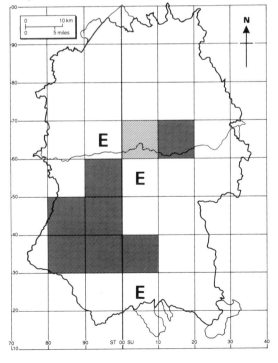

83

C. tuberosum is a perennial herbaceous plant with grooved, unwinged stems covered in cottony (arachnoid) hairs. The plants can reach a large size, particularly in ungrazed grasslands where several hundred flowering scapes may be seen on one plant, covering an area of up to one metre square and reaching a metre in height. In grazed grassland, the plants are usually smaller. The leaves are dull green with sparse, cottony hairs underneath and deeply pinnatified. The flowering heads are pink-purple, usually solitary, the receptacle is rounded with cottony hairs and appressed purple-tinged bracts which narrow to an out-turned point. An elongated receptacle indicates that hybridisation has occurred with *C. acaule* (see Figure 7).

Of six characters tested by Ann Hutchison in 1986, only two, the shape of receptacle/flowering head and type of hairs present, were found to be reliable in differentiating *C. tuberosum* from the hybrid thistle (on fresh material only). She discarded leaf outline, stem length, floret colour and flowering time as unreliable characters.

Although *C. tuberosum* is only known from seven Wiltshire sites, a further ten localities hold populations of the hybrid thistle and, historically, both were known from additional sites on the Wiltshire chalk. One atypical site, consisting of two damp lowland meadows at Rowde, situated at the foot of the chalk scarp, was known until the 1930s. However, the underlying geology at the foot of the downs is usually highly calcareous due to the presence of chalk material accumulated from erosion processes on the chalk downs.

Grose (1957) considered that the most characteristic associates of *C. tuberosum* (excluding 'species which are generally distributed on the downs') were saw-wort *Serratula tinctoria* and devils'-bit scabious *Succisa pratensis*. This was confirmed in 1986 when other characteristic associates zigzag clover *Trifolium medium*, dyer's greenweed *Genista tinctoria* and betony *Stachys officinalis* were also noted. Although all these species were not present on every site, they were often seen on the same pieces of downland as *C. tuberosum* or the hybrid thistle, and their presence is considered indicative of comparatively mesotrophic conditions for chalk grassland, probably related to climate and the predominantly northerly and westerly aspects of the sites. The presence of a chalk heath community on one site is thought to be associated with underlying flinty material, possibly residual Clay-with-flints or a flint layer in the chalk. Depth of soil may also be an important factor but the soil has not been investigated on any of the sites.

The typical grassland community where *C. tuberosum* grows is sheep's-fescue-meadow

Figure 7. Aid to identifying *C. tuberosum* (Hutchison 1986). Drawings by Valerie Headland.

(a) *Cirsium acaule*

Receptacle and flowerhead elongated; Jointed hairs only.

(b) The hybrid (*C. tuberosum* x *C. acaule*)

Receptacle and flowerhead elongated (the extent of elongation is related to the closeness of the hybrid to *C. tuberosum* or *C. acaule*). Jointed and arachnoid hairs present.

(c) *C. tuberosum*

Receptacle and flowerhead rounded and almost cylindrical (flowerhead knapweed-like). Arachnoid hairs only.

oat-grass *Festuca ovina-Helictotrichon pratensis* (NVC CG2), devils'-bit scabious-oxeye daisy *Succisa pratensis-Leucanthemum vulgare* sub-community, grading into *Bromopsis erecta* grassland (NVC CG3). According to Rodwell (1992) the *Succisa-Leucanthemum* community is virtually restricted to parts of the Wiltshire and Dorset chalk and presumably this is related to the wetter, more oceanic climate in comparison with the chalk grasslands of mid-south and south-eastern England. Many of the usual chalk downland plants and grasses are present in varying abundance, with decreasing species-richness on those sites where grazing has been abandoned for some time. For example, in 1986 Site B was rank and species-poor grassland, dominated by *B. erecta* and false-oat grass *Arrhenatherum elatius*. *C. tuberosum* was associated with the most herb-rich areas. This site is the most well-known of the *C. tuberosum* sites and lies within the Imber Ranges on the SPTA. A second site (Site D) within the same training area was 'rank grassland ... dominated by *Bromopsis erecta* and *Arrhenatherum elatius* with *Festuca rubra* locally abundant'. Dropwort *Filipendula vulgaris* was constant and abundant over most of this site and tall fescue *Festuca arundinacea* was also a frequent associate. Other herbs which were particularly common were *Trifolium medium* and common knapweed *Centaurea nigra*. Site A, located on a private north-west facing slope, presented the most spectacular display of chalkland flowers, being species-rich grassland with many thousands of *C. tuberosum* plants scattered within the herb-rich sward. The sward height was about 100-150 mm with no one particular grass being dominant. The condition of this down was by far and away the most healthy of any of the *C. tuberosum* sites and appeared to have been grazed more recently than Sites B and D.

This plant appears to prefer a sward which is ungrazed or lightly grazed. Complete lack of grazing would inevitably lead to the loss of colonies as a result of natural succession, but temporary cessation of grazing may be beneficial. Anecdotal observations on Site B over the past decade or so

indicate that *C. tuberosum* has probably spread over this particular site, which has had no grazing for a considerable period (pers. comm. Lane 1991). At Site C, the thistle was abundant on a steep ungrazed north-facing slope which was becoming invaded by scrub and which had not been grazed for a long time. On the same site, only hybrid plants could be found on the heavily grazed, south-facing slope on the opposite side of the valley.

The lack of any documentation on historical grazing management at most of the sites means that when grazing is reintroduced with the aim of benefiting the species, it will be at best a matter of trial and error. It is, therefore, very important that accurate records of stocking levels and grazing regimes on such sites are kept. Similarly, there needs to be adequate scientific monitoring of the thistle populations, preferably by fixed point quadrats or transects and fixed point photographs that can be repeated at regular intervals. Such monitoring needs to involve a healthy partnership between the conservation agencies and owners or occupiers of the sites.

Hybridisation with Cirsium acaule

One of the main threats to *C. tuberosum* is reported to be its hybridisation with *Cirsium acaule* var. *caulescens*, a form which often has long stems. The hybrid *C. tuberosum* x *C. acaule* was confirmed from 16 sites in 1986. This included all the Wiltshire localities where *C. tuberosum* also grew.

C. acaule is most commonly found on chalk grasslands where there is high grazing pressure and, consequently, a short, herb-rich turf. In contrast, *C. tuberosum* appears to survive best in grassland which is ungrazed or which has a very light grazing regime although the situation at Site E seems to confound this statement. *C. acaule* is usually rare or absent under the latter conditions but, where it does persist in tall grassland on the Wiltshire chalk, it is universally the form var. *caulescens* which has long stems. Grose (1942) commented that this form of *C. acaule* grew on sites where 'the grass was long or the soil deep' and that its stems could reach 'almost a foot in height'. Undoubtedly this morphological adaptation enables the survival of the species in long, erratically grazed swards where C. acaule would not normally survive.

Hybridisation between the two species, C. tuberosum and C. acaule, may have occurred in the past when neglected or lightly grazed grasslands holding colonies of C. tuberosum were grazed after a long period of time, promoting shorter swards attractive for the establishment and spread of C. acaule (assuming hybrids were infertile and could not spread through the dispersal of fertile wind-blown seeds). Alternatively, C. tuberosum could have invaded tall grassland where C. acaule (var. caulescens) had survived. Vague assumptions maybe, but the lack of historical data and paucity of research precludes definitive statements on the hybridisation issue and on many other aspects relating to the ecology of C. tuberosum.

On all but one of the seven sites in Wiltshire where C. tuberosum is known, the hybrid also occurs. It is also known from another nine sites which could indicate that hybridisation may have caused the extinction of originally 'pure' colonies. Grose (1957) considered that hybridisation had probably caused the extinction of C. tuberosum from former, notably the most north-westerly, sites in km squares SU06 and SU16. However, at least two of these sites suffered physical depredations which may have reduced the size of the pure colonies. North Down, Cherhill was partly ploughed during the Second World War and at Avebury, archeological excavations and the rapacious collection of specimens may have caused the extinction of C. tuberosum on the ancient earthworks in the early part of this century. The latter site is now subject to heavy visitor pressure and a grazing regime which is unfavourable to the species, and which may have also contributed its apparent demise there.

A major problem in confirming the presence or absence of C. tuberosum is that very few sites have been visited by the same person on a repeated basis, either during one season or over a period of seasons. Unfortunately, visiting botanists rarely map and accurately document their observations. In any case, single visits and isolated observations can be deceptive. For example, Hutchison and Gillam (pers. comm. 1986) considered that repeated visits to individual sites over one year or over successive years may reveal variation in purity not noticeable from one visit. Two visits by them to Site E in 1986 provided some interesting observations. On the first visit on 11 August, sheep had been grazing the site three weeks earlier and only hybrid plants were seen. In contrast, on 25 September Hutchison saw mainly pure plants and only a few hybrids. These observations give hope that C. tuberosum may also persist on grazed sites where only the hybrid was recorded in 1986, most notably at the Calstone/Oldbury Downs complex and at Avebury. At Calstone and Oldbury, Grose had only found the hybrid thistle, but in the 1970s an extensive colony of C. tuberosum was observed. Horton (1985) wrote, 'Before the 1970s hybrid thistles were known here. In the early 1970s the site changed hands and no grazing occurred for a season. As a result, the plant flowered over a wide area and also appeared to be largely pure. The flowering was so prolific that a dark patch on the side of the down could be seen from Morgan's Hill some two miles away. The new owner introduced heavy sheep-grazing, with aerial fertilizer applications and by the next year only a handful of short-stemmed flowers were present'. The precise location of the 'pure' site was never mapped. During the 1986 survey, parts of Calstone Down and Oldbury Castle were surveyed and revealed only low numbers of hybrid plants. However, there are substantial downlands in this area, most of them heavily grazed. The possibility of C. tuberosum persisting should not be discounted.

Hybridisation with Cirsium palustre

The hybrid C. tuberosum x C. palustre marsh thistle has been recorded from three sites in the British Isles. Glamorgan, VC4 (1933), Wiltshire, ST93 (found by Grose in 1947), Wiltshire, ST93 – one plant which I found in 1986 in a different site from that recorded by Grose. Accounts of the first two can be found in Grose (1949) and Stace (1957). Some sample foliage, stem and flowers were collected from the plant seen in 1986 and are now held at the herbarium at the Royal Botanic Gardens, Kew.

Looking to the Future

C. tuberosum is surely one of Britain's most attractive rare plants. To ensure its long-term survival, its remaining sites require diligent monitoring and appropriate conservation management. Detailed research into the ecology of the species, its habitat and management requirements would also be beneficial. This and the completion of a conservation action plan for the species should be a priority for Wiltshire botanists and conservation agencies before the twentieth century draws to a close.

Cirsium tuberosum in Wiltshire (extant sites)

Note. Italicised recorder's name and date in brackets denotes the latest detailed records referred to in the text.

SITE A. Private site. Aspect NW. Extent 4 ha. No. of plants thousands. Conservation status none.
Many thousands of plants on a steep downland slope. *C. tuberosum* is a sub-dominant component in the sward. The hybrid thistle is present but not abundant and only a few plants of *C. acaule* were seen. The grassland is typical species-rich chalk grassland with other, less characteristic species being frequent. These included *Centaurea nigra*, *Serratula tinctoria*, *Trifolium medium* and *Genista tinctoria* (*Everett 1986*). The site is lightly grazed by sheep (Lane, pers. comm. 1991).

SITE B. Warden's Down. Aspect S, SE, W. Extent 4 ha. No. of plants several thousand. Conservation status SSSI SPTA (W).

Two slopes at the mouth of a small chalk combe. The plants grow on gently sloping and level ungrazed grassland. Much of the grassland is rank and species-poor, dominated by *Bromopsis erecta* and *Arrhenatherum elatius*. The hybrid thistle is scattered throughout one of the *C. tuberosum* colonies but largely absent from the other. This locality is vulnerable to troop manoeuvres and tanks being driven over the site from time to time (*Everett 1986*).

SITE C. Private site. Aspect NW. Extent 3 ha. No. of plants several thousand. Conservation status SSSI with management agreement.
This is an extensive colony of several thousand pure and hybrid plants scattered through rank grassland and scrub on a steep slope. In 1986 the grassland had not been grazed for some considerable time and there was significant scrub invasion. However, this condition had apparently favoured *C. tuberosum*. In contrast, a grazed species-rich chalk slope on the opposite side of the combe was observed to hold the hybrid thistle only. A programme of scrub removal has since been instigated, under the supervision of English Nature, with a view to re-introducing light grazing on the slope where the *C. tuberosum* occurs. The total area of this site, including that covered by hybrids, is 6 hectares and part of it is a National Nature Reserve (*Everett and Wild 1986*).

SITE D. Ladywell Down. Aspect NW, N. Extent c. 4 ha. No. of plants several hundred. Conservation status SSSI SPTA (W).
C. tuberosum is scattered along a moderately steep slope and on a flatter crest above. There are also a number of small 'outlier' colonies away from the main ones. Some of the plants are large, some having over 300 scapes and being 3 m in diameter. The hybrid thistle is frequent and scattered amongst the *C. tuberosum* plants. The site is rank, ungrazed grassland dominated by *B. erecta*, *A. elatius* and abundant *F. rubra*. A significant part of the area was fenced and planted with conifer and broadleaved trees in the early 1980s but recent observations indicate that a high

proportion of these plantings are failing (*Everett and Porley 1986; Gillam 1991*).

SITE E. Private site. Aspect N. Extent less than 25 ha. No. of plants *c.* 100.
Pure and hybrid plants on sheep-grazed down. *C. tuberosum* was seen on a second visit where only the hybrid thistle had been seen previously (*Gillam and Hutchison 1986*).

SITE F. Private site. No. of plants *c.* 17. Conservation status nil.
An atypical site of overgrown chalk heath. Species present include heather *Calluna vulgaris* and western gorse *Ulex gallii*, Yorkshire-fog *Holcus lanatus*, tormentil *Potentilla erecta* and perforate St John's-wort *Hypericum perforatum* as well as a range of typical chalkland shrubs and tree seedlings. In 1986, only leaves of suspected *C. tuberosum* were seen. Some scrub clearance has been carried out since 1986 but long-term conservation management on this site needs to be secured.

SITE G. Pewsey Downs National Nature Reserve.
About 100 plants of the hybrid thistle are scattered over 3 hectares of chalk grassland. One suspected plant of *C. tuberosum* was seen by Payne and Rose in 1986.

Other localities on the SPTA(W).
Additional localities were reported by Jack Pile in 1992. Records were received of a total of ten colonies of mostly pure plants scattered in rough grassland on the Imber ranges within 2 km of the well-established and well-known sites at Ladywell and Warden's/High Downs. Owing to the proximity of some of these colonies to one another I have considered that they form four new 'sites'. Several of them were close to the larger well-known sites and I considered these as outliers of those sites rather than as new localities *per se*. The colonies discovered by Jack Pile were located in a total of five km squares. Seven of the colonies were at least 1 km away from the well-known sites. The colonies were described as ranging from '12 stems' and 'half-a-dozen plants' to 'medium-sized' colonies.

In two of the colonies, *C. tuberosum* was found but *C. acaule* was also common. Both pure and hybrids were reported from the others with pure plants always more frequent.

These new discoveries pose several questions. Are there additional colonies on this large expanse of unimproved, rough chalk grassland? Are these small, scattered colonies the remnants of larger ones or are they satellites of the larger well-known localities? Finally, is the number of colonies increasing and will someone be prepared to monitor them accurately on a regular basis in order to find the answer?

The Hybrid Thistle in Wiltshire

In addition to the sites mentioned above, the hybrid thistle *Cirsium tuberosum* x *C. acaule* is known from the following localities.

Avebury Ring. Fourteen plants on bank of ancient earthwork (Pankhurst 1983). A few plants, very close to and almost indistinguishable from dwarf thistle (Everett 1986). This contrasts with observations by Grose (1942) who reported, 'botanists believe pure examples to be still fairly plentiful, but I fear that they are gradually being supplanted by hybrid forms. These forms are ... very near the true plant'.

Roundway Down. Three hybrid plants (Everett and Green 1986). Oliver's Castle. Seven hybrid plants, very close to *C. acaule* on slope below path around the earthworks (Everett and Green 1986).

Tytherington Down. Three plants (Everett, Hutchison and Last 1986).

Stockton Down. About 150 plants observed in 1986 (Everett), many of which were quite close to the pure form. Grose recorded pure plants from this site.

Oldbury Castle/Calstone Downs. Twenty-one plants below and to the west of the monument

(Everett and Green 1986) and about 40 more plants, closer to *C. acaule*, on a steep north-west facing slope. This area would pay closer scrutiny as a large colony of pure plants was seen in the 1970s. Suitable grassland in 1 km squares SU0469, SU0368 and SU0468 needs to be thoroughly searched.

Down in ST93 (i). Sixteen hybrids close to *C. acaule* in species-rich grassland lightly grazed by rabbits (Everett 1986).

Down in ST93 (ii). One hybrid plant with about 20 scapes on north-west facing slope adjacent to woodland (Everett 1986).

Milk Hill, Pewsey Downs NNR. One plant with six flowers (Payne 1986).

Extinct and Unconfirmed Localities

Note. In some cases it was not clear from the sources whether *C. tuberosum* or the hybrid had been recorded.

Avebury Ring. *C. tuberosum* was common here in the early part of this century but archaeological excavations and the plundering of specimens may have caused its extinction. More recently, unsuitably high grazing pressure may have promoted hybridisation and eradication of *C. tuberosum* and make accurate observations impossible. The hybrid thistle remains (Everett 1986).

Upton Cow Down, Redhorn Hill, Brouncker's Down (Stearn 1975). These localities were searched in 1986 by the NCC's chalk grassland survey team but no plants were located.

Marden Down. An unconfirmed and dubious record checked out in 1986.

North Down, Cherhill. Twelve or thirteen plants of *C. tuberosum* in 1927, reduced to two in 1940. 'Formerly many hundreds of hybrid plants' (Grose 1942), 'almost eradicated by ploughing' (Grose 1957).

East Codford Down. Small colony on slope which looked pure (Harris 1983). Searched in 1986 but no plants could be found. Grose recorded *C. tuberosum* here in 1954.

Golden Ball Hill. Hybrid plants just above a well-worn track on very steep west side of hill (Gillam 1975). Grose (1957) stated that the hybrid occurred 'on the gentle north slope'. The site was heavily sheep-grazed in 1986 and was not surveyed. First recorded 1919, when a small colony of *C. tuberosum* plants were reported 'at the foot of the hill' (Grose 1942).

Maple Wood, Sandridge. Several plants were first recorded in 1930 in a field adjoining Maple Wood but were destroyed when the site was converted to a chicken run (Grose 1942). 'May have been *C. acaule* x *tuberosum*' (Grose 1957).

Netherstreet. One *C. tuberosum* plant at the foot of the downs above the village found by Thorold *c.* 1922. Not recorded since (see Grose 1942, 1957).

Bidcombe Hill. A rumoured colony which was identified as being *C. palustre* by Hutchison in 1986.

Mere Down. *C. tuberosum*, last recorded 1897. Grose (1957) noted 'in a chalk-pit near the top of the hill ... destroyed by digging'.

Combe Hill. Border of cornfield, recorded by Hughes in 1953. Grose (1957) reported 'seed was probably wind-borne from the station on the downs a mile distant'.

Silbury Hill. One small patch of the hybrid (Grose 1942). No recent data.

Huish Hill. Undocumented record. No other data.

King's Play Hill. Hybrid plants, last seen at the top of the hill in 1977 but ploughed up since (Gillam 1986).

Rowde. *C. tuberosum* was frequent in two damp meadows at the foot of the downs. By 1939 one of them had been ploughed (Grose 1939) and the other site was lost long ago.

Corton Down. *C. tuberosum* recorded in 1953 (Grose 1957).

Chickengrove Bottom. One plant was seen in 1977 and by Wilkinson in 1984 but has since disappeared. In all probability this plant was introduced.

Imber Ranges. A colony of 'half a dozen pure plants' known by Jack Pile between 1984 and 1989, which he was unable to relocate in 1992.

Specimens Held in Herbaria

Many specimens of *C. tuberosum* were collected in the early 1900s. For example, specimens from Avebury are held at the National Museum of Wales, Devizes Museum, the British Museum (Royal Botanic Gardens, Kew), Swindon Museum, at Marlborough College and in private collections. Specimens from sites including Avebury were also distributed amongst the Botanical Exchange Club in the early part of this century. Specimens from other sites are also held at these herbaria and at Oxford, Cambridge and Reading. Some specimens collected during the 1986 survey are lodged at Devizes Museum and a specimen of the hybrid *C. tuberosum* x *C. palustre* was given to Kew. Photocopies of specimens collected in 1986 are held by English Nature at their Peterborough and Devizes offices, as are full records of all the sites visited during the 1986 survey.

Colour plates, page 36.

Acknowledgements

Thanks to Gilbert Green for advice on geology and to Ann Hutchison for help in identifying specimens and assessing the reliability of characters for identification. Thanks also to Ann Hutchison for surviving my off-the-road driving and rescue by horse and land-rover when the going got tough! Thanks also to site owners and occupiers for giving me the privilege of seeing the glorious flowering of Wiltshire's flagship plant in 1986.

References

Grose, D (1942). The tuberous thistle in Wiltshire. *Wiltshire Archaeological Magazine,* **49**: 557-561.

Grose, D (1949). A hybrid thistle in Wiltshire. *Watsonia,* **1**: 91.

Grose, D (1957). *The Flora of Wiltshire.* Wiltshire Archaeological and Natural History Society, Devizes.

Perring, F and Farrell, L (1983). *British Red Data Books, 1: Vascular Plants.* Royal Society for Nature Conservation, Lincoln.

Rodwell, J S (ed) (1992). Introduction to calcicolous grasslands. In *British Plant Communities, Vol. 3: Grasslands and Montane Communities.* Cambridge University Press, Cambridge.

Stace, C (1957). *Hybridisation and the Flora of the British Isles.* Academic Press in collaboration with the BSBI, London.

Stearn, W (ed) (1975). *Supplement to the Flora of Wiltshire.* Wiltshire Archaeological and Natural History Society, Devizes.

Addendum

One other locality outside Wiltshire, west of Blandford in Dorset, was also reported in 1992, where one plant was seen growing on a chalk grassland bank by Dr H Bowen, BSBI recorder for Dorset (pers. comm. D Pearman).

CAREX FILIFORMIS L. Downy-fruited Sedge and CAREX HUMILIS Leyss. Dwarf Sedge

R W David

The county of Wiltshire has particular connections with these two sedges, which in Britain are extremely local. Downy-fruited sedge *Carex filiformis* L. was first recorded as a British native at Marston Meysey in north Wiltshire by Robert Teesdale in 1799 (Smith 1900). Since the publication of *Flora Europaea* vol. 5 in 1980, *Carex tomentosa* has been generally accepted as the correct name for this sedge, but recent research has established that *C. filiformis* has the better claim. Dwarf sedge *Carex humilis* Leyss. occurs in enormous quantities in South Wiltshire, the centre of its British distribution.

Carex filiformis

This sedge extends throughout Europe and into Asia, from eastern Spain and France in the west to Western Siberia in the east and from southern Sweden, Poland and Baltic Russia in the north to central Italy, Greece, European Turkey and the Crimea in the south. In England it reaches its north-western limit, with a main concentration in east Gloucestershire, extensions into west Gloucestershire, north Wiltshire and isolated colonies in Oxfordshire and formerly in Middlesex and Surrey.

Continental botanists have characterised it as a plant of damp meadows and open woodland. In England the habitats are surprisingly varied. The commonest does indeed appear to be damp meadow, especially on gravel where the subsoil is continuously irrigated. J E Lousley, who rediscovered Teesdale's site in 1936, noted (*in litt.*

1937) that the plant was most abundant in damp depressions in the field. This meadow has long since been drained and ploughed, but the same phenomenon may be observed in other Thames valley localities including a second Wiltshire station, the richest in Britain, discovered near Somerford Keynes by D Wells in 1969. *C. filiformis* has, however, also been seen in downland described as being conspicuously dry. Several Gloucestershire woods have produced substantial colonies, and E Nelmes' wartime explorations of that county found that the sedge was frequently present on road verges, although the spraying routines of the 1960s destroyed the established vegetation and replaced it with coarse plants such as upright brome *Bromopsis erecta* and hogweed *Heracleum sphondylium* with which the sedge can no longer compete.

Carex filiformis is a very distinctive, if inconspicuous, plant. A member of subgenus *Carex* proper, in which male and female spikes are clearly differentiated, it usually appears as a scattered colony, which is in fact a congregation of small tufts arising from slender, creeping rhizomes. The leaves, narrow (2 mm wide or less), crowded, upright, more or less glaucous, spring from red or red-purple basal sheaths, a character that will always serve to distinguish the sometimes shy-flowering *C. filiformis* from glaucous sedge *C. flacca*, the sedge that most frequently accompanies it and most nearly resembles it. When produced, the flowering stems are thin, 150-300 mm tall and rigidly erect. They bear a single terminal male spike (very occasionally two) with, close below, one or two globose or shortly ovoid, sessile, more or less contiguous female spikes. The small (2-3 mm) rounded utricles are covered with a short greyish tomentum. At anthesis, which may be as early as mid-May, the whole plant is a curiously matt greyish-green that effectively camouflages it among the grasses with which it grows. In fruit the heads assume a brownish coloration that makes the plant easier to see, but by the end of July not only are the utricles likely to have fallen but the whole flowering spike may well have disintegrated. Such a plant is easily overlooked, and Wiltshire botanists are urged to keep a sharp eye open for it, especially in the vicinity of the Cotswold Water Park.

Carex humilis

The circumstances of *Carex humilis* Leyss. are in some respects very different from those of *C. filiformis*, for the vice-county of South Wiltshire contains over a hundred colonies (and formerly one in North Wiltshire, now destroyed) and some of these may extend for half a mile or more and number thousands of plants.

In continental Europe it occurs over much the same area as *C. filiformis* but has a wider longitudinal range for it extends well into Manchuria. It is, however, absent from Scandinavia. It is a plant of open grassland on chalk or limestone with a high pH (in England between 7.3 and 7.9) and though commonest on south-facing slopes, may be found even where the aspect is northerly. Like *C. filiformis*, it reaches its north-western limit in southern England where it has an equally restricted distribution, being concentrated on the downland of Wiltshire and the neighbouring portions of Dorset and Hampshire with small outliers on the carboniferous limestone of north Somerset and the Avon and Wye gorges. It is wholly absent from the downs of Sussex and Kent. This oddly confined distribution in Britain has been attributed (Coombe 1954) in some measure to the chronology of ancient clearances at a time when, as has been suggested by Wells (1975), more favourable climatic conditions enabled the sedge

to set seed more readily than it appears to do today. Certainly to find a seeding plant seems nowadays to be difficult, while the ability to regenerate from the re-rooting of small, severed pieces may be observed in recently ploughed areas. To this faculty must be attributed the rapid recolonisation of the wartime bomb-craters on Parsonage Down, near Shrewton, and the fact that the lawns of Blandford Camp in Dorset, regularly mown with military precision, are carpeted with the sedge.

Two recent changes in farming practice pose some threat to *C. humilis* in Wiltshire despite its present abundance. On many areas of downland the traditional sheep have been replaced by cattle, whose hooves pockmark and puddle the slopes and even the ancient earthworks sometimes used as winter stockyards, and whose method of grazing tears out the turf instead of merely cropping it. Even more damaging is the spraying of fertiliser from the air. While the level tops of the downs have been cultivated from time immemorial, the ancient dykes and tumuli have been spared and have provided a refuge from the plough, and the steep sides of the coombes remain unploughable. From the aerial sprays, however, no ground can escape. The irony is that the effect of spraying is wholly deleterious, for while the original plants are destroyed, only docks and nettles arise to replace them.

Carex humilis makes low, close tufts or patches of very fine (less than 1.5 mm broad) but stiff, arcuate leaves from short, woody rhizomes. This, too, is a member of subgenus *Carex*, and at anthesis, which may be as early as mid-March while the developing leaves are still short, the anthers of the single terminal male spike, bright lemon-yellow in colour and curved over on relatively long filaments, show like little flags against the winter-browned herbage. The two to four female spikes below the male and distant from each other are few-flowered with short, hairy utricles enclosed in conspicuously scarious glumes, but are largely hidden in the foliage. By May the flowers are over but the leaves, now extending, become a vivid emerald-green that again make the plants stand out from their surroundings. They remain conspicuous even in later summer when the leaves have turned to bronze and have extended in length to as much as 300 mm. By September, however, if there are autumn rains and the grasses begin to show new growth, the sedge may become hard to detect until, at the turn of the year, it develops a characteristic reddish-brown colour that enables an observer to pick out, even at some distance, any slope where the plant is at all abundant.

Colour plate, page 34.

References

Coombe, D E (1954). *Carex humilis* Leyss. In Pigott, C D and Walters, S M. On the interpretation of the distribution shown by certain British species of open habitats. *Journal of Ecology,* **42**: 111-113.

Smith, J E (1900). Descriptions of five new British species of Carex. *Transactions of the Linnean Society,* **5**: 264-273.

Wells, T C E (1975). The floristic composition of chalk grassland in Wiltshire. In Stearn, L F (ed) *Supplement to the Flora of Wiltshire.* Wiltshire Archaeological and Natural History Society, Devizes.

Regrettably R W (Dick) David died before the publication of this book. Ed.

FRITILLARIA MELEAGRIS L.
Fritillary

Noel King and Derek Wells

Few would dispute the view that fritillary *Fritillaria meleagris* L. is one of Britain's most beautiful wild plants. A fritillary meadow in full flower during late April and early May is one of the most impressive and distinctive sights to be found amongst the vegetation communities in the country. The Latin name is derived from *fritillus*, a dice box or chess board and *meleagris* from Meleager who, in Greek mythology, had sisters who were turned into guinea-fowls – birds with speckled feathers. Grigson (1955) lists over 30 local names for *F. meleagris* in Britain, but Grose (1957) refers to only three for Wiltshire, namely Oaksey lily, Toad's Head and Toad's Mouth. The only other name that seems to have popularity in the county is Snake's Head.

The first record of the species growing wild in Britain is in a list of plants made for the Ruislip area of Middlesex by John Blackstone in 1737. The comparative lateness of a wild record has caused some doubts to be raised in the past about the native status of the plant in this country. Grigson, in his excellent *Englishman's Flora*, suggests that the plant may have become naturalised in suitable habitats as the result of garden escapes from nearby manorial or monastic gardens. However, Oswald (1992) in a detailed and reasoned historical account believes *F. meleagris* to be native. It is worth noting that the plant is above ground for a short period of time and instantly recognisable only in the very short flowering period. Botanists may note down records, country folk rarely do! The close phyto-geographical relationship between its natural distribution in Britain and that of the continent also strongly suggests that it is a truly native species.

The genus *Fritillaria* belongs to the Liliaceae family and is widely distributed throughout the northern temperate zones of the world, from China to the western United States. It contains over 90 species varying widely in their ecological requirements and covering a range of habitats from grasslands and woodlands to high alpine conditions. *F. meleagris* is the only species found in Britain. Its natural range extends from this country, through central and northern Europe to Russia in the east and southern Sweden in the north. In Britain, its distribution is confined to England with a clearly eastern and southern influence, having a particularly strong association with the alluvial meadows of the River Thames and its tributaries. There are other centres of distribution in Suffolk, Staffordshire, Hereford-shire, Buckinghamshire and Cambridgeshire. A few of these sites may be suspect as 'natural', but even if included, the number of sites in Britain with more than 100 plants does not total more than 20. Wiltshire is of particular importance for *F. meleagris* containing some 30% of the sites and around 80% of the total British population. Pride of place must go to the 44 hectare National Nature Reserve at North Meadow, Cricklade. Never mind seeing Rome before you die!

The soil type favoured by *F. meleagris* is a deep alluvium with a pH ranging from 5.8 to 7.0. Seasonal winter flooding is normal, but water rarely stands for long periods as the soils are free-draining and water is drawn down when levels fall in the adjacent water courses. It is doubtful if flooding is essential to the maintenance of *F. meleagris*. The more likely link is that grassland subject to flooding was more given to being put up for hay in days gone by. Ploughing would not have been an option.

F. meleagris is, arguably, the most notable species of the vegetation community characteristic of agriculturally unimproved alluvial meadows of southern England. This community is species-rich with many grasses, including red fescue *Festuca rubra*, meadow foxtail *Alopecurus pratensis* and sweet vernal-grass *Anthoxanthum odoratum* together with the more uncommon grass, smooth brome *Bromus racemosus*. Of the many herbs present, great burnet *Sanguisorba officinalis*, pepper-saxifrage *Silaum silaus*, yellow-rattle *Rhinanthus minor* and the little grassland fern, adder's-tongue *Ophioglossum vulgatum* are very characteristic. This community is now recognised in the National Vegetation Classification as Mesotrophic grasslands, MG 4 (Rodwell 1992).

F. meleagris is a communal species flowering in late April to early May. Its single, or rarely two-flowered, head is carried on a stem arising from a two or three-scaled bulb 10-20 mm in size. The plant first appears above ground in March and the stem eventually reaches a height of between 200 and 500 mm before flowering. The stem and leaves are glabrous and glaucous with the three to six leaves being 80-200 mm in length and placed alternately on the stem. The bud in its final development bends downward, giving the plant its characteristic hanging appearance in flower. The flower consists of six tepals 30-50 mm in length, pink to purple with a dark chequered pattern as a background. White forms occur in most populations usually in low numbers. In a few sites, notably at the Wiltshire Trust for Nature Conservation's Upper Waterhay reserve, the white form predominates.

After pollination, normally by bumble bees, the stalk of the trigonous seed capsule straightens and the capsule develops in an upright position. By mid-June it is ripe and the 50-110 seeds are shaken out by wind or the hay-making process. In all populations a proportion of plants are non-flowering. These are either young plants, with a single leaf some 80 mm in length, or stems with leaves and no flowers. This life cycle is well adapted to the traditional hay-making/aftermath grazing routine. The plant emerges in mid-March when the meadow is set up for hay and produces seeds before hay-making at which time it has died back to the underground bulb.

Recent reports make it clear that the plant has markedly declined throughout its range. Hope-Simpson (1950) reported that the large concentration of fritillary meadows described by Flower (1872) as one of the most abundant concentrations of the plant in Britain, on the west side of the Oaksey/Minety road, had been ploughed up just after the Second World War. In the late 1960s, Nature Conservancy staff with considerable help and dedication from Ted Browning, carried out a field by field survey of riverside meadows in Wiltshire. This revealed a total of 13 sites involving 37 meadows. In 1992, the authors resurveyed these areas and found six sites involving 11 meadows. However, five of these meadows had received fertiliser in the intervening period and the vegetation was no longer floristically rich, being dominated by meadow-grass *Poa* spp., *Alopecurus pratensis* and perennial rye-grass *Lolium perenne*. The fritillaries are still present, although in reduced numbers, but without the glorious backdrop of associated herbs and grasses. We surveyed the remaining sites in England and found a similar story. In our view, there are only 12 sites in England where the fritillary is to be found in reasonable numbers (over 1,000) and in characteristic vegetation. It is significant that of the 12 sites, eight are controlled by conservation bodies, one is in an Oxford college and the remainder are in private ownership. There are two main causes for the drastic decline of fritillary sites in England. The first, and by far the greatest, cause of decline is the enormous advance in agricultural technology which has resulted in wholesale improvement by ploughing, fertilising and reseeding of meadows, with the concomitant loss of herb-rich swards. The second cause of loss is the exploitation of sand and gravel resources which has affected some Wiltshire sites. We know of no site in Europe with a greater concentration of *F. meleagris* than that at North Meadow. With its associated flora and known management history, this site is surely of international importance.

Colour plate, page 37.

References

Blackstone, J (1737). *Fasciculus Plantarum circa Harefield sponte nascentium,...* London.

Flower, T B (1857-1874). The Flora of Wiltshire. *Wiltshire Archaeological and Natural History Magazine.*

Grigson, G (1955). *The Englishman's Flora.* Dent, London.

Grose, D (1957). *The Flora of Wiltshire.* Wiltshire Archaeological and Natural History Society, Devizes.

Hope-Simpson, J F (1950). Unpublished report to the Nature Conservancy.

Oswald, P (1992). The Fritillary in Britain – a historical perspective. *British Wildlife,* 3: 200-210.

Rodwell, J S (ed) (1992). *British Plant Communities, Vol. 3: Grasslands and Montane Communities.* Cambridge University Press, Cambridge.

ORNITHOGALUM PYRENAICUM L.
Spiked Star-of-Bethlehem or Bath Asparagus

David Green

The genus *Ornithogalum* is a member of the family Liliaceae. In Europe the plant occurs in Belgium, south-west Switzerland, Austria and in the mountains of Spain, Portugal, Italy and Greece. It is also found in the Crimea, Asia Minor and Morocco. In the British Isles, the distribution of this native plant is very localised. *The Atlas of the British Flora* 1976 shows spiked Star-of-Bethlehem *Ornithogalum pyrenaicum* L. as occurring in 22 10 km squares, of which eleven lie in Wiltshire and a further six occur in adjacent 10 km squares in Somerset, Gloucestershire and Berkshire. The remaining colonies are in Sussex, Norfolk and Bedfordshire.

In Wiltshire the plant grows mainly in two distinct types of colony, small linear hedgerow and green lane colonies and in much more extensive colonies in woodland. In some old and ancient woodlands it can vie for dominance with the bluebell. It is also found along river banks and on unimproved pasture. In the Bristol Avon valley, from Monkton Farleigh through Murhill, Freshford, Avoncliff and on the Bradford-on-Avon plain, the plant may be found in almost every hedge, copse and wood. Multiple colonies are found east of Little Bedwyn, near Wroughton, south of Devizes, near Farley and in an area bordering the western county boundary from Slaughterford in the north to Wingfield in the south.

About Bradford-on-Avon and along the Bristol Avon valley, *O. pyrenaicum* grows on Oolitic Limestone which is overlain with calcareous clays. In other sites in Wiltshire it grows on the Lower Chalk and on greensand. The locality of the first Wiltshire record is given by Thomas Johnson in his *Mercurius Botanicus* 1634 where he states 'It growes in the way betweene Bathe and Bradford not farre from little Ashley'. It still grows in this area in great quantity.

The best time of year to count colonies and study the plant's distribution is in early spring. The blue-green rosette of leaves appears earlier than bluebell leaves with which it is almost always found. These leaves continue to grow until, by May, they are 350-400 mm long, lax and collapsing. The leaves begin to die back while the flowering spike is growing to its full height of up to 1,000 mm. The flowers, which are arranged in a compact raceme, usually open in the third or fourth week of June and last for three to four weeks. The pedicels are slender, spreading or ascending and the florets, starlike in shape and opening from the bottom of the spike first, are 6-10 mm across.

The seeds, roughly pyramidal in shape and charcoal in colour, are 2 mm across and take many years to develop into a mature bulb. The large size of the seed must contribute to the plant's restricted distribution. However, in some situations, for instance along green lanes, it would seem that the movement of farm stock may help dispersal. Seeds falling in autumn become mixed with the mud of the trackway and from there may be carried by hooves or vehicle tyres to new locations.

In woodlands, single seedlings growing *en masse* can be seen in early spring. The leaves are only 1-1.5 mm across and up to 75 mm long. A seedling requires several seasons in order to develop its single, hooded monocotyledon leaf, 10 mm wide and 100 mm long, arising from a bulb underground. The enlargement of a colony by vegetative means is by lateral buds developed each spring from the mature bulbs, which can measure up to 50 mm across. Further work is needed to discover how long it takes for these lateral buds to develop into independent bulbs. The length of time it takes for a seedling to develop into a mature flowering plant depends on light, moisture and habitat. These factors may explain why extensive colonies grow, but do not flower, under the dense shade found in some woods.

In Bath, in the adjacent county of Avon, the unopened flower spikes used to be collected and sold as Bath asparagus. This custom ceased commercially in recent years.

It is quite possible that this species, like many others regarded as questionable natives, was in fact introduced to England at the time of the Roman occupation of this locality. It grows in greater abundance near Bath than anywhere else in the British Isles. Here it is found around the southern facing slopes that were supposed to have been planted with grape vines in Roman times but are now mostly woodland and mixed pasture. I wonder whether the bulb of O. *pyrenaicum* arrived via the earth ball of a Roman vine, or whether it was deliberately introduced for its own culinary value.

Colour plate, page 33.

References

Clapham, A R, Tutin, T G and Warburg, E F (1962). *Flora of the British Isles.* Cambridge University Press, Cambridge.

Grose, D (1957). *The Flora of Wiltshire.* Wiltshire Archaeological and Natural History Society, Devizes.

Perring, F H and Walters, S M (1976). *Atlas of the British Flora.* Botanical Society of the British Isles, London.

Riddledell, H J, Hedley, G W and Price, W R (1948). *Flora of Gloucestershire.* Chalford House Press, Bristol.

Roe, R G B (1981). *The Flora of Somerset.* Somerset Archaeological and Natural History Society, Taunton.

Stearn, L F (1975). *Supplement to the Flora of Wiltshire.* Wiltshire Archaeological and Natural History Society, Devizes.

LEUCOJUM AESTIVUM L.
Summer Snowflake

Rosemary FitzGerald

The status of summer snowflake *Leucojum aestivum* L. has often been questioned since its discovery in England in the eighteenth century. *Leucojum* is an attractive genus and various members have been in cultivation for centuries. As early as 1599 Gerard confirmed the horticultural popularity of three species, *L. aestivum, L. autumnale* and *L. vernum*, in England. 'These plants do growe wilde in Italie and the places adiacent, notwithstanding our London gardens have taken possession of them all, many years past' (Gerard 1599). The early names were 'summer sottekins' or 'early summer fooles', presumably because they fool people by their similarity to snowdrops. 'Snowflake' was coined by William Curtis, who found the plant on the Thames in 1788, the first English record.

However, Curtis was satisfied that the species was native, 'undoubtedly wild ... just above the high water mark ... where no garden, in all probability, could ever have existed ...' (Curtis 1788), and modern opinion tends to agree with this assessment. *L. aestivum* is distributed throughout Europe, in a 'uniform habitat – namely either freshwater swamps in estuarine lands which are occasionally overflowed by the tide, or the flooded margins of lakes and rivers' (Knowles and Phillips 1910). English and Irish sites appear to be closely similar in habitat and community to those known on the continent and form part of an almost continuous distribution from east to west. Knowles and Phillips (1910) make this premise the main argument of their excellent paper, 'It is the view of some botanists that *Leucojum aestivum* has possibly been introduced into the British Isles by man – that it may have been planted, or may have escaped

from hypothetical gardens ... but we propose to show that the habitat and distribution of the plant on the continent ..., where it is admitted to be native, agree with its occurrences in England and Ireland, and that in its principal stations in both these countries, its abundance, its associates, the situations it affects, and the general conditions under which it grows, are such as to preclude all idea of its being an introduced plant.'

Much of the argument about the status of the summer snowflake (sometimes known as the Loddon lily from its abundance on that river) gives the impression of being based on prejudice rather than science, the plant being considered 'too pretty' to be wild (Grigson 1958; FitzGerald 1990). As indicated above, the phytogeographical evidence is perfectly agreeable to its being a native plant. There are two points which are helpful when examining the possible sources of this prejudice, and the first one is very simple – time of flowering.

Leucojum aestivum flowers early, in April, in sites which are unappealing at that time of year. Many are flooded in winter and in spring are a waste of muddy silt and dead stalks of the previous year's rather dull vegetation (typically such species as greater pond-sedge *Carex riparia*, cleavers *Galium aparine*, hemlock water-dropwort *Oenanthe crocata*, reed canary-grass *Phalaris arundinacea* or common reed *Phragmites australis* and the ubiquitous common nettle *Urtica dioica*). Even the few more species-rich water meadow sites, away from willow or alder carr and swampy islands, are pretty bleak so early, and by mid-May when botanising in wet areas is more tempting, the surrounding vegetation conceals the snowflakes.

Curtis himself (1788) comments 'How so ornamental a plant ... could have escaped the prying eyes of the many Botanists who have resided in London for such a length of time seems strange', but Knowles and Phillips sensibly point out 'That L. *aestivum* has been overlooked for so long in these islands does not seem surprising when we remember that it flowers early ... and that the situations in which it grows are wet, unpleasant, and often inaccessible at that time of the year ...'. They also note the great difficulty of relocating even previously marked clumps in the tall vegetation of July. Grigson gives an incomparable picture of a typical site, 'Imagine, if you have never seen a Loddon Lily, a black swamp on the edge of the Thames, alders and willows overhead, a swamp which quivers and soggs and stinks. In the gloom, not the more usual light of Marsh Marigolds but white flowers hanging in a severe purity from the end of long stems.' It seems reasonable to accept that the comparatively late discovery of some British sites is more likely to be because no one was looking at the right time, than because the plants were not there, being still in the hypothetical gardens.

The second point was brought to my notice by Dr D E Coombe and has proved very helpful in recent fieldwork undertaken to refind historic sites in Dorset and to assess their status. There are two subspecies of *Leucojum aestivum* present in Britain, ssp. *aestivum* and ssp. *pulchellum* (Salisb.) Briq.. The latter is much the more frequent in gardens, and is often assumed to be *L. aestivum* sensu stricto. Knowles and Phillips record it so labelled in 'more than one Botanic Garden'. The subspecies are satisfactorily distinct in the field, and when it is known that ssp. *aestivum* is the rare wild plant but that ssp. *pulchellum* is a relatively frequent garden escape (usually in the form of a persistent clump or two rather than a spreading population), a rational distinction can often be made between sites as likely to be casual or native. Much of the doubtful reputation of *L. aestivum* then disappears.

The most important field character to separate the subspecies is that ssp. *aestivum* has translucent scarious teeth along the edge of the spathe while ssp. *pulchellum* has a perfectly entire edge. The teeth are easily seen with a lens, or even when held up to the light, and can also be felt. Other differences, all of which have proved useful in the field, are summarised by Knowles and Phillips 'When seen growing side by side, the difference between the two species is quite apparent, ...*pulchellum* being smaller in all its parts, its leaves narrower, of a brighter green and more glossy. Its scapes are more slender, and bear only three or, very rarely four flowers, which are much smaller, and are usually produced three or four weeks earlier than those of ...*aestivum*'. Flowers of ssp. *aestivum* number 3-7 on each stem and measure 25-27 mm as opposed to the 14-15 mm in ssp. *pulchellum*.

In Wiltshire *Leucojum aestivum* has been known and generally given good status, since it was found by a Mr Richardson of Marlborough College in 1887 between Ramsbury and Chilton Foliat on the R. Kennet. Interestingly, the find was communicated to the *Journal of Botany* for that year by E S Marshall, who was himself to discover the first native site in Ireland ten years later. This original site is still extant. Farrell (1979) summarising the habitat and distribution of the summer snowflake in Britain, listed another site at Chilton Foliat further downstream, but says, 'although again in a willow thicket, [it] looks as though it may have spread naturally from one originally planted clump'. The finest population currently known is at Woodford Green on the R. Avon north of Salisbury, where the plant occurs on both sides of the river. Farrell considered the approximate two thousand plants she saw here 'certainly native'.

It is hoped that this interesting species will maintain its populations in Great Britain and Ireland. The specialised niche which it inhabits so successfully in such inhospitable terrain – winter-flooded, silt-choked, shaded – has survived so far because many of the sites are inaccessible and intractable. However, modern reclamation and drainage techniques, the control of rivers and the rebuilding of their banks and the general greed for land suitable for development now threaten all such places. It is urgent that this beautiful plant should be given a high conservation priority. If current county records can be purged of any '*pulchellum*' impurities, then energy and resources can be devoted to the survival of true *Leucojum aestivum* ssp. *aestivum*, freed from being dismissed as 'only an escape'.

Colour plate, page 38.

References

Curtis, W (1788). *Flora Londinensis*, Vol. V.

Farrell, L (1979). The distribution of *Leucojum aestivum* L. in the British Isles. *Watsonia*, **12**: 325-332.

FitzGerald, R (1990). The status of *Leucojum aestivum* in Dorset. Nature Conservancy Council Commissioned Research, CSD Report 1061. *Rare Plant Survey of SW England*, **4**. Nature Conservancy Council, Peterborough.

Gerard, J (1596-9). *Catalogue of Plants*.

Grigson, G (1958). *The Englishman's Flora*, Phoenix House Ltd, London.

Knowles, M C and Phillips, R A (1910). On the claim of the snowflake (*Leucojum aestivum*) to be native in Ireland. *Proceedings of the Royal Irish Academy*, **XXVIII**, Sect.B, No.8: 387-399.

Marshall, E S (1887). *Leucojum aestivum* in N Wilts. *Journal of Botany*, **183**.

THE FERNS
OF WILTSHIRE

Patricia Woodruffe

Ferns are among the earliest vascular plants to have evolved. Although generally thought of as 'ancient', they never became a dominant feature of British vegetation and this is certainly the case in Wiltshire today. However, their distribution is widespread and they have adapted to a range of habitats, from freshwater to quite dry conditions.

In common with close allies such as the horsetails and clubmosses, the ferns have retained some primitive characteristics, particularly in their reproductive cycles. Details of these cycles can be found by reference to Freethy 1987 and Hyde and Wade 1978. The most significant feature is the occurrence of two quite independent plants, the conspicuous and familiar spore-bearing plant or sporophyte and the less evident tiny green prothallus or gametophyte. The latter may be regarded both as a hindrance to the evolution of the fern group and as an interesting relic of an ancestral mode of reproduction. The gametophyte is highly vulnerable to desiccation and consequently is limited in its distribution to damp, shaded places. The distribution of the sporophyte is, of course, related to that of the gametophyte. The life cycle of a fern, with its aquatic and terrestrial phases, has been likened to that of an amphibian.

Ferns (sporophytes) normally bear spores on the fronds which, in the majority of cases, are vegetative structures, analogous to leaves and having the dual functions of reproduction and photosynthesis. The fronds develop in a tightly coiled manner which is not found in many other groups of vascular plants. When expansion takes place, the frond uncurls because there is more elongation on the inner side of the leaf than on the outer side. This results in the characteristic crozier-like formations in spring.

In a few species, the fertile material is separate and easily distinguished from the vegetative fronds. In hard fern *Blechnum spicant* the fertile fronds are larger, more erect and have narrower segments or pinnae. In royal fern *Osmunda regalis* the spores are borne only by the upper pinnae of the fertile fronds and in members of the adder's-tongue family there are distinct fertile spikes and sterile blades. Whilst this tendency towards the isolation of vegetative and reproductive material might be considered as an evolutionary advance, it is widely held that these species are amongst the most ancient of all ferns. The fossil records for the *Osmunda* group are remarkably complete and indicate that they can truly be described as 'living fossils' (Sporne 1966).

It is, of course, the distribution of the sporophyte which has been recorded in the Wiltshire Flora Mapping Project (WFMP). Seventeen species occur quite frequently in Wiltshire, four others are rare and two are introductions. Of the many factors which govern their range, rainfall, soil and land-use are likely to be of greatest significance. Some species, particularly those which grow on walls, show a north-westerly distribution whilst others can be associated more readily with clayey soils or greensands where woodlands are better developed. The expanses of chalk downland, with well-drained soils and a preponderance of arable farming and unmanaged grassland used by the military are home to relatively few species.

In Wiltshire, as elsewhere, the habitats with which ferns are most usually associated are woodlands, old meadows, walls and, in the case of water fern *Azolla filiculoides*, freshwater.

Woodland Ferns

The majority of ferns found in the county fall into this category. Lack of rainfall prevents specimens attaining the luxuriance of their more south-westerly distributed counterparts, but a good range of species can be found in some woodlands especially in the 'New Forest fringe' in the south-east of the county. Here the soils are underlain by either clays, sands or gravels and have supported woodland over a long period of time. Even where stands of conifers have replaced native broadleaved species there is ample evidence to show that these are ancient woodlands which have had no other land-use for 300 or more years (Figure 4, page 16).

Some woodland ferns are regarded as indicator species of ancient woodland because they do not colonise readily and therefore are characteristic of relatively undisturbed sites (Nature Conservancy Council 1983). Such species include hard fern *Blechnum spicant*, scaly male-fern *Dryopteris affinis*, narrow buckler-fern *Dryopteris carthusiana*, lemon-scented fern *Oreopteris limbosperma*, hart's-tongue *Phyllitis scolopendrium*, hard shield-fern *Polystichum aculeatum* and soft shield-fern *Polystichum setiferum*. There are records of all these species in the county and indeed, there are a few woods which contain the majority of them. The most abundant is *Phyllitis scolopendrium* which is common in the west, where it often forms large colonies, but becomes progressively less so to the north-east. It is not confined to woodland but occurs also on stream banks, in quarries and on walls. The least common of the group is *Oreopteris limbosperma* which Grose (1957) recorded as rare, but present at a number of sites on acidic soils throughout the county. During the WFMP the plant has been found at only two sites, both close to the New Forest. At one of these the specimens are numerous and well-developed.

Another rare species, hay-scented buckler-fern *Dryopteris aemula*, has been recorded in the same area.

Identification of two species of shield-fern, *Polystichum aculeatum* and *Polystichum setiferum*, is confusing because the distinguishing features are minor and 'of degree' rather than 'present or absent'. They include the texture of the frond and the angle at which the pinnules are attached to the pinna. Grose (1957) records that *Polystichum setiferum* is far less common than *Polystichum aculeatum* but the results of the WFMP do not confirm this (Maps 14 and 15, page 129). The two species occupy similar habitats but *Polystichum setiferum* is more frequent and the plants are numerous and well-developed. The records of *Polystichum aculeatum* are scattered and the plants are limited both in number and size.

The genus *Dryopteris* is well represented in woodlands where male-fern *Dryopteris filix-mas* and broad buckler-fern *Dryopteris dilatata* are widespread. However, two other closely related species which are indicators of ancient woodland, *Dryopteris affinis* and *Dryopteris carthusiana*, have a limited distribution (Maps 17 and 18, page 129). Many fern species, particularly those of the genus *Dryopteris*, hybridise freely, leading to the development of distinct sub-species which have not been recorded by the WFMP.

Other woodland species include lady-fern *Athyrium filix-femina* and polypody *Polypodium* agg. *Athyrium filix-femina* can be located on clays, sandy soils and on superficials overlying the chalk. Its growth is often associated with old banks, hedges and walls as well as being epiphytic on trees. For the purposes of the WFMP, little attempt has been made to distinguish other species, although it is known that *Polypodium vulgare* is not the sole representative of the genus.

Ferns of Meadows and Open Spaces

One of the best known ferns is bracken *Pteridium aquilinum*, a plant with the reputation of being one of the world's most important weeds (Taylor 1989). Its distribution in Wiltshire is checked by its intolerance of chalk and of intensive agricultural practices. Although normally associated with heathlands and moorlands, it is also found along hedgerows, woodland rides and in clear-felled areas.

The plants spread by spores and by an extensive rhizome system. Eradication is not easy despite the availability of herbicides of doubtful specificity (Nature Conservancy Council 1986). A labour-intensive, but effective, technique is that of whipping or trampling the fronds two or three times during the growing season (British Trust for Conservation Volunteers 1980). The procedure, repeated annually, will weaken the plants, if not eradicate them.

Pteridium aquilinum has been used in the past for bedding material for animals and humans, for compost, as a source of potash (when burnt) and a yellow dye (Page 1988). It possesses a remarkable chemical armoury which includes a range of toxic substances, including carcinogens and insecticides. These can be ingested, inhaled or transmitted to animals via milk and water (Taylor 1989). Field trials involving the larvae of a South African moth are being conducted in this country and could lead to an environmentally acceptable method of controlling a weed which spreads at the rate of about 53 square kilometres a year.

Another fern associated with open sites is adder's-tongue *Ophioglossum vulgatum*. It frequents damp, unimproved grassland, where it can be abundant in the north of the county, but is also found on chalk downland and in woodland. It is regarded as an indicator species of old meadows and can sometimes be found in churchyards although, surprisingly, only one WFMP record comes from such a site. It may be that rigorous churchyard management is not conducive to its survival. The plant is quite atypical of ferns, having a small stature and a frond that does not uncurl as it grows. A close relative, moonwort *Botrychum lunaria,* is currently confined to one known site in the county.

Ferns on Walls

The four species of fern occurring mainly or exclusively on walls are black spleenwort *Asplenium adiantum-nigrum*, wall-rue *Asplenium ruta-muraria*, maidenhair spleenwort *Asplenium trichomanes* and rustyback *Ceterach officinarum*. Of these, only *Asplenium adiantum-nigrum* occurs in significant numbers in habitats other than walls. It can also be found in hedges and along stream banks but, despite this, it is relatively uncommon in the county. It is interesting to note that a number of records come from railway bridges constructed of acidic, blue bricks (Green 1991). The stronghold for both *Asplenium trichomanes* and *Ceterach officinarum* is the north-west, where, on the fringe of the Cotswolds, there are stone walls and a higher rainfall than elsewhere. Of the four species, *Asplenium ruta-muraria* is the most widespread, avoiding only extensive tracts of chalk. Churchyard walls are some of the best places to search for these species and it is unfortunate that the recording technique of the WFMP has not provided any information on precise locations for them. One other fern which grows on walls and in quarries is brittle bladder-fern *Cystopteris fragilis*. It is now known from only four localities in the county but has been considered for many years to be rare (Grose 1957).

Colour plate, page 40.

Water Fern

Azolla filiculoides is a native of tropical America and was first recorded on the Kennet and Avon Canal at Limpley Stoke in 1939. It spread eastwards reaching Devizes in 1942, Pewsey Wharf in 1946 and Wootton Rivers in 1949 but, as it advanced, its frequency at former sites declined. Such changes are not unusual for this species. There are many records of fluctuations and disappearances lasting many years (Grose 1957). Present WFMP records consist of only nine observations, although some of these cover extensive areas; it is interesting to see that it is no longer confined to the canal system but has been found on ponds and along the rivers Avon and Wylye near Salisbury.

Extinctions

In the early 1990s it would seem that no ferns had become extinct in the county since the publication of the *Flora of Wiltshire* (Grose 1957). A number of species which had not been recorded for a considerable time, or were known to have been lost from the only recorded sites at that time, were not found during the WFMP. These include beech fern *Phegopteris connectilis*, pillwort *Pilularia globulifera* and marsh fern *Thelypteris palustris*.

Osmunda regalis, believed by Grose (1957) to be extinct in natural habitats, is still present in the county at sites where it may be regarded as a long-term introduction.

Maidenhair fern *Adiantum capillus-veneris*, was recorded in Salisbury and, although no longer present, has been found to be thriving at a site where it is known to be an introduction.

References

British Trust for Conservation Volunteers (1980). *Woodlands. A Practical Conservation Handbook*. British Trust for Conservation Volunteers, Wallingford.

Freethy, R (1987). *British Ferns*. The Crowood Press, Marlborough.

Grose, D (1957). *The Flora of Wiltshire*. Wiltshire Archaeological and Natural History Society, Devizes.

Hyde, H A and Wade, A E (1978). *Welsh Ferns*. The National Museum of Wales, Cardiff.

Nature Conservancy Council (1987). *The Use of Herbicides on Nature Reserves*. Interpretive Branch, Nature Conservancy Council, Peterborough.

Page, C N (1988). *Ferns*. New Naturalist Series, Collins, London.

Sporne, K R (1966). *The Morphology of Pteridophytes*. Hutchinson, London.

Taylor, J A (1989). The British Bracken Problem. *Geography Review*, 2(5).

PART THREE

The Flora

THE FLORA

David Green and Ann Hutchison

Background

Compiled by David Green, Sally Scott-White and Patricia Woodruffe.

We hope that this section will prove to be a mine of useful information for anyone with an interest in the flora of Wiltshire. The following descriptions of the distribution and frequency of species, with technical data and anecdotal comments, give an overview of the 1,200 flowering and allied plants recorded in the county during the 8 years 1984-91. They confirm the presence of all the vascular plants which occur in the county and indicate some of the significant changes in status which have taken place since World War II and the publication of the last Wiltshire flora. Details of geology, soil and habitat types are included, information which is useful in tracking down the distribution of a plant. A broad picture has been built up of the occurrence of plants throughout the county which, with data being integrated into the national Biological Record, will add to the updated information on plant distribution throughout Great Britain.

The fact that a species merits special protection because it is regarded as nationally scarce is indicated. This status may be because its numbers have declined due to loss or change of habitat, or because the plant occurs on the edge of its geographical range. Conversely, it is shown how other species, which have adapted well to the changing landscape, have increasing populations. This information will be valuable to those who take responsibility for safeguarding Wiltshire's natural heritage for the future.

In 1852, H C Watson divided Great Britain into 112 areas, the vice-counties (VC), of roughly equal dimensions which would serve as comparative areas of plant distribution. Many of these are not enclosed within current county boundaries. The areas covered in this flora are VC7 (north Wiltshire) and VC8 (south Wiltshire), both of which include parts of neighbouring counties Gloucestershire and Berkshire in the north and Somerset, Hampshire and Berkshire in the south see Figure 8.

Figure 8. Map of Wiltshire, showing the vice-county and administrative county boundaries.

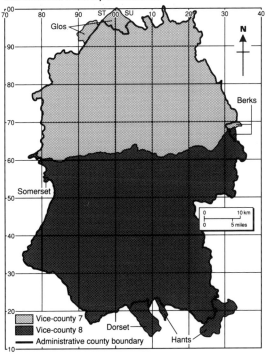

111

The authors of The Flora are two members of the Botanical Society of the British Isles (BSBI) who hold the society's honorary position of VC recorders for Wiltshire. It is the responsibility of a VC recorder to keep up-to-date records on plants in their VC and to accept, check and verify new records. Their duties during the Wiltshire Flora Mapping Project (WFMP) included checking and verifying the accuracy of all records, especially where identification was questionable, giving guidance and alerting other members of the Science Group to possible misidentifications. Some difficult genera have species which are so similar in structure and in other characteristics that identification is critical and requires determination from a national or county expert before the record can be accepted. The VC recorders monitored the progress of recording in each tetrad and, through herbarium workshops and field meetings, assisted members to tackle difficult taxa such as grasses, sedges and rushes.

Determination of Species Categories

The method of recording is described on page 4 and the cards used are illustrated on page 4. In order to determine the species to be assigned to A and B categories the WFMP coordinator, Susan Cross, obtained data on all the county's recorded plant species from the National Biological Records Centre at the Institute of Terrestrial Ecology, Monkswood. The VC recorders drew up a list of plants which they felt warranted inclusion in either the A or B category for each VC and from these the final lists of A and B species for the entire county were agreed. Any plant not included in either list was referred to as a C species.

Nomenclature

During the initial years of the WFMP, Latin nomenclature was taken from the second edition of the much-loved Flora of the British Isles by Clapham, Tutin and Warburg 1962 with which some of us had grown up. However, with the appearance of Clive Stace's New Flora of the British Isles in 1991, it became evident that the nomenclature would need to be up-dated. It was recognised that Stace would be the standard reference book for many years and the decision was made to use his nomenclature in The Wiltshire Flora. In this section of the book, where an older name used during the WFMP has been updated by Stace it follows the new name and is printed in italics. During final checking of the text prior to publication, reference was made to D H Kent's A List of Vascular Plants of the British Isles (1992 published by the BSBI) which varies from Stace in a few instances. The names given to these species by Kent have been incorporated in the text.

English nomenclature used throughout the project is that adopted by Dony, Jury and Perring 1974 in English Names of Wild Flowers, 2nd edition. Names for species not included in this publication have been attributed English names according to Stace.

Storage and Handling of Records

All records made during the WFMP were entered onto the Wiltshire Biological Records Centre (WRBC) database. dBase III+, a commercial database program for PCs, was used to manage the data.

Species were separated into three files on the computer according to which of the three different recording levels had been used: tetrad for A species, 1 km square for B species and 6 figure grid reference for C species.

Data entry of approximately 250,000 records took place from 1987 to 1992 during the winter months when the recording cards were available from the tetrad recorders. This was accomplished by the following team of temporary personnel on the Employment Training Scheme: Kim Beadie, Terry Koerner, Sharon Mulholland, Alison Stickler, Gill Wade and Brenda Whitton to whom, together with those volunteers from the WFMP, some of whom worked at home and sent in discs, Sally Scott-White expresses her thanks for their dedicated efforts.

Data for A and B species was entered by typing the code number printed on the cards, the recorder's name and the location by 10 km² and tetrad or 1 km². C species records were coded using numbers from the *List of British Vascular Plants*, J E Dandy 1958. Data was typed into special data entry screens developed for the WFMP by the WBRC. Data entered for each C species included the date, site name, 6 figure grid reference, recorder's and verifier's names, details of subspecies, hybrid or variety and any other comments referring to colony size, history, etc. Records for A and B species were cumulative over the period of the project and were not dated.

An approximate breakdown of the 250,000 records into the three species categories were: A 130,000, B 110,000 and C 10,000.

Data Checking

Routines were developed at WBRC for summarising data, checking and producing distribution maps for the flora.

Data checking consisted of comparing record totals for each group of species for each tetrad against the totals given by the 10 km² coordinators on tetrad summary sheets. Where there was a significant difference this was followed by checking the entire set of records for each tetrad against the record card. This could not, of course, detect a substitution of one species for another due to recorder error in completing the card, or typing errors made during data entry. However, duplication or omission during data entry was detected and corrected. Thanks go to John Rayner for his help in checking many of the tetrads.

Some A and B species which were believed to have a restricted distribution were subjected to checking of every single record. Distribution maps were displayed at an AGM and the names of suspect species were circulated to coordinators who were asked to confirm them. Prior to the 1990 recording season the following species were considered to fall into this category and recorders were asked to confirm that they could distinguish one from another, usually more common species, with which confusion was suspected.

Species possibly misidentified	Similar, common species
Agrostis canina	Agrostis capillaris
Asplenium adiantum-nigrum	A. ruta-muraria
Chenopodium bonus-henricus	C. rubrum
Crepis biennis	C. capillaris or C. vesicaria
Epilobium obscurum } E. roseum	E. ciliatum
E. obscurum } E. roseum	E. tetragonum
Galium saxatile	G. palustre or G. uliginosum
Geranium rotundifolium	G. molle or G. pyrenaicum
Glyceria notata	G. fluitans or G. declinata
Malva neglecta	dwarf forms of M. sylvestris
Matricaria recutita	Tripleurospermum inodorum or Anthemis cotula
Mentha x verticillata	M. spicata x piperita
Myosotis secunda	M. laxa
Persicaria bistorta	P. amphibia or P. maculosa
Senecio aquaticus	S. jacobaea or S. erucifolius
Solidago virgaurea	S. canadensis or S. gigantea

Species, for which doubt about the accuracy of recording remains, have a note included to this effect in the text under the heading for the genus. Only C species approved by the VC recorders were entered on the database. Where there was any doubt about the correct identification of a species, they requested a specimen, visited the site themselves or, for some of the critical species, sought advice from a specialist.

Possible Sources of Error in the Accuracy of the Text

A printing mistake occurred on the B recording card where the same code number was given for two species. C recording cards were not preprinted with the species name or other details. Handwriting was unclear on some cards. Guidance on an OS map series to be used for place names and the inclusion of parish names would perhaps have resulted in more accurate data on locations. Shortage of time and lack of personnel prevented the checking of every grid reference for accuracy.

Major changes of classification and nomenclature during the years of the project were time-consuming. Decisions to change from the *Flora of the British Isles*, 2nd edition by Clapham, Tutin and Warburg 1962 to the *Flora of the British Isles* 3rd edition by Clapham, Tutin and Moore 1987 and finally to the *New Flora of the*

British Isles by Stace 1991 slowed the rate of progress of data handling and checking.

Checking of records was not as extensive as had been planned. Had time allowed, C card entries would have been printed for return to coordinators and recorders for confirmation before the end of the last year of recording, while they retained the relevant notebooks and memories were still fresh. The sheer volume of data generated combined with staff changes at the WBRC and the extensive use of temporary staff made this impossible to achieve.

In spite of these shortcomings the general level of error in the database is estimated to be below 1%.

Analysis of the Quality of Recording

In order to help the VC recorders to assess 'completeness' of the recording in a tetrad easily and with reasonable accuracy, recorders completed a simple form which provided details of the different habitats within each tetrad. The greater the diversity of habitats, the greater the potential number of species to be located. At the end of each recording season, 10 km square co-ordinators were asked to indicate the number of A, B and C species and the total number of grasses and sedges recorded in each tetrad. It was hoped that this information would give some measure of the quality and completeness of recording and provide opportunities for more experienced persons to assist with the field work in the following season.

In September 1991, when the recording work had been completed and after the data had been entered onto the database, it became possible to determine the total number of A, B and C species recorded per tetrad. These figures are represented in Figures 9 and 10. From the latter, it is too simplistic to assume that tetrads with fewer than average records were 'under-recorded'. The reader is urged to consult the topographical and geological maps (pages 8 and 12) to gain some insight into possible habitat diversity before passing such judgement.

From a total of 948 tetrads in which recording took place, the average (mean) number of records

per tetrad was 216. Thirty-eight tetrads had scores of less than 100. Of these, 24 were either tetrads through which the county boundary runs and were recorded only in part, or were contained within the two VCs but not within the present-day county of Wiltshire. Therefore, there are 14 tetrads

Figure 9. Number of species recorded per tetrad.

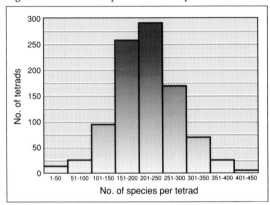

Figure 10. Map showing number of species recorded per tetrad.

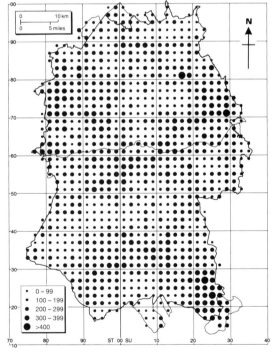

lying entirely within the recording area, within which fewer than 100 species were recorded in each and for which some degree of under-recording must be acknowledged. In some of these, difficulties of access were experienced which could not be overcome.

Figure 11. Number of 'grasses and allied species' recorded per tetrad as a percentage of the total of 87.

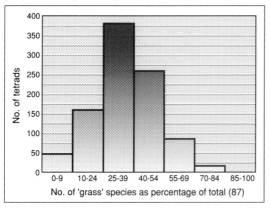

Figure 12. Map showing number of 'grasses and allied species' recorded per tetrad as a percentage of the total of 87.

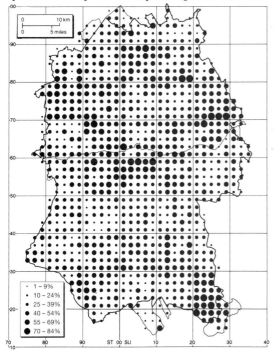

The range of completely acceptable recording levels which can be related to the nature and diversity of habitats in a tetrad is illustrated by the following examples.

An area of relatively low numbers of species per tetrad is found within the Larkhill/Westdown Ranges on the Salisbury Plain Training Area where there are extensive tracts of rough chalk grassland, a little secondary woodland and virtually no wetland or habitation. Here, a tally of 150-200 species was usual. The lower level of 100-150 species was recorded in tetrads where the dominant form of land-use was arable farming. There are other parts of the county where habitat diversity is high and species totals per tetrad are in excess of 300 and a few tetrads have over 400. Such areas usually include some ancient woodland, downland or old meadows, rivers, wetlands and some habitation. Some of the most notable parts of the county include the areas around Ramsbury and Aldbourne, the Cotswold valleys, the Cotswold Water Park, the area around Potterne and Urchfont, the Salisbury Avon valley and the extreme south-east of the county bordering on the New Forest.

An investigation was made into the completeness of recording of the four plant families, grasses, rushes, sedges and horsetails, which have inconspicuous reproductive structures. The total number of species of Poaceae, Juncaceae, Cyperaceae and Equisetaceae listed on the A and B record cards was 87. These are subsequently referred to as 'grasses and allied species'. At the end of the recording period the number of these 87 species which had been recorded in each tetrad was extracted from the database. Figure 11 demonstrates the level of recording of these species throughout the county and the map (Figure 12) indicates the number of species recorded per tetrad within the county which, in many cases, can be related to the diversity of habitats in a locality. It seemed probable that there was a high degree of correlation between the total number of species recorded in a tetrad and the number of 'grasses and allied species' occurring within it. A graph of the percentage of these species, plotted against the percentage of the total species recorded, was prepared and the regression coefficient was calculated to be 0.79. Although the suggested relationship is probably valid in many instances, there are others where this is not so. For example, in a sample of tetrads with a predominance of arable farming and some of the lowest total species counts, a tally of between 20 and 30 or 23% – 34% of the total 87 'grasses and allied species' was recorded, which represents between 12% and 18% of the total plants found. A tetrad with a very high proportion of second-rate downland which was re-establishing after a period of arable farming yielded 39 (45%) of the total number of 'grasses and allied species' or 18% of the total plants. Therefore, it can be demonstrated that there were tetrads with rather low total counts which can be rich in such species. Conversely, in the 100 tetrads with 300 or more species recorded, the number of 'grasses and allied species' ranged between 37 (43%) and 71 (82%) or 11% and 20% of the total number of records of all species.

There were 47 tetrads with fewer than 10% of the 'grasses and allied species' recorded. Of these, 30 had a total of fewer than 100 species recorded, and the majority were tetrads which lie on the county boundary and were recorded only in part.

In attempting this analysis of the level of recording, it is tempting to provide some guide-lines concerning an 'acceptable minimum'. This has not been done, but the possible variation and the range of factors which interact in any tetrad has been demonstrated and the reader is left to judge the results.

Compilation of the Text

The following species accounts were written with reference to printouts from the WRBC containing details of the records already described, the number of species per 1 km or 2 km square, the number of 10 km squares in which each species was recorded and, in many cases, copies of the distribution maps. From these it was possible to analyse in a county context the dynamic influences which bear upon the distribution of individual species and plant groups. For example, clear distinctions became apparent between the distribution of chalk-loving plants and those which prefer clay, sand or heath. The course of major rivers and the position of the Kennet and Avon Canal are highlighted by the concentration of some aquatic species. The presence of ancient woodlands is confirmed by the frequency of known ancient woodland indicator species.

Drawing on this data, and on the authors' own field experience, the accounts were roughed out, worked on, sometimes argued over and finally agreed by the members of the Science Group. References are made to records from the authors' own BSBI index files which predate by many years, and ran parallel with, the WFMP. Contributions from recorders who were not WFMP members are gratefully acknowledged.

Selection of Distribution Maps for Publication

The Science Group had the difficult task of assessing which of the enormous number of maps should be published in the Flora. It was felt that the following categories should not be included:

- Introduced trees and shrubs
- Aliens, garden throw-outs and other introduced species of infrequent occurrence
- Relic crops
- Some rare native species. The few locations for these could be explained more satisfactorily in the text
- Most native species which are so common that a distribution map would be of little value.

The majority of other species have a distribution map.

Appendices can be found on pages 365 - 371

Appendix I. Records of species in the first four groups listed above.

Appendix II. British Red Data Book species and plants found in the county which are included on the provisional list of nationally scarce species.

Appendix III. Species recorded during the WFMP but not recorded in *The Flora of Wiltshire* or the Supplement.

Appendix IV. Species recorded in *The Flora of Wiltshire* 1957 by Grose and in *The Supplement to The Flora of Wiltshire* 1975 but not recorded during the WFMP.

The Vice-county Recorders' Review of the Wiltshire Flora Mapping Project

From its inception, the Wiltshire Flora Mapping Project (WFMP) was seen as a vehicle for informing and educating amateur botanists while gathering data on the distribution of the county's flora that could be used to compile a new flora to succeed that of D Grose (1957) which was becoming outdated. Prior to 1984 there were experienced botanists active in the county and others who had good local knowledge and 'looked at' plants but did not keep records of what they had seen. In 1982 the N Wilts VC recorder received notes from just two individuals. The WFMP brought these and other people together and, in order to increase their knowledge and confidence and by sharing expertise, it arranged field meetings and indoor workshops.

Organisation of the project's fieldwork through a dedicated coordinator for each 10 km square was very successful. During the eight years some of the original coordinators left Wiltshire but, remarkably, in every case someone else stepped in to fill the gap. In S. Wilts, where there are nearly 100 more tetrads that in N. Wilts, special thanks are given to those who worked so hard to ensure that the coverage was completed. Recruits who had finished tetrads in their own allocated 10 km squares volunteered to travel many miles to help. There are areas in the south, including the Salisbury Plain Training Area (SPTA) where the only access to a tetrad is by crossing another tetrad on foot. This was not such a problem in N. Wilts where most of the countryside is criss-crossed by roads and lanes or there is open access.

It is appreciated that recording the flora of any county could never be complete and that inexperience will inevitably lead to some mis-identification and to the lack of recognition that there were different, though superficially similar, species within the critical groups for which even experts are not always agreed on the determination. These are treated as aggregates.

A choice of field guides was available for recorders but, by good timing on his part, Francis Rose had produced *The Wild Flower Key* in 1981

which proved a popular and valuable tool for many recorders. However, well-used copies of David McClintock and RSR Fitter's *The Pocket Guide to Wild Flowers* appeared from many a haversack during field meetings and was used to settle the identification of a plant. The purchase by recorders of BSBI handbooks and other reference books including *Plant Crib* (1988) which were on sale at the annual Lackham meetings, could be linked to the improvement in the standard of recording from year to year.

In the early years there were those who questioned the decision to use the 1 km square as the unit for recording the 'B', or intermediately common category of plants, but, as the project progressed, recorders' enthusiasm increased and they enjoyed the challenge of trying to fill the four boxes on their 'B' cards. The extra information obtained has enabled a much clearer picture of the distribution of these plants to be understood.

At the start of the project there was no certainty that it would be possible for the data to be stored in a county database since the Wiltshire Biological Records Centre (WBRC) had not then been established. In retrospect, the design of the 'C' cards was not ideal either for use by the recorders or for transferring the data to a computer. Greater accuracy might have been achieved, and a great deal of time saved, had they been designed for computer input.

It was anticipated that the WFMP fieldwork would take approximately eight years. Annual progress was displayed on a map at the Lackham meetings using a different coloured dot for each year to show the tetrads that had been recorded. This, and their annual inspection of the record cards, gradually convinced the VC recorders that the original estimate was correct. In late 1989, when there were two more seasons left for recording, plans for the production of *The Wiltshire Flora* were begun. It would need to set the scene for the flora as described in the 1980s by including introductory articles and articles on some of the plants 'special' to Wiltshire at that time.

Compilation of The Flora section of this publication was carried out by the VC recorders and checked by the science group, with the help of the WBRC, and represents only a portion of the vast data bank. Great care was taken over accuracy between the text and the distribution maps but no apology is made where dots have been omitted and comments left deliberately vague so as to protect the locations of rare or threatened species and private land to which access was only given on the understanding that it would not be identified.

The project was highly successful in gathering information and resulted in many sites of conservation interest being brought to the attention of the statutory bodies, a number being designated Sites of Special Scientific Interest (SSSI). Records gathered have formed a useful database from which county and national organisations have been able to assess the importance of sites and make informed decisions on such issues as road and industrial developments and water extraction. Since the completion of the mapping of the flora and, to some extent, as a result of it, 19,690 hectares of chalk downland on the SPTA became an SSSI in January 1993 and the southern stretch of the Salisbury Avon and part of the S. Wiltshire downs have been accepted into the Environmentally Sensitive Area scheme.

The publication of a book of this nature is a stimulus to further recording and the updating process will continue with guidance from the VC recorders, the WBRC and the Wiltshire Botanical Society.

We would like to be notified of any errors and omissions that are bound to be present.

David Green
After moving to Bath in 1976 David Green began to study the flora of Avon, Somerset and Wiltshire and contributed to *The Flora of Somerset* written by Captain RGB Roe and published in 1981. In that year the BSBI appointed him VC recorder for N. Wilts. He works as an ecologist and was the Wiltshire Botanical Society's first chairman.

Ann Hutchison
Ann Hutchison has lived, botanised in and enjoyed S. Wiltshire, mostly from Salisbury, for more than 30 years. She was appointed VC recorder for S. Wilts in 1972. She had taken early retirement from her work as a librarian just prior to the start of the WFMP. She was a founder member of the Wiltshire Trust for Nature Conservation and retains her interest in conservation.

Both VC recorders were central to the running of the Wiltshire Flora Mapping Project.

Acknowledgements

Without the integrity, patience and thoroughness of Roy Fussell, this Flora would not have been completed in the time available. Patricia Woodruffe gave extra support and assistance in the south. Thanks are due to Hampshire botanists for records in VC8 (Hants) and their help in S. Wilts is much appreciated. Paul Bowman, VC recorder for Hants, allowed us to include a number of records before the publication of the *Flora of Hampshire* by Lady A Brewis, Dr F Rose and RP Bowman, Harley Books. David Green thanks his wife Alison for her nine years of patient support and encouragement.

Contributors

Some records in the text are attributed to named contributors who are identified by the initials printed in bold type in the following list of names. All other contributors are included in the list of WFMP recorders on pages v and vi.

J **A**cornley	H **B**ennett
I **A**dgie	D **B**lackford
B Allen	H J M **B**owen
D **A**llen	J **B**owker
P **A**ndrew	R P **B**owman
C **A**ndrewes (Sir)	**Box A**rchaeological
R **A**nscombe	and **N**atural **H**istory
J E **B**aker	Society
N Baldock	R **B**rockbank
L **B**alfe	E **B**romley
S Baynes	A **B**rown

M Browne
P Bunce
A Byfield
C M Cannicott
B K Chadwick
N L Chadwick
R N Chadwick
S Chandler
P Chave
W Clarke
P Cleverly
A Clifton
D G Cooper
R Cooper
Cotswold
  Water Park/Survey
  Team
D Counsell
M Cragg-Barber
S A Cross
E W Culling
E Curtis
P Darby
R Dauncey
M Dodd
J Dodd
G Domanievski
B Easterbrook
E Elliott
S Everett
P Farey
S Farr
R FitzGerald (Lady)
D Forbes
J Fraser
P M W Froud
R Fussell
B Gale
K Gifford
B Gillam
V Gleed
G Goodfellow
M Gray (Lady)
D Green
C Greenwell
J Greenwood

R Grose
D O Graiff
J Hall
J Hammond
M Hardstaff
B G Harris
S Harvey
V E Headland
R T Henly
D Herrod-Taylor
P Hewett
J B Hindley
D Hodgson
S C Holland
V Hopkinson
R Hornby
J W Howitt
K Howitt
C J Hughes
D L Hughes
D P Hughes
A Hutchison
J Jenkin
M Jenkinson
J Jenkyns
B Karn
H Kay
S Kirkman
C Kitchen
M Kitchen
M Lambert
N Langdon
B Last
R Laurence
J Lippitt
J Lovell
J Maitland (Lady)
M Marks
K Marsh
C McQuitty
O Menhinick
P R Merritt
M Mobsby
P Mobsby
K M More
S Nash

Nature Conservancy
  Council/Survey
  Team
M Newbery
D Newman
J Newton
G Nicholls
K Nicol
J E Oliver
J Ounsted
E Overend
R F Packham
S M Palmer
J M Papé
C Patrick
K Payne
G Pearce
C J Perraton
B Phillips
P Phillipson
D Pickering
J Pile
P Pitman
M Ponting
R Porley
J Presland
C Preston
F Price
S Price
C Quest-Ritson
R Randall
J Rawlings
D Read
T C G Rich
E Rollo
F Rose
J Roseaman
G Rycroft
J Rycroft
J Sajo
A Sawyer
V Scott
M Sewell
O Simmonds
D Simpson-Green
A Skinner

M H Smith
P Sneyd
D Sodon
D Spooner
G Steven
D P E Stevens
C Storey
M W Storey
I Stratton
A J Summers
J Sykes
M D Thomas
R Tidswell
P Toynton
J Tozer
M Tyte
R Veall
P Wakefield
J Wall
R Walls
D Wells
L White
W White
P A Whitehead
S Whitworth
L Wild
R Wild
J E Wilder
M Wilkinson
V Williams
Wiltshire Trust for
  Nature Conservation/
  Survey Team
P Wilson
K Wise
S Wolfe-Barry
D J Wood
R Woods
J G Woodgate
P M Woodruffe
E Woolford
H Wright
J Wright
A Wycherley
G Yerrington
S Young

Glossary

acid soil /alkaline soil
All materials in the presence of water can be either neutral, acid or alkaline, the degree of acidity being expressed in terms of a scale called pH. Neutral soil is pH 7, numbers above this indicate alkalinity and below, acidity

ancient woodland
Land having had continuous woodland for at least 300 years

base-rich soil
Soil having a relatively large amount of available mineral nutrients

biennial
Plant that completes its life-cycle within 2 years from seed germination to seed production

bog
Area of water-logged, acid peat

calcareous
Having a high content of calcium as one or more of its chemical compounds

calcicole
Plant associated with calcareous soil

calcifuge
Plant intolerant of calcareous soil

carr
Alder or willow woodland developed in very wet conditions

casual
Alien plant not naturalised or well-established

climax woodland
Woodland containing those species that result from natural processes of succession without human interference

coppice
Thicket of broad-leaved woodland understorey resulting from periodic cutting to near ground level and allowed to grow again from the stool

critical group
Related species with differences existing but difficult to detect and define

downland
Unimproved pasture/grassland, traditionally sheep-grazed, on chalk or limestone

ephemeral
Short-lived plant. Some species have several generations in one year

eutrophic
Nutrient-rich

fen
Area of water-logged peat with alkaline or neutral water-flow

green lane
Unmetalled ancient track, sometimes bounded by hedges on lowland. Many used in the past as drovers' roads and now as access to fields and woodland

heath
Lowland acid grassland with heather, and sometimes gorse or bracken, usually on sands or gravels

hybrid swarm
Series of plants originating by hybridisation between two species and subsequent recrossing with the parents and between themselves so that a continuous series of forms arises

improved grassland
Permanent or reseeded grassland. Agriculturally improved by drainage and/or application of herbicides and artificial fertilisers

indicator species
Plant indicative of a particular habitat

introduction
Of non-native origin, introduced deliberately or accidentally

marsh
Low-lying land on mineral-rich soil, but not peaty, flooded in winter

meadow
Grassland cut for hay

mesotrophic
Of intermediate status – neither nutrient-rich nor nutrient-poor

native
Not known to have been introduced by human agency

naturalised
Introduced plant that has become established

neutral soil
Ecological term for soil having pH values between 6 and 7

pasture
Grassland grazed by sheep and/or cattle

perennial
Plant that lives for more than 2 years

riparian
Growing on river/stream bank

saprophyte
Plant that derives its nourishment from dead or decaying material

secondary woodland
Woodland on a site which has been wooded for less than 300 years

unimproved grassland
Permanent or semi-natural grassland fertilised only by dung of grazing animals

Abbreviations

agg.	aggregate. Including two or more species which closely resemble each other
auct.	of various authors but not the original one
BM	British Museum
BR	British Rail
BSBI	Botanical Society of the British Isles
BTCV	British Trust for Conservation Volunteers
conf.	confirmed by a recognised BSBI recorder
comm. or pers. comm.	personal communication
CWP	Cotswold Water Park
det.	determined. Material sent to BM or BSBI for identification
FC	Forestry Commission
GB	Great Britain
Hb.	herbarium
id.	identified by the recorder
ITE	Institute of Terrestrial Ecology
K & A	Kennet and Avon
MOD	Ministry of Defence
NCC	Nature Conservancy Council (now English Nature)
NNR	National Nature Reserve
NT	National Trust
NVC	National Vegetation Classification
sp.	species (singular)
spp.	species (plural)
SPTA(C)	Salisbury Plain Training Area (Central)
SPTA(E)	Salisbury Plain Training Area (East)
SPTA(W)	Salisbury Plain Training Area (West)
ssp.	sub-species (singular)
sspp.	sub-species (plural)
SSSI	Site of Special Scientific Interest
WBRC	Wiltshire Biological Records Centre
WCC	Wiltshire County Council
WFMP	Wiltshire Flora Mapping Project
WTNC	Wiltshire Trust for Nature Conservation (now Wiltshire Wildlife Trust)
var.	variety
VC	Vice-county
ver.	verified. Confirmed by VC recorder

Guidance Notes for Users of The Flora

The taxa in this flora follow the order adopted by Clive Stace in the *New Flora of the British Isles* 1991. Details are set out in the order shown in the example below.

FUMARIACEAE[1]

Fumaria L.[2]

Fumaria densiflora DC.[3]
F. micrantha Lagasca[4]
Dense-flowered Fumitory[5]

Nationally scarce plant.[6]
Native.[7] Cornfield weed on chalk soil.[8]
N. One VC7 record . . .
S. A marked concentration . . . [9]
10 km² 7 (13%)[10] **1 km² 26 (<1%)**[11] Map 56, page 147[12]

(1) **Family name** printed in CAPITALS.
(2) **Generic name** and name of authority.
(3) **Latin species name** according to the nomenclature adopted by Stace in *The New Flora of the British Isles,* followed by the name of authority.
(4) **Alternative Latin species name,** printed in *italics,* is the older name used during the WFMP.
(5) **English name** according to the nomenclature adopted by Dony, Jury and Perring in *English Names of Wild Flowers,* 2nd edition.
Sub-species, varieties, forms, white-flowered specimens.
(6) **Nationally scarce plant or British Red Data Book species.**
A nationally scarce plant is one that occurs in 16 - 100 10 km².
A British Red Data Book species is one that occurs in 15 or fewer 10 km² nationally.

(7) **Status** of the species in Wiltshire. A species native in GB but an introduction in Wilts is indicated.
(8) **Habitat/s** in which the species occurs.
(9) Account of frequency, distribution, etc. of the species. Some of the less common species are dealt with separately for the two vice counties following the headings **N.** and **S.** Some **contributors** are identified by initials, their full names are listed on page 118.
A **glossary** can be found on page 120.
Abbreviations used in the text are explained on page 121.
(10) **The number of 10 km²** in which the species was recorded followed, (in brackets), by its percentage of the county's total of 52.
(11) **The number of 1 km² or 2 km²** in which the species was recorded followed (in brackets) by the percentage of the county's totals, 3659 1 km² or 948 2 km².
In general, numbers for sspp. are included in the totals and on the distribution maps for the species, e.g. *Ranunculus penicillatus* ssp. *penicillatus* and ssp. *pseudofluitans* on page 138. There are a few exceptions for which the sspp. have their own numbers, e.g. *Papaver dubium* ssp. *dubium* and ssp. *lecoqii* on page 141.
(12) **Distribution maps** are included for over half the species. Each dot is placed centrally in a tetrad (2 km²), therefore some of those on the vice-county boundary appear to lie on the wrong side of, or outside, it. The number of 1 km squares within a tetrad in which a species was found is not shown.
Where a dot might indicate too accurately the location of a vulnerable species it has been omitted from the map.

The mention of a location does not indicate a right of access.

EQUISETACEAE

Equisetum L.

Equisetum fluviatile L.
Water Horsetail

Native. Ponds, streams, canals, bogs and marshes. A localised but common component of the emergent vegetation in these habitats in areas of more acidic heavy clay, sometimes in huge numbers covering entire ponds.
10 km² 29 (56%) 1 km² 96 (3%) **Map 1, page 125**

Equisetum arvense L.
Field Horsetail

Native. Roadside banks, cultivated and waste ground. Frequent and widespread except on the chalk.
10 km² 46 (88%) 2 km² 525 (55%) **Map 2, page 125**

Equisetum sylvaticum L.
Wood Horsetail

Native. Damp woods, particularly near streams within them.
S. Four records of this rarity, three are confirmations of previously known areas in SW: Castle Wood 1985 FR and 20-30 plants near stream in same wood 1991 PMW. Single plant amongst *E. arvense* Tucking Mill 1991 PMW. New site at Urchfont, by damp and shady overgrown footpath 1990 JMP.
10 km² 2 (4%) 1 km² 3 (<1%)

Equisetum palustre L.
Marsh Horsetail

Native. Confined to marshes, bogs, rivers, streams and wet areas where it grows in abundance.
10 km² 37 (71%) 2 km² 182 (19%) **Map 3, page 125**

Equisetum telmateia Ehrh.
Great Horsetail

Native. Wet woodlands, canal margins, marshes, ditches and springs.
N. Very common along the greensand/clay spring line near Lacock and the Corallian/clay junction near Lyneham. Elsewhere, more frequent on heavier clay.
S. Highest concentrations are on roadside verges and in damp places on the Kimmeridge Clay and Portland/Purbeck Beds in the Semley area where they form eye-catching colonies. Has spread to drier areas such as at the base of Alderbury by-pass embankment.
10 km² 34 (65%) 1 km² 168 (5%) **Map 4, page 125**

OPHIOGLOSSACEAE

Ophioglossum L.

Ophioglossum vulgatum L.
Adder's-tongue

Native. Unimproved grassland and open woods.
N. Very difficult to find even when its exact location is known. Most frequent on neutral/acid clay in the Minety area of Braydon Forest.
S. Most frequent on SPTA(C&E) on chalk grassland even where it has been burnt or the soil disturbed. Small colony water-meadow Winterbourne Gunner 1986 PM. Known for many years Blackmoor Copse WTNC reserve.
10 km² 23 (44%) 1 km² 61 (2%) **Map 5, page 125**

Botrychium Sw.

Botrychium lunaria (L.) Sw.
Moonwort

Native. Unimproved grassland.
N. Fifteen plants in a mossy corner of an unimproved meadow near Purton May 1992 PW.
S. Unimproved hay meadow, with *Carex caryophyllea* and *Pedicularis sylvatica* near Ansty 1986 MM. A new site and first record in VC8 for

55 years. For many years this plant was considered to be extinct in Wilts. How many other colonies, old and new, remain to be discovered?
10 km² 2 (4%)   1 km² 2 (<1%)

OSMUNDACEAE

Osmunda L.

Osmunda regalis L.
Royal Fern

Native/introduction. Native populations were plundered by collectors many years ago. The fern has been planted in the grounds of a few estates.
N. Single plant near gamekeeper's cottage, Chilton Foliat 1984 DG, known here for many years.
S. Introduced several sites in Stourhead Gardens 1988-91 DG & PS. A record for VC8 (Hants) 1989 VW thought to be native.
10 km² 3 (6%)   1 km² 5 (<1%)

ADIANTACEAE

Adiantum L.

Adiantum capillus-veneris L.
Maidenhair Fern

Nationally scarce plant.
Native in GB, introduction in Wilts. Established in shade of an old greenhouse Marden Mill 1985 RF.
10 km² 1 (2%)   1 km² 1 (<1%)

POLYPODIACEAE

Polypodium L.

Polypodium L. agg.
Polypody

Native. Found on stone walls, roofs and branches of trees, especially oak. Much commoner in the Cotswold district and Vale of Wardour than elsewhere. Aggregate includes *P. interjectum* except where the latter was specifically verified.
10 km² 39 (75%) 2 km² 222 (23%)   Map 6, page 125

Polypodium interjectum Shivas
Polypodium vulgare L. ssp. *prionodes* (Asch.) Rothm.
Intermediate Polypody

Native. Occurs within the county but the true distribution is not known. Only accurately determined material has been accepted.
10 km² 5 (10%)   1 km² 6 (<1%)

DENNSTAEDTIACEAE

Pteridium Gled. ex Scop.

Pteridium aquilinum (L.) Kuhn
Bracken

Native. Woods, heaths and banks on neutral and acid soil but less vigorous on heavy clay. Only occurs on the chalk where it is capped by superficial deposits. The only European fern to grow in extensive, spreading stands.
N. Common on sandy soils. Elsewhere, most frequent in Savernake Forest.
S. Most frequent in SW and SE. A troublesome weed in several woodland nature reserves, especially at Blackmoor Copse. Spreading on New Forest heathland due to lack of management.
10 km² 46 (88%) 1 km² 807 (22%)   Map 7, page 125

THELYPTERIDACEAE

Oreopteris Holub

Oreopteris limbosperma (Bellardi ex All.) Holub
Thelypteris oreopteris (Ehrh.) Slosson
Lemon-scented Fern

Native. Lightly-shaded situations associated with

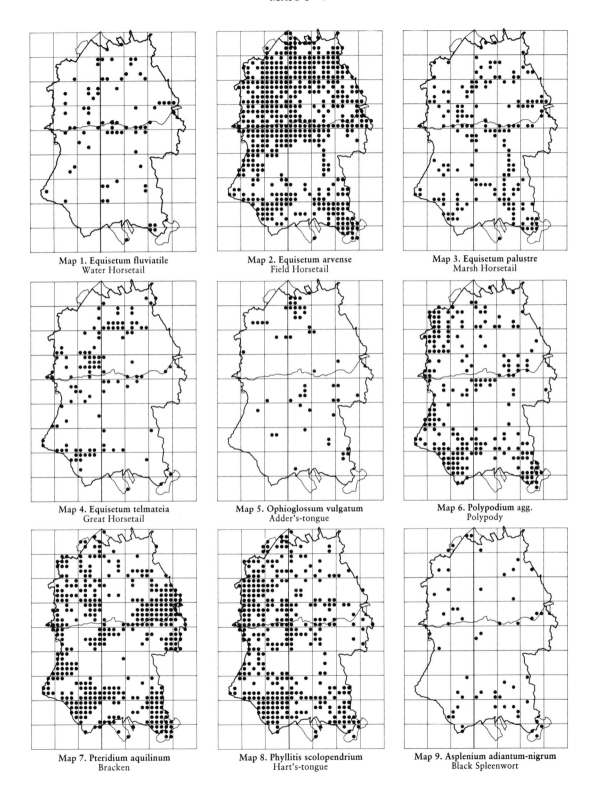

Map 1. Equisetum fluviatile
Water Horsetail

Map 2. Equisetum arvense
Field Horsetail

Map 3. Equisetum palustre
Marsh Horsetail

Map 4. Equisetum telmateia
Great Horsetail

Map 5. Ophioglossum vulgatum
Adder's-tongue

Map 6. Polypodium agg.
Polypody

Map 7. Pteridium aquilinum
Bracken

Map 8. Phyllitis scolopendrium
Hart's-tongue

Map 9. Asplenium adiantum-nigrum
Black Spleenwort

tracksides and adjacent ditches. An indicator species of ancient woodland.

S. Confined to two localities, both in ungrazed woodland. Stourton in the W and private woodland on the N fringe of the New Forest in the SE where it is unknown in heavily grazed areas further to the S. Populations vary from single plants to colonies of 40+.

10 km² 3 (6%)   1 km² 7 (<1%)

ASPLENIACEAE

Phyllitis Hill

Phyllitis scolopendrium (L.) Newman
Hart's-tongue

Native. Damp woodland having rocky outcrops, quarries, streamsides, bases of stonework. Base-rich soil. More common in the western half of the county due to the damper climate and presence of oolitic and greensand soils. Evidence of this is shown by the marked increase in frequency between Wilton and Mere where the fern becomes more common on a variety of habitats such as green-sand banks, a disused quarry and streamside walls.

10 km² 47 (90%) 1 km² 563 (15%)   Map 8, page 125

Asplenium L.

Asplenium adiantum-nigrum L.
Black Spleenwort

Native. Walls, banks, railway cuttings and the brickwork of bridges. Very locally distributed, more frequent in S. Only abundant on the 'blue brick' of railway bridges that occur throughout much of the county and on some walls. Re-recorded after 50 years on walls of Bishopstone (near Salisbury) and Stratford Tony churches.

10 km² 26 (50%) 1 km² 63 (2%)   Map 9, page 125

Asplenium trichomanes L.
Maidenhair Spleenwort

Native. Walls and rocks. Recorded as a single species during WFMP but has since been determined as three sspp. of which two may occur in Wilts.
Ssp. **quadrivalens** D. Meyer.
Common.
Ssp. **pachyrachis** (Christ) Lovis & Reichst.
Occurs in western GB, possibly occurs in Wilts.
N. Common on the Cotswold stone walls in towns and villages in the NW. Grows in mortar lines of the brick bridges over the K & A Canal and railways.
S. Almost entirely restricted to walls, both acid and lime, mortared or not.

10 km² 34 (65%) 1 km² 147 (4%)   Map 10, page 129

Asplenium ruta-muraria L.
Wall-rue
Native. Most frequent and widespread in Cotswold villages which have a wealth of dry stone walls. Also grows on brick bridges, church walls and other stone structures.

10 km² 44 (85%) 2 km² 234 (25%)   Map 11, page 129

Ceterach Willd.

Ceterach officinarum Willd.
Rustyback

Native. Limestone quarries, walls and mortar cracks in masonry including those in railway bridges. Plants destroyed when walls are repointed.
N. Common on dry stone walls in Cotswold villages in the NW. Less common elsewhere but occurs in Swindon and Marlborough and their surrounding villages.
S. Occurs mainly in the R. Nadder valley and in the area around Salisbury. Absent from the chalk.

10 km² 36 (69%) 1 km² 161 (4%)   Map 12, page 129

WOODSIACEAE

Athyrium Roth

Athyrium filix-femina (L.) Roth
Lady-fern

Native. Damp woods, shady streamsides, hedge bottoms and green lanes especially on acid soils.
N. Main concentrations around Malmesbury, in the Braydon Forest area, on the Lower Greensand in the Spye Park area and in Savernake Forest.
S. Main concentrations in the SE corner and on the Portland and Purbeck outcrops around Tisbury.
10 km² 33 (63%) 1 km² 163 (5%)   Map 13, page 129

Cystopteris Bernh.

Cystopteris fragilis (L.) Bernh.
Brittle Bladder-fern

Native. Stonework.
N. Growing on old stone bridge near North Wraxall 1983 JP. First record for VC7 since 1940. Sites on the county boundary with Avon at Brown's Folly and quarries at Box have been repeatedly searched but no plants found 1992 DG.
S. Growing in shop basement, High Street, Devizes 1983 DG. Site later destroyed. Phillips House, Dinton 1987 MDT. Not refound on walls Fonthill Gifford 1986 AH & DS.
10 km² 3 (8%)   1 km² 3 (<1%)

DRYOPTERIDACEAE

Polystichum Roth

Polystichum setiferum (Forsskål) Moore ex Woynar
Soft Shield-fern

Native. Woods, hedgebanks and wooded stream-sides. The commoner of the two *Polystichum* species.

N. Suitable habitats occur mainly in the W. Occurs on almost bare limestone scree in ash woodland and steep woodland banks on greensand.
S. Most common in the Vale of Wardour and the SE, avoiding the chalk. Plants always better developed than *P. aculeatum*.
10 km² 27 (52%) 1 km² 183 (5%)   Map 14, page 129

Polystichum aculeatum (L.) Roth
Hard Shield-fern

Native. Woods, steep cuttings, ditches, shaded banks and roadside verges.
N. Infrequent, usually occurring in small numbers on stream banks in woodland and on Clay-with-flints in West Woods and Savernake Forest.
S. Most common in the Vale of Wardour and the SE. Rarely found in colonies.
10 km² 24 (46%) 1 km² 94 (3%)   Map 15, page 129

Dryopteris Adans.

Dryopteris filix-mas (L.) Schott
Male-fern

Native. A frequent and widely-distributed species of woods and hedges but less common on chalk soils.
10 km² 50 (96%) 2 km² 553 (58%) Map 16, page 129

Dryopteris affinis (Lowe) Fraser-Jenkins
Scaly Male-fern

Subspecies recorded as an aggregate for the WFMP include:
Ssp. **affinis**
Dryopteris pseudomas (Wollaston) Holub & Pouzar
Ssp. **borreri** (Newman) Fraser-Jenkins
Ssp. *robusta* Oberholzer & Tavel ex Fraser-Jenkins.
Native. Old, damp woodland on neutral to acid soils.

N. Woods on clay soil. Localised in its distribution, abundant at Spye Park, Bird's Marsh near Chippenham and Braydon Forest area, sparingly elsewhere.

S. Most records refer to only a few plants, but recorded as 'numerous' in Compton Wood MDT. Much more frequent in the New Forest area, many colonies having robust, conspicuous specimens.

10 km² 16 (31%) 1 km² 70 (2%)   Map 17, page 129

Dryopteris aemula (Aiton) Kuntze
Hay-scented Buckler-fern

Native.

S. Very shallow stream valley with sloping, damp, acid banks. Close to New Forest 1985 FR, RH. This may be the 'Landford, Simms 1894' site included by Grose in *The Flora of Wiltshire*.

10 km² 1 (2%)   1 km² 1 (<1%)

Dryopteris carthusiana (Villars) H. P. Fuchs
Narrow Buckler-fern

Native. Damp woodland, acidic marshes and fens.

N. Occurs very locally in woods in Braydon Forest including Ravensroost, Somerford Common, Stonehill and Little Withywood. Occasionally rooted in *Carex paniculata* tussocks in some sites beside R. Kennet at Knighton, Chilton Foliat and Froxfield. Dried-up pond Savernake Forest, single location Spye Park.

S. Many ancient woodland sites including Stourton, Great Ridge and Bentley Woods. Most records refer to only a few plants. Common and widespread Hamptworth 1990 DJW.

10 km² 14 (27%) 1 km² 41 (1%)   Map 18, page 129

Dryopteris dilatata (Hoffm.) A. Gray
Broad Buckler-fern

Native. Woodland, hedgebanks, streamsides on acid, neutral and calcareous soils. A common

member of the plant community of these habitats.

10 km² 47 (90%) 1 km² 502 (14%)   Map 19, page 133

BLECHNACEAE

Blechnum L.

Blechnum spicant (L.) Roth
Hard Fern

Native. Old woodland on acid soils. Generally regarded as a very good indicator species of ancient woodland.

N. Very rare. West Woods 1984 WTNC/ST, Chisbury Wood near Great Bedwyn 1985 MP, Hens Wood 1989 JN, Raspberry Copse, Bowood 1990 DG.

S. Stronghold in the New Forest area especially in ditches and on streamsides in woods where it is common and widespread. N of this area much less frequent in Clarendon and Bentley Woods. On greensand in the SW at Stourton, Great Bradley, Southleigh and Little Ridge Woods, and around Wardour.

10 km² 11 (21%) 1 km² 47 (1%)   Map 20, page 133

AZOLLACEAE

Azolla Lam.

Azolla filiculoides Lam.
Water Fern

Introduction. History in Wilts documented by Grose. First record from K & A Canal at Limpley Stoke 1939 (C I Sandwith, Green & Buckle). See Aquatic Plants of the Kennet & Avon Canal p.57.

N. Since 1939 has occurred throughout the length of the canal, probably never in such abundance as in the first few years. From 1984-91 it appeared on the Long Pound E of Devizes between Horton and All Cannings, its position being partly controlled by the strength and direction of the wind 1987 BG. Introduced in farm garden pond Yatesbury 1988 BG.

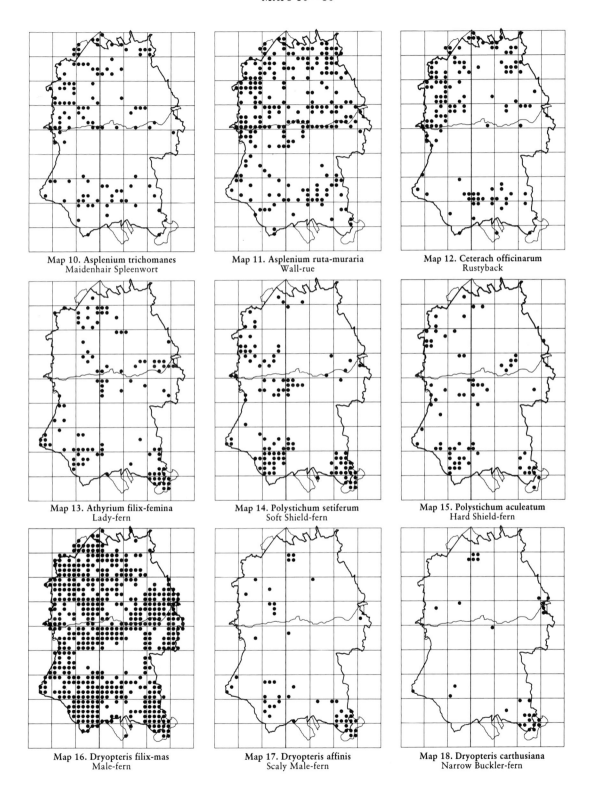

Map 10. Asplenium trichomanes
Maidenhair Spleenwort

Map 11. Asplenium ruta-muraria
Wall-rue

Map 12. Ceterach officinarum
Rustyback

Map 13. Athyrium filix-femina
Lady-fern

Map 14. Polystichum setiferum
Soft Shield-fern

Map 15. Polystichum aculeatum
Hard Shield-fern

Map 16. Dryopteris filix-mas
Male-fern

Map 17. Dryopteris affinis
Scaly Male-fern

Map 18. Dryopteris carthusiana
Narrow Buckler-fern

S. Now three sites in R. Wylye: Stockton 1985 AS, near Stockton 1987 JO & BSBI, E of Boyton 1987 DN & BSBI. Four sites in R. Avon area S of Salisbury: North & South Charlton water-meadows, mill-leat Downton and Trafalgar 1984 NLC & BKC. Daw's Nursery, Frome Road, Trowbridge 1989 EC.

10 km² 7 (13%)   1 km² 15 (<1%)   Map 21, page 133

PINACEAE

Picea A. Dietr.

Picea abies (L.) Karsten
Norway Spruce

Introduction. Woodland plantations. Usually planted, but self-sown in Bentley Wood.
10 km² 40 (77%) 1 km² 251 (7%)

Larix Miller

Larix decidua Miller
European Larch

Introduction. All trees have been planted, some in single-species stands, some in softwood mixtures. Widely-distributed.
10 km² 47 (90%) 1 km² 505 (14%)

Pinus L.

Pinus sylvestris L.
Scots Pine

Introduction (much planted) and native. Prefers sandy, well-drained soils.
N. A tree in Spye Park, with a 6 metre girth and a height of 22 metres was, in 1953, calculated to be 260-300 years old and, from incomplete investigations, was considered by a forester to be most probably 'a representative – perhaps the last one – of a native English strain to occur in Wilts.'

(Ref. A Botanical Survey of Spye Park by D Grose, Wiltshire Archaeological and Natural History Magazine, 55, 263-269).
S. Seedlings present in the New Forest where the species was re-introduced in 1770. Grows quickly for several years on well-drained soil then more slowly. Usually short-lived on chalk. Colonising chalk at Blackball Firs SPTA(C), Milston Down SPTA(E), Porton Down and Pepperbox Hill.
10 km² 46 (88%) 1 km² 719 (20%)   Map 22, page 133

CUPRESSACEAE

Juniperus L.

Juniperus communis L.
Juniper

Native. Unimproved chalk downland. Seedlings survive only in the absence of grazing stock. Becomes overshadowed by yew and other tree species as the succession proceeds towards its climax.
N. In quantity only at the W end of the Marlborough Downs: Beacon Hill, King's Play Hill, Morgan's Hill (seedlings on Mid-Wilts Golf Course), Calstone, Knoll and Bassett Downs. Single or few Clifford's Hill, Huish Hill and Giant's Grave. Many colonies are only remnants of more vigorous past populations.
S. Numbers of bushes range from 1-2 to scattered or frequent. Of sufficient interest to merit four SSSIs. Largest colony in S England of exceptional and national interest benefiting by having two areas of very old bushes and another of younger age Porton Ranges (SSSI). Large colony of high quality stretching 1 km along Beacon Hill (SSSI) with many seedlings here and on SPTA(E). Pepperbox Hill and Dean Hill (SSSI) and scattered N of Baverstock (SSSI). Most westerly at Great Ridge. N-facing at Burcombe. Grovely Wood, High Post Golf Course, Pinecrest, Figsbury Ring, Stock Bottom and in the N at Pewsey Hill.
10 km² 14 (27%) 1 km² 52 (1%)   Map 23, page 133

TAXACEAE

Taxus L.

Taxus baccata L.
Yew

Native. A tree of woodland and scrub on chalk and limestone downland, cliffs and rocky outcrops. Frequently planted, especially in and close to churchyards.
N. Abundant only very locally on parts of the limestone escarpment and on steep slopes along the valley of the Bristol Avon and its tributaries.
S. On steep chalk slopes, often associated with *Sorbus aria*. Great Yews, an SSSI S of Salisbury, is of great interest, because it is totally natural in origin and the sole survivor of pure yew woodland in the county on fairly level ground.
10 km² 49 (94%) 1 km² 724 (20%) Map 24, page 133

ARISTOLOCHIACEAE

Asarum L.

Asarum europaeum L.
Asarabacca

Native/introduction of historical interest. Both William Turner and Nicholas Culpepper, 16th century, wrote that 'it groweth in England only in gardines that I wotte of' and that 'it groweth frequently in gardines. Gives ripe seed June-July.' An intriguing rarity with unusual cyclamen-shaped leaves and hidden brown flowers. Once grown medicinally.
S. Two contrasting records and sites.
1. Near Redlynch, one of the county's botanical show-pieces known since 1782. Colony stretching for many metres under a hedge was monitored for some years by NLC & BKC. By 1985, plants were growing in hazel copse on other side of lane but were later eaten by goats. The colony produces seeds and seedlings.
2. A single clump in a wood near Ebbesbourne

Wake. It is more robust vegetatively and produces flowers, comm. BF, AH.
10 km² 2 (4%) 1 km² 2 (<1%)

NYMPHAEACEAE

Nymphaea L.

Nymphea alba L.
White Water-lily

Native/introduction. Static water, rarely in slow-moving water.
N. Uncommon. Planted in many village and privately-owned ponds by landowners who aim to enhance the environment. Probably only native on K & A Canal at Horton, Allington and All Cannings. Other records: ponds at Braydon, Battle Lake, Red Lodge, Ridge, Burderop Hospital and Box Bottom in Savernake Forest.
S. Planted at Cowesfield Green, Whiteparish PMW, Melchet Pond 1988 RV, small village pond Poulshot Green 1986 BGH, Cresset Pond 1987 and lake Donhead St Andrew 1990 MM, large pond Poulshot 1991 BGH, four sites Stourhead Gardens 1991 PS. Downton water-meadows and shallow, slow-flowing stream from R. Avon New Court Farm 1984 NLC/BKC, Bristol Avon at Limpley Stoke 1986 JM.
10 km² 13 (25%) 1 km² 22 (<1%) Map 25, page 133

Nuphar Smith

Nuphar lutea (L.) Smith
Yellow Water-lily

Native/introduction. Lakes, large ponds and slow-flowing water courses.
N. Common only in the Bristol Avon and its tributaries. Infrequent in the K & A Canal. Probably introduced to some larger ponds and lakes.
S. Less frequent. 'Backwaters of the Avon' S of Salisbury (Grose) still applies 30 years on.
10 km² 27 (52%) 1 km² 108 (3%) Map 26, page 133

CERATOPHYLLACEAE

Ceratophyllum L.

Ceratophyllum demersum L.
Rigid Hornwort

Native. Static and slow-moving water.
N. Abundant throughout the length of the K & A Canal and in all the CWP lakes. Scarce in some of the sluggish streams.
S. Single record. Common in dewpond on Urchfont Hill 1989 BG.
10 km² 12 (23%) 1 km² 54 (2%)   Map 27, page 133

RANUNCULACEAE

Caltha L.

Caltha palustris L.
Marsh-marigold

Native. Frequent but sparsely distributed due to the county's limited wetland habitats.
10 km² 47 (90%) 2 km² 355 (37%)   Map 28, page 136

Helleborus L.

Helleborus foetidus L.
Stinking Hellebore

Nationally scarce plant.
Native. Woodland on calcareous soil. Introduced in most localities.
N. Steep, wooded hillsides in By Brook valley. Although appearing to be native, the origin of these plants may have been the gardens of old cottages and mills. Known 1835 by Babington in Cloud Quarry, renamed Backpath Wood, where small colony adjacent to the road persisted for many years. Larger colony 150+ plants higher up the wooded slope 1983 DG. Long Dean 1983, Ford and Rack Hill 1984 ASk & GG, Castle Combe 1985 LW, Murhill House overlooking the Bristol

Avon valley 1986 JM where the plant has been known for a long time but questionably native.
S. Everleigh Ashes 1986 KN, Wylye 1988 BL, several plants along top of railway embankment Roman Road NE of Idmiston 1988 OS, probably planted c. 200 m from Amesbury Abbey 1990 BL, number of plants on slope above public footpath Arn Hill, Warminster 1991 VEH, fine colony extending to 100 m in woodland by side of track Tollard Farm/Park View Point close to Dorset boundary 1991 JO & AH.
10 km² 8 (16%) 1 km² 13 (<1%)   Map 29, page 136

Helleborus viridis L.
Green Hellebore

Native. Woodland on calcareous soil.
N. Main concentration on limestone is similar to that of *H. foetidus*. Colerne Park, Slaughterford 1984 DG, Wick Wood and adjacent road verge near West Kington 1984 MB, Conkwell 1987 JP. On Lower Chalk: large colony of long-standing in Clouts Wood near Wroughton 1984 DG, streamside Liddington 1989 SC, Breech Cottage woodland strip once part of West Woods, Savernake 1989 JEO.
S. Some hedgebank sites doubtfully native. Large clumps, wooded slope Peppercombe Lane, Urchfont 1984 RF, steep bank trampled by cattle and between R. Nadder and railway 1985 MM. Roadside banks: one old-established colony Fonthill Gifford 1987 JJe, one clump on verge of Ridge/Chilmark road 1988 VH. Old hedgebank of arable field, Upper Chute 1986 JSy, two plants in gateway Orcheston 1988 AW.
10 km² 10 (19%) 1 km² 16 (<1%)   Map 30, page 136

Eranthis Salisb.

Eranthis hyemalis (L.) Salisb.
Winter Aconite

Introduction. Sparsely distributed. Often associated with churchyards and sites of previous

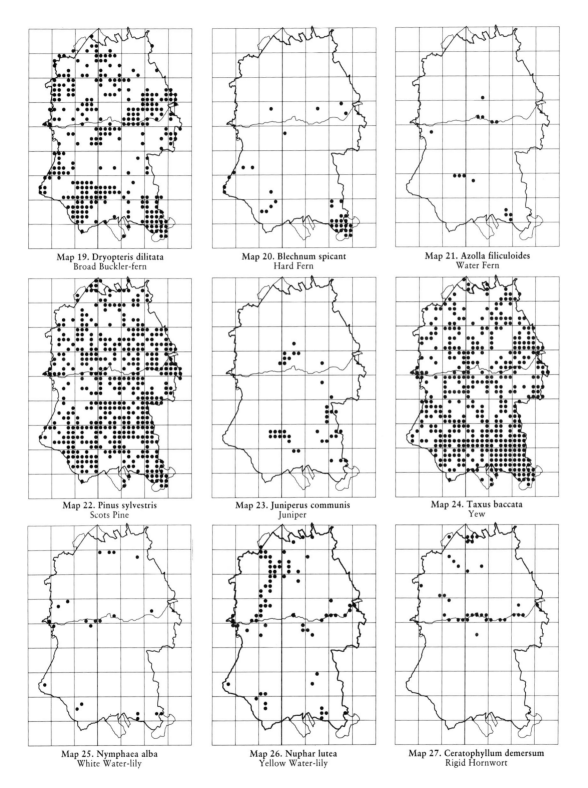

Map 19. Dryopteris dilitata
Broad Buckler-fern

Map 20. Blechnum spicant
Hard Fern

Map 21. Azolla filiculoides
Water Fern

Map 22. Pinus sylvestris
Scots Pine

Map 23. Juniperus communis
Juniper

Map 24. Taxus baccata
Yew

Map 25. Nymphaea alba
White Water-lily

Map 26. Nuphar lutea
Yellow Water-lily

Map 27. Ceratophyllum demersum
Rigid Hornwort

gardens. Found in ornamental woodlands where plantings have become long-established.

S. Wood near Lake House, refind of record referred to by Grose.

10 km² 10 (19%) 1 km² 14 (<1%)

Aconitum L.

Aconitum napellus L. ssp. **napellus**
Monk's-hood

Nationally scarce plant.
Native and introduction. Shaded damp river and stream banks. Status in some of its locations questionable.

N. Native along brooks Nettleton and West Kington. Doubtfully native Slaughterford and Rowde, both near ruined mills. Garden throw-out Savernake 1984 DG.

S. Native at two known sites, Bishopstone 1984 ABr, spreading 6 m x 2 m and second smaller colony near Bristow Copse, N of Pewsey JEO & KP 1985-86. Edge of ride in conifer wood opposite Pilton Lodge 1987 PW & MR, Figheldean 1988 BE, probably a garden survival Imber village 1988 JL, woodland wild garden Iford Manor 1987-89 JM and Wingfield 1990 PF. Known at least 25 years between lane and Brook House, Storridge Lane, Westbury 1990 EC. Scattered clumps in two areas in mixed woodland Great Ridge Wood 1990 VH.

10 km² 10 (19%) 1 km² 16 (<1%)   Map 31, page 136

Consolida (DC.) Gray

Consolida ajacis (L.) Schur
Consolida ambigua (L.) P. Ball & Heyw.
Larkspur

Introduction. Formerly occurring as a casual cornfield weed which survived for only a year or two at a site.

N. Garden weed Bromham 1987 DG.

10 km² 1 (2%)   1 km² 1 (<1%)

Anemone L.

Anemone nemorosa L.
Wood Anemone

Native. A common species of dry, deciduous woodland. Also occurs under hedges and rarely in unimproved neutral pasture.

10 km² 49 (94%) 2 km² 407 (43%)   Map 32, page 136

Pulsatilla Miller

Pulsatilla vulgaris Miller
Anemone pulsatilla L.
Pasqueflower

Nationally scarce plant.
Native. Dry chalk grassland.

S. First VC8 (Hants) record 1983 PT conf. RPB, JO.

10 km² 1 (2%)   1 km² 1 (<1%)

Clematis L.

Clematis vitalba L.
Traveller's-joy

Native. Woodland, hedgerows and scrub on calcareous soils. Striking display of seed heads.

10 km² 50 (96%) 2 km² 525 (55%)   Map 33, page 136

Ranunculus L.

Terrestrial and emergent aquatic species were accurately recorded. Subaquatic species presented problems due to difficulty of collecting specimens, the short flowering period and the variation in form according to environmental conditions.

Ranunculus acris L.
Meadow Buttercup

Native. A plant of neutral, damp, unimproved grassland. Less frequent on chalk downland where

it occurs only among coarse grass. Improvement of grassland has reduced its abundance. Common and widely-distributed.
10 km² 50 (96%) 2 km² 804 (85%)   Map 34, page 136

Ranunculus repens L.
Creeping Buttercup

Native. Very common, especially in damp or shaded habitats and on waste ground.
Form with double flowers: Garden Devizes 1992 BG, Chapmanslade 1986 CQ-R.
10 km² 52 (100%) 2 km² 881 (93%)

Ranunculus bulbosus L.
Bulbous Buttercup

Native. A common species on all types of semi-improved and unimproved grassland. More common on chalk grassland than *R. acris* and *R. repens*. This plant dies back in summer.
10 km² 49 (94%) 2 km² 558 (59%)   Map 35, page 136

Ranunculus sardous Crantz
Hairy Buttercup

Probable native.
S. Very rare. Around ponds W of Furzley village, first record for 23 years 1989 VW, Plaitford Common 1991 AB.
10 km² 1 (2%)   1 km² 2 (<1%)

Ranunculus arvensis L.
Corn Buttercup

Nationally scarce plant.
Native. Disturbed lime-rich soil. Declined since the 1960s to relic status nationally due to use of herbicides.
N. Market garden Malmesbury 1985 JH, cornfield Malmesbury Common 1988 JW.
S. King's Corner, Pewsey 1986 KN, Carvers Hill Farm, Shalbourne 1987 CM, two plants edge of cornfield, no trace after potato crop in following year Old Dilton 1987 VEH.
10 km² 4 (8%)   1 km² 5 (<1%)

Ranunculus auricomus L.
Goldilocks Buttercup

Native. Woodland and the base of old hedges.
N. Most highly concentrated in association with ancient woodlands from the western border of the county E to the Braydon Forest area.
S. Less frequent. Largely confined to ancient woodland sites near Trowbridge, S of Pewsey, around Chute and area between Porton Down and Redlynch.
10 km² 44 (85%) 1 km² 278 (8%)   Map 36, page 136

Ranunculus sceleratus L.
Celery-leaved Buttercup

Native. Silty edges of rivers, streams, ponds, canals and gravel pits.
N. Abundant along the Bristol Avon and in the area between Malmesbury and Cricklade. Scattered along the K & A Canal and in CWP. Occasional in ponds on the lowland clay.
S. Along the Salisbury Avon. Sparse elsewhere except on clay soils between Devizes and Trowbridge where it is frequent.
10 km² 32 (62%) 1 km² 190 (5%)   Map 37, page 139

Ranunculus lingua L.
Greater Spearwort

Native and introduction. Sold in garden centres. All records are probable introductions.
N. Gravel pit Inwood, near Lacock 1988 DG, small pond near Charlton 1990 JRy.
S. Recorded for 15 years Harnham, Salisbury 1989 IS, large spectacular population Newhouse Lake 1989 DJW, and single plant introduced to pond Bentley Wood 1987 PMW.
10 km² 4 (8%)   1 km² 5 (<1%)

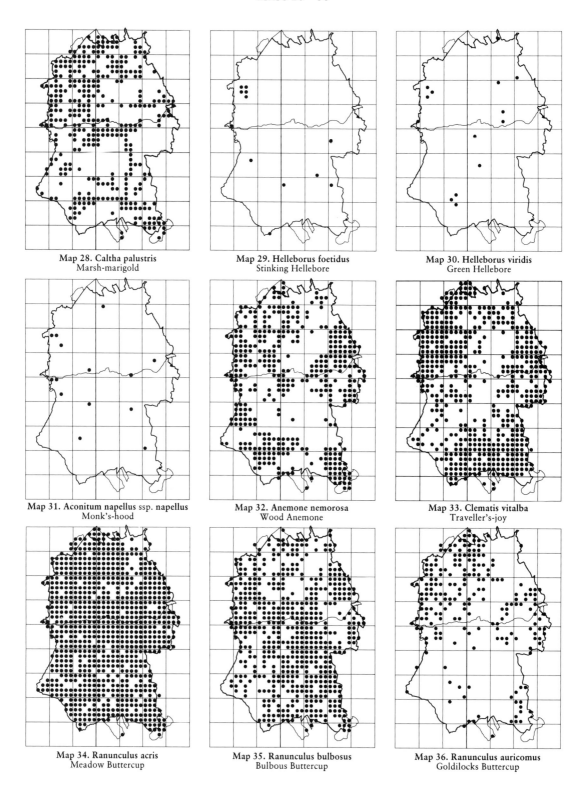

Map 28. Caltha palustris
Marsh-marigold

Map 29. Helleborus foetidus
Stinking Hellebore

Map 30. Helleborus viridis
Green Hellebore

Map 31. Aconitum napellus ssp. napellus
Monk's-hood

Map 32. Anemone nemorosa
Wood Anemone

Map 33. Clematis vitalba
Traveller's-joy

Map 34. Ranunculus acris
Meadow Buttercup

Map 35. Ranunculus bulbosus
Bulbous Buttercup

Map 36. Ranunculus auricomus
Goldilocks Buttercup

Ranunculus flammula L.
Lesser Spearwort

Native. Damp open woodland, pond margins, ditches and wet flushes in fields on neutral to acid soils.
N. Abundant along open rides in Braydon Forest woodlands, especially at Somerford Common. On Lower Greensand at Spye Park. Only one record from the area of acid soil in Savernake Forest.
S. Most frequent in SE corner of county on clay and in Vale of Wardour in SW.
10 km² 33 (63%) 1 km² 148 (4%)   Map 38, page 139

Ranunculus ficaria L.
Lesser Celandine

Native. Common and widely-distributed in woods and hedgebanks. Prolific weed of churchyards and gardens.
10 km² 51 (98%) 2 km² 743 (78%)

Ranunculus hederaceus L.
Ivy-leaved Crowfoot

Native. Pond mud and shallow water on acid soils.
N. No recent records. Grose reported 18 localities but some of these may have been due to earlier misunderstanding of the genus.
S. The decline noticed in 1957 is now more dramatic. No records from peaty soil in the SW where it was once common. Cluster of sites in SE, around Redlynch and Landford sometimes in association with *R. omiophyllus*. Only other record, growing on sides of freshly dug drainage ditch by a small marsh, Woodborough 1984 RF.
10 km² 3 (6%)   1 km² 9 (<1%)

Ranunculus omiophyllus Ten.
Ranunculus lenormandii F. Schultz
Round-leaved Crowfoot

Native. Shallow water, ditches, wet mud on tracks and pond edges.

S. Confined to SE of county. First records for many years, Furzley pools 1989 AB, Loosehanger and Quar Hill Plantation 1989 DJW, Nomansland 1991 VW, Plaitford and Wellow Commons 1991 RV.
10 km² 2 (4%)   1 km² 15 (<1%)   Map 39, page 139

Ranunculus trichophyllus Chaix
Thread-leaved Water-crowfoot

Native. Ponds and ditches.
N. Most frequent in disused ponds, formerly used for watering cattle, which are a feature of low-lying clay. Elsewhere on clay Hullavington, Sutton Benger and Biddestone and on gravel CWP, North Meadow NNR at Cricklade and Lacock.
S. Characteristic plant of downland dewponds and other ponds. Appeared within two years of old dewpond being lined with butyl Parsonage Down NNR 1984. Pond at rear of surgery Whiteparish; small ponds, both dried out but plants in flower West Ashton and Bulkington, frequent roadside pond Great Hinton and village green Poulshot. Small dewpond N of Little Down, Broad Chalke.
10 km² 14 (27%) 1 km² 22 (<1%)   Map 40, page 139

Ranunculus aquatilis L.
Common Water-crowfoot

Native. Ponds, lakes, and gravel pits. Primarily a plant of field and village ponds, less common in canals, rivers and streams.
N. Most frequent in the large number of disused ponds on the lowland clays from Melksham to Cricklade.
S. Scattered, but common along the rivers Till, Wylye and Nadder.
10 km² 28 (54%) 1 km² 112 (3%)   Map 41, page 139

Ranunculus peltatus Schrank
Pond Water-crowfoot

Native.
N. Dewpond Milk Hill (Pewsey Downs NNR)

1986 KP, pond at Oaksey 1987 CK & MK.

S. Common in large pond The Warren, West Lavington 1984 RF. Stream E of ford King's Farm near East Wellow and Furzley Common 1991 RV.

10 km² 5 (10%)   1 km² 6 (<1%)

Ranunculus penicillatus (Dumort.) Bab.
Stream Water-crowfoot

Native. Fast-flowing, lime-rich rivers and streams.
N. Occurs on Bristol Avon upstream of Malmesbury and downstream of Bradford-on-Avon but rarely between these towns. R. Thames, By Brook and extensively on R. Kennet.
S. Most frequent on the southern tributaries of Bristol Avon, on Salisbury Avon, R. Wylye, R. Nadder and their tributaries.
Ssp. **penicillatus**
Has laminar and capillary leaves. Records only from the upper reaches of the R. Kennet 1988 JEO.
Ssp. **pseudofluitans** (Syme) S. Webster
The most common ssp. in Wilts.

10 km² 32 (62%)   1 km² 138 (4%)   Map 42, page 139

Ranunculus fluitans Lam.
River Water-crowfoot

Native. Lime-rich, fast-flowing water courses.
S. Bristol Avon downstream from Limpley Stoke Mill 1983 DG. In the deeper water of Salisbury Avon or carriers from Standlynch Mill upstream through Bodenham and Britford water-meadows 1984 to East Harnham Farm 1985 NLC & BKC. Shallow water R. Bourne 1985 NLC & BKC, R. Wylye near Boyton 1987 BSBI meeting, Bathampton Estate 1987 BL, R. Nadder near Donhead House 1990 MM and in deep fast-flowing water near Dinton 1988 SMP. Plentiful in stream S of Earldoms 1987 PMW, under bridge upper Salisbury Avon Puckshipton, Wilsford 1989 JMP.

10 km² 7 (13%)   1 km² 18 (<1%)   Map 43, page 139

Ranunculus circinatus Sibth.
Fan-leaved Water-crowfoot

Native. Slow-flowing and static water.
N. Most frequent in the K & A Canal but it has declined here in recent years during the canal's restoration and opening up for through traffic. Spreading in some of the shallower pits in the CWP.
S. A decline in records, possibly reflecting over-recording in the past. Dewpond Urchfont Hill, abundant in R. Wylye, Kingston Deverill 1989 BG.

10 km² 12 (23%)   1 km² 18 (<1%)

Adonis L.

Adonis annua L.
Pheasant's-eye

Introduction. Arable and disturbed land, appearance erratic.
N. Meadow at Gastard 1984 TB, Draycot Foliat 1990 JR. Both colonies very small, one on spoil dug for a fence post-hole on unimproved grassland.
S. Arable and tracksides SPTA(E), arable near High Post and Longhedge Farm, disturbed ground and arable Odstock, arable Allenford. Area near Salisbury continues to produce new records made possible by long seed-dormancy. See article on p.43.

10 km² 8 (15%)   1 km² 14 (<1%)   Map 44, page 139

Myosurus L.

Myosurus minimus L.
Mousetail

Nationally scarce plant.
Probably native. Damp arable ground.
S. Milton Lilbourne 1985 FP, first record since 1957. Farmland Rushall 1988 DGC, bare mud in entrance to arable field, East Grafton 1989 AJS, single plant between rows of daffodils Ware's Nursery, Woodborough 1991 FP.

10 km² 2 (4%)   1 km² 4 (<1%)

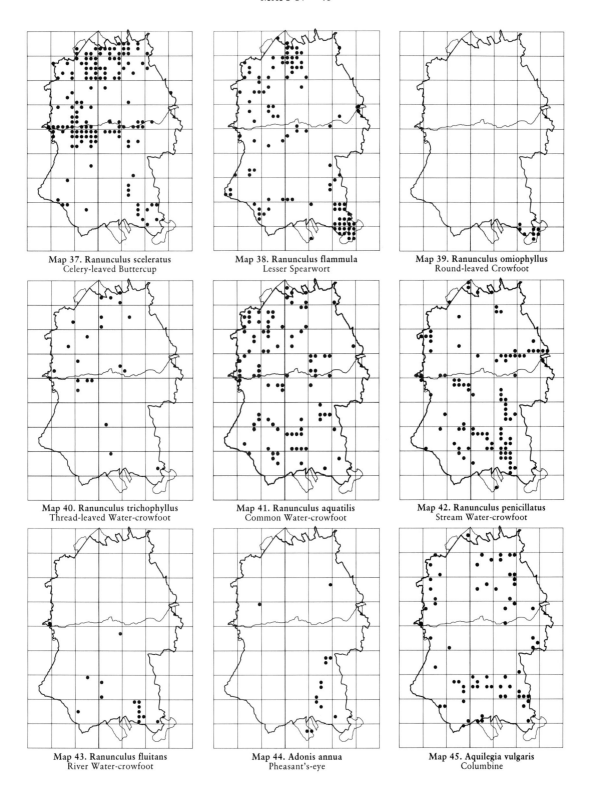

Map 37. Ranunculus sceleratus
Celery-leaved Buttercup

Map 38. Ranunculus flammula
Lesser Spearwort

Map 39. Ranunculus omiophyllus
Round-leaved Crowfoot

Map 40. Ranunculus trichophyllus
Thread-leaved Water-crowfoot

Map 41. Ranunculus aquatilis
Common Water-crowfoot

Map 42. Ranunculus penicillatus
Stream Water-crowfoot

Map 43. Ranunculus fluitans
River Water-crowfoot

Map 44. Adonis annua
Pheasant's-eye

Map 45. Aquilegia vulgaris
Columbine

Aquilegia L.

Aquilegia vulgaris L.
Columbine

Native and introduction. Native plants usually have blue/violet flowers.
N. A rare native on limestone in woods on the valley slopes of the By Brook around Castle Combe. Colonies small and their distribution transient. All other records considered to be garden escapes; many colour variations and evidence of hybridisation.
S. An indicator species of ancient woodland. Records from this habitat vary from a single plant Knighton Wood 1986 LW, colony of about 20 (mostly seedlings) Chase Wood 1991 JO to over 70 Stonedown Wood 1991 PCh & PMWF. Probably hundreds over wide area Bentley Wood, all blue-coloured 1984-85 PMW & 1990 IA. Pink-flowered plants in Grovely Wood BL and several plants dumped at Winterbourne Dauntsey PM must have been of garden origin.
10 km² 25 (48%) 1 km² 77 (2%)   Map 45, page 139

Thalictrum L.

Thalictrum flavum L.
Common Meadow-rue

Native. Neutral wet meadows, river and streamsides. Usually very local.
N. Abundant locally in the Thames/Isis flood plain especially in North Meadow NNR, Cricklade. Elsewhere, in small numbers in the Bristol Avon, By Brook and R. Kennet valleys.
S. Majority of records are from the valleys of the rivers Bourne, Wylye and Salisbury Avon.
10 km² 22 (42%) 1 km² 58 (2%)   Map 46, page 143

Thalictrum minus L.
Lesser Meadow-rue

Native in GB, introduction in Wilts occurring as a garden escape.
N. Near the Column, Savernake Forest 1985 DG *et al*. Holbutts Farm near Box 1986 JR, road verge Hazeland 1985 DG.
S. Brookmead, East Grimstead 1986 PAW.
10 km² 4 (8%)   1 km² 4 (<1%)

BERBERIDACEAE

Berberis L.

Berberis vulgaris L.
Barberry

Native and introduction. Confusion may occur due to cultivars seeding into the wild.
Frequency considerably reduced in last 40 years. This plant is the alternate host for black rust *Puccinia graminis*, a fungal disease which attacks wheat. Prior to the development of fungicides able to control the disease, farmers eradicated the plants by digging them up and burning them.
N. Shrubs in quantity in a few areas. Corston and Hullavington 1986-88 JH & JW, Kington St Michael 1987 JH, Ashton Keynes and Upper Mill 1987-89 SW, Norton Farm 1988 MC-B, Thames Head VC7 (Glos) 1990 MK, Crudwell 1991 KG.
S. None of the five records post *The Flora of Wiltshire* were refound. Two new records: several shrubs on unimproved bank by stream Stowford, Wingfield 1986 GY, Upton, East Knoyle 1990 DP.
10 km² 9 (17%)   1 km² 15 (<1%)   Map 47, page 143

Mahonia Nutt.

Mahonia aquifolium (Pursh) Nutt.
Oregon-grape

Introduction. Planted for pheasant food and cover in woodland.
10 km² 14 (27%) 1 km² 25 (<1%)

PAPAVERACEAE

Papaver L.

Papaver somniferum L. ssp. somniferum
Opium Poppy

Introduction. Persistent annual weed. Gardens, waste ground and rubbish tips.
10 km² 31 (60%) 1 km² 106 (3%)

Papaver rhoeas L.
Common Poppy

Native. Arable land and waste ground. Well-distributed throughout the county but less common than in former times due to the increased use of herbicides.
Form with white flowers near Salisbury Clump 1984 PM.
10 km² 50 (96%) 2 km² 753 (79%)

Papaver dubium L. ssp. dubium
Long-headed Poppy

Probably native. Like *P. rhoeas*, it was once a common sight in cornfields, now greatly reduced due to the use of herbicides. More frequent on limestone than *P. rhoeas*.
10 km² 42 (81%) 2 km² 267 (28%) Map 48, page 143

Papaver dubium L. ssp. lecoqii (Lamotte) Syme
Yellow-juiced Poppy

N. Occurs mainly on limestone and Cornbrash in the NW and heavy clay soils around Swindon where it is well-distributed, occurring on dumped soil and, increasingly, among cereal crops.
S. Probably under-recorded. Two reports only, Stratford Tony Down 1990 PW, Henley near Oxenwood 1989 ER.
10 km² 15 (29%) 1 km² 29 (<1%) Map 49, page 143

Papaver hybridum L.
Rough Poppy

Nationally scarce plant.
Probably native. Arable and waste ground on chalk soil.
N. New Plantation, Sherston 1990 AC.
S. Main block reaching westward as far as N of Baverstock on arable land and adjacent to Grovely Wood. Northwards to Bulford 1985 KN. Isolated western record edge of Herepath, Swallowcliffe 1988 MM.
10 km² 9 (17%) 1 km² 60 (2%) Map 50, page 143

Papaver argemone L.
Prickly Poppy

Nationally scarce plant.
Probably native. In arable crops on sand and chalk.
N. Distribution very restricted. Number of plants in a location always small. Naish Hill 1986 JMP, Derry Hill 1987 GW, Hawkstreet Farm near Bromham 1987 RFP, Stanley and Great Somerford 1990 PD, Compton Bassett 1990 DB, Horton 1991 PW.
S. The main area, of some importance, is centred around four farms in the Martin/Damerham area VC8 (Hants) with two counts of more than a thousand plants each on edges of fields and a single plant in one field 1986-87 JO. Adjoining is a much larger area with far fewer plants which are irregular in occurrence from year to year: Whitsbury Down, Wick, New Court Down, field opposite Odstock Hospital 1988 PW, Clearbury Downs 1991 JO. N and E of Salisbury: by A345 near Salisbury Clump 1984, field at top of Little Down, Durnford 1988, Normanton Down 1989 ER, rare Fussell's Lodge Farm 1990 PM, single plant in set-aside field, Cholderton 1991 AJS. W of Salisbury: with other arable weeds in gateway and field edge above Swallowcliffe 1990 MM, Ox Drove near Alvediston JEO, Charlton Down 1991 VH.
10 km² 12 (23%) 1 km² 28 (<1%) Map 51, page 143

Meconopsis Viguier

Meconopsis cambrica (L.) Viguier
Welsh Poppy

Nationally scarce plant.
Native in GB, introduction in Wilts. Garden escape, spreading into adjacent pavements, walls, churchyards and waste places.
10 km² 6 (12%)   1 km² 8 (<1%)

Chelidonium L.

Chelidonium majus L.
Greater Celandine

Introduction. Walls and grassy banks, usually near habitation and frequently adjacent to old buildings and village churches. Most frequent NE of Marlborough and around Swindon.
10 km² 44 (85%) 1 km² 353 (10%)   Map 52, page 143

FUMARIACEAE

Pseudofumaria Medikus

Pseudofumaria lutea (L.) Borkh.
Corydalis lutea (L.) DC.
Yellow Corydalis

Introduction. Old walls, usually near habitation. Frequently planted in gardens from where it has seeded to become a beautiful addition to village wall flora.
10 km² 38 (73%) 1 km² 144 (4%)   Map 53, page 143

Ceratocapnos Durieu

Ceratocapnos claviculata (L.) Lidén
Corydalis claviculata (L.) DC.
Climbing Corydalis

Native. Woodland on acid soils.

N. In one small area in Savernake Forest 1986 MS, first record for VC7.
S. Upper Holt Wood, near Teffont 1988 VH, first record for 20 years. Of geographical interest, at least 30 km E of previously recorded area where it was refound at Perfect's Copse, Little Coombe, two areas St Peter's Cross and three at Castle Wood 1991 PMW.
10 km² 3 (6%)   1 km² 8 (<1%)   Map 54, page 143

Fumaria L.

Species are similar in general appearance and probably few recorders realised that close examination of flowers and fruit is necessary for correct identification. Therefore, *F. officinalis* may have been over-recorded at the expense of other species.

Fumaria muralis Sonder ex Koch
Common Ramping-Fumitory

Native. Cultivated and waste land.
S. Abundant on spoil heaps near entrance to The Butts, Salisbury 1988 PM, ver. 1990 AH, first VC8 record and four plants in allotments Wellhead, Mere 1990 AH.
Ssp. **boraei** (Jordan) Pugsley
N. Market gardens Bremhill 1990 DG, first recent VC7 record.
S. Among arable weeds, field-edge near Swallowcliffe 1990 MM & PM.
10 km² 4 (8%)   1 km² 4 (<1%)

Fumaria officinalis L. ssp. **officinalis**
Common Fumitory

Native. Occurs throughout the county on arable and waste land, often only in small numbers.
Ssp. **wirtgenii** (Koch) Arcang.
Native.
S. Berwick Down 1990 TCGR, second VC8 record having been first recorded in 1938 by D Grose.
10 km² 49 (94%) 2 km² 495 (52%) Map 55, page 147

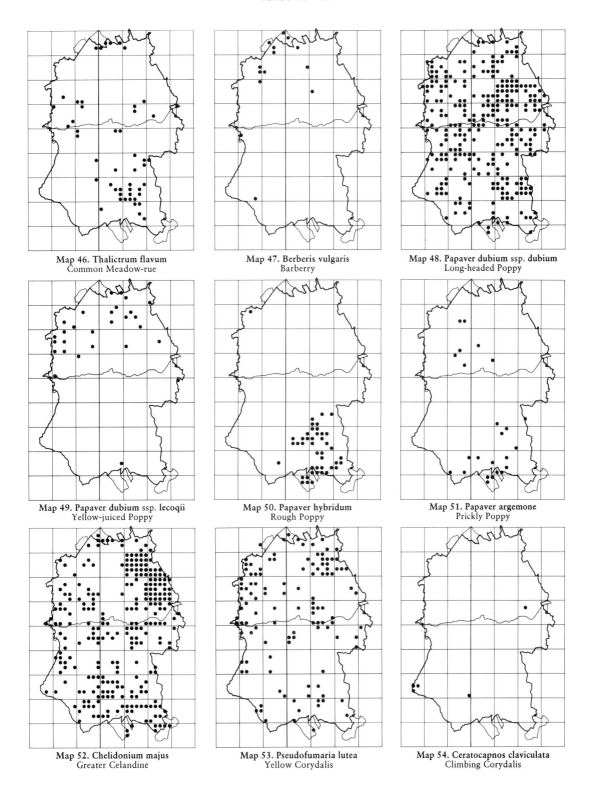

Map 46. Thalictrum flavum
Common Meadow-rue

Map 47. Berberis vulgaris
Barberry

Map 48. Papaver dubium ssp. dubium
Long-headed Poppy

Map 49. Papaver dubium ssp. lecoqii
Yellow-juiced Poppy

Map 50. Papaver hybridum
Rough Poppy

Map 51. Papaver argemone
Prickly Poppy

Map 52. Chelidonium majus
Greater Celandine

Map 53. Pseudofumaria lutea
Yellow Corydalis

Map 54. Ceratocapnos claviculata
Climbing Corydalis

Fumaria densiflora DC.
F. micrantha Lagasca
Dense-flowered Fumitory

Nationally scarce plant.
Native. Cornfield weed on chalk soil.
N. One VC7 record. Allotment weed Chippenham 1985 SB det. Dr MG Daker BSBI referee.
S. A marked concentration of records in the S, 13 in the Allenford/Damerham area VC8 (Hants), plants mostly numbering 2-3 but *c.* 200 in one field and 73 over a wide area among abundant *F. officinalis*, both at Allenford 1986-87 JO. Refound Old Sarum 1988 PM. Distribution similar to that described by Grose but there is a retraction southwards.
10 km² 7 (13%)   1 km² 26 (<1%)   Map 56, page 147

Fumaria parviflora Lam.
Fine-leaved Fumitory

Nationally scarce plant.
Native. Cornfields.
S. Field of rape with many weeds, Wick near Downton 1984 JO det. Lady Anne Brewis, second VC8 record.
10 km² 1 (2%)   1 km² 1 (<1%)

ULMACEAE

Ulmus L.

Ulmus glabra Hudson
Wych Elm

Native. Woods and hedgerows. Common on the limestone scarp where it was part of the climax ash/elm woodland until the 1970s when Dutch elm disease killed 99% of the trees. Continues in shrub form along the river valleys and on clay in N and S Wilts. Regenerating along hedgerows and as coppice from cut stumps of mature trees.
10 km² 46 (88%)   1 km² 428 (12%)   Map 57, page 147

Ulmus procera Salisb.
English Elm

Native and introduction. Since Dutch elm disease struck in 1970s almost every standard English elm in the county has been felled. However, the species survives in its sucker state and, in recent years, 6 m high young trees have become a common sight. Common and widely-distributed.
10 km² 49 (94%)   2 km² 675 (71%)   Map 58, page 147

Ulmus minor Miller ssp. **minor**
Small-leaved Elm

Native. A very variable species. Three records attributed to this species.
N. Stand of more than 50 trees previously coppiced, now full grown, Inwood, Farleigh Wick 1989 DG.
S. Scattered trees in regenerating woodland Great Netley Copse and Pitton Copse 1988 PW.
10 km² 2 (4%)   1 km² 2 (<1%)

CANNABACEAE

Humulus L.

Humulus lupulus L.
Hop

Native. Hedges and woodland edges. Most common on the clay in Braydon Forest area and on the low land between Melksham and Trowbridge. Largely absent from the chalk area except in the river valleys.
10 km² 46 (88%)   1 km² 510 (14%)   Map 59, page 147

URTICACEAE

Urtica L.

Urtica dioica L.
Common nettle

Native. Very common, especially on disturbed

ground and the somewhat enriched soil of farmyards, rabbit warrens, badger setts and river silt.
10 km² 52 (100%) 2 km² 914 (96%)

Urtica urens L.
Small nettle

Native. A species of arable land. Most common in the market gardens around Bromham and on sandy soils throughout the county. Scattered elsewhere.
10 km² 39 (75%) 2 km² 179 (19%)   Map 60, page 147

Parietaria L.

Parietaria judaica L.
Pellitory-of-the-wall

Native. Dry stone and brick walls. Scattered. Common on village walls in the Cotswolds.
10 km² 37 (71%) 2 km² 108 (11%)   Map 61, page 147

Soleirolia Gaudich.

Soleirolia soleirolii (Req.) Dandy
Mind-your-own-business

Introduction. Naturalised in damp places especially at the base of shaded walls.
N. Garden weed Castle Combe 1987 JH, Murhill Lane, Winsley 1985-88 JM.
S. Limpley Stoke 1987 and Iford Manor 1989 JM, on wall above R. Wylye, Wilton 1989 MDT.
10 km² 4 (8%)   1 km² 5 (<1%)

JUGLANDACEAE

Juglans L.

Juglans regia L.
Walnut

Introduction. Planted in gardens, orchards and

road verges. Saplings from germinated nuts occur rarely.
10 km² 40 (77%) 1 km² 104 (3%)

MYRICACEAE

Myrica L.

Myrica gale L.
Bog-myrtle

Native. Wet heathland and bogs. Rare.
S. Hamptworth Common 1986 NCC/ST. The remaining sites are in Hants: Plaitford Common, bog N of Furzley and West Wellow Common 1989 VW, Plaitford Common (two) and West Wellow Common 1991 RV.
10 km² 1 (2%)   1 km² 8 (<1%)

FAGACEAE

Fagus L.

Fagus sylvatica L.
Beech

Native and introduction. Grose considered this plant native in only a few places in S Wilts. However, it is extensively planted and regenerates especially on the chalk and chalk superficials. A locally common species.
Var. **purpurea**
Introduction. Ornamental tree. Apparently self-sown in Great Ridge Wood 1990 VH.
10 km² 51 (98%) 2 km² 767 (81%)

Castanea Miller

Castanea sativa Miller
Sweet Chestnut

Introduction. All trees planted. In woodland plantations, hedgebanks and country parks.

Thrives best on acidic soils. Occasionally coppiced.
10 km² 38 (73%) 1 km² 254 (7%)   Map 62, page 147

Quercus L.

Quercus cerris L.
Turkey Oak

Introduction. An invader of calcareous soils. Originally planted as a fast-growing oak species whose bark was used in the dyeing industry. Planted as an ornamental tree in large gardens.
10 km² 15 (29%) 1 km² 23 (<1%)

Quercus petraea (Mattuschka) Liebl.
Sessile Oak

Native. Acidic soils: sand, heavy clays and Clay-with-flints.
N. Spectacular 400-500 year old trees in Savernake Forest are centred on King and Queen Oaks near Twelve O'Clock Drive. On clay in Braydon Forest area at Old Copse 1984, Red Lodge 1987 MWS, Stonehill Wood 1988 JF. Planted tree Westonbirt village 1987 HB.
S. At least some planted. In SE, main ride Bentley Wood 1984 PMW, saplings and mature trees Whiteparish Common and roadside 1986 PMW, Standlynch Down 1986 RNC, single tree Loosehanger Copse 1990 DJW. In W, Clanger Wood 1987 EC and plantation in partly ancient woodland Penstones Wood 1991 DPH.
10 km² 7 (13%) 1 km² 14 (<1%)   Map 63, page 147

Quercus robur L.
Pedunculate Oak

Native. Common throughout the lowland clays. Less common on the chalk and greensand. Much planted in woodland, standards being a feature of SW and SE Wilts. The large number of standard trees removed during both World Wars has left few older specimens which are particularly

valuable for the support of lichens and invertebrates.
10 km² 52 (100%) 2 km² 747 (79%)   Map 64, page 150

BETULACEAE

Betula L.

Betula pendula Roth
Silver Birch

Native. Woodland on all soil types but probably not indigenous on the chalk. Most frequent on light soils and heathland.
N. Known to hybridise with *B. pubescens* in Braydon Forest.
S. According to Grose, probably native around Longleat, Lavington, Collingbourne Wood, Great Ridge Wood, Grovely Wood, the Donheads, Vernditch Chase and in SE.
10 km² 47 (90%) 1 km² 786 (22%)   Map 65, page 150

Betula pendula x B. pubescens = B. x aurata Borkh.

Native.
N. Growing with both parents Great Lodge Wood 1985 MWS (conf. DG). Only VC7 record.
10 km² 1 (2%)   1 km² 1 (<1%)

Betula pubescens Ehrh.
Downy Birch

Native. Damp situations.
N. Ancient woodland sites in the Braydon Forest area, woods near Crooked Soley and Bird's Marsh, Chippenham.
S. Proved to be more common than expected. Probably less often planted than *B. pendula* and certainly preferring damper conditions in woods, heaths and grassland. Main areas: Great Ridge Wood, Longleat/Stourton, Wardour and the SE.
10 km² 20 (38%) 1 km² 88 (2%)   Map 66, page 150

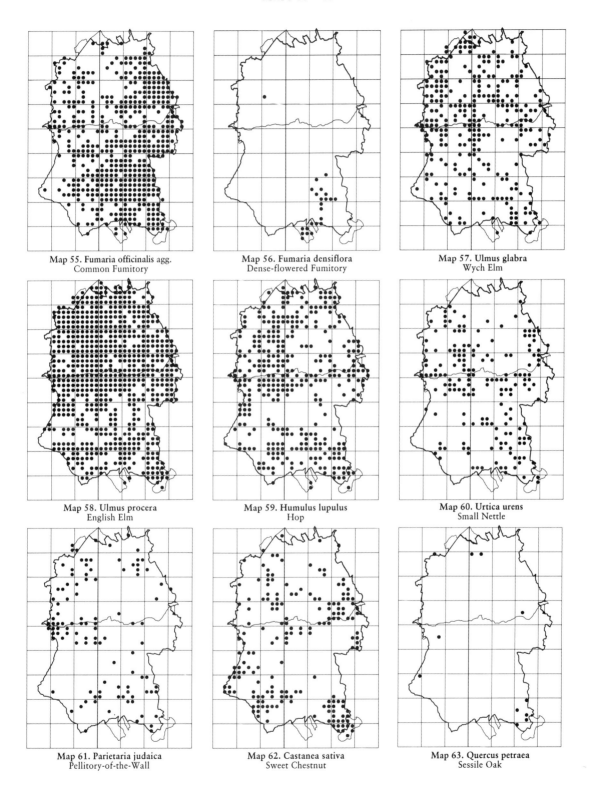

Map 55. Fumaria officinalis agg.
Common Fumitory

Map 56. Fumaria densiflora
Dense-flowered Fumitory

Map 57. Ulmus glabra
Wych Elm

Map 58. Ulmus procera
English Elm

Map 59. Humulus lupulus
Hop

Map 60. Urtica urens
Small Nettle

Map 61. Parietaria judaica
Pellitory-of-the-Wall

Map 62. Castanea sativa
Sweet Chestnut

Map 63. Quercus petraea
Sessile Oak

Alnus Miller

Alnus glutinosa (L.) Gaertner
Alder

Native. Bogs, lakes and damp woodland on neutral to acid soils especially along river valleys. Occasionally develops into climax carr woodland.
10 km² 48 (92%) 2 km² 392 (41%)   Map 67, page 150

Alnus incana (L.) Moench
Grey Alder

Introduction. Commonly planted in towns (records not included) and rarely wet woodland.
N. Planted as a coppice and timber crop in Big Wood, Rowde where it has naturalised by suckers, 1985 DG. Oaksey Road Bridge, planted around waterworks 1985 CK.
S. Beside stream Heath Bridge 1984 BGH & AH, in overgrown hedge Eastwell 1985 BGH, first and second VC 8 records. Several trees between old and new road Heron Bridge 1986 BGH.
10 km² 4 (8%)   1 km² 6 (<1%)

Carpinus L.

Carpinus betulus L.
Hornbeam

Native and introduction. Woodland, hedgerows, open situations. Frequently planted. Often occurs as single tree of considerable age. Saplings occur in woodlands, especially near Slaughterford in By Brook valley. Sometimes coppiced as at Little Durnford.
10 km² 41 (79%) 1 km² 242 (7%)   Map 68, page 150

Corylus L.

Corylus avellana L.
Hazel

Native. Common and widely-distributed throughout woodland and, to a lesser extent, in hedges. Hazel coppice was formerly used for fuel, building materials and hurdle-making. With the cessation of coppicing after World War II, the hazel became derelict and overgrown and, with the lack of light, less interesting both for the flora and some invertebrates. The conservation value of rotational coppicing is now understood and conservation bodies are reintroducing coppice rotations in order to recreate the temporary open conditions beneficial to woodland flora and fauna.
10 km² 52 (100%) 2 km² 832 (88%)

PHYTOLACCACEAE

Phytolacca L.

Phytolacca americana L.
American Pokeweed

Introduction. Stace considers that the species recorded in GB may not be *P. americana* but an Asian species.
S. The Close, Salisbury 1986 DPES.
10 km² 1 (2%)   1 km² 1 (<1%)

CHENOPODIACEAE
The species of this family are superficially similar. This has led to identification problems and the possibility of species being under-recorded.

Chenopodium L.

Chenopodium bonus-henricus L.
Good-King-Henry

Native. Most frequently found near habitation in rural areas, in farmyards and on road verges. Its distribution reflects a long history of use by man of which it is now a relic. Scarce and seldom in great quantity. Some records may have been *C. rubrum* mis-identified as *C. bonus-henricus*.
10 km² 23 (44%) 1 km² 67 (2%)

Chenopodium rubrum L.
Red Goosefoot

Native. A common species of farmyards, dung heaps, thriving best on enriched soils.
10 km² 47 (90%) 2 km² 303 (32%) Map 69, page 150

Chenopodium polyspermum L.
Many-seeded Goosefoot

Native. Waste and cultivated land, particularly in potato and swede crops and on enriched soil around farm buildings. Most frequent on heavy clay soil and sometimes on river silt spread by winter flooding.
10 km² 36 (69%) 1 km² 170 (5%) Map 70, page 150

Chenopodium hybridum L.
Maple-leaved Goosefoot

Probably introduction. Waste and arable ground.
N. Garden weed Devizes 1989 JP.
S. Disturbed ground Britford water-meadows 1984 NLC & BKC, two areas dumped soil, one having several plants, The Butts, Salisbury (known here since 1962 AH) 1984 PM, road verge Steeple Langford, rubbish dump Stoford 1988 BL. Abundant weed along 100m field/road edge strip Middle Woodford 1988, footpath through corn inside Ogbury Camp 1988, thinly scattered disturbed roadside West Gomeldon 1990 and field edge Lake Down 1991 PM.
10 km² 6 (12%) 1 km² 12 (<1%)

Chenopodium murale L.
Nettle-leaved Goosefoot

Probably native. Waste and cultivated ground.
N. In a new flower-bed Swindon 1988 DG.
S. Along a bridleway Upper Chicksgrove 1984 DF, edge of a field of maize Fonthill Gifford 1987 AH.
10 km² 2 (6%) 1 km² 3 (<1%)

Chenopodium ficifolium Smith
Fig-leaved Goosefoot

Native. Enriched ground in farmyards and on manure heaps. An increasing species.
N. Winsley 1983 JP, first VC7 record, several more records around this area 1986 JP. Elsewhere, Semmington and Naish Hill 1987, two sites Rowde 1989 DG.
S. West Hale 1984 NLC/BKC, bridleway Upper Chicksgrove 1984 DF, in three areas Imber Ranges 1985 JL, garden weed Wilton 1986 AH, Great Mills, Milford 1986 NLC, Picket Furlong 1987 DF, near Boyton 1987 BSBI meeting, rubbish dump Stoford 1988 BL, A36 verges Chilhampton 1989 BL.
10 km² 7 (13%) 1 km² 20 (<1%) Map 71, page 150

Chenopodium album L.
Fat-hen

Native. Very widely-distributed on waste and cultivated land especially in the vicinity of farm buildings.
10 km² 48 (92%) 2 km² 718 (76%)

Atriplex L.

Atriplex prostrata Boucher ex DC.
Spear-leaved Orache

Native. A common species occurring around the edges of arable fields, waste land and farmyards.
10 km² 42 (81%) 2 km² 303 (32%) Map 72, page 150

Atriplex patula L.
Common Orache

Native. A constant species of dung heaps and enriched soil around farmyards where stock are housed. Frequent.
10 km² 48 (92%) 2 km² 445 (47%) Map 73, page 153

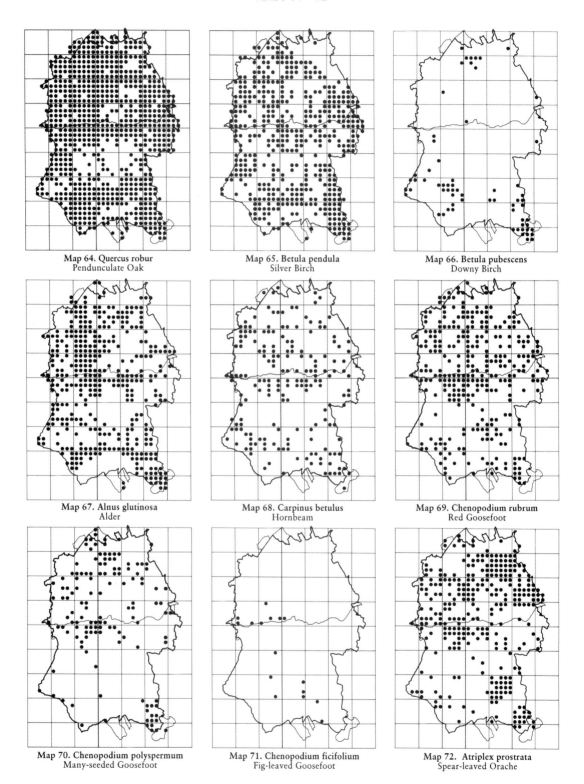

Map 64. Quercus robur
Pendunculate Oak

Map 65. Betula pendula
Silver Birch

Map 66. Betula pubescens
Downy Birch

Map 67. Alnus glutinosa
Alder

Map 68. Carpinus betulus
Hornbeam

Map 69. Chenopodium rubrum
Red Goosefoot

Map 70. Chenopodium polyspermum
Many-seeded Goosefoot

Map 71. Chenopodium ficifolium
Fig-leaved Goosefoot

Map 72. Atriplex prostrata
Spear-leaved Orache

AMARANTHACEAE

Amaranthus L.

Amaranthus retroflexus L.
Common Amaranth

Introduction.
Included in chicken and bird-seed mixtures. Grown as a 'green' vegetable by West Indian communities. Most records are from gardens and allotments.
N. Garden Aldbourne 1986 JN, old railway Outmarsh 1989 JH, Allington 1989 JH, garden Upper Minety 1989.
S. Garden Trowbridge 1986 EC. Introduced with pheasant feed at Compton Chamberlayne where it has survived for 5 years and is spreading 1991 CPa, SMP & AH. Unusual habitat near sheep trough Throope Down 1991 PW.
10 km² 7 (13%)   1 km² 8 (<1%)

PORTULACACEAE

Claytonia L.

Claytonia sibirica L.
Montia sibirica (L.) Howell
Pink Purslane

Introduction.
N. Coate Water 1984 PA, first county record ver. 1990 DG.
S. Shalbourne 1986 CM, first VC record, 20 m² patch under oak Grovely 1987 BL, ver. AH.
10 km² 3 (6%)   1 km² 3 (<1%)

Montia L.

Montia fontana L.
Blinks

Native. Acid soils, wet for at least part of the year. Sets seed early in the year, then quickly disappears especially in dry, warm conditions.

N. In large colonies adjacent to M4 Draycott Park 1986 DG.
S. Common on heathland around the New Forest, possibly extending its season in very wet conditions. Elsewhere, Clanger Wood 1987 EC.
Ssp. **minor** Hayw.
Ssp. *chondrosperma* (Fenzl) Walters
N. Track Bury Hill 1989 DG & SW.
10 km² 5 (10%)   1 km² 17 (1%)   Map 74, page 153

CARYOPHYLLACEAE

Arenaria L.

Arenaria serpyllifolia L. ssp. **serpyllifolia**
Arenaria serpyllifolia L.
Thyme-leaved Sandwort

Native. Quarries, railway tracks, tops of walls, open short grassland, especially on calcareous soil. Common in these habitats.
10 km² 46 (88%)   2 km² 342 (36%)   Map 75, page 153

Arenaria serpyllifolia L. ssp. **leptoclados** (Reichb.) Nyman
Arenaria leptoclados (Reichb.) Guss
Slender Sandwort

Native. Bare places, quarries, tops of walls, anthills and bare chalk downland. Much less common than ssp. *serpyllifolia* with which mis-identification is possible.
10 km² 37 (71%)   2 km² 101 (11%)

Moehringia L.

Moehringia trinervia (L.) Clairv.
Three-nerved Sandwort

Native. Widespread in damp woodland and hedgebanks usually in the shade, rarely occurring in other habitats.
10 km² 50 (96%)   2 km² 337 (36%)   Map 76, page 153

Minuartia L.

Minuartia hybrida (Villars) Schischkin
Fine-leaved Sandwort

Nationally scarce plant.
Native. Dry, thin, well-drained soil with open vegetation.
S. Common only on heavily rabbit grazed, lichen-rich chalk grassland, exposed soil and chalk rubble Porton Down 1991 PW. Records elsewhere unconfirmed.
10 km² 6 (12%)   1 km² 14 (<1%)

Stellaria L.

Stellaria media (L.) Villars
Common Chickweed

Native. A species of disturbed ground and improved grassland where it can be very common.
10 km² 52 (100%) 2 km² 863 (91%)

Stellaria neglecta Weihe
Greater Chickweed

Native. Damp, shady places.
N. Records only from the extreme W on clay, in some places overlying limestone. Damp verges of roads and lanes. Common around Bradford-on-Avon, in Hayes and Cumberwell Woods 1984-85 JP, Rode Hill, Reybridge, near Bower Hill, Biddestone, Thingley and Great Chalfield 1987-88 DG, Yatton Keynell 1988 JH. Frequency decreases towards the E of its range.
S. Lye Green near Westwood 1989 JM, Great Hinton and Keevil airfield 1991 BGH. Old records from Nadder Valley were not refound.
10 km² 5 (10%)   1 km² 14 (<1%)   Map 77, page 153

Stellaria holostea L.
Greater Stitchwort

Native. Frequent and often abundant, especially along the bases of damp hedgebanks flowering in the spring.
10 km² 49 (94%) 2 km² 535 (56%)   Map 78, page 153

Stellaria graminea L.
Lesser Stitchwort

Native. Rough grassland, unimproved neutral meadows and hedgebanks on sandy soil and on leached chalk.
N. Well-distributed especially in neutral grassland and on Clay-with-flints around Savernake and on downland N of Marlborough.
S. Common in meadows and open woods on neutral and acid soil. On the chalk only where the soil has been leached.
10 km² 47 (90%) 1 km² 746 (20%)   Map 79, page 153

Stellaria uliginosa Murray
Stellaria alsine Grimm
Bog Stitchwort

Native. Marshes, silty streamsides and other wet areas having lime-rich water.
N. Scattered with concentrations on the Lower Greensand near Lacock and E of Marlborough.
S. Wet woods, streamsides and wet meadows SW of Devizes and on clays, sand and gravel in SE. R. Avon and R. Nadder valleys.
10 km² 31 (60%) 1 km² 206 (6%)   Map 80, page 153

Cerastium L.

Cerastium arvense L.
Field Mouse-ear

Native. Dry chalk grassland, rough grassland perhaps once improved, arable on chalk and tracksides.
S. High Post Golf Course, Boscombe Down airfield, Figsbury Ring and Stock Bottom 1984-87 PM, Chicksgrove Quarry 1985 NCC/ST, near Yarnbury Castle 1986 BG, three sites N of Baverstock 1988

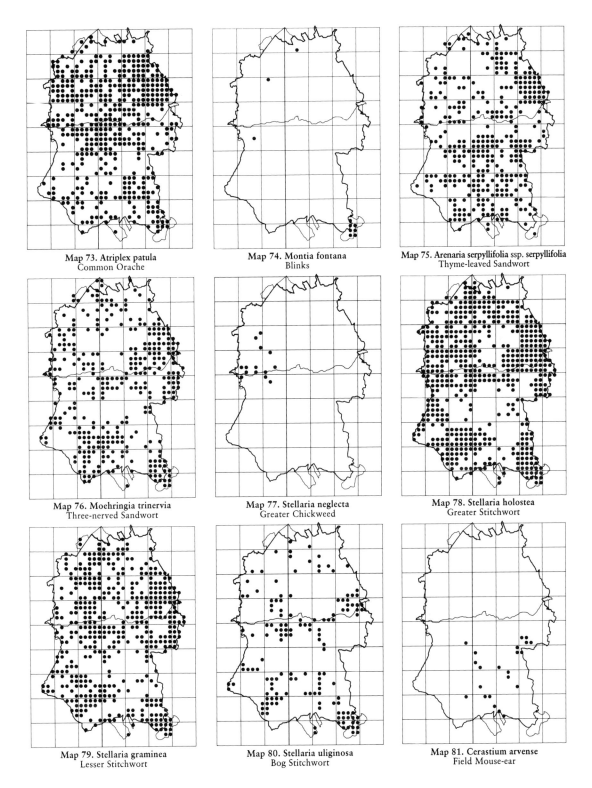

Map 73. Atriplex patula
Common Orache

Map 74. Montia fontana
Blinks

Map 75. Arenaria serpyllifolia ssp. serpyllifolia
Thyme-leaved Sandwort

Map 76. Moehringia trinervia
Three-nerved Sandwort

Map 77. Stellaria neglecta
Greater Chickweed

Map 78. Stellaria holostea
Greater Stitchwort

Map 79. Stellaria graminea
Lesser Stitchwort

Map 80. Stellaria uliginosa
Bog Stitchwort

Map 81. Cerastium arvense
Field Mouse-ear

SMP, Throope Hill 1990 PW, Grims Farm lane and Gallows Hill 1990 BKC & JO, both sides of track near Hoopside 1991 BG, Ox Drove E of Compton Chamberlayne. SPTA(E): profuse flowering Bourne Bottom and near Weather Hill 1987 ER, occurs elsewhere on the Ranges 1990 AJS.

10 km² 10 (19%) 1 km² 29 (<1%)   Map 81, page 153

Cerastium fontanum Baumg.
Common Mouse-ear

Native. Common throughout the county in short grassland, on rocky outcrops and railway embankments, especially on neutral and calcareous soils.

10 km² 52 (100%)2 km² 841 (89%)

Cerastium glomeratum Thuill.
Sticky Mouse-ear

Native. Dry short acid and neutral grassland, cultivated and waste ground.
N. Frequent and often abundant especially on stony ground and arable clay.
S. Occurs on walls. Uncommon on chalk.
Less common than C. *fontanum*. Under-recorded.

10 km² 48 (92%) 2 km² 322 (34%) Map 82, page 157

Cerastium diffusum Pers.
Sea Mouse-ear

Native.
N. Found on anthills in two localities on Milk Hill (Pewsey Downs NNR) 1984-85 KP, first county record. Not uncommon nationally but, as the English name suggests, most frequent near the sea.

10 km² 2 (4%)   1 km² 2 (<1%)

Cerastium pumilum Curtis
Dwarf Mouse-ear

Nationally scarce plant.

Native. Growing on anthills Milk Hill (Pewsey Downs NNR) 1984 KP. Abundant some years.

10 km² 1 (2%)   1 km² 1 (<1%)

Cerastium semidecandrum L.
Little Mouse-ear

Native. Bare places on chalk and sandy soils.
N. Tan Hill (Pewsey Downs NNR) 1985 KP, on a sandy bank Okus (Swindon) 1986 DG.
S. Dry track in Grovely Wood BL, Sidbury Hill SPTA(E) AJS, anthills Great Fore Down SPTA(C) and Breach Hill SPTA(W) BG.

10 km² 6 (12%)   1 km² 6 (<1%)

Myosoton Moench

Myosoton aquaticum (L.) Moench
Water Chickweed

Native. River, stream and pond sides, marshes, damp road verges and ditches.
N. Abundant along some water-courses, especially the Bristol Avon.
S. Most frequent on the low land around Trowbridge. The courses of the R. Avon and R. Wylye are well-outlined on the distribution map.

10 km² 33 (63%) 1 km² 212 (6%)   Map 83, page 157

Moenchia Ehrh.

Moenchia erecta (L.) Gaertner, Meyer & Scherb.
Upright Chickweed

Nationally scarce plant.
Native. Sandy soils with little vegetative competition.
S. Penn and Canada Commons and near Porter's Farm 1991 RV, near Barford Farms 1991 VW. All VC8 (Hants).

10 km² 1 (2%)   1 km² 4 (<1%)

Sagina L.

Sagina nodosa (L.) Fenzl
Knotted Pearlwort

Native. Damp, light soils.
N. Two colonies on disturbed gravel in the CWP. Colony seen by Grose on Oaksey Moor in 1948 was excavated for gravel in late 1950s when the site and the plants were thought to have been destroyed. Rediscovered and second colony found Pike Corner 1987 DG.
S. Damp sandy track near Gasper 1991 AH. Probably overlooked. Positive searching might update a number of old records.
10 km² 3 (6%)   1 km² 5 (<1%)

Sagina procumbens L.
Procumbent Pearlwort

Native. Damp bases of walls, paths, between paving-stones, damp gravels, marshland and heathland. Locally common in the damp recesses of walls. Less frequent in other habitats. Perhaps overlooked.
10 km² 43 (83%) 2 km² 231 (24%) Map 84, page 157

Sagina apetala Ard. ssp. erecta F. Herm.
Annual Pearlwort

Native. Cracks in paving-stones, dry stony farm tracks, paths, bare and trodden places. A garden weed. Absent from chalk. Widely scattered. Perhaps overlooked.
10 km² 30 (58%) 1 km² 76 (2%)   Map 85, page 157

Scleranthus L.

Scleranthus annuus L.
Annual Knawel

Native. Arable land and dry, open places.
N. Many hundreds of plants, cornfield edge near the monument, Savernake Forest 1985 DG & JN.

S. Cornfield edge near Rag Copse (Collingbourne Wood) 1985 FP, single plant on waste ground with arable weeds by railway bridge Winterbourne Dauntsey 1988 PM, edge of Home Farm, Hamptworth 1990 DJW.
10 km² 4 (8%)   1 km² 5 (<1%)

Spergula L.

Spergula arvensis L.
Corn Spurrey

Native. Market gardens, arable and other disturbed land on light, acidic, sandy soils.
N. Only common where no herbicides have been used N of Devizes to Bremhill, including Bromham market gardens.
S. Especially common on the sandy soils in the SE corner.
10 km² 19 (37%) 1 km² 64 (2%)   Map 86, page 157

Spergularia (Pers.) J. S. & C. Presl

Spergularia rubra (L.) J. S. & C. Presl
Sand Spurrey

Native. Short turf and cultivated land on sandy soils.
N. Three localities on Lower Greensand in Spye Park 1984 DG. Confirmation of Grose's 1950s records.
S. Canada, Furzley and West Wellow Commons 1991 RV.
10 km² 2 (4%)   1 km² 6 (<1%)

Lychnis L.

Lychnis flos-cuculi L.
Ragged-Robin

Native. Unimproved marshy and damp grassland, open wet woodland, and occasionally in drier pastures. Abundant in some unimproved meadows

on the clay. Can survive in ditches adjacent to fields where it once grew. Elsewhere largely restricted to the marshy areas of river valleys. A pleasing number of records considering the loss of suitable habitat by drainage for agriculture and building.
10 km² 42 (81%) 1 km² 387 (11%) Map 87, page 157

Agrostemma L.

Agrostemma githago L.
Corncockle

British Red Data Book species.
Introduction. Formerly a common plant in arable crops, becoming scarce as cleaner seed was introduced in the 1920s, but reappearing during World War II when old pasture was ploughed. Its disappearance from arable land in 1950s-1960s was possibly due to the use of herbicides.
N. Four records all attributed to bird-seed origin or garden escapes.
S. Many plants of this species and *Centaurea cyanus* appeared on newly-turned soil following the grubbing out of a hedge on the edge of Westbury recreation ground 1986 EC & VEH. A record of much interest.
10 km² 4 (8%)   1 km² 5 (<1%)

Silene L.

Silene vulgaris Garcke
Bladder Campion

Native. Road verges, rough grassland mainly on calcareous soils. Occurs in small numbers in most of its locations.
10 km² 46 (88%) 1 km² 844 (23%) Map 88, page 157

Silene noctiflora L.
Night-flowering Catchfly

Nationally scarce plant.
Native. Arable land mainly on calcareous soils.
N. On Cornbrash in cereal crop near Ford 1985

DG and in pea crop Neston 1986 CG, Poole Keynes CWP 1986 SW, on limestone gravel Hullavington 1987 JH.
S. High number of records, all from cornfields except where stated. Near Grovely Hill 1984 DS-G, large colony/hundreds stretching 400 m along road/field edge A360 near Camp Hill, Salisbury 1984 PM, A338 roadside Stag Inn, Charlton 1986 JO, N of Baverstock 1987 MDT; two farms Martin/Damerham (Hants) area one with plants in two fields the other spread over 700 m 1987 JO; opposite Odstock Hospital 1988 PW, disturbed soil railway embankment London Road, Salisbury 1990 MS, Heron Bridge 1990 BGH, colonies of one, six and hundreds Steeple Ashton 1991 EC.
10 km² 10 (19%) 1 km² 20 (<1%) Map 89, page 157

Silene latifolia Poiret
Silene alba (Miller) E. H. Krause
White Campion

Native. Widely-distributed on hedgebanks, waste places and disturbed soil. Less common than *Silene dioica*, which flowers 2-3 weeks earlier.
10 km² 49 (94%) 2 km² 679 (72%)

Silene latifolia x S. dioica = S. x hampeana
Meusel & K. Werner
Hybrid Campion

Native. Disturbed areas, road verges, arable land. Common where both parents are present. Under-recorded.
10 km² 43 (83%) 1 km² 268 (7%) Map 90, page 157

Silene dioica (L.) Clairv.
Red Campion

Native. Common and widely-distributed on hedgebanks, streamsides and in open woods and woodland clearings. Less common on chalk soils. Form with white flowers, Kilmington 1986 CQ-R.
10 km² 52 (100%) 2 km² 740 (78%)

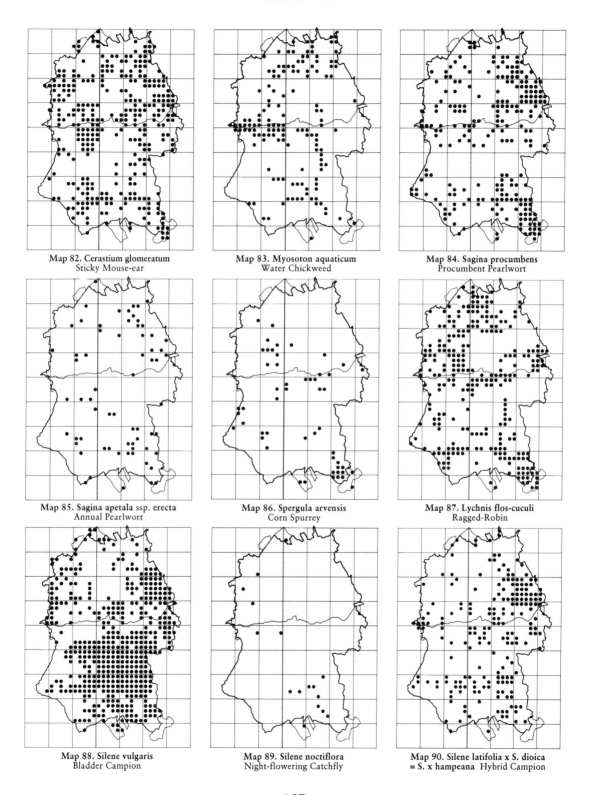

Map 82. Cerastium glomeratum
Sticky Mouse-ear

Map 83. Myosoton aquaticum
Water Chickweed

Map 84. Sagina procumbens
Procumbent Pearlwort

Map 85. Sagina apetala ssp. erecta
Annual Pearlwort

Map 86. Spergula arvensis
Corn Spurrey

Map 87. Lychnis flos-cuculi
Ragged-Robin

Map 88. Silene vulgaris
Bladder Campion

Map 89. Silene noctiflora
Night-flowering Catchfly

Map 90. Silene latifolia x S. dioica
= S. x hampeana Hybrid Campion

Silene gallica L.
Small-flowered Catchfly

Nationally scarce plant.
Native. Cultivated land on acid soil.
N. Single plant Nuthills Farm, Sandy Lane 1988
AJS. First record since Grose found it in same
location 1951.
10 km² 1 (2%)   1 km² 1 (<1%)

Saponaria L.

Saponaria officinalis L.
Soapwort

Introduction. Garden escape or throw-out found on
road verges and woodland edges where it spreads,
often forming large long-lasting stands. Form with
double flowers is common. Widely-distributed.
10 km² 26 (50%) 1 km² 64 (2%)   Map 91, page 161

Dianthus L.

Dianthus deltoides L.
Maiden Pink

Nationally scarce plant.
Possibly native in Wilts.
S. Bourne Bottom SPTA(E) 1982 MDT. Checked
annually, number of plants fluctuate 1992 AJS.
Possibly the site referred to in Grose, 'It has not
been seen since about 1888'.
10 km² 1 (2%)   1 km² 1 (<1%)

POLYGONACEAE

Persicaria Miller

Persicaria bistorta (L.) Samp.
Polygonum bistorta L.
Common Bistort

Native. Unimproved grassland, adjacent to streams
and on damp roadside verges. Sometimes covers
large areas of grassland. Possibly over-recorded in
error for the terrestrial form of *P. amphibia*.
10 km² 19 (37%) 1 km² 35 (1%)

Persicaria amphibia (L.) Gray
Polygonum amphibium L.
Amphibious Bistort

Native. Rivers, streams, ponds, gravel pits and canals.
The species has two forms which may cause confusion
in identification. Aquatic, floating form in ponds
and slow rivers. Terrestrial form in damp habitats.
N. Aquatic form frequent along the length of the
K & A Canal. Terrestrial form common between
Malmesbury and Minety.
S. The distribution along the rivers Avon, Bourne,
Wylye and Nadder is clearly shown on the map.
10 km² 30 (58%) 1 km² 143 (4%)   Map 92, page 161

Persicaria maculosa Gray
Polygonum persicaria L.
Redshank

Native. Widely-distributed in cultivated, disturbed
and damp habitats.
10 km² 51 (98%) 2 km² 679 (72%)

Persicaria lapathifolia (L.) Gray
Polygonum lapathifolium L.
Pale Persicaria

Native. Cultivated and waste ground, especially
wetter places. A weed of cultivation and heaps of
farmyard waste.
10 km² 45 (87%) 1 km² 357 (10%) Map 93, page 161

Persicaria hydropiper (L.) Spach
Polygonum hydropiper L.
Water-pepper

Native. This species needs soil disturbance for its

seeds to germinate. Localised to stream and river banks, ponds, damp woodland tracks and other watery places with silted conditions.

10 km² 41 (79%) 2 km² 204 (21%)   Map 94, page 161

Persicaria minor (Hudson) Opiz
Polygonum minus Hudson
Small Water-pepper

Nationally scarce plant.
Native. Pondsides, damp tracks.
S. Several plants along track near road junction Barford Farms, Bramshaw 1985 RV. Ponds W of Furzley village VC8 (Hants) 1989 VW & AB.

10 km² 1 (2%)   1 km² 2 (<1%)

Fagopyrum Miller

Fagopyrum esculentum Moench
Buckwheat

Introduction.
N. Sown as a fodder crop for pheasants especially on chalk in the Pewsey area. Elsewhere at Sandridge, near Flisteridge Wood, Savernake and Sevenhampton.
S. Waste ground near R. Till, Shrewton 1984 SG and beside Ox Drove adjacent to barley Teffont Down 1984 MM. On chalk following ploughing for the first time for many years New Copse SPTA(C) 1986 RF. Garden weed, possibly introduced in wild bird-seed Potterne BGH 1988. Apparently planted for game The Wig SPTA(E) 1987 ER, single plant waste ground West Lavington 1989 RF, between track and bank Coombe, SPTA(E) 1990 DGC.

10 km² 12 (23%) 1 km² 13 (<1%)

Polygonum L.

Polygonum arenastrum Boreau
Equal-leaved Knotgrass

Native. Arable and waste land. Quickly colonises well-trampled soil in farmland gateways. In somewhat drier places than *P. aviculare*.

10 km² 48 (92%) 2 km² 457 (48%)

Polygonum aviculare L.
Knotgrass

Native. Arable and waste land. Quickly colonises well-trampled soil in farmland gateways. More common than *P. arenastrum* which occupies a similar habitat.

10 km² 51 (98%) 2 km² 743 (78%)

Polygonum rurivagum Jordan ex Boreau
Cornfield Knotgrass

Nationally scarce plant.
Native. Weed of cultivation.
N. The finding of this plant in a cabbage crop at Biddestone 1988 DG was the second VC7 record. Road verge A420 1989 JH, Grittenham 1989 DG.
S. The occurrence of this plant in an arable field on Odstock Down 1989 GS(NCC) was the first VC8 record for 33 years.
Under-recorded due to similarity with other more common *Polygonum* species.

10 km² 4 (8%)   1 km² 5 (<1%)

Fallopia Adans.

Fallopia japonica (Houtt.) Ronse Decraene
Reynoutria japonica Houtt.
Japanese Knotweed

Introduction. Damp areas, streamsides, roadsides, waste places, often near habitation. An increasing species both in number of sites and in area covered at a site. Dominates some areas, especially near streams. Importation now banned due to its ability to spread and its resistance to all herbicides.

10 km² 35 (67%) 1 km² 132 (4%)   Map 95, page 161

Fallopia baldschuanica (Regel) Holub
Fallopia aubertii (L. Henry) Holub
Russian-vine

Introduction. Popular garden climber sprawling over garden walls and hedges and spreading to scrubby vegetation nearby.
10 km² 8 (15%)   1 km² 12 (<1%)

Fallopia convolvulus (L.) Á. Löve
Black-bindweed

Native. A frequent weed of arable land.
10 km² 49 (94%)   2 km² 515 (54%)   Map 96, page 161

Rumex L.

Rumex acetosella L.
Sheep's Sorrel

Native. Heathland, acid grassland, railway clinker and superficial deposits over chalk.
N. Frequent only around Savernake Forest and on Lower Greensand at Bromham. Sparse in the Braydon Forest area and along the railway system.
S. Most frequent on acid grassland and heathland in SE and SW. Chalk superficials on SPTA(C) and Great Ridge Wood.
10 km² 39 (75%)   1 km² 216 (6%)   Map 97, page 161

Rumex acetosa L. ssp. **acetosa**
Common Sorrel

Native. Grassland and woodland glades on neutral soils. Occasionally on more acidic soil. Common.
10 km² 50 (96%)   2 km² 800 (84%)

Rumex hydrolapathum Hudson
Water Dock

Native. Rivers, canals, ponds and gravel pits.
N. Most abundant in the K & A Canal. Frequent

in the R. Kennet and its tributaries, Bristol Avon downstream from Malmesbury, a section of R. Ray and disused canal from Sutton Benger E to Swindon.
S. Concentrated on R. Avon from Standlynch Mill to Alderbury meadows 1984 NLC & BKC, upstream to Wilsford Manor 1991 PM. Common in small meadow flooded in winter Hood's Farm, Stert 1985 RF. R. Wylye and Steeple Langford gravel pits 1987 BL, R. Nadder at Town Path, Salisbury and carrier Netherhampton, well-established introduction Blackmoor Copse 1990 IA.
10 km² 21 (40%)   1 km² 87 (2%)   Map 98, page 161

Rumex crispus L.
Curled Dock

Native. A common species of rough grassland, railway embankments and waste ground.
10 km² 49 (94%)   2 km² 714 (75%)

Rumex crispus x R. obtusifolius = R. x pratensis Mert. & Koch

Native. The commonest hybrid of this genus but not recognised by most WFMP recorders. Majority of records attributed to JEO.
10 km² 8 (15%)   1 km² 18 (<1%)

Rumex conglomeratus Murray
Clustered Dock

Native. Stream and pond sides. Damp hollows in grassland. Distribution restricted by the plant's habitat requirements. Possibly over-recorded due to mis-identification.
10 km² 49 (94%)   2 km² 508 (54%)   Map 99, page 161

Rumex sanguineus L. var. **viridis** (Sibth.) Koch
Wood Dock

Native. Open woodland, hedges and rough

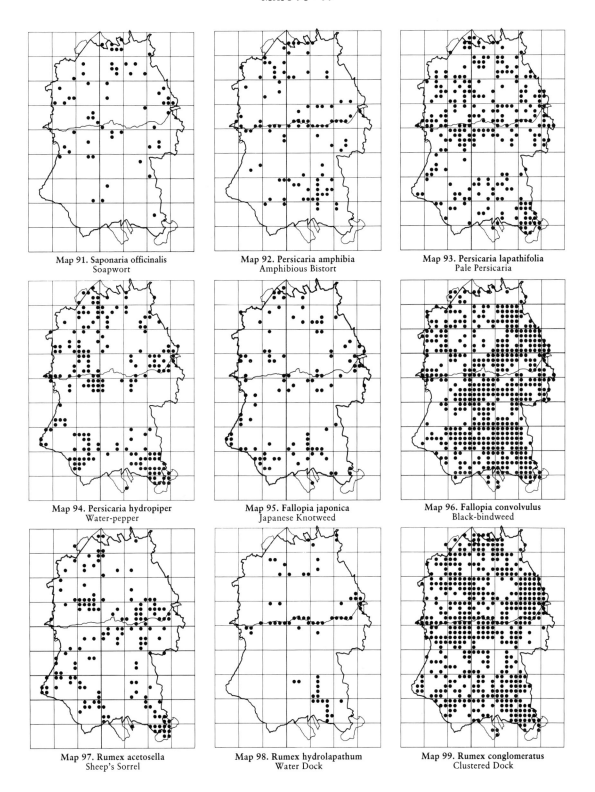

Map 91. *Saponaria officinalis*
Soapwort

Map 92. *Persicaria amphibia*
Amphibious Bistort

Map 93. *Persicaria lapathifolia*
Pale Persicaria

Map 94. *Persicaria hydropiper*
Water-pepper

Map 95. *Fallopia japonica*
Japanese Knotweed

Map 96. *Fallopia convolvulus*
Black-bindweed

Map 97. *Rumex acetosella*
Sheep's Sorrel

Map 98. *Rumex hydrolapathum*
Water Dock

Map 99. *Rumex conglomeratus*
Clustered Dock

grass banks. Common.
Var. sanguineus
Introduction.
N. The only record of this rare variety was from a nursery in Malmesbury where it grew as a weed 1990 MC-B, (ver. DG).
10 km² 48 (92%) 1 km² 695 (19%)   Map 100, page 165

Rumex pulcher L.
Fiddle Dock

Native. Grassy places and waste ground.
N. Rare. South Wraxall, pasture near Coate Water and SE of Corsham, grass field on hill above Avoncliff 1984-90 DG.
S. A record from water-meadows at Charlton 1984 JWr comm. NLC/BKC. A good specimen growing in rich ground by barns near Ogbury Camp 1987 PM was only the third record since 1959.
10 km² 5 (10%)   1 km² 6 (<1%)

Rumex obtusifolius L.
Broad-leaved Dock

Native. Very common on wasteland, road verges, rough grassland and areas of pasture poached by cattle.
10 km² 52 (100%)2 km² 849 (89%)

Rumex maritimus L.
Golden Dock

Nationally scarce plant.
Native.
N. Known to occur only at Coate Water, Swindon. This plant was noted by Grose in 1944 and 1956 on the bare mud exposed when the water level was lowered for lake maintenance. It was refound 1984 by DG in three places on mud trampled by cattle on the edge of the extension to Coate Water.
10 km² 1 (2%)   1 km² 1 (<1%)

CLUSIACEAE

Hypericum L.

Hypericum calycinum L.
Rose-of-Sharon

Introduction. Commonly planted in public places.
N. Spreading at Burderop Hospital. Persistent for many years on road verge Ramsbury 1988 JN.
S. The dominant shrub in a small wood Market Lavington 1984 RF. An extensive linear colony beside the railway line Norton Bavant 1991 JEO.
10 km² 7 (13%)   1 km² 7 (<1%)

Hypericum androsaemum L.
Tutsan

Native. Old woodland, in Wilts on acid soils only.
N. Recorded prior to 1983 but found in only one site since at Great Wood, Grittenham 1991 DG.
S. Records of one or several plants in old woodlands, the majority from the fringe of the New Forest. One of the larger colonies, 28 plants, Lowdens Copse DJW.
10 km² 11 (21%) 1 km² 39 (1%)   Map 101, page 165

Hypericum perforatum L.
Perforate St John's-wort

Native. Frequent throughout much of the county in grassland, open woodland and scrub, especially on calcareous soils.
10 km² 50 (96%) 2 km² 627 (66%)

Hypericum maculatum Crantz
Imperforate St John's-wort

Native. Green lanes, railway embankments and woodland rides where grass is long and rank. Very localised.
N. Sites between Chippenham and Malmesbury: Kington St Michael 1986 JH, Stockton Marsh

1987 DH, railway cuttings Hullavington and Rodbourne 1985-89 DG, Charlton Park 1989 HB, Green Lane Luckington 1990 DG. Pitter's Copse, Sandy Lane 1991 DG, refind of Grose's record.
S. Chalk pit Whiteparish 1988 PMW, trackside Little Down, Stoke Farthing 1989 GS, wet open woodland Hook Copse, Semley 1990 MM.
10 km² 8 (15%)   1 km² 14 (<1%)   Map 102, page 165

Hypericum tetrapterum Fries
Square-stalked St John's-wort

Native. Ungrazed marshes, fens, streamsides and damp open woodland. Frequent and widespread in wet localities.
10 km² 47 (90%) 2 km² 291 (31%)   Map 103, page 165

Hypericum humifusum L.
Trailing St John's-wort

Native. Open woodland, heathland and cultivated land on acidic soils.
N. Spye Park, Savernake Forest and on heavy clay in Braydon Forest.
S. Most of the records are from the heaths and woods of SE. Scattered in many woodlands: Stourton Woods, Deerwood Common, Penstones Wood, Longleat, Great Ridge, Chase Woods, Whaddon Common, Bentley Wood, Collingbourne Wood and Bedwyn Brail.
10 km² 15 (29%)   1 km² 57 (2%)   Map 104, page 165

Hypericum pulchrum L.
Slender St John's-wort

Native. Open woodland, heaths and hedgebanks on neutral to acid soils. Similar distribution to that of *H. humifusum*.
N. Most common in the Braydon Forest area, Spye Park and Savernake Forest. Relic sites occur in woodland on the slightly acidic soil NE of Chippenham.
S. In all main woodland areas from Polesdon Estate

1987 CH in NE to Castle Wood 1991 PMW in SW and from Clanger Wood 1990 GY in NW to Brook (Hants) 1991 RV in SE. Most records are from SE area including Bentley Wood. Great Ridge Wood has six records in one tetrad but some records are of only a single plant, with two plants on nearby downland 1990 VH. Cleared beechwood Grovely Wood 1984 DS-G, woodland clearing Little Yews 1986 JT, chalk-heath Chirton Down SPTA(C) 1986 RF.
10 km² 26 (50%) 1 km² 90 (2%)   Map 105, page 165

Hypericum hirsutum L.
Hairy St John's-wort

Native. Open woodland and grassland with scrub on chalk, limestone and clay. Frequent in these habitats but usually occurring in small numbers.
10 km² 46 (88%) 2 km² 315 (33%) Map 106, page 165

Hypericum elodes L.
Marsh St John's-wort

Native. Only occurs in the New Forest in the SE of the county in drainage channels on acidic peat soils. Unlikely to tolerate drying out. Not widespread and populations are relatively small.
10 km² 1 (2%)   1 km² 10 (<1%)   Map 107, page 165

TILIACEAE

Tilia L.

Tilia platyphyllos Scop.
Large-leaved Lime

Nationally scarce plant.
There is some doubt over the accurate identification of this rare species, in part due to it being incorrectly included in the WFMP list of 'B' species instead of *T. x vulgaris*. Therefore the true county distribution is not known and all records for *T. platyphyllos* have been listed as *T. x vulgaris*.

Tilia platyphyllos x T. cordata = T. x vulgaris
Hayne
Tilia x *europaea* auct. non L.
Lime

Introduction. Frequently planted in churchyards, parklands and formal avenues and occasionally in woodland where care is necessary in identifying it from *T. cordata*. Widely-distributed except on chalk.
10 km² 13 (25%) 1 km² 50 (1%)   Map 108, page 165

Tilia cordata Miller
Small-leaved Lime

Native. Ancient woodland, old boundary and green lane hedgerows. Tolerant of limestone, sandstone and clay soils.
N. Occurs in many of the woods in the Braydon Forest area, especially Stonehill and Ravensroost. Climax woodland in Webb's Wood but has been heavily coppiced by the FC. Single trees in Silk Wood and beside a lake at Wootton Bassett. Native in Gopher Wood but other records in SU16/SU26 are for plantings on Pewsey Downs NNR (by NCC) and in Savernake Forest (by FC).
S.   All the known sites for coppiced stools occur in woodland in SE corner in two localities: one small stool and 9-10 stools Whiteparish Common 1986 WTNC/ST, the first and second VC records, and Barnsell Copse. Most records are of single mature trees as at Quidhampton. Plantings occur Southcott near Pewsey, Longford and Wilbury Estates, Yarnbury Grange, West Gomeldon and recent plantation Grafton Camp. See article on p.71.
10 km² 17 (33%) 1 km² 40 (1%)   Map 109, page 167

MALVACEAE

Malva L.

Malva moschata L.
Musk Mallow

Native. Roadside verges, hedgebanks and pasture.

Locally plentiful around Aldbourne. Scattered elsewhere. Usually occurs in small colonies of 4-6 plants separated from the nearest plants by a considerable distance.
Form with white flowers, CWP 1985 JS.
Var. **heterophylla** Lej. & Court.
This form flowers in July/August, later than *M. moschata*.
N. Three records: woods near Bradford-on-Avon 1984 DG, Kingsdown Lane, Swindon 1990 JN. Form with white flowers, Bupton Earthworks 1990 JR.
10 km² 42 (81%) 1 km² 317 (9%)   Map 110, page 167

Malva sylvestris L.
Common Mallow

Native. Dry road and track verges and waste ground. Frequent and widely-distributed but usually in small numbers.
10 km² 49 (94%) 2 km² 531 (56%)   Map 111, page 167

Malva neglecta Wallr.
Dwarf Mallow

Native. Cracks in paving-stones, the base of walls, farmyards, cultivated and waste land. Usually near habitation. Market gardens on Lower Greensand at Bromham. Rare on the chalk.
10 km² 23 (44%) 1 km² 54 (2%)   Map 112, page 167

DROSERACEAE

Drosera L.

Drosera rotundifolia L.
Round-leaved Sundew

Native. Sphagnum bogs.
S. Restricted by habitat requirements to the New Forest and its environs. Apparently commoner than *D. intermedia*.
10 km² 1 (2%)   1 km² 11 (<1%)   Map 113, page 167

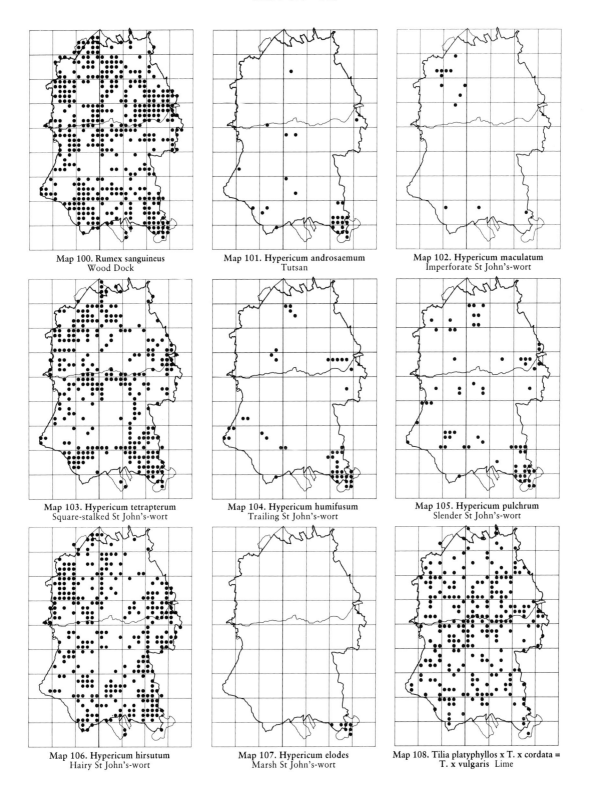

Map 100. Rumex sanguineus
Wood Dock

Map 101. Hypericum androsaemum
Tutsan

Map 102. Hypericum maculatum
Imperforate St John's-wort

Map 103. Hypericum tetrapterum
Square-stalked St John's-wort

Map 104. Hypericum humifusum
Trailing St John's-wort

Map 105. Hypericum pulchrum
Slender St John's-wort

Map 106. Hypericum hirsutum
Hairy St John's-wort

Map 107. Hypericum elodes
Marsh St John's-wort

Map 108. Tilia platyphyllos x T. x cordata =
T. x vulgaris Lime

Drosera intermedia Hayne
Oblong-leaved Sundew

Native. Wet, peaty heaths.
S. Restricted to these habitats in the New
Forest, adjacent commons and at the edge of small
bog pools. Colonies consist of numerous rosettes.
Continues to occur Plaitford and Hamptworth
Commons, not recorded at Landford Common or
Pound Bottom.
10 km² 1 (2%)   1 km² 10 (<1%)

CISTACEAE

Helianthemum Miller

Helianthemum nummularium (L.) Miller
Common Rock-rose

Native. Chalk and limestone downland and scrub.
Frequent in these habitats. Unpalatable to rabbits
resulting in its dominance in some areas. Dominant
species of some 'fairy rings' and frequent on the
well-drained soil of anthills.
10 km² 42 (81%) 1 km² 720 (20%)

VIOLACEAE

Viola L.

Viola odorata L.
Sweet Violet

Native. Frequent and widely-distributed on banks
on calcareous to neutral soil in open woodland
and woodland clearings. In some areas the form
with white flowers predominates.
10 km² 49 (94%) 2 km² 487 (51%)   Map 114, page 167

Viola odorata x V. hirta = V. scabra F. Braun
Viola x *permixta* Jordan

Native.

S. Racecourse, Netherhampton 1989 JEO.
10 km² 1 (2%)   1 km² 1 (<1%)

Viola hirta L.
Hairy Violet

Native. Open woodland, scrub, railway banks,
rough and grazed unimproved calcareous
grassland. One of the earliest downland
species to come into flower. Often frequent,
especially on chalk and limestone downland. A
rare plant of unimproved ridge-and-furrow pasture
in the N.
10 km² 39 (75%) 1 km² 453 (12%)   Map 115, page 167

Viola riviniana Reichb.
Common Dog-violet

Native. Restricted mainly to woodlands and older
green lanes with hedges. Frequent and very
abundant locally.
10 km² 51 (98%) 2 km² 509 (54%)   Map 116, page 167

Viola riviniana x V. canina = V. intersita
G. Beck
Viola x *weinhartii* W. Becker

Native.
N. The only record was from a bank in a cutting
on the M4 motorway near Upper Seagry 1992
DG.
10 km² 1 (2%)   1 km² 1 (<1%)

Viola reichenbachiana Jordan ex Boreau
Early Dog-violet

Native. Woods, woodland and hedge banks.
Predominantly a species of old woodland. Its
occurrence is most frequent on calcareous soils
especially on limestone and on clay in the SE of the
county.
10 km² 44 (85%) 1 km² 306 (8%)   Map 117, page 167

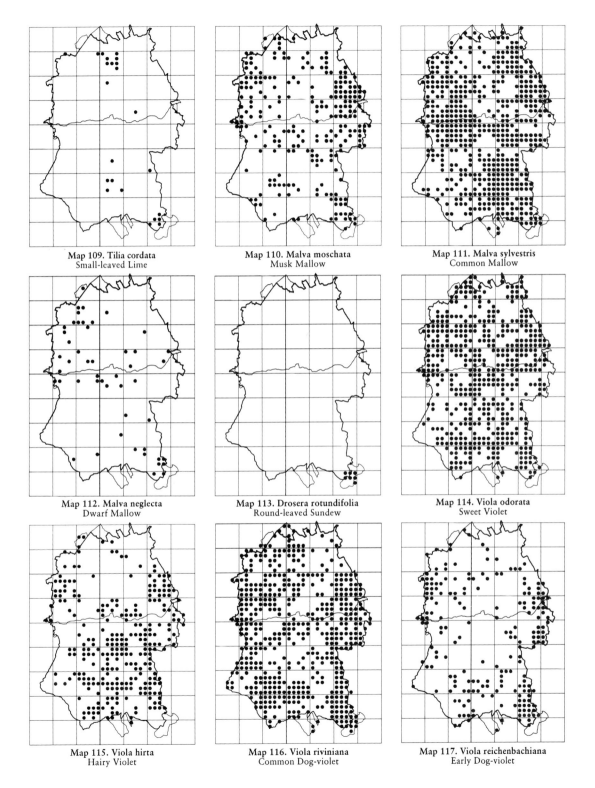

Map 109. Tilia cordata
Small-leaved Lime

Map 110. Malva moschata
Musk Mallow

Map 111. Malva sylvestris
Common Mallow

Map 112. Malva neglecta
Dwarf Mallow

Map 113. Drosera rotundifolia
Round-leaved Sundew

Map 114. Viola odorata
Sweet Violet

Map 115. Viola hirta
Hairy Violet

Map 116. Viola riviniana
Common Dog-violet

Map 117. Viola reichenbachiana
Early Dog-violet

Viola canina L.
Heath Dog-violet

Native. Heaths, acidic grassland and open woodland on Clay-with-flints.
N. The only sizeable numbers occur in Savernake Forest.
S. Sparingly and absent from chalk except on overlying superficials. There may have been identification problems with this species.
10 km² 9 (17%)   1 km² 22 (<1%)

Viola palustris L.
Marsh Violet

Native. Bogs, fens, wet heaths and woodland on acid soils.
N. Very rare. Grows under old alder carr Spye Park 1985 DG, refind of Grose's 1945 record.
S. A species we are delighted still exists in the county. Refinds in the SW in Stourton Woods 1985 FR and two groups on Gutch Common 1987 PWa (NCC). In the SE: Plaitford Common, two sites West Wellow Common 1989 VW and bog N of Furzley 1989 VW & AB, all VC8 (Hants).
10 km² 4 (8%)   1 km² 10 (<1%)

Viola tricolor L. ssp. **tricolor**
Wild Pansy

Native. Arable and waste land. Some records may be of garden escapes.
N. Bunny Lane, Minety 1987 SW, Hullavington 1989 MC-B, Aldbourne 1990 JN.
S. Tittle Path Hill, Semley 1987 JO, Westwood nursery near Trowbridge 1989 JM.
10 km² 5 (10%)   1 km² 5 (<1%)

Viola arvensis Murray
Field Pansy

Native. Arable land. Frequent.
10 km² 49 (94%)   2 km² 602 (63%)

CUCURBITACEAE

Bryonia L.

Bryonia dioica Jacq.
White Bryony

Native. Hedges, scrub and woodland edges. Well-distributed throughout the county in these habitats but often in small quantity.
10 km² 47 (90%)   1 km² 908 (25%)   Map 118, page 171

SALICACEAE

Populus L.

Populus alba L.
White Poplar

Introduction. Planted, especially adjacent to streams, spreading by suckering. Probably more common than records suggest.
10 km² 11 (21%)   1 km² 15 (<1%)

Populus alba x P. tremula = P. x canescens (Aiton) Smith
Grey Poplar

Introduction. River and stream banks, hedges and damp woodland. Generally in small quantity. Its ability to regenerate by suckers 10 m from the parent tree creates problems for the forester.
10 km² 37 (71%) 1 km² 192 (5%)   Map 119, page 171

Populus tremula L.
Aspen

Native. Damp woodland, streamsides and roadside verges. Often planted.
N. Scattered. Only frequent on low-lying damp clay in Braydon Forest area.
S. Frequent in ideal habitats in the SE.
10 km² 36 (69%) 1 km² 143 (4%)   Map 120, page 171

Populus nigra L. ssp. **betulifolia** (Pursh) W. Wettst.
Black-poplar

Native. River valleys and flood plains. Many of the locations in which surviving elegant old trees are now found bear little resemblance to the previously winter-flooded riverside meadows. Since the lowering of the water-table through over-extraction and drainage, the trees now stand in hedgerows on dry farmed land.
N. During the WFMP's 8 years, a remarkable number of previously unknown trees have been added to the few known records in the Swindon area and CWP. Groups of trees S of Wootton Bassett, R. Kennet near Ramsbury, between Minety/Ashton Keynes, Westhay, N of Seagry Wood, Hannington Wick and near Great Wood, Grittenham. All records were confirmed by BSBI referee E Milne-Redhead.
S. Three trees Gomeldon 1987 JF, accepted as refinds E Milne-Redhead. Some old records not refound but two areas produced new sites mainly for single trees at Worton Common and Potterne Wick 1985-90 BGH, Etchilhampton and Patney 1985 RF, Stert 1986 DH-T.
10 km² 10 (19%) 1 km² 26 (<1%)   Map 121, page 171

Populus L. agg.
Poplar

All introductions. Streambanks, woodlands including plantations and hedges. Well-distributed on the clay and along water-courses. Planted in old water-meadows in Salisbury Avon valley. Rare on the chalk. All unidentified species recorded were aggregated. They include
Populus nigra x P. deltoides = P. x canadensis Moench
Hybrid Black-poplar
The most commonly planted tall poplar in Wilts reaching a height of 40 m in damp valleys.
Populus candicans Aiton
P. gileadensis Roul.
Balm-of-Gilead
Populus trichocarpa Torrey & A. Gray
Western Balsam-poplar

N. Two trees green lane Giles Green, Brinkworth 1983 DG, beside pond Red Lodge 1985 MWS, near bridge over By Brook, Ashley near Box JR.
Populus balsamifera L. **x P. trichocarpa**
Hybrid Balsam-poplar
10 km² 45 (87%) 1 km² 401 (11%)   Map 122, page 171

Salix L.

The difficulty in identifying members of this genus limited the number of records submitted during the WFMP. Hybrids presented a special problem. Workshops, using herbarium material, gave some recorders a good grounding and confidence to attempt correct identification of species.

Salix pentandra L.
Bay Willow

Native in the N of GB, introduction in Wilts.
N. Single tree in area of alder and willow adjacent to railway, Christian Malford Halt 1984 DG. Refind of Grose's (undated) record. Three trees beside R. Kennet, Knighton 1987 JN. Unconfirmed report from small wood near Sutton Benger 1989 DB.
10 km² 2 (4%)   1 km² 3 (<1%)

Salix fragilis L.
Crack Willow

Native, but more common as a planted tree. River, lake and stream banks. Always on damp ground. Many pollarded female trees are in a ruinous state. Restricted to the clay in N and along river valleys throughout the county.
10 km² 47 (90%) 1 km² 718 (20%)   Map 123, page 171

Salix alba L.
White Willow

Introduction. River valleys, stream and river banks and damp hedgerows. This species most commonly grows singly. Planted extensively.

Var. **vitellina** (L.) Stokes
Ssp. *vitellina* (L.) Arcang.
Golden Willow
N. Battle Lake Plantation 1985 MWS.
Var. **caerulea** (Smith) Dumort.
Ssp. *caerulea* (Smith) Rech. f.
Cricket-bat Willow
S. Fordbrook, Pewsey 1988 JEO.
10 km² 41 (79%) 1 km² 374 (10%) Map 124, page 171

Salix triandra L.
Almond Willow

Native and planted. Riverbanks, marshes, damp
spots in woodland. Locally frequent in parts of
the damp valleys and on the clay in N Wilts, but
uncommon elsewhere. The least recorded of all
the commoner *Salix* species in the county.
10 km² 35 (67%) 2 km² 94 (10%) Map 125, page 171

Salix purpurea L.
Purple Willow

Native. River and stream banks.
N. Native along the R. Kennet, often occurring in
large numbers. Its status elsewhere in N Wilts is
questionable. Introduced in one lake, CWP and very
probably around ponds at Braydon and Red Lodge.
S. Most frequent along R. Avon near Salisbury.
10 km² 19 (37%) 1 km² 51 (1%) Map 126, page 171

Salix viminalis L.
Osier

Native. River, stream and ditch banks. Always on
damp ground.
N. Confined to the river valleys and areas
traditionally drained by ditches as found around
Minety.
S. Frequent in Vale of Pewsey and along stretches
of the valleys of the rivers Avon, Wylye and
Nadder. Planted extensively.
10 km² 38 (73%) 1 km² 197 (5%) Map 127, page 174

Salix viminalis x S. caprea = Salix x sericans
Tausch ex A. Kerner
Salix x *laurina* auct. non Smith
Broad-leaved Osier

Native. Field boundaries and woodland edges on
damp ground. Often occurs with both parents.
N. Records are sparse, only from CWP,
Malmesbury, Wootton Bassett, Chiseldon,
Highworth, Clatford and R. Kennet. Probably
under-recorded.
10 km² 6 (12%) 1 km² 8 (<1%)

Salix viminalis x S. cinerea = S. x smithiana Willd.
Silky-leaved Osier

Native.
N. Coate Water 1989 JN, in hedgebank Littleton
Drew 1990 DG.
10 km² 2 (4%) 1 km² 2 (<1%)

Salix caprea L.
Goat Willow

Native. Woodland, hedges and open downland.
Widely-distributed throughout the county on drier
soil than many other *Salix* species.
10 km² 49 (94%) 1 km² 853 (23%) Map 128, page 174

Salix caprea x S. cinerea = S. x reichardtii
A. Kerner

Native.
N. Severalls Copse near Kemble 1988 MK.
10 km² 1 (2%) 1 km² 1 (<1%)

Salix cinerea L. ssp. **oleifolia** Macreight
Grey willow

Native. Frequent, especially on damp clay, much
less common on chalk.
10 km² 49 (94%) 2 km² 480 (51%) Map 129, page 174

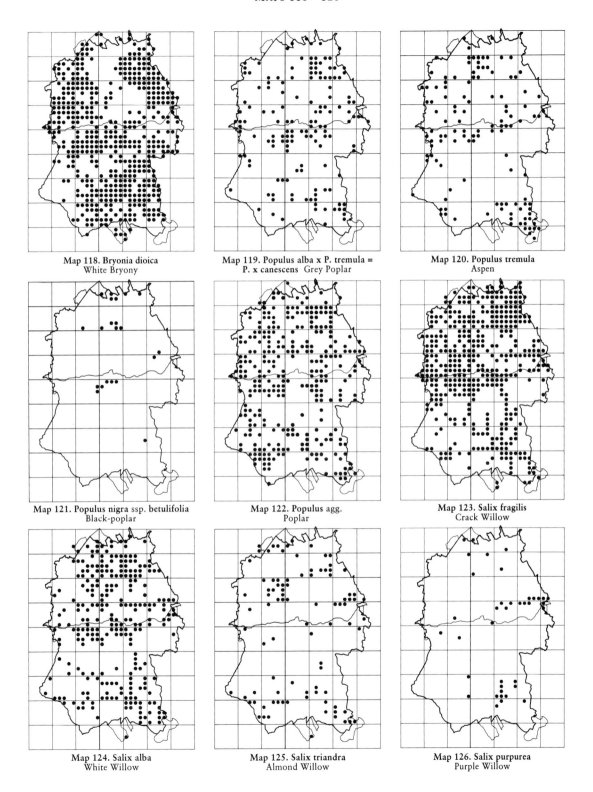

Map 118. Bryonia dioica
White Bryony

Map 119. Populus alba x P. tremula =
P. x canescens Grey Poplar

Map 120. Populus tremula
Aspen

Map 121. Populus nigra ssp. betulifolia
Black-poplar

Map 122. Populus agg.
Poplar

Map 123. Salix fragilis
Crack Willow

Map 124. Salix alba
White Willow

Map 125. Salix triandra
Almond Willow

Map 126. Salix purpurea
Purple Willow

Salix aurita L.
Eared Willow

Native. Damp woodland, scrub and heathland on acid soils.
N. Wetter areas of Braydon Forest and eastern edge of Savernake Forest. Usually in small numbers.
S. A decrease in number of records (cf. Grose) in SE corner where once common.
10 km² 13 (25%) 1 km² 28 (<1%)

Salix repens L.
Creeping Willow

Native. Wet acid grass and heathland.
N. Now extinct in all old sites. The single plant reported at Somerford Common by Grose 1964, where the forester had promised to protect it, has been shaded-out by trees 5m high 1983 DG.
S. Wet heathland in New Forest in zone between *Calluna* heath/*Sphagnum* bog, never in large patches. Hamptworth 1986 NCC/ST, Plaitford and West Wellow Commons, bog N of Furzley 1989 VW.
10 km² 1 (2%) 1 km² 9 (<1%) Map 130, page 174

BRASSICACEAE

Sisymbrium L.

Sisymbrium officinale (L.) Scop.
Hedge Mustard

Native. Hedges, road verges and waste ground. Common throughout the county.
10 km² 51 (98%) 2 km² 701 (74%)

Alliaria Heister ex Fabr.

Alliaria petiolata (M. Bieb.) Cavara & Grande
Garlic Mustard

Native. Common, especially on hedgebanks.
10 km² 52 (100%) 2 km² 782 (82%)

Arabidopsis (DC.) Heynh.

Arabidopsis thaliana (L.) Heynh.
Thale Cress

Native.
N. Uncommon and thinly distributed. Only frequent on railway ballast and on bare, acid soil as at Chittoe, where it is an arable weed, and around Swindon and Aldbourne.
S. Cultivated ground on neutral to acid soils.
10 km² 38 (73%) 2 km² 158 (17%) Map 131, page 174

Erysimum L.

Erysimum cheiranthoides L.
Treacle Mustard

Introduction. Light arable soil and waste land.
N. Two sites, Ashton Keynes 1984 SW, Somerford Keynes 1985 JS, now found annually in CWP; elsewhere Malmesbury 1989 JW, Allington 1989 JH and Swindon 1991 PA.
S. Winterbourne Stoke 1986 BG, Fonthill Clump 1986 VH, few plants in tree nursery Landford 1987 PMW and by roadside Zeals 1991 AH.
10 km² 8 (15%) 1 km² 10 (<1%)

Erysimum cheiri (L.) Crantz
Cheiranthus cheiri L.
Wallflower

Introduction. Naturalised on walls and waste ground. Old wall, Malmesbury 1987 JW, broken walls and rubble North View Hospital, Purton 1989 JEO.
10 km² 2 (4%) 1 km² 2 (<1%)

Hesperis L.

Hesperis matronalis L.
Dame's-violet

Introduction. Commonly a garden escape which

colonises shady places, therefore often found at base of hedges, frequently within 100 m of habitation.
10 km² 31 (60%) 1 km² 87 (2%)   Map 132, page 174

Barbarea R. Br.

Barbarea vulgaris R. Br.
Winter-cress

Native. Frequent but occurring in small numbers on riverbanks, disturbed damp soil, in hedgerows and woodland rides.
10 km² 46 (88%) 2 km² 387 (41%)   Map 133, page 174

Barbarea stricta Andrz.
Small-flowered Winter-cress

Probable introduction.
N. Disused railway line S of Chiseldon 1990 JEO.
10 km² 1 (2%)   1 km² 1 (<1%)

Barbarea intermedia Boreau
Medium-flowered Winter-cress

Introduction. Bare ground. First county record 1893 (Tatum).
N. Lockeridge JEO.
S. Car park Devizes Museum 1983 SAC & DG, single plant on dumped soil with other weeds Pinecrest near Figsbury Ring 1985 PM and two single plants, on bare ground and in fresh tank track, Chirton Down SPTA(C) 1986 RF. Bramshaw 1991 RV.
10 km² 5 (10%)   1 km² 6 (<1%)

Rorippa Scop.

Rorippa nasturtium-aquaticum (L.) Hayek
Nasturtium officinale R. Br.
Water-cress

Native. Unpolluted neutral to lime-rich water.

Frequent in fast-flowing rivers such as the R. Kennet in which it was grown commercially for many years and in water-bodies on the clay. Often occurs only in small numbers.
10 km² 47 (90%) 2 km² 355 (37%)   Map 134, page 174

Rorippa microphylla (Boenn.) N. Hylander ex Á. Löve & D. Löve
Nasturtium microphyllum (Boenn.) Reichb.
Narrow-fruited Water-cress

Native. Ditches and ponds.
N. Ditches Lower Pavenhill Farm, Purton 1984 and near Withy Bed Wood, Wootton Bassett 1986 MWS, ponds Sutton Benger 1987 and Alderton 1990 DG. Probably under-recorded due to the similarity of this plant to *R. nasturtium-aquaticum*.
10 km² 3 (6%)   1 km² 4 (<1%)

Rorippa palustris (L.) Besser
Rorippa islandica auct. non (Oeder ex Murray) Borbás
Marsh Yellow-cress

Native. Damp, disturbed and bare soil at water's edge.
N. Abundant at edges of some gravel pits CWP and Coate Water, Swindon. Along stretches of Bristol Avon and R. Ray. Three records from near K & A Canal Devizes 1986 DG, 1987 JL.
S. Marshy ground beside R. Avon: Alderbury meadows 1984 NLC & BKC, Stratford-sub-Castle 1985, Rushall 1986 PMWF, Little Durnford 1986, Charlton 1990 BKC and Wilsford Manor 1991 PM. R. Biss, Yarnbrook 1987 RR. Five records from Steeple Ashton/Bulkington area, one on a roadside 1990 BGH, bare ground beside pond and river edge Marden Mill 1984, Hatfield Farm and Puckshipton Pond 1985 RF. In SE habitats include dry ditch Pitton 1988 PW and wet depression on open ground Hamptworth 1991 DJW.
10 km² 17 (33%) 1 km² 40 (1%)   Map 135, page 174

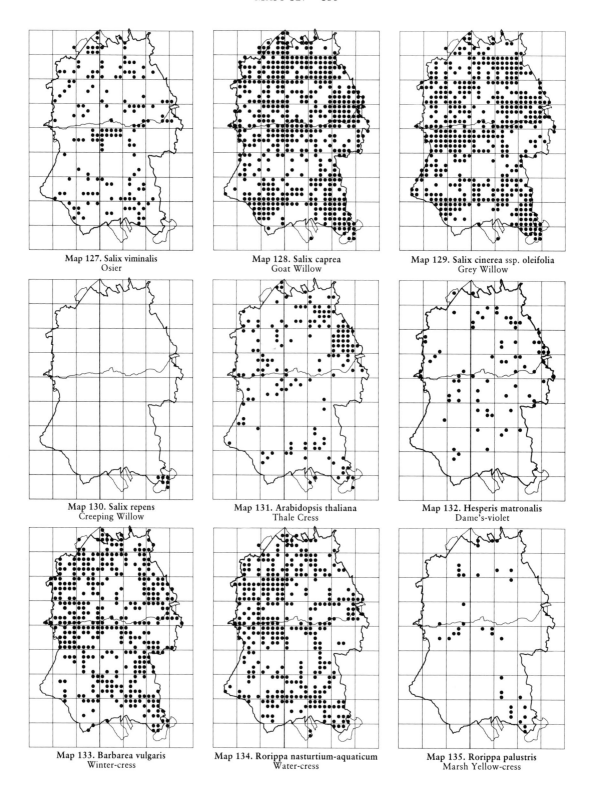

Map 127. *Salix viminalis*
Osier

Map 128. *Salix caprea*
Goat Willow

Map 129. *Salix cinerea* ssp. *oleifolia*
Grey Willow

Map 130. *Salix repens*
Creeping Willow

Map 131. *Arabidopsis thaliana*
Thale Cress

Map 132. *Hesperis matronalis*
Dame's-violet

Map 133. *Barbarea vulgaris*
Winter-cress

Map 134. *Rorippa nasturtium-aquaticum*
Water-cress

Map 135. *Rorippa palustris*
Marsh Yellow-cress

Rorippa sylvestris (L.) Besser
Creeping Yellow-cress

Native. Bare, damp places in woodland rides. Lake, river and pond banks. Waste ground.

N. Sparsely distributed. Frequent on the banks of the By Brook, local by lakes at Lyneham, Coate Water and Battle Lake, on clay in the Melksham area 1984-88 DG, on disturbed ground Burderop Hospital 1985 JEO, at Parkgate Farm 1985 MWS and on waste ground near the R.Kennet, Mildenhall 1988 JN.

S. Most recent records were from banks, marshy and muddy edges of the R. Avon from Standlynch Mill through Britford N to Bodenham Weir 1984 NLC & BKC. On dumped soil: fairly damp at Woodford Green 1984 and fairly dry at The Butts, Salisbury 1985 PM. Weeds in a newly-planted shrub border at Trowbridge Station 1989 EC, on dredged silt at Marden 1988 JMP and a single plant above a ditch at Southwick 1991 GY.

10 km² 11 (21%) 1 km² 24 (<1%)   Map 136, page 177

Rorippa amphibia (L.) Besser
Great Yellow-cress

Native. In and beside rivers, occasionally in ponds and ditches.

N. Along stretches of the Bristol Avon, R. Thames/Isis downstream to Cricklade, lake at Coate Water, Swindon.

S. Hatfield Farm, Etchilhampton 1989 AJS.

10 km² 9 (17%) 1 km² 20 (1%)   Map 137, page 177

Rorippa austriaca (Crantz) Besser
Austrian Yellow-cress

British Red Data Book species.
Native.

N. The only record was from disturbed soil on a new housing estate Lydiard Tregoze 1990 PA.

10 km² 1 (2%)   1 km² 1 (<1%)

Armoracia Gaertner, Meyer & Scherb.

Armoracia rusticana Gaertner, Meyer & Scherb.
Horse-radish

Introduction. Persisting on road verges, waste ground, streambanks and railway embankments. Well-distributed and frequent.

10 km² 46 (88%) 1 km² 486 (13%)   Map 138, page 177

Cardamine L.

Cardamine bulbifera (L.) Crantz
Coralroot

Nationally scarce plant.
Native in GB, introduction in Wilts.
N. Gardens of Lackham College, not planted, first noted 1985 EWC.

10 km² 1 (2%)   1 km² 1 (<1%)

Cardamine pratensis L.
Cuckooflower

Native. Frequent in unimproved damp grassland, in places occurring in large drifts, and in open, moist woodland. Has decreased due to the 'improvement' of lowland pastures.

10 km² 49 (94%) 2 km² 503 (53%)   Map 139, page 177

Cardamine flexuosa With.
Wavy Bitter-cress

Native. Woodland rivulets, silt along stream edges, wasteland and as a garden weed. Frequent except on the chalk from which it is largely absent.

10 km² 46 (88%) 2 km² 349 (37%)   Map 140, page 177

Cardamine hirsuta L.
Hairy Bitter-cress

Native. Wasteland and gardens. Frequent and

widely-distributed except on Salisbury Plain.
10 km² 49 (94%) 2 km² 498 (52%)   Map 141, page 177

Arabis L.

Arabis glabra (L.) Bernh.
Tower Mustard

Nationally scarce plant.
Native.
N. Known from Chittoe, near Bromham, since 1650
(How) on a roadside verge. The verge was protected
by WCC in 1970s but the plant died out due to the
absence of disturbed soil until 1985 when DG found
it on freshly dumped soil. Here it survived until the
soil was removed in 1991, but seven plants were
found in 1992 on the site of the removed soil DG.
10 km² 1 (2%)   1 km² 1 (<1%)

Arabis hirsuta (L.) Scop.
Hairy Rock-cress

Native. Chalk and limestone downland, railway
embankments, tracks and walls. Most frequent
on SPTA, uncommon elsewhere.
10 km² 23 (44%) 1 km² 65 (2%)   Map 142, page 177

Lunaria L.

Lunaria annua L.
Honesty

Introduction. Garden escape. Has spread by seed
to road verges, often far from houses.
10 km² 24 (46%) 1 km² 41 (1%)

Draba L.

Draba muralis L.
Wall Whitlowgrass

Nationally scarce plant.

Native. Large colonies on low stone walls adjacent
to Shipham Wood in VC7 (Glos) 1987 CK.
10 km² 1 (2%)   1 km² 1 (<1%)

Erophila DC.

Erophila DC. agg.
Common Whitlowgrass

The following species may occur in the county. They
were recorded as an aggregate during the WFMP.
E. verna is considered to be the most common.
Erophila majuscula Jordan
Erophila verna (L.) DC.
Erophila verna (L.) DC. var. **praecox** (Steven)
Diklic
Erophila glabrescens Jordan
Native. Walls, bare and waste ground, quarries,
chalk pits, anthills and tracks. This ephemeral
species is abundant on thin and bare calcareous
soil and walls throughout the county. Also on
sandy soil in the S.
10 km 2 41 (79%) 1 km² 290 (8%)   Map 143, page 177

Capsella Medikus

Capsella bursa-pastoris (L.) Medikus
Shepherd's-purse

Native. Very common on disturbed ground.
10 km² 51 (98%) 2 km² 866 (91%)

Thlaspi L.

Thlaspi arvense L.
Field Penny-cress

Introduction. An arable weed, more often found
among root than cereal crops, along field
boundaries and on disturbed soil resulting from
roadworks, pipe-laying and ditch clearance.
Occurs on most soil types, less common on chalk.
10 km² 26 (50%) 1 km² 83 (2%)   Map 144, page 177

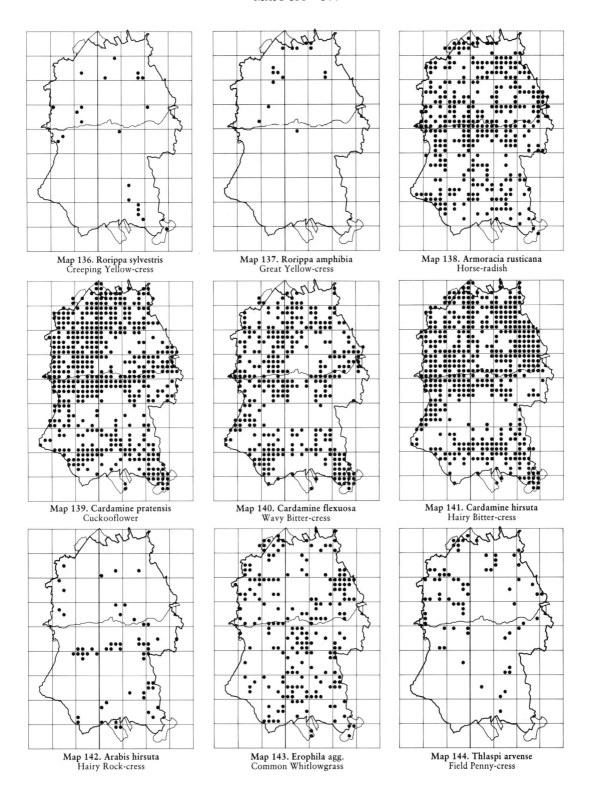

Map 136. Rorippa sylvestris
Creeping Yellow-cress

Map 137. Rorippa amphibia
Great Yellow-cress

Map 138. Armoracia rusticana
Horse-radish

Map 139. Cardamine pratensis
Cuckooflower

Map 140. Cardamine flexuosa
Wavy Bitter-cress

Map 141. Cardamine hirsuta
Hairy Bitter-cress

Map 142. Arabis hirsuta
Hairy Rock-cress

Map 143. Erophila agg.
Common Whitlowgrass

Map 144. Thlaspi arvense
Field Penny-cress

Iberis L.

Iberis amara L.
Wild Candytuft

Nationally scarce plant.
Native. Bare chalky ground.
S. Well-documented site (originally two) for 30 years on Porton Ranges, 3-4 plants per year, then rectangular ditch dug followed by display of hundreds of plants in flower. New road made 200 m away throwing up bare chalk banks, first one and then both sides of road colonised by plants 1992 DOG.
10 km² 2 (4%)   1 km² 2 (<1%)

Lepidium L.

Lepidium sativum L.
Garden Cress

Introduction. Throw-out from cultivation of mustard and cress. This annual species does not become naturalised in the wild in Wilts. Garden escape into places such as farmyards. Surprisingly few records.
10 km² 7 (13%)   1 km² 8 (<1%)

Lepidium campestre (L.) R. Br.
Field Pepperwort

Native. Railway embankments, tracks, disturbed and waste ground on calcareous soils. An ephemeral species rarely re-occurring in the same place and usually in small numbers.
10 km² 14 (27%) 1 km² 25 (<1%)

Lepidium heterophyllum Benth.
Lepidium smithii Hook.
Smith's Pepperwort

Native. Disturbed ground by roads, tracks and railways.

S. Both sides of main NW/SE track Imber Ranges SPTA(W) 1986 JL & BG (ver. AH), first VC record. Single fruiting plant by road SPTA(W) 1986 BG, two plants roadside S of Imber village, three plants Tinkers Firs SPTA(W) 1989 JL. Elsewhere on waste land near railway N of Westbury 1990 PS.
10 km² 2 (4%)   1 km² 5 (<1%)

Lepidium ruderale L.
Narrow-leaved Pepperwort

Probable introduction. Only recorded from man-made habitats, pavement cracks, car parks.
N. Nettleton 1988 JH, first VC7 record since 1919, Ramsbury 1991 JN.
S. Pavement/wall junction Snuff Street, Devizes 1991 PD.
10 km² 3 (6%)   1 km² 3 (<1%)

Lepidium latifolium L.
Dittander

Nationally scarce plant.
Native in GB, introduction in Wilts.
N. The site reported in *The Supplement to the Flora of Wiltshire* on the banks of the Bristol Avon below Melksham refound 1989 DG on the river bank opposite Monkton House.
10 km² 1 (2%)   1 km² 1 (<1%)

Lepidium draba L. ssp. **draba**
Cardaria draba (L.) Desv.
Hoary Cress

Introduction. Disturbed ground beside tracks and roads, in waste places and railway sidings. Spreads by an extensive system of runners to produce large stands. Scattered, mainly between Chippenham and Westbury, in the Vale of Pewsey, southern edge of Salisbury Plain and on soil disturbed by military vehicles on SPTA(E).
10 km² 17 (33%) 1 km² 54 (2%)   Map 145, page 181

Coronopus Zinn.

Coronopus squamatus (Forsskål) Asch.
Swine-cress

Probably native. Tracks, bare and disturbed ground. Frequent in trampled field entrances.
10 km² 41 (79%) 1 km² 392 (11%) **Map 146, page 181**

Coronopus didymus (L.) Smith
Lesser Swine-cress

Introduction. Disturbed and waste ground, dumped soil, garden weed.
N. Surprisingly infrequent. Murhill 1985 JM, Hullavington 1987 JW, Stanton St Quintin, Garsdon and near Braydon House 1985-90 JW, Winsley 1988 JP.
S. A high number of records from a variety of habitats indicate a successful weed which produces a large number of seeds. Examples of the different habitats: roadside lay-by Heron Bridge near Potterne 1985 BGH, gravel ride Nightwood copse 1986 MD, dumped gravel South Newton 1989 BL, pavement crack Laverstock 1989 PM, car park near Westbury White Horse 1990 DC.
10 km² 12 (23%) 1 km² 37 (1%) **Map 147, page 181**

Diplotaxis DC.

Diplotaxis tenuifolia (L.) DC.
Perennial Wall-rocket

Possibly native. Waste ground, often on rubble of derelict and disused buildings.
N. Roadside between Farleigh Wick and Bradford-on-Avon 1986 JP, station car park Bradford-on-Avon 1987 GY, in and around Swindon railway station 1989 JN, Hawkworth Estate 1989 JEO.
S. Railway bridge, Salisbury 1984 PM, mostly destroyed by building work 1985, one plant on overgrown downland adjacent to arable Pitt Coppice Down, Grovely 1987 BL.
10 km² 4 (8%)   1 km² 6 (<1%)

Diplotaxis muralis (L.) DC.
Annual Wall-rocket

Introduction. Dry, waste places, railway sidings and disturbed soil. Both *Diplotaxis* species have a distinct, offensive smell of coal gas or tar. Its distribution in Wilts is restricted due to the lack of derelict cinder and bare ground of which it is a pioneer coloniser and from which it does not seem to have the ability to expand.
10 km² 19 (37%) 1 km² 30 (<1%)   **Map 148, page 181**

Brassica L.

Brassica napus L. ssp. oleifera (DC.) Metzger
Rape

Introduction. A relic of cultivation along field boundaries and hedgerows. Increasingly planted as the crop 'oil-seed rape' in the last 10 years. Most frequently found as an escape in predominantly arable areas. Confusion with *B. rapa* has probably led to some mis-identification.
10 km² 42 (81%) 1 km² 324 (9%)

Brassica rapa L. ssp. rapa
Wild Turnip

Introduction. Relic of cultivation. Scattered. Possibly mis-identified as *B. napus*.
Ssp. campestris (L.) Clapham
Native. Lower reaches of Bristol Avon downstream from Bradford-on-Avon to the county boundary, the only known native location. First reported here in 1905.
10 km² 26 (50%) 1 km² 61 (2%)

Brassica nigra (L.) Koch
Black Mustard

Native. River, stream and canal banks and waste land.
N. Locally abundant on the silted banks of slow-flowing Bristol Avon and on K & A Canal, on rail-

way embankments and disturbed or derelict land.
S. Less common than in N.
10 km² 29 (56%) 1 km² 83 (2%)   Map 149, page 181

Sinapis L.

Sinapis arvensis L.
Charlock

Native. Common and widely-distributed on arable
land.
10 km² 49 (94%) 2 km² 641 (68%)

Sinapis alba L.
White Mustard

Introduction. Cultivated and waste ground. Well-
distributed but rather scarce.
10 km² 32 (62%) 1 km² 69 (2%)   Map 150, page 181

Erucastrum C. Presl

Erucastrum gallicum (Willd.) O. E. Schulz
Hairy Rocket

Introduction. Bare and disturbed soil.
S. This rather aptly-named crucifer occurs almost
exclusively on SPTA where it is widespread and
sometimes common on tank tracks, waste ground,
arable field edges, shell holes and rabbit warrens.
First recorded near Druid's Lodge 1925. Discovered
outside SPTA on disturbed ground near Cholderton
1985 AJS and on a dismantled railway line near
Newton Tony 1989 DOG.
10 km² 9 (17%) 1 km² 101 (3%)   Map 151, page 181

Hirschfeldia Moench

Hirschfeldia incana (L.) Lagr.-Fossat
Hoary Mustard

Introduction. Burderop Hospital grounds 1989

JEO, in the vicinity of Swindon station 1989 JP.
10 km² 1 (2%)   1 km² 2 (<1%)

Rapistrum Crantz

Rapistrum rugosum (L.) Bergeret
ssp. **linnaeanum** (Cosson) Rouy & Fouc.
Bastard Cabbage

Introduction.
N. Waste ground around railway station Swindon
1990 PA.
S. Large colony in flower-beds on new ring-road
embankment Trowbridge 1990 JP.
Both records conf. TCG Rich BSBI Cruciferae referee.
10 km² 2 (4%)   1 km² 2 (<1%)

Raphanus L.

Raphanus raphanistrum L.
Wild Radish

Introduction. Cultivated and rough ground on
sandy soils.
N. Common in the market gardens at Bromham
and N of Chippenham. Scarce elsewhere.
S. Common on sandy soil in the Redlynch/
Landford area.
10 km² 28 (54%) 1 km² 92 (3%)   Map 152, page 181

RESEDACEAE

Reseda L.

Reseda luteola L.
Weld

Native. Disturbed chalk soil, limestone quarries,
railway sidings and waste ground.
N. Common around Swindon, infrequent elsewhere.
S. Especially common on SPTA on disturbed
chalk soil.
10 km² 42 (81%) 1 km² 395 (11%)   Map 153, page 181

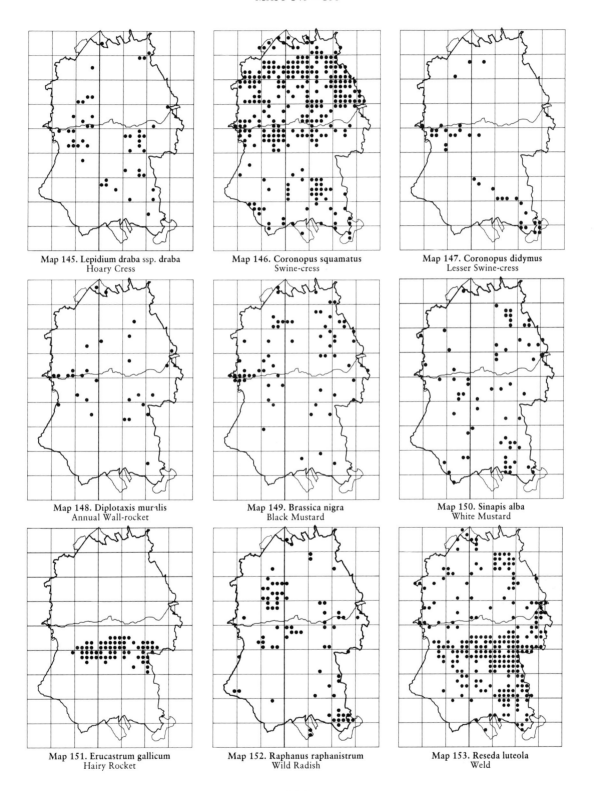

Map 145. Lepidium draba ssp. draba
Hoary Cress

Map 146. Coronopus squamatus
Swine-cress

Map 147. Coronopus didymus
Lesser Swine-cress

Map 148. Diplotaxis muralis
Annual Wall-rocket

Map 149. Brassica nigra
Black Mustard

Map 150. Sinapis alba
White Mustard

Map 151. Erucastrum gallicum
Hairy Rocket

Map 152. Raphanus raphanistrum
Wild Radish

Map 153. Reseda luteola
Weld

Reseda lutea L.
Wild Mignonette

Native. Disturbed and waste land, railway sidings, especially on the chalk. Frequent throughout the areas of calcareous soil. Occurs in large numbers on newly disturbed and compacted soils.
10 km² 44 (85%) 1 km² 869 (24%)   Map 154, page 184

ERICACEAE

Rhododendron L.

Rhododendron ponticum L.
Rhododendron

Introduction. Woodland on acid soils, where it seeds readily. Originally planted. Most frequent in the grounds of landscaped estates.
N. Bowood Park.
S. Longleat, Stourton, Hamptworth and Hare Warren, near Wilton.
10 km² 32 (62%) 1 km² 204 (6%)   Map 155, page 184

Calluna Salisb.

Calluna vulgaris (L.) Hull
Heather

Native. Grassland, heathland and open woodland on acid soils. Leached soil on the chalk.
N. Restricted to very limited areas of suitable habitat. Largest colonies are in Savernake Forest/ West Woods and on Lower Greensand in a restricted area of Spye Park. Small colonies on Kimmeridge Clay in railway cutting E of Chippenham station and on Fyfield Down NNR where sarsen stones have caused local acidification of the chalk and the land has probably never been ploughed.
S. The surprise of finding this species on the tops of chalk downs is very real until one remembers that it is not unusual for these tops to be leached. Records are from Great Ridge Wood and Grovely

areas; on SPTA at Sidbury Hill and West Down Ranges. Of particular interest are two plants on anthills on Little Langford Down WTNC Reserve. Elsewhere, small areas of acid heath in the SE and SW, both showing clusters of records and plants. An area near Teffont has produced a number of acid-loving species.
10 km² 20 (38%) 1 km² 69 (2%)   Map 156, page 184

Erica L.

Erica tetralix L.
Cross-leaved Heath

Native. Wet heaths and bogs
S. Stronghold on the New Forest heathlands, frequently in association with *E. cinerea* and *Calluna vulgaris* but able to tolerate wetter conditions. Elsewhere at Walden's Wood, West Grimstead 1988 PAW and Langley Wood 1990 MD.
10 km² 3 (6%)   1 km² 19 (<1%)   Map 157, page 184

Erica cinerea L.
Bell Heather

Native. Dry heaths.
S. Abundant on a hill near Teffont 1988 VH. All other records from the New Forest area, the more northerly being remnant populations of formerly widespread heathland. Those further S retain relatively extensive stands.
10 km² 3 (6%)   1 km² 20 (<1%)   Map 158, page 184

Vaccinium L.

Vaccinium myrtillus L.
Bilberry

Native. Heaths and open woodland on acid soils.
N. Only record is from the relic of former heathland in the Savernake area. Refound 1981 (G Lewis) and still present.

S. Most records are from open woodland and hedgebanks in the New Forest. Burning has reduced its distribution but it survives in more shaded areas and where the soil is particularly dry and acid. In many areas grazing prevents fruiting. Elsewhere recorded from Semley Hill 1987 JO, Horningsham Common Plantation 1987 VEH, Great Ridge Wood 1989 VH and Donhead St Andrew 1990 MM.

10 km² 7 (13%)   1 km² 16 (<1%)   Map 159, page 184

PYROLACEAE

Pyrola L.

Pyrola minor L.
Common Wintergreen

Native in GB. Introduction in S Wilts woods.
S. Believed introduced with conifers about 60 years ago. Not found every year even with thorough searching. Now two areas, original suffering from smothering by ivy Fonthill Terrace 1988 EE & JBH.

10 km² 1 (2%)   1 km² 1 (<1%)

MONOTROPACEAE

Monotropa L.

Monotropa hypopitys L. ssp. hypophegea (Wallr.) Holmboe
Yellow Bird's-nest

Native. Woods on calcareous soils.
N. A small colony in a disused quarry at Monkton Farleigh growing under beech 1978 has not been seen since 1984 DG. Several large colonies still present just outside the county at nearby Brown's Folly. Other earlier records have either become extinct or been overlooked, perhaps due to the plant's appearance in late summer in woodland where, in the past, colonies were more often found by mycologists than botanists.

S. Near Downton 1987 NCC/PW. Porton Range 1991 DOG.
10 km² 3 (6%)   1 km² 3 (<1%)

PRIMULACEAE

Primula L.

Primula vulgaris Hudson
Primrose

Native. Woodland coppice and clearings, hedgerows, shady banks, and to a lesser extent in damp grassland. In suitable habitats throughout the county. Most frequent in woods on clay soil. On the chalk, the species is restricted to the superficial deposits.
10 km² 51 (98%) 1 km² 1189 (33%) Map 160, page 184

Primula vulgaris x P. veris = P. x polyantha Miller
False Oxlip

Native. Woodland and pasture with scrub where, unusually, the two parents occur.
N. Not uncommon in its distribution but seldom more than a single plant in a locality. Most frequently in the more wooded NW.
S. Most frequent in SW and SE where it is long-standing in Blackmoor Copse.
10 km² 26 (50%) 1 km² 83 (2%)   Map 161, page 184

Primula veris L.
Cowslip

Native. Unimproved grassland predominantly on chalk and limestone, where it grows in abundance in some places. Although lost from many areas due to use of fertiliser and ploughing, small colonies persist in untreated field corners, along road verges and old green lanes. Commonly seeds on newly-established motorway and road verges. Remains abundant in some old ridge and furrow pastures in the N and is a feature of unimproved

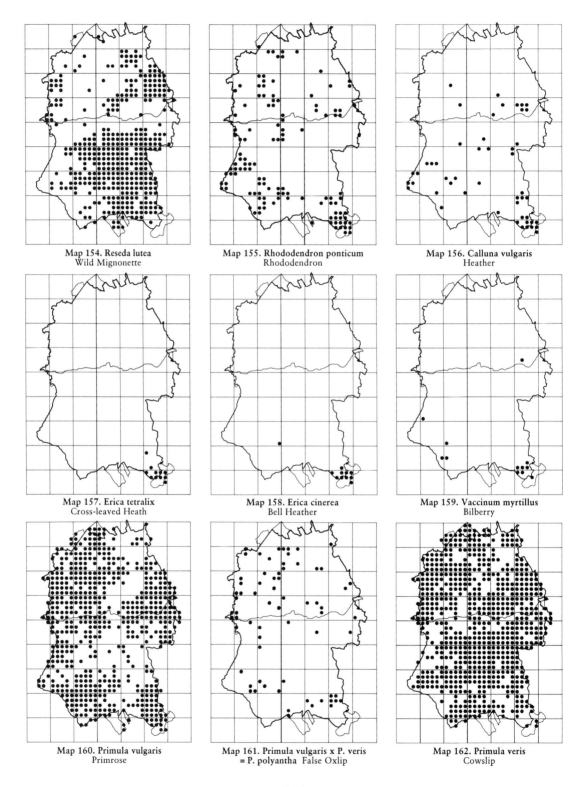

Map 154. *Reseda lutea*
Wild Mignonette

Map 155. *Rhododendron ponticum*
Rhododendron

Map 156. *Calluna vulgaris*
Heather

Map 157. *Erica tetralix*
Cross-leaved Heath

Map 158. *Erica cinerea*
Bell Heather

Map 159. *Vaccinum myrtillus*
Bilberry

Map 160. *Primula vulgaris*
Primrose

Map 161. *Primula vulgaris* x *P. veris*
= *P. polyantha* False Oxlip

Map 162. *Primula veris*
Cowslip

chalk grassland throughout the county.
10 km² 50 (96%) 1 km² 1399 (38%) **Map 162, page 184**

Lysimachia L.

Lysimachia nemorum L.
Yellow Pimpernel

Native. Woods and damp areas on acid soils.
N. Largely restricted to West Woods and
Savernake Forest and the Lower Greensand in the
Spye Park area. Colonies usually small.
S. Most frequent in Stourton to Longleat area,
Vale of Wardour, Great Ridge and Grovely Woods
and in the SE.
10 km² 38 (73%) 1 km² 232 (6%)   **Map 163, page 187**

Lysimachia nummularia L.
Creeping-Jenny

Native. Damp woodland, road banks, and marshy
ground. An indicator species of unimproved damp
meadows. Neutral to calcareous soils.
N. Most frequent in damp woods on the clay
between Melksham and Swindon and in the R.
Kennet valley.
S. Well-distributed along the R. Avon. Scattered
elsewhere in suitable habitats.
Interesting difference in distribution between this
species and *L. nemorum*.
10 km² 41 (79%) 1 km² 294 (8%)   **Map 164, page 187**

Lysimachia vulgaris L.
Yellow Loosestrife

Native. Banks of rivers, streams, ponds and gravel pits.
N. Native, but very localised beside the R. Thames,
some streams in the Braydon Forest area and some
CWP pits. There are some questionable records
especially from ornamental ponds.
S. Banks of the R. Wylye and R. Avon, by ponds
and some wet meadows as at Plaitford.
10 km² 18 (35%) 1 km² 44 (1%)   **Map 165, page 187**

Anagallis L.

Anagallis tenella (L.) L.
Bog Pimpernel

Native. Bogs and wet places.
N. The two occurrences are in very different
habitats: very wet acidic grassland Spye Park
1984 DG and several colonies on unimproved
calcareous grassland Pike Corner (CWP) 1985
RH. Recorded from nearby Poole Keynes 1914
(WJ Greenwood) *The Flora of Cirencester and its
Neighbourhood*.
S. The majority of records are for the N sector of
the New Forest where the plant grows in acidic,
boggy conditions often near streams and ditches.
Known for several years on a damp lawn Alderbury
and in a wet field West Grimstead, both on sandy
sub-soils. In bog Jones's Mill 1984 MW.
10 km² 6 (12%)   1 km² 13 (<1%)   **Map 166, page 187**

Anagallis arvensis L. ssp. arvensis
Scarlet Pimpernel

Native. Common on arable land, disturbed soil
and as a garden weed.
10 km² 51 (98%) 2 km² 688 (73%)

Anagallis arvensis L. ssp. caerulea Hartman
Ssp. *foemina* (Miller) Schinz & Thell.
Blue Pimpernel

Native. Cultivated ground. Only two confirmed
records of this ssp. Arable field, Colerne 1979-88
DG, garden Easton Royal 1987 KMM.

Samolus L.

Samolus valerandi L.
Brookweed

Native. Stream and gravel pit edges. Rarely wet
woodland rides.

N. Four pit edges in one area of CWP where the plant is found amongst the transient plant communities which develop on bare, calcareous gravel 1983 SCH, pits 2a & 40 1985 DG, Poole Keynes 1989 SW. Elsewhere, the Strings valley near Goatacre 1984 WTNC/ST, Catcombe Wood 1984 DB, woodland track Spye Park 1985 DG, damp grassland Wootton Bassett 1985 VG.

10 km² 5 (10%)   1 km² 12 (<1%)   Map 167, page 187

GROSSULARIACEAE

Ribes L.

Ribes rubrum L.
Red Currant

Possibly native. In Wilts thought to be native in many ancient woodlands. Well-distributed in woods, often abundant as an understorey species. Also in hedges and by shady streamsides. The record from the roadside S of Netherhampton near Salisbury may well be a descendant of the county's first record *c.* 1834 by Maton.

10 km² 46 (88%) 1 km² 400 (11%) Map 168, page 187

Ribes nigrum L.
Black Currant

Probable introduction. Garden relic or escape and bird-sown. Woods, hedges and shady streamsides. Usually occurs as a single shrub.
N. Possibly native Yielding Copse near Ogbourne St George 1988 JN and Conkwell Wood in the W 1987 JM. Elsewhere, naturalised on industrial sites, railway cuttings and rough urban land.
S. Half of the records are from marshy sites, others from derelict gardens, rough ground. Approximately six bushes in damp area by large willows Upavon 1985 PMWF, frequent old woodland Bushy Copse 1985 PMW.

10 km² 21 (40%) 1 km² 37 (1%)   Map 169, page 187

Ribes uva-crispa L.
Gooseberry

Native. Woods and hedges. A species occurring consistently in older woodlands throughout the county. Less frequent in hedges.

10 km² 48 (92%) 1 km² 532 (15%)   Map 170, page 187

CRASSULACEAE

Crassula L.

Crassula helmsii (Kirk) Cockayne
New Zealand Pigmyweed

Introduction. In and around ponds, becoming very invasive in some counties.
N. The discovery of this plant in a garden pond at Winsley in 1979 JP was the first county record. In a moat at Liddington 1985 GD, in a field pond S of Angrove Wood 1989 MWS and in Burderop Park 1991 DG.
S. In Hatches Pond, West Wellow 1991 VW and in a new pond Odstock Hospital near Salisbury 1991 JO.

10 km² 6 (12%) 1 km² 6 (<1%)

Umbilicus DC.

Umbilicus rupestris (Salisb.) Dandy
Navelwort

Native. Dry and mortared stone walls and railway bridges.
An oceanic species on the eastern edge of its distribution in GB.
N. Nearly always associated with old, free-standing limestone walls and occasionally on walls supporting roadside banks. Locally abundant in some Cotswold towns and villages.
S. Mainly on walls between the Donheads and Dinton.

10 km² 18 (35%) 1 km² 68 (2%)   Map 171, page 187

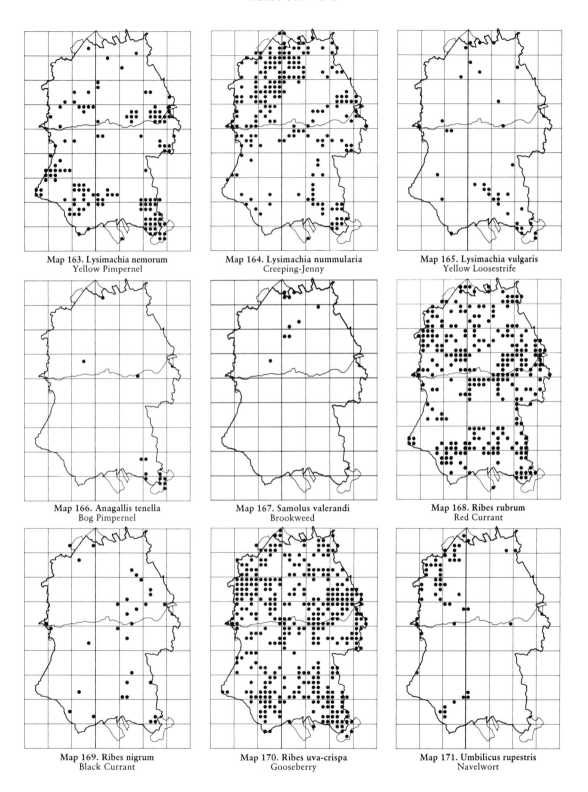

Map 163. **Lysimachia nemorum**
Yellow Pimpernel

Map 164. **Lysimachia nummularia**
Creeping-Jenny

Map 165. **Lysimachia vulgaris**
Yellow Loosestrife

Map 166. **Anagallis tenella**
Bog Pimpernel

Map 167. **Samolus valerandi**
Brookweed

Map 168. **Ribes rubrum**
Red Currant

Map 169. **Ribes nigrum**
Black Currant

Map 170. **Ribes uva-crispa**
Gooseberry

Map 171. **Umbilicus rupestris**
Navelwort

Sedum L.

Sedum telephium L.
Orpine

Native. Sandy and gravelly places on neutral/acid soils. Woodland edges and verges, usually in semi-shade.
N. Several sites Silk Wood 1983 DG, Oaksey Wood 1984 CK & MK, Stanton Park 1985 JH, Burderop Wood and West Woods 1986 JEO, Ramsbury 1988 JN.
S. Majority of records, many from verges, in SE but not extending to highly acidic soils in New Forest. Notable within woodland at Sandlands and Lowden's Copse 1987-90 DJW and Bentley Wood 1989 PMW. Elsewhere, long-known wayside Alderbury 1984 CMC, Stourton 1985 FR, Whitsbury Common 1990 JO, roadside Heath Hill Farm (VC6) 1991 PMW and base of hedge Park Hill Plain, Longleat 1991 ER.
Ssp. **fabaria** (Koch) Kirschl.
S. Brook 1991 RV.
10 km² 14 (27%) 1 km² 31 (<1%)   Map 172, page 190

Sedum rupestre L.
Sedum reflexum L.
Reflexed Stonecrop

Introduction. Planted on walls and naturalises from garden escapes and throw-outs throughout the county. Probably more frequent than records received suggest.
10 km² 14 (27%) 1 km² 17 (<1%)

Sedum forsterianum Smith
Rock Stonecrop

Nationally scarce plant
Native in GB, introduction in Wilts.
N. Walls near the lake Purton House and Purton church 1990 JEO.
10 km² 1 (2%)   1 km² 1 (<1%)

Sedum acre L.
Biting Stonecrop

Native. Roofs, tops of walls, quarries, bare soil and exposed gravel.
N. Most frequent in the Cotswold villages growing in almost any suitable stone crack and in accumulated silt in roof gutters. Elsewhere, on sparsely vegetated areas on chalk downland, bare ground in places such as discarded railway yards and on bare gravel CWP.
S. Much less frequent due to the lack of suitable walls. Road verges at Tilshead and at Porton where it also grows on downland. Has colonised roof tops especially in Salisbury.
10 km² 40 (77%) 1 km² 282 (8%)   Map 173, page 190

Sedum album L.
White Stonecrop

Introduction. Walls, stony ground. Usually associated with buildings.
N. Frequent in towns and villages on the edge of the Cotswolds. Occasional elsewhere.
S. Uncommon and scattered.
10 km² 32 (62%) 1 km² 90 (3%)   Map 174, page 190

Sedum anglicum Hudson
English Stonecrop

Native in GB, introduction in Wilts.
S. Large colonies established on disused runways Sheep Bridge SPTA(E) 1991 AJS.
10 km² 1 (2%)   1 km² 1 (<1%)

Sedum dasyphyllum L.
Thick-leaved Stonecrop

Introduction. Naturalised on walls.
N. On limestone walls in the NW around some Cotswold villages. Frequent on the W edge of Luckington 1991 DG. Elsewhere colonies are very small, having only 1-2 plants. Easton Piercy

1987 JH, Littleton Drew, Brookend, Hebden Leaze, West Kington Wick 1983-91 DG.
S. Stowford Farm, Wingfield 1986 GY.
10 km² 3 (6%)   1 km² 8 (<1%)   Map 175, page 190

SAXIFRAGACEAE

Saxifraga L.

Saxifraga cymbalaria L.
Celandine Saxifrage

Introduction.
N. Known as a garden weed Southleigh, Bradford-on-Avon since 1984. Probably originated from J Swanborough who grew it in her garden and gave seedlings to her guests.
10 km² 1 (2%)   1 km² 1 (<1%)

Saxifraga granulata L.
Meadow Saxifrage

Native. Unimproved chalk downland and occasionally roughish damp meadows. Large colonies on many chalk downlands including SPTA and on, and just below, the tops of the Pewsey Downs. Tall plants were surviving in a fertilised meadow Etchilhampton 1985 RF. In damp meadow adjacent to stream Froxfield 1986 JN & AJS.
10 km² 24 (46%) 1 km² 117 (3%)   Map 176, page 190

Saxifraga tridactylites L.
Rue-leaved Saxifrage

Native. Old walls, tracks, bare ground and quarries.
N. Only abundant in the Cotswold villages. It grows in profusion on the stone roofing tiles of a restaurant in Malmesbury.
S. Local. On the disturbed soil on active anthills on chalk downland.
10 km² 25 (48%) 1 km² 86 (2%)   Map 177, page 190

Chrysosplenium L.

Chrysosplenium oppositifolium L.
Opposite-leaved Golden-saxifrage

Native. Woodland streamsides, spring-heads and damp ditches.
N. Abundant along the streams of the Bristol Avon and By Brook where they pass through woodland and along the spring line at the junction of the greensand and clay around Bromham and near Lacock. Local elsewhere.
S. Concentrations of records on heavier clay and on greensand SW of Tisbury, around Warminster and in Vale of Pewsey.
10 km² 25 (48%) 1 km² 152 (4%)   Map 178, page 190

Chrysosplenium alternifolium L.
Alternate-leaved Golden-saxifrage

Native. Streamsides in woodland.
N. Only on Lower Greensand. Alder carr Whetham 1985. A refind of TB Flower's first record for the county (1864) in a wooded valley at Bromham 1985 and in Raspberry Copse 1991 DG.
S. Donhead St Andrew 1985 EE, S of Cools Farm, West Tisbury 1986 WTNC/ST, confirmation of 1881-82 record at Gasper 1986 EE & FR and several patches beside R. Nadder at Dinton 1988 SMP.
10 km² 4 (8%)   1 km² 7 (<1%)

ROSACEAE

Filipendula Miller

Filipendula vulgaris Moench
Dropwort

Native. Frequent on grazed and ungrazed unimproved chalk grassland.
N. Very rare on non-calcareous soil. Records only from Hullavington airfield 1987 JH, very common along railway cutting at Alderton and Luckington 1986, nearby in a neutral meadow on

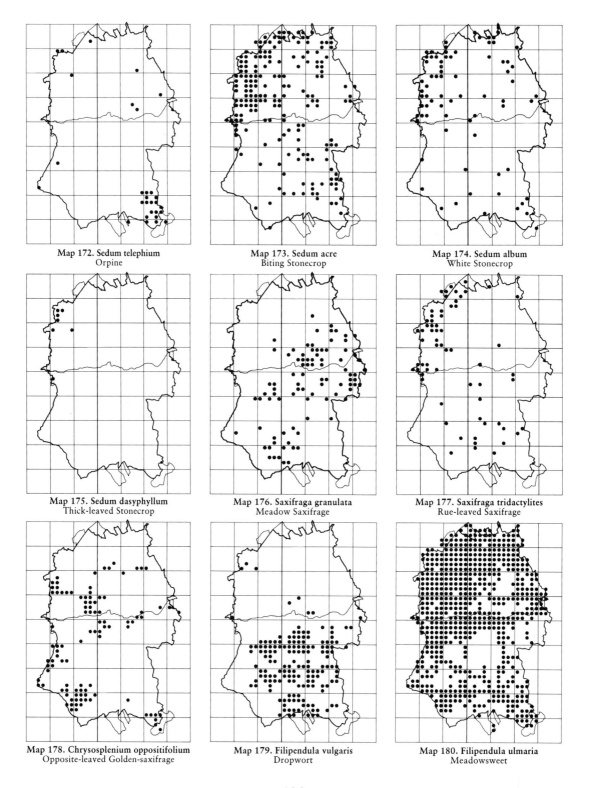

Map 172. Sedum telephium
Orpine

Map 173. Sedum acre
Biting Stonecrop

Map 174. Sedum album
White Stonecrop

Map 175. Sedum dasyphyllum
Thick-leaved Stonecrop

Map 176. Saxifraga granulata
Meadow Saxifrage

Map 177. Saxifraga tridactylites
Rue-leaved Saxifrage

Map 178. Chrysosplenium oppositifolium
Opposite-leaved Golden-saxifrage

Map 179. Filipendula vulgaris
Dropwort

Map 180. Filipendula ulmaria
Meadowsweet

the W county border 1990 DG and in wild garden Murhill 1985-87 JM. Surprisingly rare on chalk. **S.** A very common plant of the chalk grassland both grazed (Parsonage Down NNR) and ungrazed (SPTA) where it flowers in great profusion.
10 km² 23 (44%) 1 km² 281 (8%)   Map 179, page 190

Filipendula ulmaria (L.) Maxim.
Meadowsweet

Native. Frequent and often abundant in damp habitats.
10 km² 49 (94%) 2 km² 624 (66%)   Map 180, page 190

Rubus L.

Rubus idaeus L.
Raspberry

Native. Woods, their margins and scrub. Frequent on Clay-with-flints and leached chalk.
10 km² 46 (88%) 2 km² 393 (41%)   Map 181, page 195

The nomenclature used for the following *Rubus* species is that laid down by E S Edees & A Newton in Brambles of the British Isles 1988 published by the Ray Society. Extensive work on *Rubus* was undertaken in the county in the past by experts of the day but little has been done in the last 40 years. The following list shows the occurrence of *Rubus* species in Wiltshire, very little being known about their distribution. Most of the following species were recorded during a two-day field meeting of batologists in 1986. Special thanks to D Allen, A Bull, A Newton & R Randall for their records. All undetermined records were named *R. fruticosus* agg.

Rubus fruticosus agg. L.
Bramble

Native. Very common throughout the county occurring in all types of habitat.
10 km² 51 (98%) 2 km² 900 (95%)

Rubus sect. Rubus
Rubus sect. *Suberecti* Lindley

Rubus nessensis W. Hall

Series 1 Sylvatici (Mueller) Focke

Rubus albionis W. C. R. Watson
Rubus calvatus Lees ex Bloxam
Rubus confertiflorus W. C. R. Watson
First VC8 record, 1983 DA.
Rubus laciniatus Willd.
Introduction.
Rubus leucandriformis Edees & Newton
Rubus lindleianus Lees
Rubus pyramidalis Kaltenb.
Rubus silvaticus Weihe & Nees
Rubus subintegribasis Druce
First VC8 record, 1983 DA.

Series 2 Rhamnifolii (Bab.) Focke

Rubus cardiophyllus Lef. & Mueller
Rubus cornubiensis (Rogers ex Riddelsd.) Rilstone
Rubus polyanthemus Lindeb.
Rubus prolongatus Boulay & Letendre ex Corbière
Rubus subinermoides Druce

Series 4 Discolores (Mueller) Focke

Rubus armipotens W. C. Barton ex Newton
Rubus procerus Mueller ex Boulay
Rubus ulmifolius Schott
Common throughout the county if not the country.
Rubus winteri P. J. Mueller ex Focke

Series 5 Vestiti (Focke) Focke

Rubus vestitus Weihe x **R. ulmifolius** (Schott)

Series 7 Micantes Sudre ex Bouvet

Rubus norvicensis A. L. Bull & Edees
First VC7 record, 1986 A Bull.
Rubus raduloides (Rogers) Sudre

Series 8 Anisacanthi H. E. Weber

Rubus dentatifolius (Briggs) W. C. R. Watson

Series 9 Radulae (Focke) Focke

Rubus bloxamii (Bab.) Lees
Rubus cantianus (W. C. R. Watson) Edees &
Newton
Rubus echinatus Lindley
Rubus fuscicaulis Edees
Rubus insectifolius Lef. & Mueller
Rubus rudis Weihe
Rubus rufescens Lef. & Mueller

Series 10 Hystrices Focke

Rubus bercheriensis (Druce ex Rogers) Rogers
Rubus dasyphyllus (Rogers) E. S. Marshall
Rubus hylocharis W. C. R. Watson
Rubus milesii Newtown
Rubus phaeocarpus W. C. R. Watson

Series 11 Glandulosi (Wimmer & Grab.)
Focke

Rubus sect. Corylifolii Lindley

Rubus nemorosus Hayne & Willd.
First VC8 record, 1983 DA.
Rubus pruinosus Arrh.
Rubus tuberculatus Bab.

Rubus sect. Caesii Lej. & Courtois

Rubus caesius L. **x R. bloxamii** (Bab.) Lees
Rubus caesius L. **x R. fruticosa**

Rubus caesius L.
Dewberry

Native. Open woodland, rides, scrub, hedge and
roadside verge banks. Frequent on clay soils.
Infrequent on the chalk except in areas of scrub.
10 km² 45 (87%) 1 km² 366 (10%) Map 182, page 195

Potentilla L.

Potentilla anserina L.
Silverweed

Native. Road and track sides, especially where
there is bare ground.
A common constituent of the flora of damp
pastures in N.
10 km² 52 (100%)2 km² 878 (93%)

Potentilla argentea L.
Hoary Cinquefoil

Nationally scarce plant.
Native in GB, introduction in Wilts.
N. The only record was from a disused railway
line at Staverton 1988 JP.
10 km² 1 (2%)   1 km² 1 (<1%)

Potentilla recta L.
Sulphur Cinquefoil

Introduction.
N. Disused railway marshalling-yard
Hullavington 1986 JH, near railway station
Swindon 1991 JN.
10 km² 2 (4%)   1 km² 2 (<1%)

Potentilla erecta (L.) Räusch.
Tormentil

Native. Heathland, unimproved neutral and
acidic grassland, open woodland and scrub on
acid soils.
N. Distribution restricted to these habitats.
Frequent in Savernake Forest, Braydon Forest and
around Spye Park.
S. Most frequent in SW, in Bentley Wood
and copses E of Redlynch in SE. On the chalk,
restricted to areas covered with superficial
deposits.
10 km² 46 (88%) 1 km² 382 (10%) Map 183, page 195

Potentilla anglica Laich.
Trailing Tormentil

Native. Dry banks. This species may have been confused with *P. erecta* x *P. reptans* = *P. x italica* Lehm.
N. Records only from Spye Park area on Lower Greensand. N of Prickmoor Wood on acidic grassland and throughout the woodland rides in The Warren 1987 DG.
S. Semley 1987 JN/BSBI meeting, Plaitford Green (Hants) 1991 RV.
10 km² 3 (6%)   1 km² 4 (<1%)

Potentilla anglica x P. reptans = P. x mixta Nolte ex Reichb.
Hybrid Cinquefoil

Native.
N. N of Prickmoor Wood in acidic grassland 1987 DG, refind of Grose's 1964 record. A chromosome count of a specimen carried out by Mrs B Howard (BSBI *Potentilla* referee) proved to be this hybrid.
S. Grose's 1962 record from Blackmoor Copse not refound.
Under-recorded.
10 km² 1 (2%)   1 km² 1 (<1%)

Potentilla reptans L.
Creeping Cinquefoil

Native. Common and widely-distributed in rough grassland, along woodland rides and tracks, in hedgebanks and damp pasture.
10 km² 51 (98%) 2 km² 770 (81%)

Potentilla sterilis (L.) Garcke
Barren Strawberry

Native. Frequent on all soils in woodland, on steep hedgebanks and roadsides but in small colonies.
10 km² 49 (94%) 2 km² 368 (39%)   Map 184, page 195

Fragaria L.

Fragaria vesca L.
Wild Strawberry

Native. Frequent and widely-distributed along woodland edges, on open bare banks, track and roadside verges.
10 km² 50 (96%) 2 km² 401 (42%)   Map 185, page 195

Duchesnea Smith

Duchesnea indica (Andrews) Focke
Yellow-flowered Strawberry

Introduction.
N. A long history of this plant at Murhill 1985 JM.
10 km² 1 (2%)   1 km² 1 (<1%)

Geum L.

Geum rivale L.
Water Avens

Native. Wet woodland, unimproved neutral grassland, streamsides and marshes.
N. Restricted to these habitats along river valleys and woodland on heavier clay, especially around West Kington.
S. Most frequent in SE where it occurs in moist woods on clay at Blackmoor Copse. Well-distributed beside the rivers Avon, Bourne, Nadder and Wylye.
10 km² 39 (75%) 1 km² 241 (7%)   Map 186, page 195

Geum rivale x G. urbanum = G. x intermedium Ehrh.

Native. Damp and wet woodland. Less frequently on dry chalk. In some localities in the absence of either parent.
N. Very localised, most frequent in woodlands N of West Kington. Nettleton Wood, Home Wood and Stanton Park Wood 1986-88 JH, Kemble

Wood 1988 MK & CK, Alderton Grove 1990 DG, West Dunley Wood, Oldlands Wood and Grittleton 1990 JH.
S. Scattered records, usually small colonies. Most frequent in Vale of Pewsey: common in small wood Hood's Farm, Stert and plantation Etchilhampton 1984, hedgerow Chirton and in small woods Patney and Woodborough 1985 RF. Sites on dry chalk: Shortengrove, Grovely Wood 1989 BL, with both parents oak wood Bidcombe Hill 1991 DF, Vernditch Chase 1991 VS and Everleigh Ashes SPTA(E) AJS.
10 km² 12 (23%) 1 km² 22 (<1%)   Map 187, page 195

Geum urbanum L.
Wood Avens

Native. Common and very widely-distributed in woodland and hedgebanks but in small numbers.
10 km² 52 (100%) 2 km² 824 (87%)

Agrimonia L.

Agrimonia eupatoria L.
Agrimony

Native. Locally common and widely-distributed in rough grassland, scrub and woodland rides.
10 km² 51 (98%) 2 km² 755 (80%)

Agrimonia procera Wallr.
Fragrant Agrimony

Native. Open woodland, road and track sides.
N. Restricted to Clay-with-flints in Savernake Forest and West Woods. The site of Grose's 1942 record in Silk Wood in the NE was searched but the plant was not found DG.
S. Records concentrated in E end of Vale of Pewsey, SPTA(E) and in SE corner. Mainly beside tracks in the same places as A. eupatoria but much less common.
10 km² 13 (25%) 1 km² 49 (1%)   Map 188, page 195

Sanguisorba L.

Sanguisorba officinalis L.
Great Burnet

Native. Unimproved neutral grassland.
N. Nowhere common. Most frequent in Minety parish especially in ridge-and-furrow pasture. In many suitable habitats in the Braydon Forest area and CWP. Elsewhere, large colonies on railway embankments at Allington and Luckington 1986 DG and N of Sherston 1985 AC. The only dicotyledon in a field of rye-grass which had been treated with herbicide near Wootton Bassett 1986 JF, colony on road verge Calne sand pits 1986 destroyed 1990 BG, disused railway track Martinslade near Seend 1988 BG.
10 km² 12 (23%) 1 km² 49 (1%)   Map 189, page 195

Sanguisorba minor Scop. ssp. minor
Salad Burnet

Native. A constant species of unimproved chalk and limestone downland. Also occurs in unimproved neutral pasture.
Ssp. muricata (Gremli) Briq.
Fodder Burnet
Introduction. Grassy places.
S. Steeple Langford Bottom 1986 BL, grassy bank adjacent to arable Pitton 1987 PW, large population both sides of path Wishford/Ebsbury Hill 1990 BL, Southmill Hill AJS 1990. Possibly under-recorded.
10 km² 47 (90%) 2 km² 537 (57%)   Map 190, page 199

Alchemilla L.

Alchemilla filicaulis Buser ssp. vestita (Buser) Bradshaw
Hairy Lady's-mantle

Native. Unimproved neutral, acidic and, rarely, on limestone grassland, woodland rides and edges, Clay-with-flints on chalk. Very localised and in

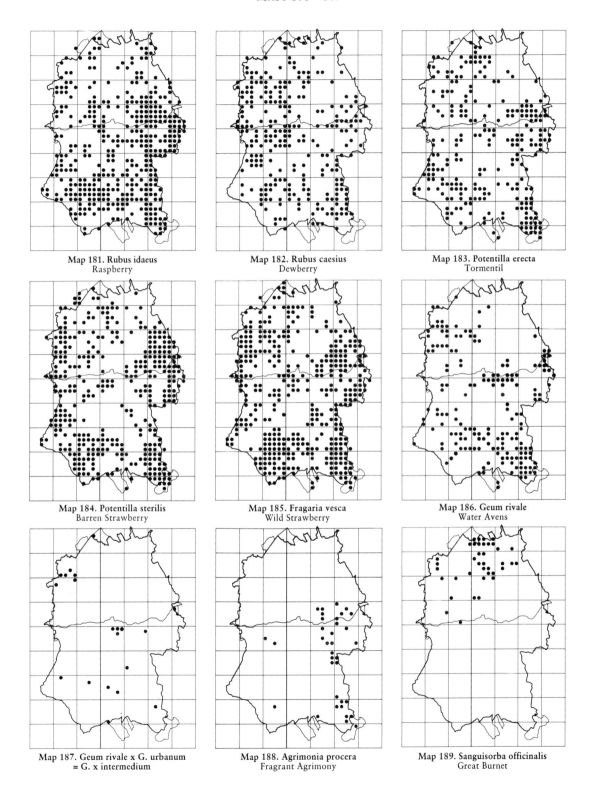

Map 181. **Rubus idaeus**
Raspberry

Map 182. **Rubus caesius**
Dewberry

Map 183. **Potentilla erecta**
Tormentil

Map 184. **Potentilla sterilis**
Barren Strawberry

Map 185. **Fragaria vesca**
Wild Strawberry

Map 186. **Geum rivale**
Water Avens

Map 187. **Geum rivale x G. urbanum**
= G. x intermedium

Map 188. **Agrimonia procera**
Fragrant Agrimony

Map 189. **Sanguisorba officinalis**
Great Burnet

very small numbers. Considered an indicator of high quality neutral and acidic grasslands.

N. Occurs on Clay-with-flints in Savernake Forest area.

S. Not unusual to find a single plant. Most frequent in woodland at Great Ridge and Collingbourne Woods and on unimproved neutral grassland in Vale of Pewsey.

10 km² 23 (44%) 1 km² 73 (2%)   Map 191, page 199

Aphanes L.

The two species in this genus have probably been under-recorded, due to their small size and inconspicuous flowers.

Aphanes arvensis L.
Parsley-piert

Native. Most common on unimproved chalk and limestone downland. Also found on anthills, thin stony soil, arable land, paths and the tops of walls.

10 km² 48 (92%) 2 km² 227 (24%)   Map 192, page 199

Aphanes inexspectata Lippert
Aphanes microcarpa auct. non (Boiss. & Reuter) Rothm.
Slender Parsley-piert

Native. Acid soils.

N. Only recorded from superficials overlying chalk Fyfield Down NNR 1986 KP, sandy soil at Spye Park 1987 DG and woodland ride Savernake Forest 1987 DG, JN & RR.

S. Restricted to light sandy soils, mainly in SE. Often an arable weed but also on tracksides, woodland rides and disturbed soil. Anthills (*Lasius flavius*) in open old meadow Bentley Wood 1988 PMW.

10 km² 6 (12%) 1 km² 23 (<1%)   Map 193, page 199

Rosa L.

This critical genus is extremely complex. Hybrids occur commonly and offspring of crosses of two

identical hybrids can be very different. Identification was attempted by very few WFMP recorders and records were accepted only from experienced botanists. The help given with this difficult group by the BSBI *Rosa* referee, Rev GG Graham, is gratefully acknowledged.

Rosa arvensis Hudson
Field-rose

Native. Hedges, woodland edges and scrubby fields. Frequent and often locally abundant.

10 km² 48 (92%) 2 km² 452 (48%)   Map 194, page 199

Rosa stylosa Desv.
Short-styled Field-rose

Native. Woodland edges, hedges, green lanes often climbing 3 m into the lower canopy of adjacent trees.

N. Winsley, near Colerne, Bird's Marsh, Ravensroost Wood, Bowood, Hullavington, Rodbourne, disused railway track near Rowde and railway cutting Luckington 1984-90 DG.

S. Edge of thin woodland strip Patney Station 1984 RF, Whitebridge Farm, Semley Common 1987 BSBI meeting, S of Hindon.

10 km² 9 (17%) 1 km² 16 (<1%)

Rosa stylosa x R. canina = R. x andegavensis Bast.

Native.

N. Edge of Ravensroost Wood 1987 DG, (conf. Rev GG Graham (BSBI *Rosa* referee).

10 km² 1 (2%) 1 km² 1 (<1%)

Rosa canina L.
Dog-rose

Native. This is the commonest rose species in Wilts and is widely-distributed throughout the county in hedges, woodland edges and on

downland. Colonises derelict land. Less frequent on acid soil.
10 km² 51 (98%) 2 km² 845 (89%)

Rosa dumetorum auct. non Thuill.

This pubescent form is now included under *R. canina*. Not uncommon.

Rosa canina x R. tomentosa = R. x scabriuscula Smith

Native.
N. Hartham Park, Breachlane Wood, Ravensroost Wood, near Alderton and Derriads, Chippenham 1987 DG. Sometimes occurs as a single bush but more commonly as a hybrid swarm with both parents growing nearby.
10 km² 4 (8%)   1 km² 6 (<1%)

Rosa canina x R. rubiginosa = R. x nitidula Besser

Native.
N. Beside chalk track from A4 to White Horse, Cherhill Down, growing with both parents 1989 DG.
10 km² 1 (2%)   1 km² 1 (<1%)

Rosa obtusifolia Desv.
Round-leaved Dog-rose

Native.
N. In hedges in three localities between the railway and Hebden Farm, Luckington 1989-90 DG.
S. West Wellow Common 1991 RV.
10 km² 2 (4%)   1 km² 4 (<1%)

Rosa tomentosa Smith
Harsh Downy-rose

Native. Heavy calcareous clay soil.

N. The commonest hairy rose species. Most localities are in the NW.
Var. **dimorpha** (Bess.) Déségl.
Found at Thingley Junction 1983 DG (det. BM). Site destroyed by landfill but single plant found beside railway line 1984 and a second colony on same railway line Lacock 1987 DG.
10 km² 11 (21%) 1 km² 27 (<1%)

Rosa sherardii Davies
Sherard's Downy-rose

Native.
N. In hedge near the railway Alderton 1985 DG. First VC7 record since 1947. Three sites at Goldborough Farm, Wootton Bassett 1986 JF & DG. These records confirmed by GG Graham (BSBI *Rosa* referee). Two plants adjacent to bridleway Shaw Farm, Lockeridge 1990 VS.
10 km² 3 (6%)   1 km² 3 (<1%)

Rosa rubiginosa L.
Sweet-briar

Native. Hedges, scrub, grassland. Mainly on calcareous soils.
N. Very rare. Goldborough Farm, Wootton Bassett 1987 JF (ver. DG), Cherhill 1989 DG.
S. Windmill Hill 1986 BG, Middle Chase Farm 1988 JJ, South Down, Ebbesbourne Wake 1988 JR, Stourhead 1988 DG, West Grimstead 1988 and Blackmoor Copse 1989 IA, Porton Ranges 1988-91 OS, Bentley Wood 1990 PMW, Throope Hill 1990 PW, SPTA(E) 1991 AJS.
10 km² 9 (17%)   1 km² 16 (<1%)

Rosa micrantha Borrer ex Smith
Small-flowered Sweet-briar

Native. Hedges, woodland edges.
N. Danks Down near Ford and Colerne 1984-90

DG, Goldborough Farm, Wootton Bassett 1984 JF.
S. Tower Hill Plantation, Porton Down 1988
BL, (ver. DG), Boscombe Down 1990 GN.
10 km² 5 (10%)   1 km² 6 (<1%)

Prunus L.

Prunus cerasifera Ehrh.
Cherry Plum

Introduction. Planted in hedges. Records from
Goldborough Farm near Wootton Bassett, Bewley
Green, Froxfield, Ugford, Heale Hill, Little
Durnford Hill and N of Pewsey Wharf.
10 km² 7 (13%)   1 km² 9 (<1%)

Prunus spinosa L.
Blackthorn

Native. Very common and widely-distributed in
woodland and hedges, creating thickets if allowed
to grow naturally.
10 km² 51 (98%)   2 km² 873 (92%)

Prunus domestica L. agg.
Wild Plum, Bullace

Introduction. Copses, hedgerows, railway
embankments and roadside verges.
The similarity of species and sub-species of the
bullace group led to confusion in identification.
All records have been shown as an aggregate.
Included in the aggregate
Prunus spinosa x P. domestica = P. x fruticans
Weihe
Prunus domestica L.
Prunus domestica L. ssp. **insititia** (L.) Bonnier
& Layens
Prunus domestica L. ssp. **domestica**
Introductions may be accidental or deliberate.
The long-standing of the species at some sites
makes its origin uncertain.
10 km² 44 (85%)   1 km² 327 (9%)   Map 195, page 199

Prunus avium (L.) L.
Wild Cherry

Native. Woods and hedges.
This tree is a widespread constituent of
ancient woodland on greensand, clay and
Clay-with-flints. It is now widely planted
in new woodlands on many different soil
types.
10 km² 46 (88%)   1 km² 461 (13%)   Map 196, page 199

Prunus padus L.
Bird Cherry

Native in GB, introduction in Wilts. Planted in
grounds of private estates.
N. Battle Lake 1984 MWS.
S. Wilcot 1985 JEO & KP, Pythouse 1987 MM,
Cowleaze Wood 1991 HW and Fairbroad Coppice
1991 VEH.
10 km² 5 (10%)   1 km² 5 (<1%)

Prunus laurocerasus L.
Cherry Laurel

Introduction. Woods and shrubberies. Much
planted in the 19th century as pheasant cover
and in ornamental woodland. Frequently
naturalised, spreading vegetatively over
large areas to the detriment of a woodland's
diversity.
10 km² 38 (73%)   1 km² 146 (4%)   Map 197, page 199

Cydonia Miller

Cydonia oblonga Miller
Quince

Introduction.
N. The only record was of one large flowering
tree and young plants in osier bed Chilton Foliat
1987 SK.
10 km² 1 (2%)   1 km² 1 (<1%)

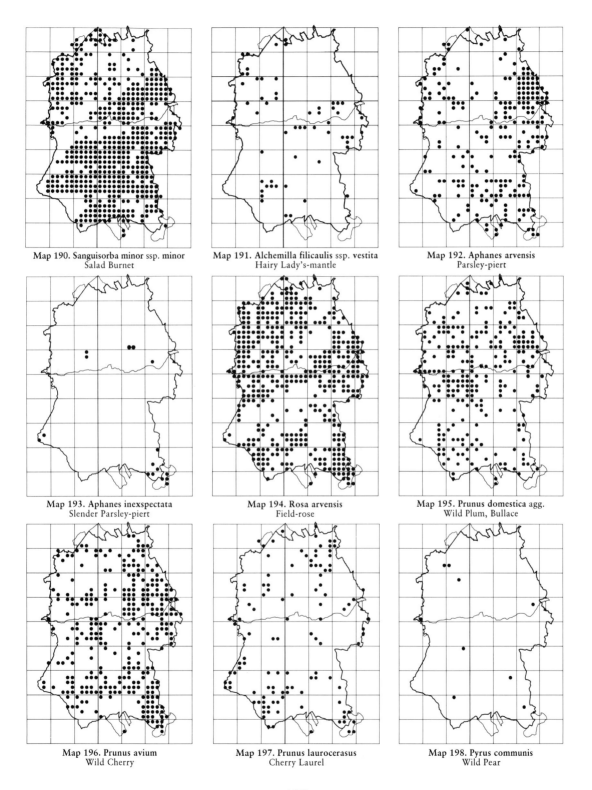

Map 190. Sanguisorba minor ssp. minor
Salad Burnet

Map 191. Alchemilla filicaulis ssp. vestita
Hairy Lady's-mantle

Map 192. Aphanes arvensis
Parsley-piert

Map 193. Aphanes inexspectata
Slender Parsley-piert

Map 194. Rosa arvensis
Field-rose

Map 195. Prunus domestica agg.
Wild Plum, Bullace

Map 196. Prunus avium
Wild Cherry

Map 197. Prunus laurocerasus
Cherry Laurel

Map 198. Pyrus communis
Wild Pear

Pyrus L.

Pyrus pyraster (L.) Burgsd.
Wild Pear

Native. The true occurrence of this tree is uncertain. Specimens at Avon, near Chippenham are probably this species 1983 DG.
10 km² 1 (2%)   1 km² 1 (<1%)

Pyrus communis L.
Pear

Introduction. Not commonly grown commercially in Wilts. A few records in hedges are probably relics of cultivation or vanished cottage gardens.
N. Near Avon Farm, Bremhill 1984 AC, Murhill House, Winsley 1985 JM, Hullavington 1989 MC-B, near Harrow Farm, Little Bedwyn JEO 1991.
S. Tucking Mill, Tisbury 1985 MM, old cottage garden Imber village 1986 JL, by track in arable area well away from buildings S of Boscombe Down 1987 PM and Tower Farm, Whiteparish 1988 DJW.
10 km² 9 (17%)   1 km² 9 (<1%)   Map 198, page 199

Malus Miller

Malus sylvestris (L.) Miller
Crab Apple

Native. Woods, hedges and railway banks. Probably well-distributed but, often being confused with *M. domestica*, the true abundance of neither species is known.

Malus domestica Borkh.
Apple

Introduction. Adjacent to railway lines and major roads where travellers have, for many years, discarded apple cores. Gradations between *M. domestica* and *M. sylvestris* prevent accuracy in assessing the distribution of either species. The figures below are combined totals for both species.
10 km² 51 (98%) 1 km² 796 (22%)   Map 199, page 203

Sorbus L.

Sorbus aucuparia L.
Rowan

Native and introduction. Open woodland and along woodland edges, usually occurring on acid soil.
N. Grose considered that this tree was non-native except possibly in Spye Park. To this can now be added sites at West Woods, Savernake Forest and woods near Seagry 1992 DG.
S. Well-known as a planted tree in suburban parks and gardens, also planted on the chalk. Bird-sown saplings establish themselves given the right growing conditions. Probably native in nine localities including Longleat, Great Bradley Wood, on the Somerset borders in the SW and New Forest.
10 km² 43 (83%) 1 km² 275 (8%)   Map 200, page 203

Sorbus intermedia (Ehrh.) Pers.
Swedish Whitebeam

Introduction. Frequently planted, increasingly so in recent years. Also self-sown.
N. A single tree at Kemble station MK & CK, a seedling at Bird's Marsh 1987 RR, a single tree on the old railway track at Marlborough 1989 VS, at Burderop hospital, NE Avebury, Monkton Down, two plantations at Gypsy Lane in Swindon, Brimble Hill, a seedling SE Lockeridge 1988-91 JEO and on railway sidings at Swindon 1991 JN.
S. Plantation Fore Hill SPTA(W) 1989 BG and common, recently planted SPTA(W) 1991 BGH.
10 km² 6 (12%)   1 km² 12 (<1%)

Sorbus aria (L.) Crantz
Common Whitebeam

Native. Woodlands, hedgerows, banks and cliffs on well-drained calcareous and acid soil.
N. Frequent on the chalk on parts of the Pewsey Downs, NE of Marlborough and on the chalk scarps notably on King's Play Hill. Frequent on the limestone in the By Brook valley downstream from Castle Combe and along the Bristol Avon valley. Occasional hedgerow bushes at Wraxhall.
S. Most frequent on chalk downs S of Salisbury Plain. Common with yew in the scrub on the slopes of Dean Hill where it was planted and is now self-sown. On sand around Nomansland on New Forest fringe.
10 km² 41 (79%) 1 km² 355 (10%) Map 201, page 203

Sorbus torminalis (L.) Crantz
Wild Service-tree

Native. Ancient woodland, boundaries and hedgerows on limestone and clay soils.
N. Good stands in some woods in the Braydon Forest area. Many colonies on clay in the valleys of the Bristol Avon and tributaries are small, some have 1-2 trees.
S. Concentration of records in Frome valley and nearby Brokerswood in W. Trees of varying ages, some well within woodland, showing some evidence of natural regeneration, Whiteparish Common 1986-89 PMW. Planted Blackmoor Copse 1990 IA, East Grimstead 1987 PAW.
Map shows only those trees considered to be native. See article on p.77.
10 km² 10 (19%) 1 km² 45 (1%) Map 202, page 203

Cotoneaster Medikus

Cotoneaster integrifolius (Roxb.) Klotz
Cotoneaster microphyllus auct. non Wallich ex Lindley
Small-leaved Cotoneaster

Introduction.

S. Lamb Down 1988 VH, Knook Horse Hill 1990 DG.
10 km² 2 (4%) 1 km² 2 (<1%)

Cotoneaster horizontalis Decne.
Wall Cotoneaster

Introduction.
N. Box Hill quarries 1984 DG, first VC7 record. Chalk pit Ogbourne St. George 1991 JEO.
S. Chalk cutting Heytesbury 1990 DG, near Amesbury 1990 ER and Fordswater 1991 AH.
10 km² 5 (10%) 1 km² 5 (<1%)

Cotoneaster simonsii Baker
Himalayan Cotoneaster

Introduction.
N. Spoilheap Box Hill quarries 1984 DG (conf. A L Grenfell). First VC7 record followed by Challenger's Grove 1984 JP. Road W of West Woods, seedlings SE of Lockeridge, W of Marlborough Common and Kingsbury Hill, Marlborough 1989-90 JEO, Burderop Hospital and chalk pit Ogbourne St. George 1989-91 JEO.
S. Lakeside Shear Water 1990 DG, two sites Plaitford Common N VC8 (Hants) 1986, 1991 RV.
10 km² 6 (12%) 1 km² 10 (<1%) Map 203, page 203

Crataegus L.

Crataegus monogyna Jacq.
Hawthorn

Native. Much used in the past for 'quick-set' hedges, planted during the Land Enclosure Acts of the 18th and 19th centuries. Very common, occurring throughout the county.
10 km² 52 (100%) 2 km² 914 (96%) Map 204, page 203

**Crataegus monogyna x C. laevigata =
C. x macrocarpa** Hegetschw.

Native. Occurs in many localities and in considerable numbers in the Braydon Forest area. DG considers this hybrid to be the commonest member of the genus in localised parts of the N of the county. Under-recorded.
10 km² 4 (8%)   1 km² 4 (<1%)

Crataegus laevigata (Poiret) DC.
Crataegus oxyacanthoides Thuill.
Midland Hawthorn

Native. Hedges and woodland on clay soils, including clay over limestone in NW. Hybridising freely with *C. monogyna* see above.
N. Occurs almost entirely on Oxford Clay, commonest in the Braydon Forest area at Ravensroost and Red Lodge Woods. Elsewhere at Malmesbury, Dauntsey, Hullavington, Luckington and Bincknoll. At Little Bowerhill Farm N of K & A Canal 1988 BG.
S. Ashton Common 1990 EC where it may have been planted.
10 km² 11 (21%) 1 km² 44 (1%)   Map 205, page 203

FABACEAE

Astragalus L.

Astragalus danicus Retz.
Purple Milk-vetch

Native. Unimproved short and rough chalk grassland. Plant reaches the southern end of its range in S Wilts.
S. Some of the sites are refinds. Isolated colony on rough grassland High Post Golf Course 1988 PM was first recorded 1928. All other sites are on SPTA(E) where the survival of the plant is likely to be secure due to lack of cultivation. Bourne Bottom 1984 ER, Beacon Hill 1984 AJS, Silk Hill Plantation 1987 ER. Alongside the Old

Marlborough Road, Figheldean Down and beside a track Bulford Field both on ground disturbed two years previously 1991 AJS.
10 km² 3 (6%) 1 km² 7 (<1%)

Astragalus glycyphyllos L.
Wild Liquorice

Native. Near hedges and borders of fields and woods.
N. Three very small colonies on limestone on the Cotswold escarpment: field boundary Turleigh 1986 JP, two at Murhill 1985-87 JM and beside lane from Slaughterford/Biddestone 1988 RR. Colony of 12 plants in a depression on the chalk scarp Bincknoll Castle 1986 DG, a refind of 1888 record (Preston).
S. Three records, all of known sites. Although Chickard Wood had been destroyed by 1985, two plants were found nearby 1988 VW. Plentiful along bridleway Lady Down, Chilmark 1984 DF, 'very striking patch' Hound Wood, Farley 1990 DPES, a refind of *c.*1932 record (B Welch).
10 km² 5 (10%)   1 km² 7 (<1%)

Onobrychis Miller

Onobrychis viciifolia Scop.
Sainfoin

Native or naturalised escape from cultivation on unimproved calcareous grassland. Localised to these habitats but often occurs in large numbers. There are two distinct forms in Wilts. A procumbent form which is considered to be native and an erect form with lighter coloured flowers, seemingly the strain that was introduced as a fodder plant from the continent around the middle of the 17th century. Widespread on SPTA. Abundant near West Down Plantation where it may once have been grown as a fodder crop 1992 BG. Form with creamy-yellow flowers, Upavon Hill 1986 KN.
10 km² 35 (67%) 1 km² 412 (11%)   Map 206, page 203

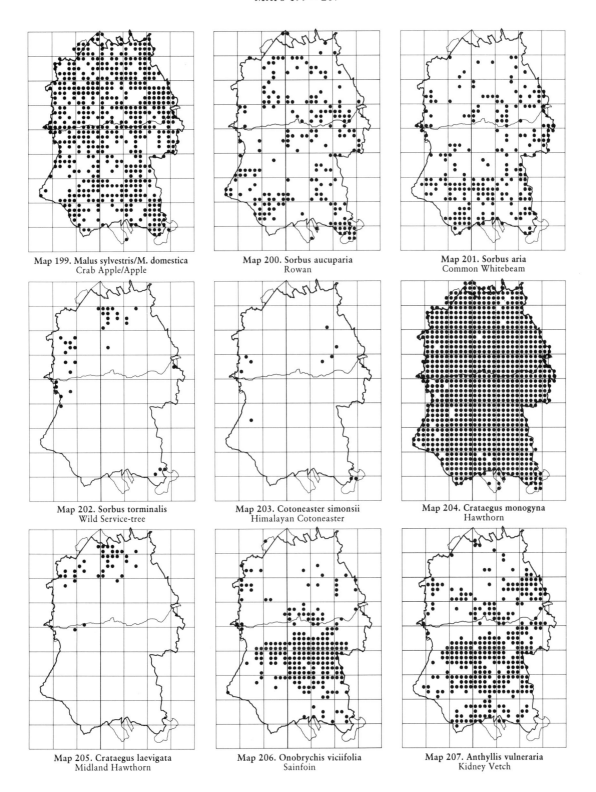

Map 199. *Malus sylvestris/M. domestica*
Crab Apple/Apple

Map 200. *Sorbus aucuparia*
Rowan

Map 201. *Sorbus aria*
Common Whitebeam

Map 202. *Sorbus torminalis*
Wild Service-tree

Map 203. *Cotoneaster simonsii*
Himalayan Cotoneaster

Map 204. *Crataegus monogyna*
Hawthorn

Map 205. *Crataegus laevigata*
Midland Hawthorn

Map 206. *Onobrychis viciifolia*
Sainfoin

Map 207. *Anthyllis vulneraria*
Kidney Vetch

Anthyllis L.

Anthyllis vulneraria L.
Kidney Vetch

Native. Frequent on unimproved chalk and limestone downland. Elsewhere restricted to habitats such as disused railway tracks and gravel workings.
10 km² 39 (75%) 2 km² 336 (36%) Map 207, page 203

Lotus L.

Lotus glaber Miller
Lotus tenuis Waldst. & Kit. ex Willd.
Narrow-leaved Bird's-foot-trefoil

Native. Hedgebanks and railway cuttings on neutral soils, scrambling over scrub. Only three known records.
N. The record by WM Stevenson in 1970 on a railway bank at Rodbourne was refound 1985 DG & RR. Kingston Lane, near Swindon 1990 JN.
S. Adjacent to disused railway line Newton Tony 1989 DOG.
10 km² 3 (6%)   1 km² 3 (<1%)

Lotus corniculatus L.
Common Bird's-foot-trefoil

Native. Common and widely-distributed in unimproved grassland.
10 km² 50 (96%) 2 km² 788 (83%)

Lotus pedunculatus Cav.
Lotus uliginosus Schk.
Greater Bird's-foot-trefoil

Native. A frequent species of marshes, ditches and wetland habitats. Occasionally found in unimproved damp pasture.
10 km² 41 (79%) 2 km² 291 (31%) Map 208, page 207

Ornithopus L.

Ornithopus perpusillus L.
Bird's-foot

Native. Free-draining acid soil.
N. Rabbit-grazed unimproved turf on sandy soil Spye Park, old sand pit near Freeth Farm, Compton Bassett 1985 DG, 1990 DB, short turf at the base of the Column, Savernake Forest 1985 JN, 1986 AJS.
S. Uncommon. Open, disturbed ground in clear-felled areas Hamptworth Estate, on sandy track sides Furzley, uncultivated area Landford tree nursery. First records for more than 30 years.
10 km² 5 (10%)   1 km² 11 (<1%)   Map 209, page 207

Hippocrepis L.

Hippocrepis comosa L.
Horseshoe Vetch

Native. Unimproved chalk and limestone grassland, bare soil on chalk road cuttings.
N. Restricted to the chalk escarpment N of the Vale of Pewsey, downland around Aldbourne and a few localities on the limestone near Box and Castle Combe.
S. Frequent. An indicator species of unimproved calcareous grassland which also has the ability to spread rapidly onto bare chalk as on a new road cutting on A303. The least common of the three yellow downland vetches (the others are *Anthyllis vulneraria* and *Lotus corniculatus*).
10 km² 35 (67%) 1 km² 435 (12%) Map 210, page 207

Securigera DC.

Securigera varia (L.) Lassen
Coronilla varia L.
Crown Vetch

Introduction.

N. Road verge near Hullavington 1985 JH. A large colony of long-standing on a protected road verge near Wootton Bassett.

S. A colony covering about 0.75 ha beside the railway line Newton Tony 1990 DOG. A303 road verge Magar 1990 RG.

10 km² 3 (6%)   1 km² 4 (<1%)

Vicia L.

Vicia cracca L.
Tufted Vetch

Rough grassland on road verges and woodland edges, often scrambling over low scrub. Common throughout the county.

10 km 2 49 (94%) 2 km² 709 (75%)

Vicia sylvatica L.
Wood Vetch

Native. Open areas in, and around the edges of woodlands, often in large numbers following coppicing. Very local.

N. Occurs in ancient woodland sites N and E of Marlborough: Rabley Wood 1984 CM, Foxbury Wood 1986 SK, Hursley Bottom in West Woods 1986 KP, Thicket Copse, East Croft Coppice, Savernake 1987 JN, Littlecote 1988 BP. A close grouping of locations on the limestone scarp overlooking the Bristol Avon valley: Inwood 1986 JP, Conkwell Grange Woods 1987 JM. Elsewhere, Silkwood 1987 HB, Great Wood, Grittenham 1990 DG, Clouts Wood 1990 PA.

S. On limestone in Slittems Wood 1986 JM, on Upper Greensand Stert near Devizes 1986 RF.

10 km² 10 (19%)   1 km² 13 (<1%)   Map 211, page 207

Vicia hirsuta (L.) Gray
Hairy Tare

Native. Roadside verges, embankments and woodland rides and clearings. Frequent but unevenly distributed.

10 km² 46 (88%) 2 km² 351 (37%)   Map 212, page 207

Vicia parviflora Cav.
Vicia tenuissima auct. non (M. Bieb.) Schinz & Thell.
Slender Tare

Nationally scarce plant.
Native in GB, introduction in Wilts.
N. One plant on dumped soil Shockerwick railway siding near Box 1983 DG.

10 km² 1 (2%)   1 km² 1 (<1%)

Vicia tetrasperma (L.) Schreber
Smooth Tare

Native. Open woodland, woodland edges, hedgerows, railway embankments and road verges. Often found scrambling over other vegetation in scrubby and overgrown areas. Most frequent on the heavy clays around Braydon Forest and in the SE.

10 km² 30 (58%) 1 km² 76 (2%)   Map 213, page 207

Vicia sepium L.
Bush Vetch

Native. Common on road verges, hedgebanks and in grassland with scrub.

10 km² 51 (98%)   2 km² 714 (75%)

Vicia sativa L.
Common Vetch

As the three subspecies were not separated for general recording, knowledge of their distribution is incomplete.
Ssp. **nigra** (L.) Ehrh.
Native. Heathland and sandy banks. Local.
N. In long grass beside ride Briary Wood 1984

JMP, Redstocks, Alderton, Alderton Grove and cornfield Rodbourne 1985-90 DG.
S. Rides in coniferous plantations Pitton Copse 1987 PW & MR.
Ssp. **segetalis** (Thuill.) Gaudin
Probable introduction. Grassy and rough places. Much more common than ssp. *nigra*.
Ssp. **sativa**
Fodder Vetch
Introduction. Formerly cultivated for fodder.
N. Edge of cornfield Rodbourne 1985 DG & RR.
10 km² 50 (96%) 1 km² 1168 (32%)

Vicia lutea L.
Yellow-vetch

Nationally scarce plant.
Native in GB, introduction in Wilts.
N. Scattered along 5 metres of road verge Wanborough Plain 1988 JN.
S. Site in quarry at Whiteparish now obliterated by landslip and chalk extraction 1984 RNC & NLC.
10 km² 2 (4%) 1 km² 2 (<1%)

Lathyrus L.

Lathyrus linifolius (Reichard) Bässler
var. **montanus** (Bernh.) Bässler
Lathyrus montanus Bernh.
Bitter-vetch

Native. Acidic to neutral woodland, heathland and neutral grassland.
N. Common in Braydon Forest, notably along rides in Ravensroost Wood and Somerford Common, in unimproved meadows and, as a woodland relic, in old hedgerows. The open, more acidic parts of Savernake Forest only support isolated colonies.
S. Heathy woodland, mainly in SE and Great Ridge Wood. 'A nice find' because infrequent, inconspicuous and colonies very small.
Var. **tenuifolius** (Roth) Garke
N. Rides in Ravensroost Wood 1987 JF & DG.

This form with very narrow leaves has been recorded in Wilts three times previously.
10 km² 15 (29%) 1 km² 62 (2%) Map 214, page 207

Lathyrus pratensis L.
Meadow Vetchling

Native. Rough unimproved grassland, roadside verges, railway cuttings and woodland rides. Common and widely-distributed.
10 km² 50 (96%) 2 km² 831 (88%)

Lathyrus tuberosus L.
Tuberous Pea

Introduction.
N. Several plants in hedge Hyde (Swindon) 1990 PD.
S. Well-established along railway Littleton Pannell 1988 BGH, two colonies on SPTA(C), one expanding in rough grassland and scrub Church Hill 1984 RF and one near Larkhill 1991 DGC.
10 km² 4 (8%) 1 km² 4 (<1%)

Lathyrus sylvestris L.
Narrow-leaved Everlasting-pea

Native. Scrub, copses, woodland tracks, rough ground.
N. Only appears to be native at one woodland site Silk Wood 1988 HB. Known for many years road verge Morgan's Hill. On waste ground near Swindon station 1989 JN.
S. A showy plant but no longer frequent in SE except in Cheyney's Wood 1985 and Battscroft Copse where a number of sites are close together 1988 DJW, large clumps Lady Down bridleway, an old site 1984 DF, Little Ridghams 1984 NLC, common in rough vegetation Urchfont 1984 RF, Odstock 1985 NLC & BKC, garden hedge bank Coombe Bissett 1986 CA, Hill Wood 1986 BGH, Great Ridge Wood 1989 CJH, 1991 CJH, DLH. Probably introduced on railway banks West Grimstead 1985 PH and Littleton Pannell 1989 BGH.
10 km² 8 (15%) 1 km² 18 (<1%) Map 215, page 207

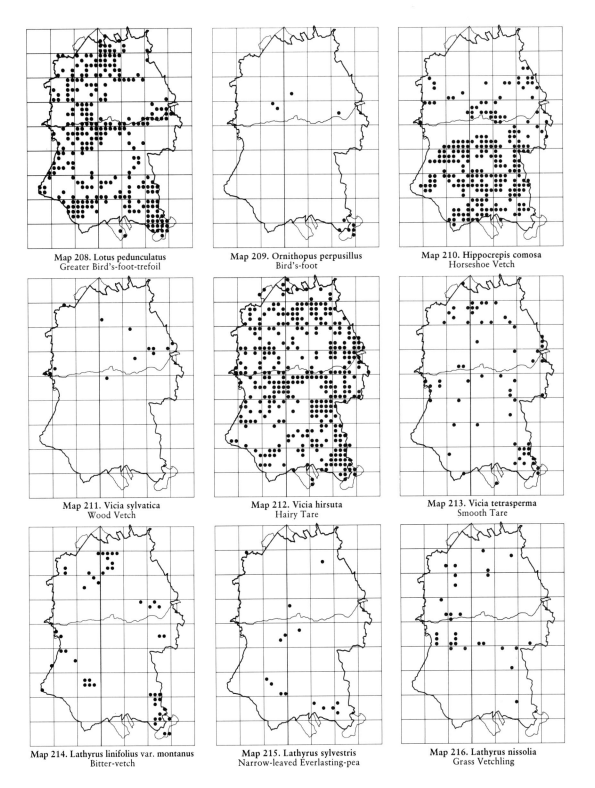

Map 208. *Lotus pedunculatus*
Greater Bird's-foot-trefoil

Map 209. *Ornithopus perpusillus*
Bird's-foot

Map 210. *Hippocrepis comosa*
Horseshoe Vetch

Map 211. *Vicia sylvatica*
Wood Vetch

Map 212. *Vicia hirsuta*
Hairy Tare

Map 213. *Vicia tetrasperma*
Smooth Tare

Map 214. *Lathyrus linifolius* var. *montanus*
Bitter-vetch

Map 215. *Lathyrus sylvestris*
Narrow-leaved Everlasting-pea

Map 216. *Lathyrus nissolia*
Grass Vetchling

Lathyrus latifolius L.
Broad-leaved Everlasting-pea

Introduction. Obviously planted in some locations. Means of introduction of others, far from present-day habitation, is puzzling.
N. This spectacular flowering pea recorded from M4 Motorway near Sutton Benger 1984 DG, Bradford-on-Avon 1985 (Mrs Bell), Murhill 1985 JM, Lidbrook and Colerne 1987-88 DG, railway cutting, dismantled railway and waste ground Swindon 1990-91 PD & JN, railway embankment Brinkworth and Barton Farm Estate 1991 JEO.
S. Large scrambling species sometimes on railway banks and thought to have been planted in gardens of huts belonging to railwaymen. Two records from disused railway line at Stert 1986 RF, 1989 JMP. Road verge Uppinton 1987 BL, waste grassland on Old Sarum 1988 PM, Steeple Ashton 1991 EC and a strong colony SPTA(C) W end of Netheravon Down 1991 BG.
10 km² 13 (25%) 1 km² 18 (<1%)

Lathyrus nissolia L.
Grass Vetchling

Native. Areas of tall, rank grass on railway banks, road-verges, green lanes and unmanaged chalk grassland. Grass-like stems and leaves blend in with surrounding vegetation. Almost impossible to see except when small, bright crimson flowers are in bloom. Some colonies have 1,000+ plants in a relatively small area.
N. Mostly on heavier clay. Railway cuttings: Pew Hill near Chippenham, Hullavington, Rodbourne and Bowerhill 1984-89 DG, Corsham Station 1988 BA and Stratton (Swindon) 1991 JN. M4 motorway cutting Draycott 1987 DG, green lanes Rowde Hill and Croft Farm, Rowde 1989 DG, steep bank Melksham 1990 JRo. Elsewhere, near Broughton Gifford 1983 JP, Derry Field Farm 1984-85 MWS, Clyffe Pypard 1989 DH and Wootton Bassett 1990 VS.
S. Wide range in plant numbers. Near Three

Crowns, Whaddon 1984 CMC, seen for several years Southwick Court Meadows 1984 MJ, Westbury Trading Estate 1984 EC, in vicinity of railway Dilton Marsh 1989 VEH. SPTA(W): clearing and wood edge Grant's Farm 1981 GP, near Imber 1986 JL, Tenantry Down 1986 NCC/ST, W of Grant's Wood and Thorncombe Farm 1988 BGH, side of track 1988 SF. N of SPTA(W) at Edington 1987 and Cowleaze Wood 1991 HW. SPTA(C): scattered near New Copse 1985 RF, West Down impact area 1989 GS, 100+ plants S of Lavington Folly DGC. SPTA(E): Bourne Bottom 1985 ER but not found 1986 when area was cattle grazed, single flowering plant at Windmill Hill Camp 1988 BG. Occurs along 300 metre strip of grassland Boscombe Down 1990 SMP.
10 km² 15 (29%) 1 km² 32 (<1%)   Map 216, page 207

Lathyrus aphaca L.
Yellow Vetchling

Nationally scarce plant.
Doubtfully native. Rough ground on road verges, tracks and arable fields.
N. Known for many years on WCC protected verge Wanborough Plain 1986 SC. Dismantled railway at nearby Chiseldon 1990 JEO and arable headland Woodborough Hill 1990 VS.
S. Further decline compared with records listed by Grose. Churchyard Chilmark 1987 DF, Littlecott 1987 JG, the remainder from rough grass at side of tracks Marden 1987 JMP, near Wick, Downton 1991 JO, PW & MR and Mere Down 1991 AH.
10 km² 8 (15%)   1 km² 8 (<1%)   Map 217, page 210

Ononis L.

Ononis spinosa L.
Spiny Restharrow

Native. Unimproved grassland and wide-verged green lanes on heavy lowland clays and both grazed and ungrazed calcareous grassland.
N. The species has disappeared from the NE

where it was once frequent due to agricultural intensification. A field at Redhouse on lowland near Melksham pink with abundance of flowers of this species 1988 DG.

S. Virtually confined to the chalk. An increase in records due to increased access to SPTA where it is frequent on SPTA(W). A feature of the grassland on Parsonage Down NNR in winter where the spiny remnants are the only ungrazed species. Map 218a shows Grose's records in *The Flora of Wiltshire* 1957 for comparison.

10 km² 25 (48%) 1 km² 98 (3%)   Map 218, page 210

Ononis repens L.
Common Restharrow

Native. Unimproved chalk, limestone and neutral grassland. Often frequent in these habitats. Increase in records probably due to better recording coverage in the county generally rather than a natural increase. Map 219a shows Grose's records in *The Flora of Wiltshire* 1957 for comparison.

10 km² 44 (85%) 1 km² 515 (14%)   Map 219, page 210

Melilotus Miller

Melilotus altissimus Thuill.
Tall Melilot

Introduction. Naturalised in disturbed and waste ground.

N. Occurs in great profusion on soil disturbed for roadworks, particularly on lighter soils.

S. Abundant on banks either side of tank tracks on SPTA creating yellow ribbons across the Plain in summer, turning black as seeds develop.

10 km² 37 (71%) 1 km² 400 (11%)   Map 220, page 210

Melilotus albus Medikus
White Melilot

Introduction. Confined to disturbed and cultivated ground, bare banks and road verges.

A declining species.

10 km² 12 (23%) 1 km² 23 (<1%)

Melilotus officinalis (L.) Lam.
Ribbed Melilot

Introduction. Disturbed ground. Occurs in same habitat as *M. altissimus* but is less common. Similarity of the two species has led to some mis-identification.

10 km² 40 (77%) 1 km² 335 (9%)   Map 221, page 210

Medicago L.

Medicago lupulina L.
Black Medick

Native. Common in grassland, on road verges and disturbed soil.

10 km² 51 (98%) 2 km² 825 (87%)

Medicago sativa L. ssp. varia (Martyn) Arcang.
M. x *varia* Martyn
Sand Lucerne

Native in GB, status in Wilts uncertain. Once considered a hybrid between the other two sspp. of *Medicago sativa*, ssp. *falcata* and ssp. *sativa*, arising naturally or introduced as seed.

S. Single plant on disturbed ground by A345 roadside near Salisbury Clumps, 1984 PM. First VC8 record.

Medicago sativa L. ssp. sativa
Lucerne

Introduction. A relic of cultivation. Field boundaries, road verges and rough grassland.

N. No longer grown as a crop. Naturalised, remaining in the same locality for many years but not spreading.

S. Continues to be grown as a crop in a few places. Widespread, in small numbers, on SPTA.

10 km² 31 (60%) 1 km² 117 (3%)   Map 222, page 210

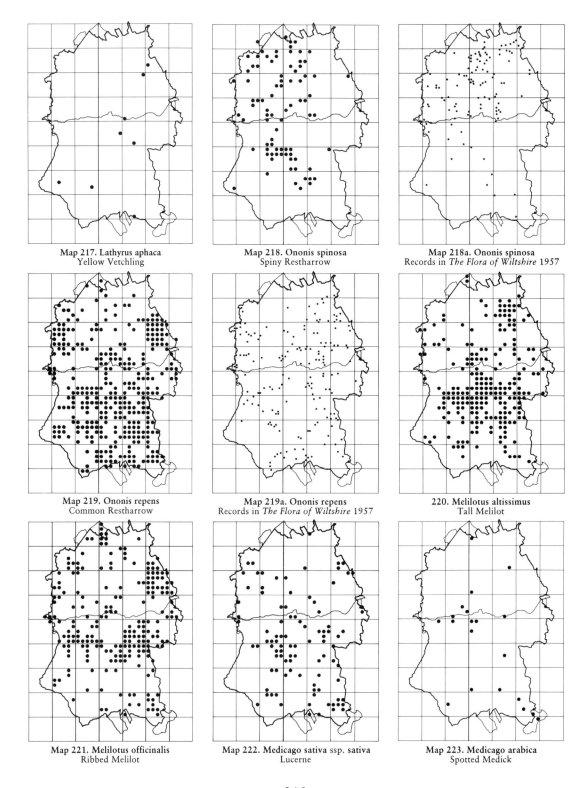

Map 217. Lathyrus aphaca
Yellow Vetchling

Map 218. Ononis spinosa
Spiny Restharrow

Map 218a. Ononis spinosa
Records in *The Flora of Wiltshire* 1957

Map 219. Ononis repens
Common Restharrow

Map 219a. Ononis repens
Records in *The Flora of Wiltshire* 1957

220. Melilotus altissimus
Tall Melilot

Map 221. Melilotus officinalis
Ribbed Melilot

Map 222. Medicago sativa ssp. sativa
Lucerne

Map 223. Medicago arabica
Spotted Medick

Medicago arabica (L.) Hudson
Spotted Medick

Native and introduction. Native on sandy soils. Readily introduced in imported soil, casual in waste places.
N. Distribution very local but regularly found on Lower Greensand at Rowde, Netherstreet and Bromham 1983-87 DG. Casual elsewhere.
S. Frequent by footpath and between graves quarry field and churchyard Hilperton EC. Bare ground in garden Market Lavington 1988 RF, common grazed grassland on steep bank S of Seend 1988 BG, Roundway Hospital 1989 BG, single plant track Lowdens Copse, Whiteparish 1988 DJW, 'clumps' recently-disturbed road verge Dinton 1989 SMP, roadside bank Donhead St Andrew 1990 JB, Seend and Stert 1990 JMP. Non-native: weed-covered bank beside track Larkhill SPTA(C) 1991 DGC and well-established in grass since 1982 The Butts, Salisbury 1984 PM with a 1962 record from this dump.
10 km² 14 (27%) 1 km² 22 (<1%)   Map 223, page 210

Trifolium L.

Trifolium ornithopodioides L.
Bird's-foot Clover

Nationally scarce plant.
Native. Sandy heathland. Unusual away from the coast.
S. Near ponds to W of Furzley village 1989 VAW & AB, near Bloodoaks and Mark's Farms W of Furzley 1991 RV, near Barford Farms, W of Furzley 1991 VAW, Bramshaw, Canada, Furzley, and West Wellow Commons 1991 VAW. First VC8 (Hants) records.
10 km² 1 (2%)   1 km² 7 (<1%)

Trifolium repens L.
White Clover

Native. Very common in all types of grassland,

frequently planted in grass mixtures to fix nitrogen in the soil.
10 km² 51 (98%) 2 km² 884 (89%)

Trifolium hybridum L.
Alsike Clover

Introduction. A relic of cultivation. Roadsides, field edges and waste places. Well-distributed throughout the county. Surviving well even though it is not sown nowadays.
10 km² 31 (60%) 1 km² 105 (3%)   Map 224, page 213

Trifolium fragiferum L.
Strawberry Clover

Native. Grassland.
N. Localised in low-lying, damp, neutral grassland mostly on heavy clay. Occasionally on dry, limestone pasture. Able to tolerate a limited amount of grassland improvement.
S. The distribution of this plant appears to be diminishing (*cf.* Grose) except in the area around Trowbridge.
10 km² 17 (33%) 1 km² 52 (1%)   Map 225, page 213

Trifolium campestre Schreber
Hop Trefoil

Native. Grassland, dry grassy banks, road verges and railway embankments where there is limited competition from other plants. This plant never occurs very abundantly. Most frequent on SPTA.
10 km² 50 (96%) 1 km² 615 (17%) Map 226, page 213

Trifolium dubium Sibth.
Lesser Trefoil

Native. A frequent species of waste ground and many types of grassland.
10 km² 49 (94%) 2 km² 529 (56%) Map 227, page 213

Trifolium micranthum Viv.
Slender Trefoil

Native. Closely cut and grazed turf, usually on sandy acid soils.

N. Very local, restricted to exposures of sand. On rabbit-grazed turf both at Freeth Farm, Compton Bassett 1985 DG and Little Frith, Savernake 1990 AJS, in sand pit Okus and sandy bank Princess Margaret Hospital, both in Swindon 1990 JN.

S. Two-thirds of records from SE: Brook Golf Course 1990 VW, Plaitford, Canada, West Wellow and Furzley Commons, Nomansland, Bramshaw area 1991 RV. Elsewhere, near Boyton 1987 BSBI meeting, Fordbrook near Pewsey 1987 JEO, lawn with short loose turf and thin top soil on chalk Wilton 1989 TCGR, churchyard lawns Steeple Langford and garden Berwick St James 1991 BL. Short mown turf edge of Laverstock Sports Club 1991 PM.

10 km² 8 (15%)   1 km² 22 (<1%)   Map 228, page 213

Trifolium pratense L.
Red Clover

Native. A constant species of most grassland. Often used in grass seed mixtures to improve the nitrogen content of the soil. Form with white flowers beside A345 N of High Post Hotel, Durnford 1984 PM.

10 km² 51 (98%)   2 km² 849 (89%)

Trifolium medium L.
Zigzag Clover

Native. Unimproved damp, rough, neutral and chalk grassland, open woodland, woodland rides, road and trackside verges and railway banks.

N. Frequent in undisturbed scrubby habitats. Railway cuttings at Luckington, open woodland rides in Somerford Common, throughout the Braydon Forest area and on the Midford Sands in the NW. Rarely on chalk downland.

S. Scattered in small numbers. Tracksides and woodland rides in Bentley Wood.

10 km² 27 (52%)   1 km² 84 (2%)   Map 229, page 213

Trifolium incarnatum L. ssp. incarnatum
Crimson Clover

Introduction. A relic of earlier cultivation as a fodder crop.

S. On edge of kale crop Marden 1988 JMP.

10 km² 1 (2%)   1 km² 1 (<1%)

Trifolium striatum L.
Knotted Clover

Native. Short grassland usually on sandy soil.

N. In a sandpit Sandridge 1989, sandpit Freeth Farm, Compton Bassett 1985 DG, short turf Okus (Swindon) 1986 DG & JN, limestone grassland Sherston 1984 DG.

S. Ironstone quarry Seend 1989 DG, edge of track Bentley Wood 1990 PMW.

10 km² 5 (10%)   1 km² 6 (<1%)   Map 230, page 213

Trifolium arvense L.
Hare's-foot Clover

Native. Bare and sandy acid soils, gravel and cinder-tracks of disused railway lines.

N. Old Minety railway station 1984 SW. Occurs on greensand Bowood 1988 JW & DH, Sandridge area 1989 DG and on sand at Okus (Swindon) 1990 DA.

S. Rare. In imported gravel on path Bentley Wood (two sites) 1984 PMW. Disturbed ground in contractor's yard Landford Wood 1987 PMW, wasteland Westbury Trading Estate 1984 EC, opposite lodge Donhead St Andrew 1984 ASk, frequent N side of wood Little Cheverell 1989 BGH, Windmill Hill 1989 AJS.

10 km² 10 (19%)   1 km² 14 (<1%)   Map 231, page 213

Trifolium subterraneum L.
Subterranean Clover

Native. Short turf.

S. Bramshaw 1991 RV, first VC8 (Hants) record.

10 km² 1 (2%)   1 km² 1 (<1%)

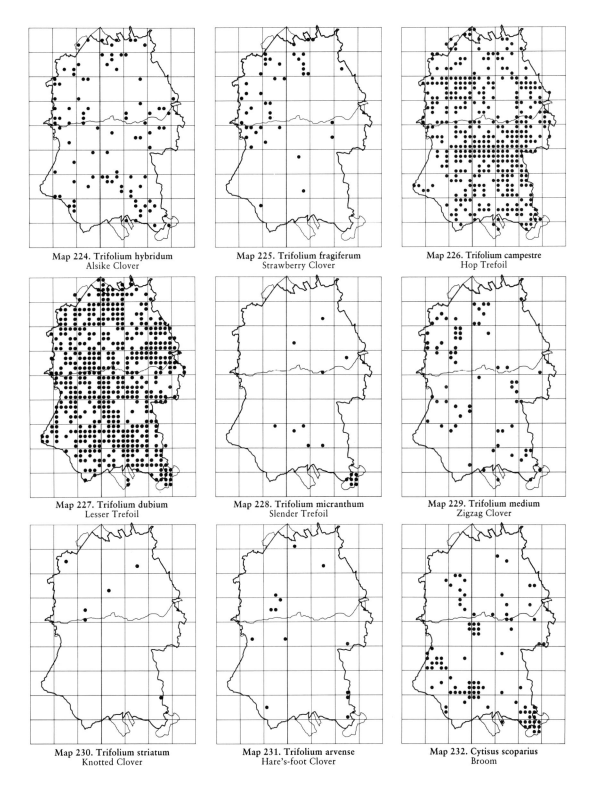

Map 224. Trifolium hybridum
Alsike Clover

Map 225. Trifolium fragiferum
Strawberry Clover

Map 226. Trifolium campestre
Hop Trefoil

Map 227. Trifolium dubium
Lesser Trefoil

Map 228. Trifolium micranthum
Slender Trefoil

Map 229. Trifolium medium
Zigzag Clover

Map 230. Trifolium striatum
Knotted Clover

Map 231. Trifolium arvense
Hare's-foot Clover

Map 232. Cytisus scoparius
Broom

Cytisus Desf.

Cytisus scoparius (L.) Link
Broom

Native. Woods, hedges and heathland scrub on acid soils.
N. Uncommon. Only found as occasional bushes. Most frequent on Lower Greensand on the scarp above Lacock and on Kimmeridge Clay stretching N to Sutton Benger where it is exposed in a cutting on the M4. Surprisingly infrequent at Savernake.
S. Locally common. A calcifuge, its main distribution following the geology. Upper Greensand in Warminster area, Nadder valley and Devizes/Lavington area, Clay-with-flints in Grovely Wood and Tertiary sands and clay in SE corner.
10 km² 29 (56%) 1 km² 131 (4%)   Map 232, page 213

Genista L.

Genista tinctoria L.
Dyer's Greenweed

Native. Chalk, limestone and neutral grassland.
N. Most frequent in unimproved, neutral meadows. Particularly abundant in the Braydon Forest area where it can colour the meadows yellow in July.
S. Grassy places, including superficial deposits on chalk. Very common in areas of SPTA(C), particularly in areas with a dense rabbit population to whom this species is unpalatable.
10 km² 27 (52%) 1 km² 136 (4%)   Map 233, page 217

Genista anglica L.
Petty Whin

Native. Sandy and peaty heathland.
S. Bog Furzely 1989 VW & AB, Furzley Common and West Wellow Common RV, Plaitford Common two sites AB & RV, woodland boundary of meadow Lord's Oak VW all 1991. First records for more than 30 years.
10 km² 1 (2%)   1 km² 5 (<1%)

Ulex L.

Ulex europaeus L.
Gorse

Native. Abundant on acid soils including leached chalk and the overlying Clay-with-flints superficials.
N. Odd bushes survive from the time before all the heaths in the Minety/Malmesbury/Draycot area were ploughed. Good colonies on leached tops of the chalk, around Savernake Forest and on the Lower Greensand at Spye Park.
S. Large colonies on the leached tops of the chalk especially on Salisbury Plain. Common on more acid soils in SW and SE. Formerly managed for fuel and as food for farm stock at a few sites.
10 km² 46 (88%) 1 km² 579 (16%)   Map 234, page 217

Ulex gallii Planchon
Western Gorse

Native. Heathy places. Rare.
S. Rides Hart Hill, Longleat Estate 1987 DG, abundant hillside Teffont 1991 VH, plantation Clarendon 1989 BKC, scattered along top of terrace near Wick Ball Camp 1991 VH.
10 km² 3 (6%)   1 km² 4 (<1%)   Map 235, page 217

Ulex minor Roth
Dwarf Gorse

Nationally scarce plant.
Native. Dry acid soil.
S. Confined to dry heathland, in quantity only in the New Forest at Cadnam, Furzley, Hamptworth, Plaitford and West Wellow Commons 1989-91 AB, RV & VW. Elsewhere, Stourton 1985 FR, 1991 PMW, Alderbury Common 1986 CMC, Bentley Wood 1988 PMW.
Var. longispinosis
N. Record for London Ride, Savernake Forest 1919, refound by Grose and in 1991 MH. The only known site.
10 km² 5 (10%) 1 km² 12 (<1%)   Map 236, page 217

ELAEAGNACEAE

Hippophae L.

Hippophae rhamnoides L.
Sea-buckthorn

Nationally scarce plant.
Native in GB, introduction in Wilts. Planted as an ornamental shrub in some larger towns. Vicarage Lane, Upavon 1985 PMWF & KP, near the church, Luckington 1988 HB.
10 km² 2 (4%)   1 km² 2 (<1%)

HALORAGACEAE

Myriophyllum L.

Myriophyllum aquaticum (Vell. Conc.) Verdc.
Parrot's-feather

Introduction.
N. New species for Wilts, found in a pond having acidic water Savernake Forest 1990 MH.
S. In new pond Odstock Hospital, Salisbury 1991 JO.
10 km² 2 (4%)   1 km² 2 (<1%)

Myriophyllum spicatum L.
Spiked Water-milfoil

Native. In static or slow-moving water.
N. Occurs in the majority of the gravel pits CWP, stretches of the Bristol Avon and K & A Canal, in dewponds Pewsey Downs NNR and ponds Swindon and Savernake.
S. R. Avon: upstream of West Chisenbury, N to near Scales Bridge 1985-90 PMWF, shallow water Wood Bridge 1988 DGC. Small quantity, chalk stream St Thomas's Bridge, Laverstock 1989 PM. R. Wylye: Ditchampton two sites, South Newton and Wylye 1989, 1990 BL.
10 km² 13 (25%) 1 km² 44 (1%)   Map 237, page 217

Myriophyllum alterniflorum DC.
Alternate Water-milfoil

Native.
S. Large amount in artificial lake Convent Bottom near Stourton 1991 PMW, first VC8 record.
10 km² 1 (2%)   1 km² 1 (<1%)

LYTHRACEAE

Lythrum L.

Lythrum salicaria L.
Purple-loosestrife

Native. Banks of rivers, streams, canals, ditches and ponds. Well-distributed, especially along the watercourses on the low-lying clay in the N and along the rivers Avon, Wylye and Nadder in the S.
10 km² 35 (67%) 1 km² 255 (7%)   Map 238, page 217

Lythrum portula (L.) D. Webb
Peplis portula L.
Water-purslane

Native. Acidic water bodies, damp woodland and rutted tracks.
N. In quantity only in Savernake Forest 1984-89 DG & AJS, very restricted in Spye Park, gravel pits near Lacock, Webb's Wood and Ravensroost Wood in Braydon Forest 1985-89 DG.
S. Wheel tracks in ride Compton Wood 1987 MDT, rides Hart Hill, Longleat 1987 DG and on muddy track in Loosehanger Copse 1989 DJW. A cluster of records in the extreme SE: infrequent on the edge of a pond Manor Farm, Plaitford 1990 PMW and ponds W of Furzley 1989 VW, Plaitford, West Wellow and Wellow Common, Penn Farm and Penn Common areas (Hants) 1991 RV.
10 km² 7 (13%)   1 km² 20 (<1%)   Map 239, page 217

THYMELAEACEAE

Daphne L.

Daphne mezereum L.
Mezereon

Nationally scarce plant.
Formerly considered native but status in Wilts is now questionable. The only remaining site of those noted in *The Flora of Wiltshire* is a wood near Ramsbury. The impenetrable state of the wood prevents an accurate count being made but the number of shrubs may exceed the 173 counted by Grose. A derelict cottage garden at the edge of the wood may have been the origin of the colony. Plants have been found in the last 30 years at Ford, West Woods, Roughmoor (near Swindon) and on dumped soil at Hullavington 1991 MC-B. All probably bird-sown and did not survive.
10 km² 2 (4%)   1 km² 2 (<1%)

Daphne laureola L.
Spurge-laurel

Native. Woodland and old hedges.
N. A significant shrub of older woodland in the limestone Cotswold valleys of the NW. Old hedges and deep green lanes in road cuttings. Scattered elsewhere.
S. Well-distributed but nowhere frequent. Absent from heavier clays. A long line of plants at the S edge of Hare Warren, Wilton may indicate an estate planting.
10 km² 36 (69%) 1 km² 104 (3%)   Map 240, page 217

ONAGRACEAE

Epilobium L.
The similarity of structure of several of the species and the tendency to hybridise, resulting in plants intermediate between their parents, makes this one of the most difficult genera for identification. *E. obscurum* and *E. roseum* were frequently

mis-identified during the WFMP. Therefore, distribution maps could not accurately be drawn and are omitted. *E. montanum*, *E. tetragonum*, *E. ciliatum* and *E. palustre* are considered to have been under-recorded.

Epilobium hirsutum L.
Great Willowherb

Native. Frequent and often abundant in damp habitats only.
10 km² 50 (96%) 2 km² 678 (71%)

Epilobium parviflorum Schreber
Hoary Willowherb

Native. A common component of marsh and streamside vegetation. Unknown in dry habitats.
10 km² 41 (79%) 2 km² 259 (27%)   Map 241, page 217

Epilobium montanum L.
Broad-leaved Willowherb

Native. Damp banks, wasteland and along the edges of woodland. Frequent and widely-distributed.
10 km² 49 (94%) 2 km² 515 (54%)   Map 242, page 220

Epilobium lanceolatum Sebast. & Mauri
Spear-leaved Willowherb

Nationally scarce plant.
Native status in Wilts is questionable. Wide variety of habitats. Rare and sparsely distributed.
N. Scrub and woodland edge Old Totterdown, Fyfield Down 1986 KP, woodland clearing Littlecote 1991 BL.
S. Garden weed West Grimstead 1987 IA (ver. AH), Harris Hill near Sutton Mandeville 1990 MM, waste ground Bonham and Fordswater near Stourton 1991 AH.
10 km² 5 (10%)   1 km² 5 (<1%)

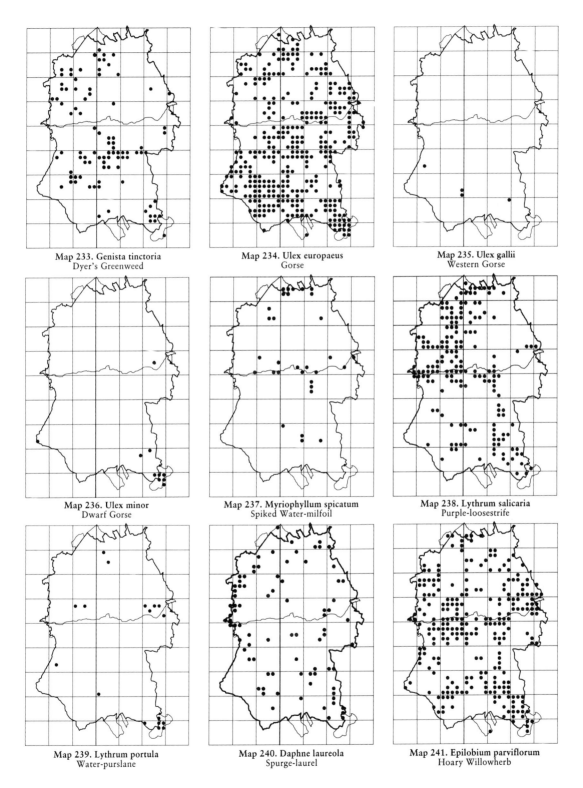

Map 233. Genista tinctoria
Dyer's Greenweed

Map 234. Ulex europaeus
Gorse

Map 235. Ulex gallii
Western Gorse

Map 236. Ulex minor
Dwarf Gorse

Map 237. Myriophyllum spicatum
Spiked Water-milfoil

Map 238. Lythrum salicaria
Purple-loosestrife

Map 239. Lythrum portula
Water-purslane

Map 240. Daphne laureola
Spurge-laurel

Map 241. Epilobium parviflorum
Hoary Willowherb

Epilobium tetragonum L.
Square-stalked Willowherb

Native. Ponds, marshes, ditches. Locally distributed in these habitats.
10 km² 37 (71%) 2 km² 121 (13%)   Map 243, page 220

Epilobium obscurum Schreber
Short-fruited Willowherb

Native. Due to mis-identification by recorders, the true distribution of this species is unknown.

Epilobium roseum Schreber
Pale Willowherb

Native. Due to mis-identification by recorders, the true distribution of this species is unknown.
N. The only positive record is from beside a track in Savernake Forest 1987 DG, JN & RR.

Epilobium ciliatum Raf.
American Willowherb

Introduction. Waste places, bare ground, railway tracks and disturbed areas in woodland. Distribution scattered and patchy.
10 km² 41 (79%) 1 km² 222 (6%)   Map 244, page 220

Epilobium palustre L.
Marsh Willowherb

Native. Localised to wet woodland and heathland, stream and pond fringes on acid soils. Uncommon habitats in the county except in the SE.
N. Abundant under alder in Spye Park 1985, pond Draycot Park 1986, near Stock Common, Savernake 1988 DG and Froxfield 1989 CM.
S. Of the records from the SE corner, which has the largest area of acid heathland, these two are typical: wet area at edge of wood Shearwood Copse 1989 and marshy area beside pond Lower

Pensworth 1989 DJW. Four records from scattered, localised sites: damp grassland Hook Copse 1990 MM, river bank water-meadow S of Heytesbury 1986 JWH, rare in fen Beechingstoke 1984 WTNC/ST and an atypical site on old railway line, Bemerton now destroyed 1985 JHi.
10 km² 10 (19%) 1 km² 18 (<1%)   Map 245, page 220

Chamerion (Raf.) Raf.

Chamerion angustifolium (L.) Holub
Chamaenerion angustifolium (L.) Scop.
Rosebay Willowherb

Native. Locally common on disturbed ground, roadsides and railway cuttings, often occurring in large stands.
10 km² 50 (96%) 2 km² 781 (82%)

Oenothera L.

Oenothera L. agg.
Evening-primrose

Introduction. Bare and disturbed ground, waste ground, railway sidings, sandy and imported soil. Scattered. Can persist and regenerate over a number of years. A critical genus for which few specimens were forwarded for verification. Some species are now grown experimentally as an oil-seed crop.
The following species may be expected to be found.
Oenothera glazioviana Micheli ex C. Martius
Oenothera erythrosepala Borbás
Large-flowered Evening-primrose
Oenothera fallax Renner
Intermediate Evening-primrose
Oenothera biennis L.
Common Evening-primrose
Oenothera cambrica Rostánski
Oenothera novae-scotiae auct. non Gates
Small-flowered Evening-primrose
Oenothera stricta Ledeb. ex Link
Fragrant Evening-primrose
10 km² 30 (58%) 1 km² 66 (2%)   Map 246, page 220

Circaea L.

Circaea lutetiana L.
Enchanter's-nightshade

Native. Common in woodland habitats.
10 km² 50 (96%) 2 km² 487 (51%) Map 247, page 220

CORNACEAE

Cornus L.

Cornus sanguinea L.
Dogwood

Native. A common component of hedges and woodland edges, especially in chalk and limestone areas. Widely-distributed throughout the county.
10 km² 51 (98%) 2 km² 700 (74%)

SANTALACEAE

Thesium L.

Thesium humifusum DC.
Bastard-toadflax

Nationally scarce plant.
Native. Unimproved chalk and limestone downland. Easily overlooked before the flowers open, especially where it occurs only sparsely. On downland where it is frequent, the mass of lime-green leaves stand out amongst the darker green foliage of the rest of the flora. A very large proportion of the country's population occurs in Wilts.
N. Two localities only on limestone: West Yatton Down 1983 DG & RR and Truckle Hill 1985 ASk both near Castle Combe. Main concentration on the downs N of Devizes at Oliver's Castle E to Knap Hill, including King's Play Hill, Cherhill/Calstone Downs, Tan, Milk and Walker's Hills. Two sites on E Marlborough Downs: Bailey and Marriage Hills.

S. More widespread and frequent. A speciality of unimproved downland on Salisbury Plain, between the rivers Wylye/Nadder and Nadder/Ebble and around Salisbury. Sites include Grovely Down and Great Cheverell Hill, both WTNC reserves. See article on p.79.
10 km² 23 (44%) 1 km² 96 (3%) Map 248, page 220

VISCACEAE

Viscum L.

Viscum album L.
Mistletoe

Native. Semi-parasitic on trees, most commonly apple and lime. Also on poplar, elm, willow and hawthorn. Very local.
10 km² 21 (40%) 1 km² 47 (1%) Map 249, page 220

CELASTRACEAE

Euonymus L.

Euonymus europaeus L.
Spindle

Native. Common. Hedges, woodland edges and scrub, more frequent on the chalk and limestone, usually in small numbers.
10 km² 50 (96%) 1 km² 953 (26%) Map 250, page 220

AQUIFOLIACEAE

Ilex L.

Ilex aquifolium L.
Holly

Native. Woods, hedges and scrub. Often planted. Attains tree stature only on acid soil where it is also most frequent in woodland and may form a dominant understorey as in the New Forest and

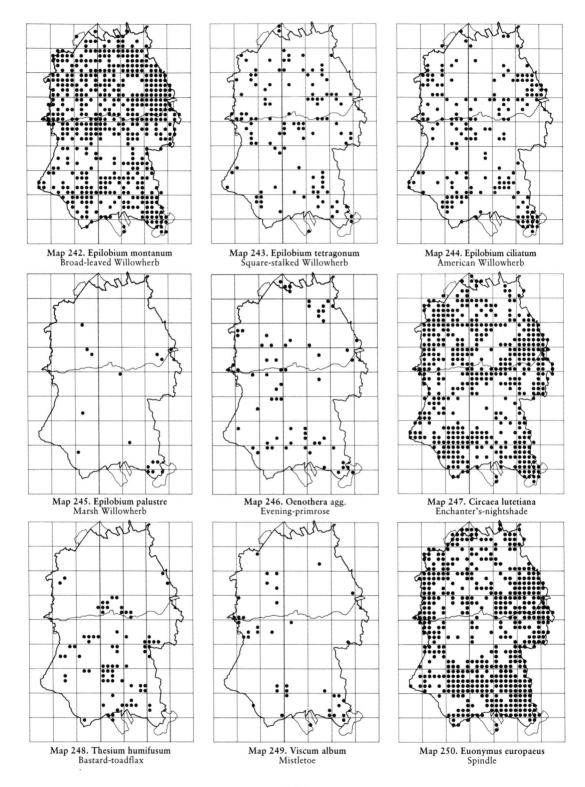

Map 242. Epilobium montanum
Broad-leaved Willowherb

Map 243. Epilobium tetragonum
Square-stalked Willowherb

Map 244. Epilobium ciliatum
American Willowherb

Map 245. Epilobium palustre
Marsh Willowherb

Map 246. Oenothera agg.
Evening-primrose

Map 247. Circaea lutetiana
Enchanter's-nightshade

Map 248. Thesium humifusum
Bastard-toadflax

Map 249. Viscum album
Mistletoe

Map 250. Euonymus europaeus
Spindle

Bird's Marsh, a woodland on acid soil N of Chippenham. Less common on the chalk.
10 km² 51 (98%) 1 km² 1383 (38%) Map 251, page 223

BUXACEAE

Buxus L.

Buxus sempervirens L.
Box

Native in GB, probable introduction in Wilts. Woods, churchyards, landscaped countryside on chalk and limestone. Well-distributed.
N. Large stands in some woods, old bushes shading out all ground flora and seedlings spreading on to open grassland at Roundway Hill.
S. Regenerating very successfully in some places. An old, large stand near Fonthill bears no resemblance to planted, clipped hedges.
10 km² 45 (87%) 1 km² 292 (8%) Map 252, page 223

EUPHORBIACEAE

Mercurialis L.

Mercurialis perennis L.
Dog's Mercury

Native. A frequent, often dominant herb layer species of ancient woodland, older secondary woodland and the base of old hedges. Widely-distributed.
10 km² 52 (100%) 2 km² 684 (72%) Map 253, page 223

Mercurialis annua L.
Annual Mercury

Possibly native. Cultivated and disturbed soil, including gardens. An increasing species.
N. Most frequent in W and around Highworth, rare on the chalk.
S. 'Common about Salisbury' (H Smith 1817),

still applies today.
10 km² 41 (79%) 1 km² 199 (5%) Map 254, page 223

Euphorbia L.

Euphorbia platyphyllos L.
Broad-leaved Spurge

Nationally scarce plant.
Native. A plant of arable land, decreasing nationally.
S. It is good to have six records: South Down, Ebbesborne Wake 1988 JEO, four colonies in wheatfields having one, six, ten and 15 plants on two farms near Damerham 1986-87 JO and several plants arable field edge Wedhampton 1986 RF.
10 km² 3 (6%) 1 km² 5 (<1%)

Euphorbia serrulata Thuill.
Upright Spurge

British Red Data Book species.
Native in GB, introduction in Wilts. Very rare plant sometimes grown in gardens where it is able to seed. Garden escape Lockeridge 1989 VS.
10 km² 1 (2%) 1 km² 1 (<1%)

Euphorbia helioscopia L.
Sun Spurge

Native. A common species of arable land. Frequent and widely-distributed.
10 km² 46 (88%) 2 km² 448 (47%) Map 255, page 223

Euphorbia lathyris L.
Caper Spurge

Possibly native. Disturbed soil. Weed in gardens and churchyards.
N. Increased in recent years, usually on disturbed ground not far from habitation surviving only a few years as the bare soil becomes stabilised. Thought to be native in ash woodland Warleigh Wood in Avon

just over the county border, known 150 years.
S. First recorded 1867 Clarendon where thought
to be native 1990 PM.
10 km² 16 (31%) 1 km² 35 (1%)

Euphorbia exigua L.
Dwarf Spurge

Introduction. Mainly on arable land, occurs on
disturbed soil SPTA(W&C). Widely-distributed in
corn fields on chalk and limestone. Rare elsewhere.
10 km² 41 (79%) 1 km² 303 (8%)   Map 256, page 223

Euphorbia peplus L.
Petty Spurge

Native. Arable land and other disturbed areas of
soil. Occurs throughout the county.
10 km² 45 (87%) 2 km² 333 (35%)   Map 257, page 223

Euphorbia esula x E. waldsteinii (Soják) R.-Smith = E. x pseudovirgata (Schur) Soó
Euphorbia x *uralensis* auct. non Fischer ex Link
Twiggy Spurge

Introduction. Its origin in places a considerable
distance from habitation is unknown. Spreads
vigorously once established.
N. Road verge bank near Blacklands now protected
by WWC known for 50 years, Mountain Bowyer
1985 JM, footpath near railway Staverton 1988 EC.
S. Embankment Barford Down 1984 NLC,
Bourne Bottom SPTA(E) 1987 ER.
10 km² 5 (10%)   1 km² 5 (<1%)

Euphorbia cyparissias L.
Cypress Spurge

Introduction. Possibly native in chalk grassland in
E Kent. Garden plant able to become a pernicious
weed.
S. Naturalised over areas of SPTA producing

large colonies. Recorded from Larkhill Ranges for
more than 40 years: Netheravon Down and Farm
Ridge 1984 LWh, Well Bottom 1985 DR, locally
common at three sites near Shrewton Folly and
near tank tracks at Honeydown Bottom 1986 BG
& AW, Summer Down 1986 RF. Bulford Range
E of Dumbell Copse AJS.
10 km² 4 (8%)   1 km² 9 (<1%)

Euphorbia amygdaloides L.
Wood Spurge

Native. A frequent and sometimes abundant
species of older woodland throughout the county.
10 km² 44 (85%) 2 km² 253 (27%) Map 258, page 223

RHAMNACEAE

Rhamnus L.

Rhamnus cathartica L.
Buckthorn

Native. Hedges, woods and scrub on calcareous
soils.
N. Shrub usually grows singly in hedges. Most
frequent on the Marlborough Downs.
S. Widespread on the chalk but in low numbers
on much of SPTA.
10 km² 47 (90%) 1 km² 742 (20%) Map 259, page 223

Frangula Miller

Frangula alnus Miller
Alder Buckthorn

Native. Hedgerows on damp, acid soils.
S. Widespread in the New Forest area but less
frequent further N. Recorded from the western
edge of the county at Great Bradley Wood, Black
Dog Woods, Hatts Farm and on the Hants/Wilts
border at Whitsbury Common.
10 km² 6 (12%)   1 km² 27 (<1%)   Map 260, page 226

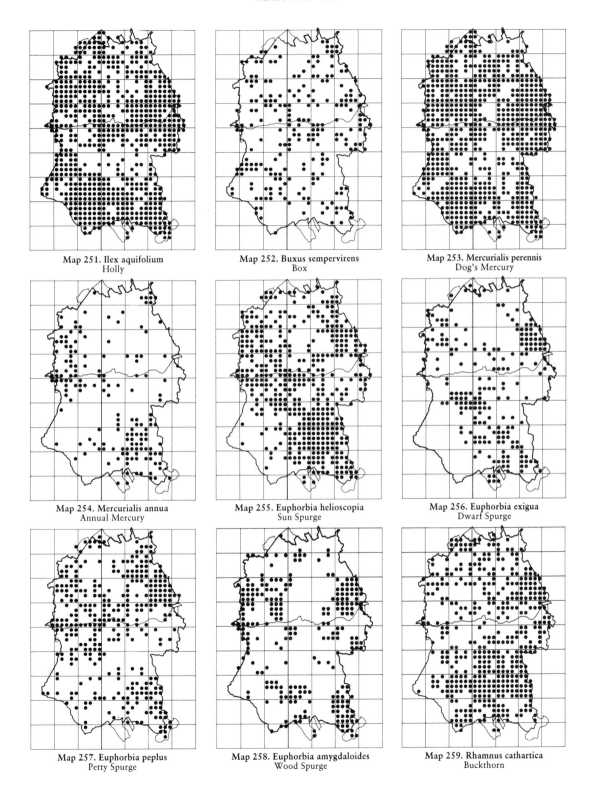

Map 251. Ilex aquifolium
Holly

Map 252. Buxus sempervirens
Box

Map 253. Mercurialis perennis
Dog's Mercury

Map 254. Mercurialis annua
Annual Mercury

Map 255. Euphorbia helioscopia
Sun Spurge

Map 256. Euphorbia exigua
Dwarf Spurge

Map 257. Euphorbia peplus
Petty Spurge

Map 258. Euphorbia amygdaloides
Wood Spurge

Map 259. Rhamnus cathartica
Buckthorn

LINACEAE

Linum L.

Linum bienne Miller
Pale Flax

Native. Rare casual. Difficult to separate from *L. usitatissimum*. Records accepted only from verified specimens.
N. Long Dean 1989 JH, first VC7 record since 1948.
S. Edge of track 1987 and *c.* 20 plants along 100 m stretch 1988 S of Beach's Barn SPTA(E) FP & SP, beside track Great Ridge Wood 1991 CJH & DLH. Records from Imber 1979 DG & RR not refound.
10 km² 4 (8%)   1 km² 4 (<1%)

Linum usitatissimum L.
Flax

Introduction. Planted as a crop in World War II. Almost unknown for a number of years but reintroduced as a crop in the 1980s and 1990s on calcareous soil.
S. Records for SPTA are the result of the war-time crops. Roadside verge Ashton Common 1991 EC.
10 km² 7 (13%)   1 km² 18 (<1%)

Linum catharticum L.
Fairy Flax

Native. One of the few annual species of unimproved chalk and limestone grassland. Less common in meadows on neutral soils.
10 km² 45 (87%) 2 km² 440 (46%)   Map 261, page 226

Radiola Hill

Radiola linoides Roth
Allseed

Native.

S. Furzley Common 1990 and in trodden turf on damp heath West Wellow Common 1991 RV. One plant on bare, raised access track Plaitford Common 1991 RPB. All Hants.
10 km² 1 (2%)   1 km² 3 (<1%)

POLYGALACEAE

Polygala L.

Polygala vulgaris L.
Common Milkwort

Native. Unimproved calcareous grassland, more common on chalk. Occasionally occurs in unimproved neutral ridge-and-furrow pasture and acidic grassland. Peak flowering period is three weeks later than that of *P. calcarea*.
10 km² 40 (77%) 1 km² 374 (10%)   Map 262, page 226

Polygala serpyllifolia Hose
Heath Milkwort

Native. Grassland and damp, open woodland on acid soils, heathland and clay superficials on the chalk.
N. Most frequent in Savernake Forest.
S. Most common on heathland and in woodland including Bentley Wood in the SE.
There may have been some mis-identification due to confusion with *P. vulgaris*.
10 km² 12 (23%) 1 km² 34 (<1%)

Polygala calcarea F. Schultz
Chalk Milkwort

Nationally scarce plant.
Native. Unimproved chalk and limestone downland.
N. Frequent on the chalk, particularly abundant on the S facing scarp of the Pewsey Downs. Rare on limestone, only occurring around Castle Combe.

S. A large proportion of GB's population occurs in S Wilts. One of the joys of short turf on unimproved chalk grassland. Expands onto bare chalk.

10 km² 31 (60%) 1 km² 409 (11%)   Map 263, page 226

HIPPOCASTANACEAE

Aesculus L.

Aesculus hippocastanum L.
Horse-chestnut

Introduction. Planted in parkland and roadsides and occurs as self-sown trees. Will grow quite well anywhere except on very acid or dry soil. Unevenly distributed, grey squirrels and members of the crow family sometimes acting as vectors aiding distribution.

10 km² 48 (92%) 1 km² 862 (24%)   Map 264, page 226

ACERACEAE

Acer L.

Acer platanoides L.
Norway Maple

Introduction. Abundantly planted. Self-sown in woodland and hedges. Introduced to GB *c.*1680. A decorative tree, growing well and self-sown, on chalk and acid soils. Not noted in Grose's *The Flora of Wiltshire* or in *The Supplement to the Flora of Wiltshire.*

10 km² 35 (67%) 1 km² 114 (3%)   Map 265, page 226

Acer campestre L.
Field Maple

Native. Locally common and widely-distributed in woodlands and hedges. Most frequently on nutrient-rich clay soils, often those overlying the chalk, and in association with ash in ancient woodlands. Common as a standard tree in woods in N, less common in S.

10 km² 51 (98%) 2 km² 788 (83%)   Map 266, page 226

Acer pseudoplatanus L.
Sycamore

Introduction. Common over much of the county. Has apparently increased in abundance since the demise of the elm. This species' ability to produce vast amounts of viable seed has made it an invasive threat to woodland.

10 km² 51 (98%) 2 km² 825 (87%)

OXALIDACEAE

Oxalis L.

Oxalis acetosella L.
Wood-sorrel

Native. In partial shade in dry woodland on acid soils.

Occurs in calcareous areas only on Clay-with-flints, rotting wood or amongst mosses on tree roots. Often localised in a wood in very small numbers. Carpetting the ground in parts of Savernake Forest.

10 km² 40 (77%) 1 km² 405 (11%)   Map 267, page 226

GERANIACEAE

Geranium L.

Geranium rotundifolium L.
Round-leaved Crane's-bill

Native. Dry banks, road verges, bases of walls. Frequent only in villages adjacent to the Bristol Avon in the W. Rare elsewhere, often occurring in small numbers but persisting in a locality for many years.

10 km² 18 (35%) 1 km² 42 (1%)   Map 268, page 226

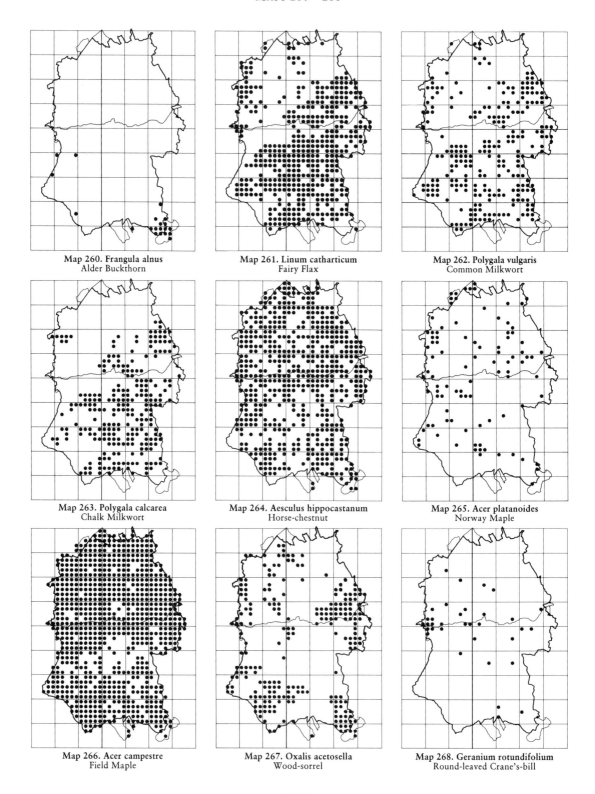

Map 260. **Frangula alnus**
Alder Buckthorn

Map 261. **Linum catharticum**
Fairy Flax

Map 262. **Polygala vulgaris**
Common Milkwort

Map 263. **Polygala calcarea**
Chalk Milkwort

Map 264. **Aesculus hippocastanum**
Horse-chestnut

Map 265. **Acer platanoides**
Norway Maple

Map 266. **Acer campestre**
Field Maple

Map 267. **Oxalis acetosella**
Wood-sorrel

Map 268. **Geranium rotundifolium**
Round-leaved Crane's-bill

Geranium sylvaticum L.
Wood Crane's-bill

Native in GB, introduction in Wilts.
S. Fisherton de la Mere 1990 BL.
10 km² 1 (2%)　　1 km² 1 (<1%)

Geranium pratense L.
Meadow Crane's-bill

Native. Road verges, rough and unimproved grassland in valley bottoms and on dry chalkland. Frequency on road verges reduced in last 25 years due to use of herbicides and unsympathetic cutting. Frequent in N and central Wilts but less common in S.
Form with petals having purple veins Gypsy Lane, Swindon 1990 JN.
Form with white flowers protected verge Lockeridge.
10 km² 46 (88%)　1 km² 1219 (33%)　Map 269, page 229

Geranium sanguineum L.
Bloody Crane's-bill

Native in GB, introduction in Wilts.
S. Waste ground near houses Stoford 1988 BL.
10 km² 1 (2%)　　1 km² 1 (<1%)

Geranium columbinum L.
Long-stalked Crane's-bill

Native. Bared areas of stony ground, thin soil and heavy grazing. Predominantly on chalk and limestone downland and arable land on chalk.
N. Restricted to many steep, eroded limestone downland areas and as a cornfield weed near Marlborough and Aldbourne.
S. Many records grouped along the SE county boundary. Increasingly recorded on set-aside land, Cholderton 1990 AJS.
10 km² 36 (69%)　1 km² 128 (4%)　　Map 270, page 229

Geranium dissectum L.
Cut-leaved Crane's-bill

Native. Locally common, especially on arable and waste land.
Form with white flowers, RAF Chilmark, Dinton 1987 SMP.
10 km² 50 (96%)　2 km² 810 (85%)

Geranium pyrenaicum Burman f.
Hedgerow Crane's-bill

Introduction. Road verges, hedgebanks and rough ground. 19th century botanists recorded it as scarce in the county but it now appears to be fully naturalised and is frequent.
10 km² 46 (88%)　1 km² 652 (18%)　Map 271, page 229

Geranium pusillum L.
Small-flowered Crane's-bill

Native. Cultivated land, tracks, road verges and grassland on sandy acid soil.
N. Garden weed Hullavington 1985 JH, Littlecote Estate 1985 BP, abundant on Lower Greensand Bromham area WFMP meeting 1986, Rowde 1987 DG.
S. Car park Warminster Station 1984 EB, Dilton Vale Farm, Westbury 1984 MG, rare on dry grassland by railway Beechingstoke 1984 WTNC/ ST, Rank Copse 1985 FP, disused road Landford 1986 PMW, edge of track near Semley 1987 JN/ BSBI, road bank Fiddington Common 1990 JMP, West Wellow Common (Hants) 1991 RV, tree nursery Chapmanslade 1991 BG.
10 km² 12 (23%)　1 km² 20 (<1%)　　Map 272, page 229

Geranium molle L.
Dove's-foot Crane's-bill

Native. A frequent component of the flora of disturbed soil. Also on chalk and limestone grassland.
10 km² 51 (98%)　2 km² 567 (60%)

Geranium lucidum L.
Shining Crane's-bill

Native. Stone walls, bare ground, tracks. Mainly on limestone.
N. Very common on walls on limestone in the W.
S. Distribution sporadic and local. Track edges on Clay-with-flints in Grovely Wood. Most frequent W of Warminster where it is frequent on roadside banks.
10 km² 35 (67%) 1 km² 230 (6%)   Map 273, page 229

Geranium robertianum L.
Herb-Robert

Native. Very common in many habitats including woodlands, road verges, railway embankments and stone walls.
10 km² 52 (100%)2 km² 865 (91%)

Erodium L'Hér.

Erodium cicutarium (L.) L'Hér.
Common Stork's-bill

Native. Tracks, cultivated land, sand pits and imported soil.
N. Mainly sandy soil. Most frequent on Lower Greensand between Rowde and Bremhill.
S. Predominantly on cultivated land and on bare soil. Its frequency on the chalk is unusual.
10 km² 28 (54%) 1 km² 100 (3%)   Map 274, page 229

BALSAMINACEAE

Impatiens L.

Impatiens capensis Meerb.
Orange Balsam

Introduction. River and stream banks. An increasing species nationally but not in Wilts.
N. Kingsdown 1986 ML, first VC7 record.

S. First recorded 1862 on R. Avon near Little Durnford and still present here. A group of records further downstream and on R. Nadder.
10 km² 3 (6%)   1 km² 23 (<1%)   Map 275, page 229

Impatiens parviflora DC.
Small Balsam

Introduction. Probably the only naturalised colony is in Belvedere Wood, Devizes 1984 BG from where it has spread to the adjacent cemetery 1985 PC. Introduction to churchyard Clyffe Pypard 1989 DH, in ditch beside lane between Wellow/Plaitford 1990 PMW.
10 km² 3 (6%)   1 km² 4 (<1%)

Impatiens glandulifera Royle
Indian Balsam

Introduction from Himalayas. River and stream banks, waste ground. Frequent in the Bristol Avon catchment area especially near the confluence of the R. Avon and R. Frome at Freshford on silt-covered banks that flood in winter. Well-distributed along R. Blackwater near Landford. Sometimes large stands.
10 km² 35 (67%) 1 km² 117 (3%)   Map 276, page 229

ARALIACEAE

Hedera L.

Hedera helix L.
Ivy

Native. A constant species of hedges and woodlands. Very common over most of the county.
10 km² 52 (100%) 2 km² 888 (94%)

APIACEAE

This large family contains several genera that are

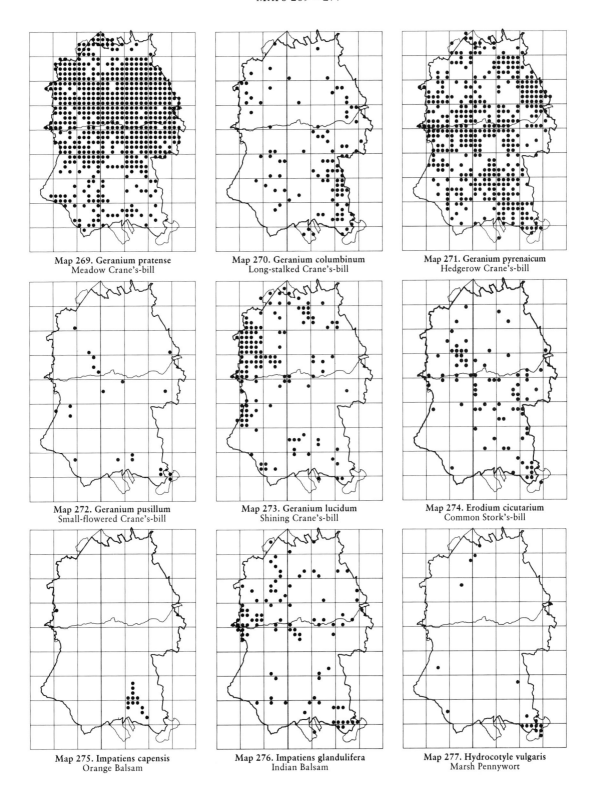

Map 269. **Geranium pratense**
Meadow Crane's-bill

Map 270. **Geranium columbinum**
Long-stalked Crane's-bill

Map 271. **Geranium pyrenaicum**
Hedgerow Crane's-bill

Map 272. **Geranium pusillum**
Small-flowered Crane's-bill

Map 273. **Geranium lucidum**
Shining Crane's-bill

Map 274. **Erodium cicutarium**
Common Stork's-bill

Map 275. **Impatiens capensis**
Orange Balsam

Map 276. **Impatiens glandulifera**
Indian Balsam

Map 277. **Hydrocotyle vulgaris**
Marsh Pennywort

superficially very similar in structure, the most critical being *Oenanthe*. Recorders were encouraged to use ripe fruits as an important key to identification and it is considered that the family as a whole was well-recorded during the WFMP.

Hydrocotyle L.

Hydrocotyle vulgaris L.
Marsh Pennywort

Native. Bogs, fens and unimproved water-meadows.
N. Unimproved grassland on the Thames flood plain, Pike Corner (CWP), water-meadow Chilton Foliat, pond edge Avon near Chippenham and Braydon Pond 1984-86 DG.
S. Most frequent in suitable habitats in the New Forest area. Isolated populations elsewhere, unimproved water-meadows near Porton 1987 JF, wet meadows Donhead St Mary 1987 PMW and Aucombe Marsh, Shear Water 1991 ER.
10 km^2 10 (19%) 1 km^2 24 (<1%)   Map 277, page 229

Sanicula L.

Sanicula europaea L.
Sanicle

Native. Ancient and the older secondary woodland. Most frequent in woods on calcareous soils.
10 km^2 44 (85%) 1 km^2 323 (9%)   Map 278, page 233

Chaerophyllum L.

Chaerophyllum temulum L.
Chaerophyllum temulentum L.
Rough Chervil

Native. Frequent and sometimes abundant, though

much less common than *Anthriscus sylvestris* with which it often grows, flowering some four weeks later.
10 km^2 48 (92%) 2 km^2 576 (61%)   Map 279, page 233

Anthriscus Pers.

Anthriscus sylvestris (L.) Hoffm.
Cow Parsley

Native. This is our commonest umbellifer and occurs in drifts along roadsides in May. Very common throughout the county.
10 km^2 52 (100%)2 km^2 889 (93%)

Anthriscus caucalis M. Bieb.
Bur Chervil

Native in GB, introduction in Wilts.
S. Hedgerow plant Coombe Bissett 1986 CA, garden weed Berwick St James, may have arrived in soil with plants brought from a garden in Isle of Sheppey 1987 BL.
10 km^2 2 (4%)   1 km^2 2 (<1%)

Scandix L.

Scandix pecten-veneris L.
Shepherd's-needle

Nationally scarce plant.
Possibly native.
N. Single plant in garden near Ramsbury 1991 SK.
10 km^2 1 (2%)   1 km^2 1 (<1%)

Smyrnium L.

Smyrnium olusatrum L.
Alexanders

Introduction.

N. A colony known for over 20 years along a right of way Lockeridge 1986 JEO.
10 km² 1 (2%)   1 km² 1 (<1%)

Conopodium Koch

Conopodium majus (Gouan) Loret
Pignut

Native. Frequent and widespread in woods and grassland.
10 km² 50 (96%) 2 km² 460 (48%)   Map 280, page 233

Pimpinella L.

Pimpinella major (L.) Hudson
Greater Burnet-saxifrage

Native. Hedgerows.
S. The only record was from Back and Jones' Lanes, Worton 1989 BK but was not confirmed.
10 km² 1 (2%)   1 km² 1 (<1%)

Pimpinella saxifraga L.
Burnet-saxifrage

Native. A frequent species of chalk and limestone downland and grassy banks on calcareous soil throughout the county. Occurs sparingly in unimproved meadows.
10 km² 47 (90%) 2 km² 506 (53%)   Map 281, page 233

Aegopodium L.

Aegopodium podagraria L.
Ground-elder

Introduction. A frequent species, always found near habitation or on rubbish dumps. A pernicious garden weed.
10 km² 50 (96%) 2 km² 642 (68%)

Berula Besser ex Koch

Berula erecta (Hudson) Cov.
Lesser Water-parsnip

Native. Most commonly in deep silt in rivers, streams, lakes, ponds, ditches and canals particularly those with a flow of lime-rich water.
N. Abundant in parts of the old Wilts/Berks canal between Chippenham and Swindon and frequent in ditches S of Lyneham. Elsewhere, occurs locally along most of the main river courses.
S. Two main localities, R. Avon N of Salisbury and E of Trowbridge extending into Vale of Pewsey. Rare elsewhere.
10 km² 24 (46%) 1 km² 74 (2%)   Map 282, page 233

Oenanthe L.

Oenanthe fistulosa L.
Tubular Water-dropwort

Native. Damp, unimproved neutral meadows, ditches and pond edges. Apparently able to withstand a fair amount of grassland 'improvement.'
N. Most common on the low-lying area of clay extending from Minety to Trowbridge.
S. More localised, most records from Nadder valley and Vale of Pewsey.
10 km² 14 (27%) 1 km² 31 (<1%)   Map 283, page 233

Oenanthe pimpinelloides L.
Corky-fruited Water-dropwort

Nationally scarce plant.
Native. Unimproved and semi-improved grassland on clay soils.
N. Single earlier record, Bewley Common 1958 (Grudgings). Twelve colonies found on intensively farmed land both along green lanes and in semi-improved grassland. The largest colony 200 plants, Melksham Without 1988 DG.
S. Two main locations. Around the 'Donheads' in SW and the New Forest in SE. Good-sized

population found West Grimstead in ungrazed pasture 1992 IA.

Possibly under-recorded, especially in situations where it flowers only irregularly. Further searching when species is in fruit could bring more records.

10 km² 6 (10%)   1 km² 13 (<1%)   Map 284, page 233

Oenanthe lachenalii C. Gmelin
Parsley Water-dropwort

Native. Damp unimproved neutral grassland, fens, gravel pits.

N. The records are from the upper Thames area where the plant was thought to have been destroyed by intensive agriculture and, in the CWP, by gravel extraction. Disused gravel workings have provided a suitable new habitat. Oaksey Moor and Derry Fields 1984 DG, in and adjacent to unimproved grassland Pike Corner (CWP) held thousands of plants 1985 DG. Flaxlands N of Wootton Bassett 1984 DG. One site outside this area Pond Farm, Charlton 1987 JF.

10 km² 3 (6%)   1 km² 4 (<1%)

Oenanthe crocata L.
Hemlock Water-dropwort

Native. A frequent and often abundant member of the semi-aquatic flora along the banks of rivers, streams and canals, especially where the water is lime-rich. Less frequent in pond and gravel pit habitats.

10 km² 43 (83%)   2 km² 327 (34%)   Map 285, page 233

Oenanthe fluviatilis (Bab.) Coleman
River Water-dropwort

Nationally scarce plant.
Native. Rivers and ditches.

N. The two tributaries of the Bristol Avon which flow through Sherston and Tetbury and on the river at Malmesbury PD, JEO & JW. Swill Brook, Ashton Keynes DG, R. Churn at North Meadow NNR, Cricklade KP.

S. In fast-flowing straight stretch of R. Wylye at Smallbrook meadows and submerged at Boreham Mill 1989 VEH. Edge of slow-flowing brook Upton Lovell 1988 JWH & KH, marshy ditch Charlton water-meadows 1990 BKC.

10 km² 5 (10%)   1 km² 10 (<1%)   Map 286, page 233

Oenanthe aquatica (L.) Poiret
Fine-leaved Water-dropwort

Native.
S. Edge of slow-flowing stream Upton Lovell 1988 JWH.

10 km² 1 (2%)   1 km² 1 (<1%)

Aethusa L.

Aethusa cynapium L.
Fool's Parsley

Native. Cultivated and waste land usually on light soils, but occurring on all soil types. Less frequent among cereal crops than formerly due to increased use of herbicides but still common on disturbed soil elsewhere.

10 km² 45 (87%)   1 km² 644 (18%)   Map 287, page 236

Foeniculum Miller

Foeniculum vulgare Miller
Fennel

Introduction. Garden escape, able to survive in a location for a long time.

N. Burderop Hospital 1985 and Mill Lane, Winterbourne Monkton 1990 JEO.

S. One specimen established since at least 1981 on grassy waste ground The Butts, Salisbury 1988 PM, on disturbed soil South Newton 1989 BL and large stand which had been sprayed Hinks Mill, Mere 1989 JHa.

10 km² 5 (10%)   1 km² 5 (<1%)

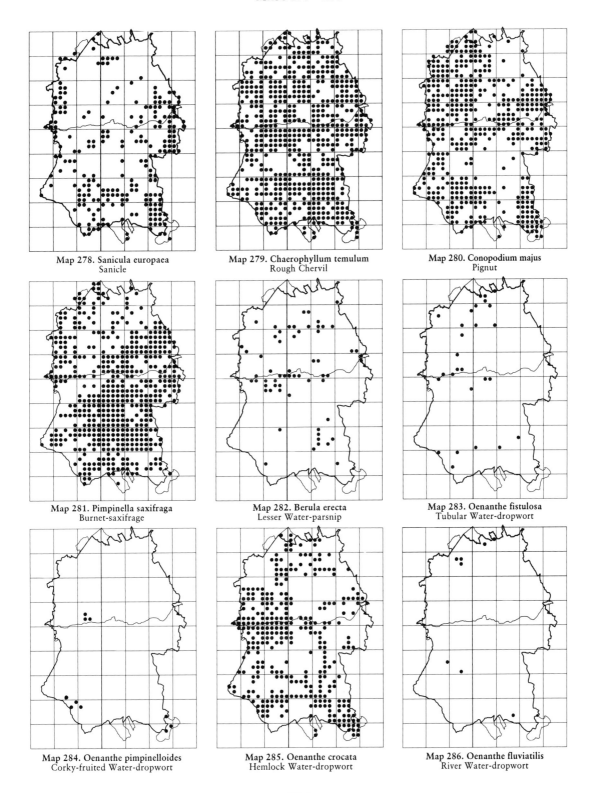

Map 278. Sanicula europaea
Sanicle

Map 279. Chaerophyllum temulum
Rough Chervil

Map 280. Conopodium majus
Pignut

Map 281. Pimpinella saxifraga
Burnet-saxifrage

Map 282. Berula erecta
Lesser Water-parsnip

Map 283. Oenanthe fistulosa
Tubular Water-dropwort

Map 284. Oenanthe pimpinelloides
Corky-fruited Water-dropwort

Map 285. Oenanthe crocata
Hemlock Water-dropwort

Map 286. Oenanthe fluviatilis
River Water-dropwort

Silaum Miller

Silaum silaus (L.) Schinz & Thell.
Pepper-saxifrage

Native. Low-lying, damp neutral and calcareous grasslands and road verges. Able to survive some agricultural 'improvement' of grassland.
N. Highest concentration stretches from Braydon Forest N to the county border including the CWP and stretches of the R. Thames. Good colonies in the By Brook valley and on lowland around Melksham.
S. Much less common than in the N, most frequent in SE corner of county.
10 km² 24 (46%) 1 km² 136 (4%)   Map 288, page 236

Conium L.

Conium maculatum L.
Hemlock

Native. A plant primarily of damp places. Streamsides, ditches, silt along river margins and also on waste land. Probably only native in damp areas but it has spread into man-made habitats including areas that have been enriched by feeding silage to cattle. Most frequent in the NW, less frequent on the chalk.
10 km² 45 (87%) 1 km² 627 (17%)   Map 289, page 236

Apium L.

Apium graveolens L.
Wild Celery

Native in Britain, introduction in Wilts. Damp places.
S. Road verge Norway Lane, Marston 1989 BK, one plant in a ditch, Marston 1990 BGH. There is a 1940 record from Marston confirmed by D Grose.
10 km² 1 (2%)   1 km² 2 (<1%)

Apium nodiflorum (L.) Lagasca
Fool's Water-cress

Native. A common species of running, lime-rich water. Occasionally in ponds.
10 km² 47 (90%) 2 km² 417 (44%)   Map 290, page 236

Apium inundatum (L.) Reichb. f.
Lesser Marshwort

Native. Static and slow-moving water and in mud on acid soils.
N. Refind of Grose's (undated) record in pond Durley 1986 AJS.
S. Wet ditch in meadow East Grimstead 1984 PAW, Standlynch Mill, R. Avon 1984 BKC & NLC, Quar Hill Plantation 1989 and Tinneys Plantation 1991 DJW, both near Hamptworth.
10 km² 4 (8%)   1 km² 5 (<1%)

Petroselinum Hill

Petroselinum segetum (L.) Koch
Corn Parsley

Native. Arable land and waste ground.
N. Rare. Ephemeral in a location. Garden weed Winsley 1983 JP, arable field margins near Hullavington 1985 DG, near Kemble airfield 1985 MK & CK, S of Highworth 1987 MWS and Somerford Keynes RR.
S. Main distribution around Salisbury area: allotments The Butts, Salisbury and Salterton Farm 1984 PM, Great Durnford and Figsbury Ring 1985 PM, South Allenford 1986 JO, Coombe Bissett 1986 CA, near Cherry Lodge Farm, Shrewton 1986 BG, Roman Road NE of Idmiston 1988 OS, three sites Odstock Hospital 1988 JO, PW, including 20+ plants in 10 x 5 m patch 1991 JO, Burcombe Without and Ugford 1989 MDT, Faulston 1991 PW. Elsewhere, on verge where hedge and bank had been removed Stert 1990 JMP, on canal bank Widbrook near Bradford-on-Avon 1990 GY.
10 km² 14 (27%) 1 km² 21 (<1%)   Map 291, page 236

Sison L.

Sison amomum L.
Stone Parsley

Native. Road verges, green lanes, edges of woodland, scrub and fields. Most frequent on heavy clay especially railway banks and headlands on arable land. Rare on the chalk.
10 km² 23 (44%) 1 km² 144 (4%)   Map 292, page 236

Carum L.

Carum carvi L.
Caraway

Introduction. Weed introduced with bird-seed and found in the wild as a garden escape due to increasing use of herbs in oriental-type cooking.
N. Near Swindon station 1989 JN, edge of cultivated field near Eastridge Farm 1986 SK.
S. Pavement in Trowbridge 1989 EC.
10 km² 3 (6%)   1 km² 3 (<1%)

Angelica L.

Angelica sylvestris L.
Wild Angelica

Native. Frequent and widely-distributed along stream and river banks, on marshy land, damp road verges and in woodland. Uncommon on the chalk.
10 km² 49 (94%) 2 km² 536 (56%) Map 293, page 236

Pastinaca L.

Pastinaca sativa L.
Wild Parsnip

Native. Frequent and often abundant species of chalk in S of county. A coloniser of new road embankments and disturbed soil. Uncommon elsewhere.
10 km² 41 (79%) 2 km² 350 (37%) Map 294, page 236

Heracleum L.

Heracleum sphondylium L. ssp. sphondylium
Hogweed

Native. Very common, particularly along road verges.
Var. **angustifolium** Huds.
N. Roadside Spye Park 1985 DG, Lockeridge 1986 and edge of bridle path East Kennet 1990 JEO.
S. Centre of track Pertwood Wood, Chicklade 1987 VW & RW, roadside verge S of Pitton village 1987 VW and Hindon Terraces 1988 JH. Probably under-recorded.
Ssp. **sibiricum** (L.) Simonkai
Native.
S. One plant in centre of track Pertwood Wood, Chicklade 1987 VW & RW, (ver. AH), first county record.
Useful for identification to have the two subspecies and the variety growing together.
10 km² 52 (100%) 2 km² 902 (95%)

Heracleum mantegazzianum Sommier & Levier
Giant Hogweed

A spectacular plant introduced from Russia in the 19th century to gardens on large estates. Apparently spreading by copius viable seed, taking 4-5 years to flower on stems 4 m high. A poisonous and potentially invasive species now banned from importation to GB.
10 km² 13 (25%) 1 km² 20 (<1%)   Map 295, page 236

Torilis Adans.

Torilis japonica (Houtt.) DC.
Upright Hedge-parsley

Native. Frequent and widely-distributed in hedges, scrub and on road verges.
10 km² 51 (98%) 2 km² 598 (63%)

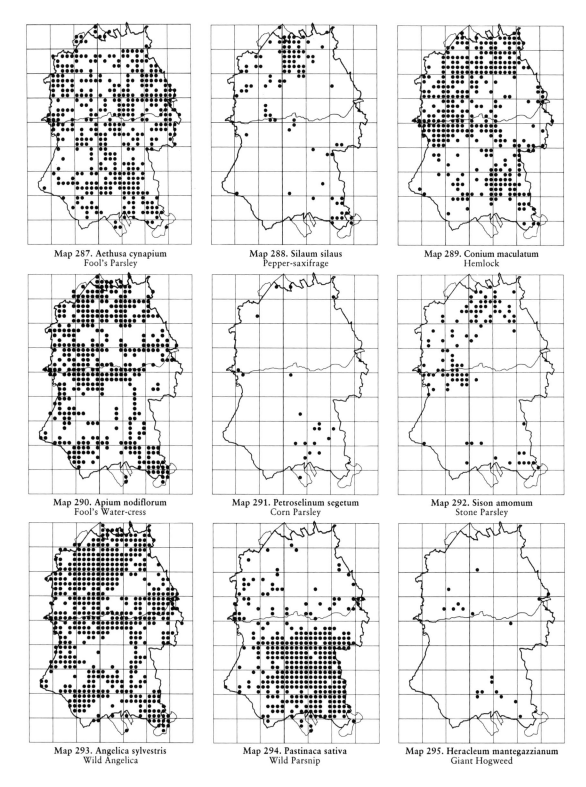

Map 287. **Aethusa cynapium**
Fool's Parsley

Map 288. **Silaum silaus**
Pepper-saxifrage

Map 289. **Conium maculatum**
Hemlock

Map 290. **Apium nodiflorum**
Fool's Water-cress

Map 291. **Petroselinum segetum**
Corn Parsley

Map 292. **Sison amomum**
Stone Parsley

Map 293. **Angelica sylvestris**
Wild Angelica

Map 294. **Pastinaca sativa**
Wild Parsnip

Map 295. **Heracleum mantegazzianum**
Giant Hogweed

Torilis arvensis (Hudson) Link
Spreading Hedge-parsley

Nationally scarce plant.
Probable introduction. Arable weed, once widespread.
S. Steep roadside bank at Bratton 1990 PS. Found by J Swanborough 1972 and has been observed regularly since. The bank is a WCC protected verge. Coombe Bissett 1986 CA.
10 km² 2 (4%)   1 km² 2 (<1%)

Torilis nodosa (L.) Gaertner
Knotted Hedge-parsley

Native. Bare ground and dry banks. Surprisingly few records.
N. Gateway to Tacklemore Wood near Lacock 1985 JMP, Townsend Farm, Horton 1991 PW.
S. Water-meadow Harnham 1991 DJW.
10 km² 3 (6%)   1 km² 3 (<1%)

Daucus L.

Daucus carota L. spp. **carota**
Wild Carrot

Native. Frequent but mainly in habitats on calcareous soils. A constant species of most unimproved chalk and limestone grassland but not in any great quantity. Abundant on disturbed chalk, e.g. SPTA(C) and area of Morgan's Hill that was ploughed in 1960s.
10 km² 46 (88%) 2 km² 544 (57%)   Map 296, page 241

GENTIANACEAE

Centaurium Hill

Centaurium erythraea Rafn
Common Centaury

Native. A common species of chalk and limestone

downland, woodland tracks on heavy clay and acidic sand and gravel. Elsewhere, very localised.
10 km² 46 (88%) 2 km² 256 (27%)   Map 297, page 241

Centaurium pulchellum (Sw.) Druce
Lesser Centaury

Native. Open woodland rides and marshy areas on damp clay.
N. Hussey Hill Wood, Thickwood and Colerne, all in the By Brook valley 1984-89 DG. On track CWP 1986 SCH, damp ground near Thingley 1989 DG, few plants on ride Ravensroost Wood 1990 JW.
10 km² 3 (6%)   1 km² 6 (<1%)

Blackstonia Hudson

Blackstonia perfoliata (L.) Hudson
Yellow-wort

Native. Unimproved chalk and limestone grassland, often on bare, stony ground within these habitats and on railway cuttings on calcareous outcrops.
N. Abundant in some areas in the Cotswold valleys around Castle Combe and on the thin chalk soil on the W-facing scarp N of Devizes. Rare on the Pewsey Downs and almost unknown on the main Marlborough Downs.
S. Most frequent on SPTA(W) where soil has been scraped to make banks on which hedges have been planted for military training.
10 km² 23 (44%) 1 km² 113 (3%)   Map 298, page 241

Gentianella Moench

Gentianella amarella (L.) Boerner
Autumn Gentian

Native. Unimproved chalk and limestone grassland.
N. Large colonies on chalk and limestone. Most

frequent on Pewsey Downs, on the Marlborough Downs around Aldbourne and around Box/Castle Combe. One colony on compacted river gravel in the CWP.

S. Sometimes hundreds of plants in a colony on chalk downland. Very common on SPTA, spreading by seed on bare, shallow chalk soil. More likely to behave as a biennial than an annual in grassland. Form with white flowers, New Copse SPTA(C) 1986 RF, Wylye Down 1987 BL.

10 km² 37 (71%) 1 km² 372 (10%) Map 299, page 241

Gentianella anglica (Pugsley) E. Warb.
ssp. **anglica**
Early Gentian

Nationally scarce plant.

Native. Endemic, restricted to chalk and limestone soils in S & SW England. Only on chalk in Wilts occurring on short unimproved turf and nearly always scattered.

N. Tan, Milk and Walker's Hills on Pewsey Downs NNR 1983 DG & RR. Downland near Aldbourne 1985 JN, a welcome new record.

S. Number at Parsonage Down NNR greatly reduced since 1981 BG. N-facing slopes include Marleycombe Hill near Bowerchalke. Long-known records from Wylye Down NNR and Great Cheverell Hill. Other sites include above Chetcombe Bottom, Cold Kitchen Hill, SPTA(C) where it occurs on dry ditches and banks, short turf and shell craters on Chirton, Wilsford, Charlton and Great Fore Downs and near New Copse.

10 km² 11 (21%) 1 km² 22 (<1%) Map 300, page 241

APOCYNACEAE

Vinca L.

Vinca minor L.
Lesser Periwinkle

Introduction. Always planted or a throw-out.

Naturalised in woodland, road and hedgebanks often near houses. Is sometimes dominant in limited areas.

10 km² 35 (67%) 1 km² 89 (2%)

Vinca major L.
Greater Periwinkle

Introduction. Always planted or a throw-out. Naturalised in woodland and road banks. Appears to be most frequent around Swindon, elsewhere sparsely distributed.

10 km² 34 (65%) 1 km² 109 (3%)

SOLANACEAE

Lycium L.

Lycium barbarum L.
Duke of Argyll's Teaplant

Introduction. Planted in hedges in villages. Large, long hedge Codford St Mary known for 30 years. Some plants have become naturalised along woodland edges. Similar to *L. chinense* with which this plant may have been confused. Distribution of both species is not fully known.

10 km² 14 (27%) 1 km² 22 (<1%)

Atropa L.

Atropa belladonna L.
Deadly Nightshade

Native. Open grassland, woodland edges, road verges, waste ground and disturbed soil.

N. Distribution very localised but the plant persists in some localities. Large colony in pasture and adjacent woodland Widdenham near Box 1980 BANHS, refound 1986. Road verge near Conkwell Grange 1984 and single plant on new road embankment Lacock 1988 DG.

S. Some records are of refinds and examples of

persistence. Near Clarendon Palace (1888 J Hussey) 1984 PM, Dean Hill 1985 MD, waste ground Stoford 1988 BL, four sites on chalk downland Porton Range, two of these on rabbit warrens 1989 OS, on disturbed soil Cockey Down 1990 PM, several plants Shrub Down 1990 JM.

10 km² 10 (19%) 1 km² 14 (<1%)   Map 301, page 241

Hyoscyamus L.

Hyoscyamus niger L.
Henbane

Nationally scarce plant.
Native. Cultivated land. Ephemeral, usually occurring only once in a locality.
N. Field beside footpath Latton church 1989 KG. Appeared in beet crop Castle Combe 1992 EO.
S. Garden weed Trowbridge 1985 EC, edge of field of barley Coombe Bissett Down 1989 JA, on disturbed ground on Esso pipeline S. Tidworth 1987 AJS.

10 km² 5 (10%)   1 km² 5 (<1%)

Solanum L.

Solanum nigrum L.
Black Nightshade

Native. Cultivated and waste land on clay and sandy soils.
N. Abundant on Lower Greensand at Bromham. Often in potato crops on heavier soil. Local in its distribution.
S. Frequent on clay E of Trowbridge, on Upper Greensand in Vale of Pewsey and on Tertiary clay and sand in SE corner of county.

10 km² 43 (83%) 1 km² 271 (7%)   Map 302, page 241

Solanum sarachoides Sendtner
Green Nightshade

Introduction. Known to have grown in abundance in market gardens at Bromham since first found 1964 PC, refound 1986 DG & RR. A few plants on dumped soil Naish Hill near Spye Park 1990 DG.

10 km² 1 (2%) 1 km² 2 (<1%)

Solanum dulcamara L.
Bittersweet

Native. More common in damp than dry rank vegetation, where it scrambles over scrub. A semi-aquatic form grows in ponds and ditches. Common throughout most of the county.

10 km² 52 (100%)2 km² 800 (84%)

Datura L.

Datura stramonium L.
Thorn-apple

Introduction. An ephemeral species of waste and disturbed ground.
N. Appeared in garden flower-bed, Witcha Cottage, Whittonditch near Ramsbury 1989 SK.
S. Disturbed ground Fittleton 1986 DSp, garden near East Combe Wood 1984 comm. B Fergusson, on site of old Carter Barracks, Bulford 1987 AJS, appeared after garden rotavated Imber Road, Warminster 1989 AS, bank of R. Bourne Newton Tony 1990 DOG.

10 km² 5 (10%)   1 km² 5 (<1%)

CONVOLVULACEAE

Convolvulus L.

Convolvulus arvensis L.
Field Bindweed

Native. Cultivated land and waste ground. Common and widely-distributed.

10 km² 51 (98%) 2 km² 826 (87%)

Calystegia R. Br.

Calystegia sepium (L.) R. Br.
Hedge Bindweed

Native. Hedges, ditches, waste ground. Common throughout most of the county.
10 km² 50 (96%) 2 km² 703 (74%)

Calystegia pulchra Brummitt & Heyw.
Calystegia sepium (L.) R. Br. ssp. *pulchra* (Brummitt & Heyw.) Tutin, nom. inval.
Hairy Bindweed

Introduction.
N. NW of Marlborough 1991 JEO.
10 km² 1 (2%) 1 km² 1 (<1%)

Calystegia silvatica (Kit.) Griseb.
C. sepium (L.) R. Br. ssp. *silvatica* (Kit.) Battand.
Large Bindweed

Introduction. Hedgerows, fences and scrub on disturbed soil. Locally abundant, especially in built-up areas, less common on chalk soil.
10 km² 22 (42%) 1 km² 64 (2%)

CUSCUTACEAE

Cuscuta L.

Cuscuta europaea L.
Greater Dodder

Nationally scarce plant.
Native. Parasitises broad-leaved herbs on river banks, stinging-nettle being its main host. The only locations are beside the Bristol Avon from Monkton House (between Melksham/Holt) downstream to Staverton, Great Bradford Wood, Bradford-on-Avon, Avoncliff, Winsley Bridge, Dundas Aqueduct and Warleigh 1983–89 DG. It continues across the county boundary into Avon.

TB Flower's 1839 record for 'second meadow beyond the Dundas Aqueduct' can still be found. The plant may disappear from a site for several years and later reappear.
10 km² 3 (6%) 1 km² 7 (<1%)   Map 303, page 241

Cuscuta epithymum (L.) L.
Dodder

Native. Calcareous grassland.
N. Single location at Ford in By Brook valley 1992 EO. Formerly grew on limestone grassland Winsley Hill. Still present in this habitat in adjacent counties of Avon/Somerset.
S. Grose stated 'locally common on heathy ground in SE Wilts, but rare elsewhere and probably decreasing on the downs.' This is not confirmed by WFMP records. All seven records are from chalk grassland: Grovely Down 1985 PPh, Charlton Down SPTA(C) 1986 RF, with two groups nearby sprawling over large anthill 1990 BG and widespread Rushall Down 1990 DGC. Widespread over steep well-grazed downland Starveall 1989 VH, extensive 1990 but decreased 1991 Haxton Down SPTA(E) AJS. A fourfold increase, parasitising many species including *Asperula cynanchica* and *Carex flacca* on earthwork bank Parsonage Down NNR 1984-92 BG.
10 km² 7 (12%) 1 km² 7 (<1%)   Map 304, page 241

MENYANTHACEAE

Menyanthes L.

Menyanthes trifoliata L.
Bogbean

Native and introduction. Fen and bog conditions in water-meadows and heathland pools.
N. Water-meadows R. Kennet: Ramsbury 1983 JN, Chilton Foliat 1983 DG and Froxfield 1984 LW. Pond in wood adjacent to railway Hullavington 1985 DG is a very unusual situation

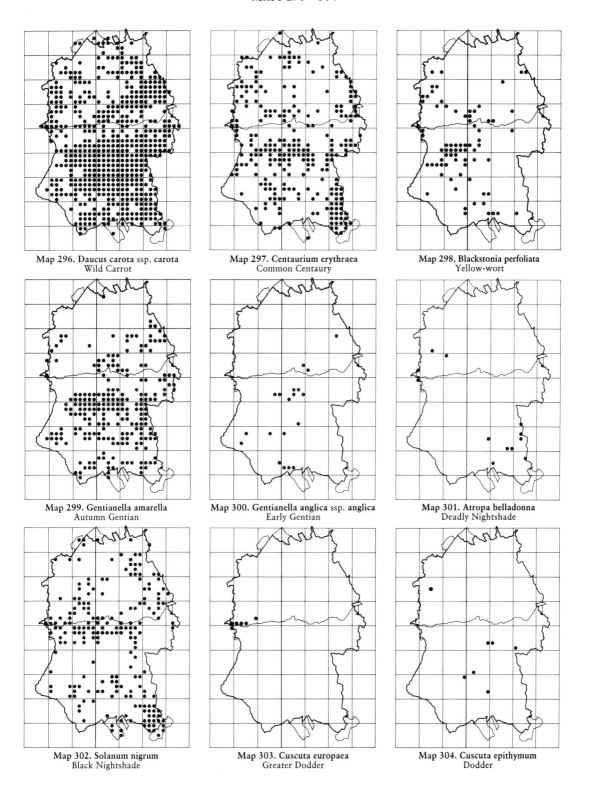

Map 296. **Daucus carota** ssp. **carota**
Wild Carrot

Map 297. **Centaurium erythraea**
Common Centaury

Map 298. **Blackstonia perfoliata**
Yellow-wort

Map 299. **Gentianella amarella**
Autumn Gentian

Map 300. **Gentianella anglica** ssp. **anglica**
Early Gentian

Map 301. **Atropa belladonna**
Deadly Nightshade

Map 302. **Solanum nigrum**
Black Nightshade

Map 303. **Cuscuta europaea**
Greater Dodder

Map 304. **Cuscuta epithymum**
Dodder

but plant appears to be native and is becoming over-grown. Pond adjacent to pit 40, CWP 1986 DG. Introduction Battle Lake, Red Lodge and Godwins Farm, Braydon.

S. Jones's Mill, Pewsey 1984 SH. R. Wylye: Stockton 1985 AS and Sherrington Mill 1987 BG. Water-meadows R. Bourne: Gomeldon and Porton 1987 JF. In a meadow Cowesfield 1989 PMW, Landford Bog 1990 VW, Cadnam Common and Furzley 1991 RV. Probable introductions: covering shallow lake Newhouse, Redlynch 1989 DJW, pond Six Wells Bottom 1991 PMW, widespread in and near lakes Stourhead Gardens 1991 PS.

10 km² 12 (23%) 1 km² 20 (<1%)   Map 305, page 245

Nymphoides Séguier

Nymphoides peltata Kuntze
Fringed Water-lily

Nationally scarce plant.
Native in GB, introduction in Wilts. Planted in ornamental and village ponds.
N. First county record K & A Canal 1983 MW. Ponds in Monk's Park, Corsham 1984 JR, Kington Langley 1985 and Olivemead, Luckington 1990 DG.

10 km² 3 (6%)   1 km² 4 (<1%)

POLEMONIACEAE

Polemonium L.

Polemonium caeruleum L.
Jacob's-ladder

British Red Data Book species.
Native in GB, introduction in Wilts. Garden escape or planting. Woods and quarries.
S. Chicksgrove Quarry 1985 MM, a few scattered on woodland bank possibly planted with *Aquilegia* and *Pulmonaria* Deptford 1990 BL. In old quarry, from dumped garden rubbish, established stand

with 1 m flowering stems pushing through tough grass and nettles Great Durnford 1984, still well-established 1987 PM. Present in wild garden without planting or sowing for 31 years East Grimstead PAW.

10 km² 4 (8%)   1 km² 4 (<1%)

BORAGINACEAE

Lithospermum L.

Lithospermum officinale L.
Common Gromwell

Native. Scrub and rides in open woodland, road verges. Most frequent on calcareous soils, largely absent from heavy clay. Colonies usually small.
N. Locally frequent in By Brook valley and on Clay-with-flints in West Woods and Savernake Forest.
S. Track sides in Bentley Wood, Grovely Wood and Chase Woods. Disturbed ground where scrub removed Old Sarum. Possibly decreased or under-recorded.

10 km² 31 (60%) 1 km² 131 (4%)   Map 306, page 245

Lithospermum arvense L.
Field Gromwell

Native. Mainly in cornfields on chalk and limestone. A declining species in this habitat due to modern farming practices.

10 km² 31 (60%) 1 km² 147 (4%)   Map 307, page 245

Echium L.

Echium vulgare L.
Viper's-bugloss

Native. Disturbed calcareous soil in open situations.
N. Very local. On thin, shallow soils. Regular

occurrence only around Box Common and in parts of By Brook valley.
S. Flowering abundance varies from year to year due to its biennial cycle. A very common species on SPTA colonising soil churned up by military vehicles. Large colonies on roadside verges on Porton Down.
10 km² 26 (50%) 1 km² 259 (7%)   Map 308, page 245

Pulmonaria L.

Pulmonaria officinalis L.
Lungwort

Introduction. Planted, especially in ornamental woodland. A garden throw-out, often persisting for a long time.
10 km² 17 (33%) 1 km² 31 (<1%)

Symphytum L.

Symphytum officinale L.
Common Comfrey

Native. A frequent and often abundant plant of damp habitats.
10 km² 49 (94%) 2 km² 539 (57%)   Map 309, page 245

**Symphytum officinale x S. asperum =
S. x uplandicum** Nyman
Russian Comfrey

Introduction, originally as fodder. Wet and dry habitats. Invasive on roadsides and a dominant species in some river valleys. Increased during the last 40 years.
10 km² 24 (46%) 1 km² 68 (2%)   Map 310, page 245

Symphytum tuberosum L.
Tuberous Comfrey

Native in GB, introduction in Wilts. Escape from cultivation.

N. Road verge Allington near Chippenham 1986 JP, first VC7 record.
S. Road verge Berwick St Leonard and field corner Fonthill Bishop 1987 VH ver. AH, first VC8 records.
10 km² 2 (4%)   1 km² 3 (<1%)

Symphytum grandiflorum DC.
Creeping Comfrey

Introduction. Garden escape, naturalises in woods and hedge bottoms.
N. Allington 1989 DG, Easton Grey 1990 PD.
S. Great Bradley Wood 1985 VEH, West Ashton 1987 EC, Fonthill Gifford 1987 JBH, Ludwell 1991 MM.
10 km² 6 (12%) 1 km² 6 (<1%)

Symphytum orientale L.
White Comfrey

Introduction. Self-sown and naturalised on hedgerow banks.
N. Waste land Back Lane, Marlborough 1990 VS.
S. Garden escape Honey Street 1989 VS, old railway track Grafton 1991 FP.
10 km² 2 (4%)   1 km² 3 (<1%)

Anchusa L.

Anchusa officinalis L.
Alkanet

Introduction. Waste and disturbed ground.
N. Possibly originally planted Winterbourne Bassett 1990 JEO.
S. Probable garden escapes at Steeple Langford, South Newton and Stoford 1987-89 BL. On disturbed chalk downland Blackball Firs 1984 AW, known for at least 5 years. Group of plants on edge of Landford Lodge tree nursery 1987 PMW.
10 km² 4 (8%)   1 km² 6 (<1%)

Anchusa arvensis (L.) M. Bieb.
Bugloss

Native. Open situations on light acid and, occasionally, on calcareous soils.
N. Almost exclusively on greensand. Occasionally found growing on imported topsoil. Frequent on cultivated land in the Compton Bassett area, Bowood and market gardens in Bromham and Rowde.
S. Two main areas of records: in the N at Market Lavington, Easterton, Stert, Urchfont and Chirton with outliers at Upper Baynton, Coulston Hill and Great Cheverell. In the SE, area includes Loosehanger and Whiteparish, with one record from a set-aside field. At Landford Lodge tree nursery the species occurs with *A. officinalis*, and near Damerham with a variety of arable weeds. A tree nursery weed at Chapmanslade and in a lay-by on the Warminster by-pass.
10 km² 12 (23%) 1 km² 38 (1%) Map 311, page 245

Pentaglottis Tausch

Pentaglottis sempervirens (L.) Tausch ex L. Bailey
Green Alkanet

Introduction. Road verges and rough ground, usually near habitation as a garden throw-out. Apparently unable to fully naturalise and spread from where it was discarded.
10 km² 35 (67%) 1 km² 98 (3%) Map 312, page 245

Trachystemon D. Don

Trachystemon orientalis (L.) Don
Abraham-Isaac-Jacob

Introduction. Damp woods.
S. Well-established and spreading Erlestoke Park 1982 EC, 18 flower heads Quarry Wood Fonthill 1987 JJ (recorded here 1960 RSR Fitter)

and beside Fonthill Lake 1988 VH.
10 km² 2 (4%) 1 km² 3 (<1%)

Amsinckia Lehm.

Amsinckia micrantha Suksd.
Amsinckia menziesii auct. non (Lehm.) Nelson & McBride; *Amsinckia intermedia* auct. non Fischer & C. Meyer; *Amsinckia calycina* auct. non (Moris) Chater
Common Fiddleneck

Introduction. Arable and turned soil on Upper and Lower Greensand. First county record 1917.
N. This plant is locally abundant on Lower Greensand at Compton Bassett, Bowood and Spye Park.
S. A cluster of records on the Upper Greensand N of Salisbury Plain at Urchfont, Easterton and Lavington Sands. Elsewhere it has been found on imported soil.
10 km² 6 (12%) 1 km² 13 (<1%) Map 313, page 245

Myosotis L.

Myosotis scorpioides L.
Water Forget-me-not

Native. Rivers, streams, lakes, gravel pits and canals. Found in most lime-rich waters, preferring flowing-water.
10 km² 44 (85%) 2 km² 366 (39%) Map 314, page 248

Myosotis secunda A. Murray
Creeping Forget-me-not

Native. Bogs, marshes and pond edges on acid soils.
N. Rare. Only occurs at Coate Water, Swindon and in a few ponds on heavy clay.
S. Rare except on the border of the New Forest.
10 km² 10 (19%) 1 km² 18 (<1%) Map 315, page 248

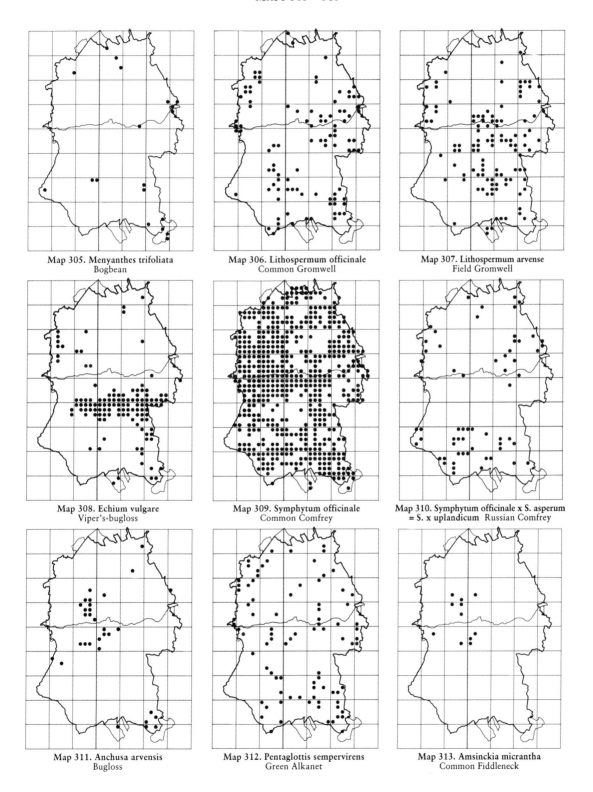

Map 305. Menyanthes trifoliata
Bogbean

Map 306. Lithospermum officinale
Common Gromwell

Map 307. Lithospermum arvense
Field Gromwell

Map 308. Echium vulgare
Viper's-bugloss

Map 309. Symphytum officinale
Common Comfrey

Map 310. Symphytum officinale x S. asperum
= S. x uplandicum Russian Comfrey

Map 311. Anchusa arvensis
Bugloss

Map 312. Pentaglottis sempervirens
Green Alkanet

Map 313. Amsinckia micrantha
Common Fiddleneck

Myosotis laxa Lehm. ssp. **caespitosa** (Schultz) N. Hylander ex Nordh.
Tufted Forget-me-not

Native. Rivers, streams, ponds, marshes and gravel pits. This species occurs in more neutral to acidic habitats than *M. scorpioides*. More common in ponds and marshes on clay soils than in flowing water.
10 km² 33 (63%) 1 km² 105 (3%) Map 316, page 248

Myosotis sylvatica Hoffm.
Wood Forget-me-not

Native. Shady places in woodland, on road verges and banks. Grose considered this plant to be native in Wilts only on the E border near Shalbourne.
N. Specimens found by JEO were identified by Dr A Silverside (BSBI referee) as *M. sylvatica* and var. *culta*. Occurs further N and W than expected: West Woods, Lockeridge, Wroughton, Winterbourne Bassett, Chiseldon, Savernake, Avebury, Axford, Rockley, Barbury and Marlborough JEO.
S. Native at Kingston's Copse, Bagshot. Other records considered to be of garden origin: Stourhead Gardens, Imber Village, roadside WCC dump near Etchilhampton, Salisbury main car park, S of Pitton.
Var. **italica**
Salisbury Race course 1989 JEO (conf. A Silverside).
Var. **culta**
Salisbury central car park 1990 JEO (conf. A Silverside).
10 km² 11 (21%) 1 km² 28 (<1%) Map 317, page 248

Myosotis arvensis (L.) Hill
Field Forget-me-not

Native. Disturbed soil, especially cultivated land. Common and widely-distributed.
10 km² 51 (98%) 2 km² 829 (87%)

Myosotis arvensis (L.) Hill var. **sylvestris** Schldl.

Introduction. Garden escape which has spread to many habitats far from habitation, sometimes becoming invasive due to the production of large numbers of viable seeds. Has caused identification problems with *M. sylvatica*.

Myosotis ramosissima Rochel
Early Forget-me-not

Native. Dry, bare areas, including on active anthills, on unimproved chalk and limestone grassland and railway chippings.
N. Localised, most frequent on unimproved, leached chalk downland where it grows with other ephemeral species including *Erophila verna*. An unusual site for Wilts on Lower Greensand at Bowood.
S. Most common on Porton Ranges, scattered elsewhere in suitable habitats but less common on SPTA where many remaining anthills are overgrown or blasted by shells.
10 km² 38 (73%) 1 km² 119 (3%) Map 318, page 248

Myosotis discolor Pers.
Changing Forget-me-not

Native. Cultivated sandy soils, neutral grassland and woodland rides on acid soils. Occasional on leached chalk.
N. Local in occurrence. A blue haze seen from a distance of 400 m at Spye Park consisted of a field left fallow for a year with tens of thousands of this species growing to the exclusion of almost every other annual. Most frequent on neutral pastures. On heavy clays in Braydon Forest.
S. Fairly generally distributed on clay and greensand soils especially in Vale of Pewsey and in SE.
10 km² 30 (58%) 1 km² 108 (3%) Map 319, page 248

Cynoglossum L.

Cynoglossum officinale L.
Hound's-tongue

Native. Disturbed calcareous soil on downland

and among scrub, especially around rabbit warrens.

N. Very rare. Mostly found in association with warrens on the downs N of Pewsey.

S. Still widespread on the chalk, particularly SPTA(C&E) and Porton Ranges.

10 km² 25 (48%) 1 km² 104 (3%)   Map 320, page 248

VERBENACEAE

Verbena L.

Verbena officinalis L.
Vervain

Native. Trackside edges, rough grassy places, base of hedges and disturbed areas. Most frequent on calcareous soil. Colonies always very small.

N. Very localised. Mainly in the W, along the Bristol Avon valley and near Bradford-on-Avon.

S. Most frequent around Salisbury on bare disturbed chalk.

10 km² 29 (56%) 1 km² 103 (3%)   Map 321, page 248

LAMIACEAE

Stachys L.

Stachys officinalis (L.) Trev. St. Léon
Betony

Native. Unimproved grassland and woodland glades on calcareous, neutral and acid soils.

N. Frequent on the clay in Braydon Forest area where large populations occur in some of the unimproved meadows.

S. Widely-distributed on chalk and acid soils. Some populations are very small. Large colony on superficial deposits Parsonage Down NNR. Considered to be an indicator species of ancient woodland where it occurs frequently along rides.

10 km² 44 (85%) 1 km² 456 (13%)   Map 322, page 248

Stachys sylvatica L.
Hedge Woundwort

Native. Hedges, ditches, woodland edges and rides. Very common.

10 km² 52 (100%) 2 km² 853 (90%)

Stachys sylvatica x S. palustris = S. x ambigua Smith
Hybrid Woundwort

Native. Grows in habitats of either parent, often in absence of one or both.

N. Lane-side Nettleton 1988 JH.

S. Railway embankments Pouldens, West Tisbury and Tisbury 1988 MM, churchyard Fonthill Bishop 1987 VH. Large clumps in moist grassland beside woodland track Longdean Bottom, Great Ridge where S. palustris unlikely, 1990 PM. Conifer plantation Great Durnford 1988 PM.

10 km² 4 (8%)   1 km² 12 (<1%)   Map 323, page 251

Stachys palustris L.
Marsh Woundwort

Native. Beside flowing and standing water, on damp ground with impeded drainage and in rank vegetation in dry places.

N. Abundant only around Malmesbury and Cricklade, localised to river valleys.

S. More records from dry habitats such as SPTA(W) than in N Wilts but wet areas still the predominant habitat. Mainly in small numbers.

10 km² 42 (81%) 1 km² 278 (8%)   Map 324, page 251

Stachys arvensis (L.) L.
Field Woundwort

Native. Arable land mainly on non-calcareous soils. An annual, ephemeral in its appearance.

N. Near Cottles Wood, Atworth 1980-84 DG, on

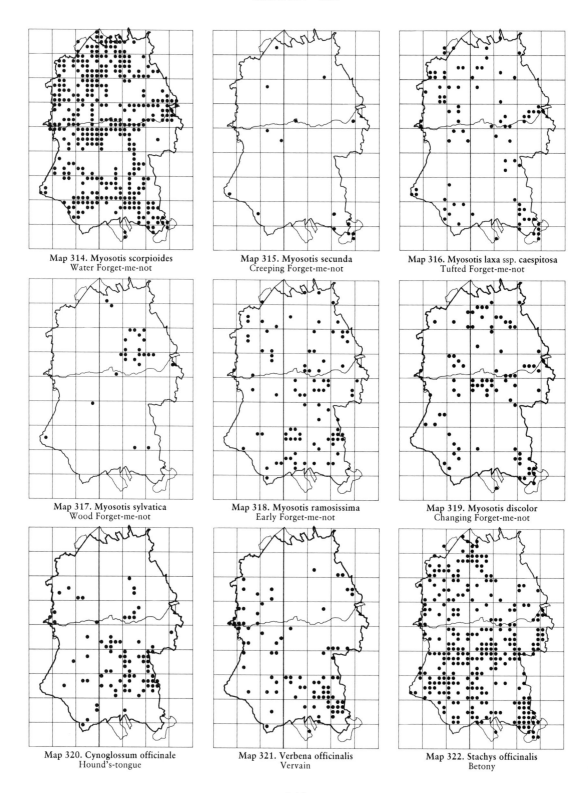

Map 314. Myosotis scorpioides
Water Forget-me-not

Map 315. Myosotis secunda
Creeping Forget-me-not

Map 316. Myosotis laxa ssp. caespitosa
Tufted Forget-me-not

Map 317. Myosotis sylvatica
Wood Forget-me-not

Map 318. Myosotis ramosissima
Early Forget-me-not

Map 319. Myosotis discolor
Changing Forget-me-not

Map 320. Cynoglossum officinale
Hound's-tongue

Map 321. Verbena officinalis
Vervain

Map 322. Stachys officinalis
Betony

sand Spye Park 1984 DG, bridlepath Stowell Farm near Hullavington 1986 JH, near Bullpark Wood, Didmarton 1987 HB, N of Sutton Benger 1987 DB & DH.
S. Five plants in one field Allenford 1986 JO, not refound 1987, Canada Common (Hants) 1986 RV, cornfield W of Lowdens Copse 1986, 2 farms in Redlynch parish 1990 DJW.
10 km² 9 (17%)   1 km² 11 (<1%)   Map 325, page 251

Ballota L.

Ballota nigra L.
Black Horehound

Native. Hedgerows, rough and bare ground. Usually occurs singly or in small colonies.
N. Well-distributed on the Cotswold edge and around Chippenham and N and W of Swindon. Rare on the chalk.
S. Most frequent in area around Salisbury.
10 km² 46 (88%) 1 km² 378 (10%)   Map 326, page 251

Lamiastrum Heister ex Fabr.

Lamiastrum galeobdolon (L.) Ehrend. & Polatschek ssp. montanum (Pers.) Ehrend. & Polatschek
Yellow Archangel

Native. Woodland and hedgebanks. An indicator species of ancient woodland with relic populations in hedgebanks.
N. Most frequent in old woodland on limestone near Castle Combe and on chalk, clay, and Clay-with-flints E of Marlborough.
S. Records scarce from the upper Salisbury Avon area due to lack of woodland. Most often on greensand and clays in SW and SE.
Ssp. argentatum (Smejkal) Stace
Introduction. Garden throw-out which naturalises aggressively in hedgebanks and woodland edges.
10 km² 50 (96%) 1 km² 542 (15%)   Map 327, page 251

Lamium L.

Lamium album L.
White Dead-nettle

Native. Hedgebanks and waste ground. Very common and widely-distributed.
10 km² 52 (100%) 2 km² 884 (93%)

Lamium maculatum (L.) L.
Spotted Dead-nettle

Introduction. Garden throw-out which does not naturalise as easily as Lamiastrum galeobdolon ssp. argentatum.
10 km² 9 (17%)   1 km² 16 (<1%)

Lamium purpureum L.
Red Dead-nettle

Native. Disturbed soil. A common weed. Form with white flowers on waste ground The Butts, Salisbury 1985 PM.
10 km² 50 (96%) 2 km² 757 (80%)

Lamium hybridum Villars
Cut-leaved Dead-nettle

Native. Cultivated and waste land.
N. Rare. There are only two known locations where it seems to persist at Tanis near Rowde, a locality known by Grose 1939 which was refound 1987 DG, and at Highworth 1989 MWS.
S. Apart from a field of rape Rood Ashton 1992 DG, the few records, some of single plants, are restricted to three main localities. In the Vale of Pewsey at Potterne, Chirton, Marden and Wilsford 1985-89 BGH, JMP, CS & MWS, near Salisbury at Clarendon Park and at Upper Woodford 1990 PM where hundreds of plants, thinly scattered, were found.
10 km² 5 (10%)   1 km² 12 (<1%)   Map 328, page 251

Lamium amplexicaule L.
Henbit Dead-nettle

Native. Cultivated land.
N. Common in arable crops on calcareous soils around Aldbourne and on sandy soil in market gardens at Bromham. Very localised elsewhere.
S. An abundant field weed especially on S half of Salisbury Plain.
10 km² 41 (79%) 1 km² 392 (11%) Map 329, page 251

Galeopsis L.

Galeopsis angustifolia Ehrh. ex Hoffm.
Red Hemp-nettle

Nationally scarce plant.
Native. Arable land and open ground. Decreased nationally in recent years.
S. Cut cornfield near Coldharbour Copse SPTA(E) S of Collingbourne Ducis 1985 AJS, two farms one with three fields having 2-4 and up to 24 plants mostly in kale patch Martin/Damerham area 1986-87 JO, track Corton 1988 WFMP meeting, single plant edge of maize patch Teffont Down 1988 AH, widespread in NW of SPTA(W) at Ladywell, Summer Down, W and N of Imber village 1992 BGH, BG & JPi.
10 km² 4 (8%)   1 km² 14 (<1%)   Map 330, page 251

Galeopsis speciosa Miller
Large-flowered Hemp-nettle

Native in GB, introduction in Wilts.
S. Three plants on a shaded track Compton Chamberlayne on greensand growing with *G. tetrahit* 1991 CP.
10 km² 1 (2%)   1 km² 1 (<1%)

Galeopsis tetrahit L.
Common Hemp-nettle

Native. Cultivated land, woodland clearings, partly-shaded tracks.
N. Common in E on chalk around Aldbourne and on Clay-with-flints at Savernake.
S. Most frequent in SW. Occurs on wide range of soils.
10 km² 47 (90%) 1 km² 694 (19%) Map 331, page 251

Galeopsis bifida Boenn.
Bifid Hemp-nettle

Native.
N. All records are from the Savernake Forest area on Clay-with-flints where the more common *G. tetrahit* also occurs. The distinction between the two species is often blurred.
10 km² 3 (6%)   1 km² 6 (<1%)

Melittis L.

Melittis melissophyllum L.
Bastard Balm

Nationally scarce plant.
Native. Woodland edges.
S. Cheyney's Wood 1986 and very pale-flowered form edge of wood Coles's Bury, Whiteparish 1988 DJW.
10 km² 1 (2%)   1 km² 1 (<1%)

Scutellaria L.

Scutellaria galericulata L.
Skullcap

Native. Banks of rivers, streams, lakes, ponds and canal. Wet woodland, fens and marshes.
N. Most frequent along the banks of the K & A Canal, R. Kennet and Bristol Avon. Frequent in damp areas in Braydon Forest and very common in the acidic alder carr at Spye Park.
S. Most records are for S of Salisbury from the R. Avon and R. Ebble.
10 km² 25 (48%) 1 km² 102 (3%)   Map 332, page 254

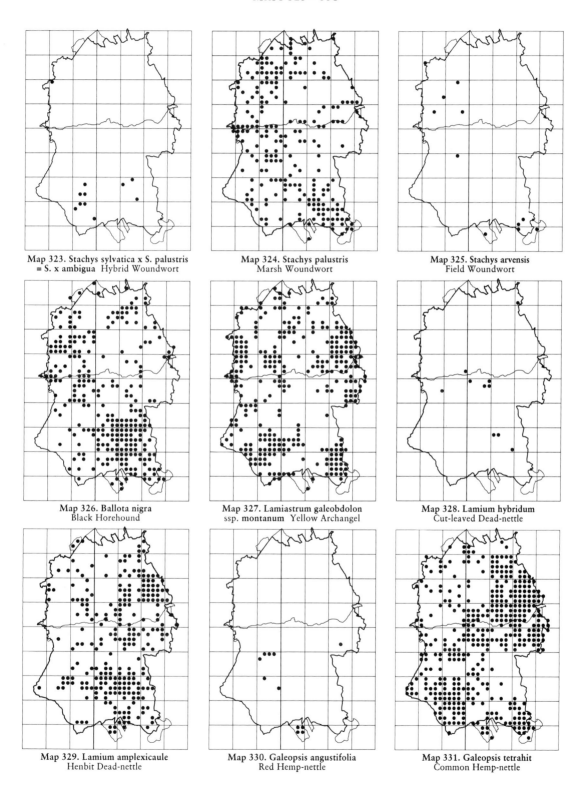

Map 323. Stachys sylvatica x S. palustris
= S. x ambigua Hybrid Woundwort

Map 324. Stachys palustris
Marsh Woundwort

Map 325. Stachys arvensis
Field Woundwort

Map 326. Ballota nigra
Black Horehound

Map 327. Lamiastrum galeobdolon
ssp. montanum Yellow Archangel

Map 328. Lamium hybridum
Cut-leaved Dead-nettle

Map 329. Lamium amplexicaule
Henbit Dead-nettle

Map 330. Galeopsis angustifolia
Red Hemp-nettle

Map 331. Galeopsis tetrahit
Common Hemp-nettle

Scutellaria minor Hudson
Lesser Skullcap

Native. Tracks in open wet woodlands, banks of streams and ditches.
S. Largely confined to SE Wilts where it extends N from the New Forest to Bentley and Clarendon Woods. Populations small and scattered. Elsewhere unconfirmed record Marston 1988 BK.
10 km² 3 (6%)   1 km² 19 (<1%)   Map 333, page 254

Teucrium L.

Teucrium scorodonia L.
Wood Sage

Native. Open woodlands, heaths, hedgerows and grassland on acid soils.
N. Most frequent on Lower Greensand at Spye Park, chalk superficials at Savernake and on clay N of Chippenham. Still present at the earliest recorded site, on limestone at Winsley (Prior 1839).
S. Most frequent on Upper Greensand on W edge of county, on chalk superficials which occur at Great Ridge and Grovely Woods and on Tertiary sand and clay in SE corner of county.
10 km² 29 (56%) 1 km² 212 (6%)   Map 334, page 254

Ajuga L.

Ajuga reptans L.
Bugle

Native. Woodland, hedgerows and unimproved neutral and acidic grassland. More common in damp places.
10 km² 51 (98%) 2 km² 524 (55%) Map 335, page 254

Nepeta L.

Nepeta cataria L.
Cat-mint

Native. Old tracks, edges of fields and farmyards

on calcareous soils. In the latter habitat the true status is doubtful, the plant being well-known as a 'herb'.
N. Local distribution. One plant in scrub Littlecote 1985 BP, edge of cultivated field near Chilton Foliat 1986 SK, track Long Dean 1986 DG, disturbed ground Hullavington 1987 and farm track Slaughterford 1988 JH.
S. Arable and verges. 2-12 plants in arable and 33 in rough hedge in the Martin/Damerham area (Hants) 1986 JO, on a verge near Deptford Manor 1987 JO/BSBI meeting, two plants in the corner of a hayfield N of Dinton 1988 MDT, along a field edge Homington 1989 JA and a verge Wilton (Burbage) windmill 1989 AJS, on a bank in a car park Odstock Hospital 1991 JO.
10 km² 9 (17%)   1 km² 16 (<1%)   Map 336, page 254

Glechoma L.

Glechoma hederacea L.
Ground-ivy

Native. Woodlands, hedgerows and heavily rabbit-grazed chalk grassland. Very common and widely-distributed.
10 km² 52 (100%) 2 km² 905 (95%)

Prunella L.

Prunella vulgaris L.
Selfheal

Native. All types of grassland, woodland rides. Common and widely-distributed.
10 km² 52 (100%) 2 km² 804 (85%)

Melissa L.

Melissa officinalis L.
Balm

Introduction. Garden escape. Naturalised by

seeding on and at the base of walls and banks often near habitation, or from plants discarded on rubbish dumps and spreading to waste ground.

10 km² 16 (31%) 1 km² 32 (<1%)

Clinopodium L.

Clinopodium ascendens (Jordan) Samp.
Calamintha ascendens Jordan
Common Calamint

Native. Woodland edges, scrub, hedgebanks and rocky outcrops. Mainly on dry calcareous soils. Local, occurring on limestone, chalk and less commonly on clay.

10 km² 21 (40%) 1 km² 62 (2%)   Map 337, page 254

Clinopodium vulgare L.
Wild Basil

Native. Hedgebanks, road verges and downland scrub on chalk and limestone. Frequent in these habitats. Local on gravel in CWP and clay elsewhere.

10 km² 48 (92%) 2 km² 459 (48%) Map 338, page 254

Clinopodium acinos (L.) Kuntze
Acinos arvensis (Lam.) Dandy
Basil Thyme

Native. Sparsely vegetated areas on calcareous soil.

N. Very rare. Arable land, woodland rides, railway embankments and unimproved grassland. Sites E of Swindon and on calcareous clays in the NW.

S. The SPTA is the stronghold for this species where it quickly colonises ground disturbed by military vehicles, particularly where chalk rubble is exposed. Elsewhere small colonies in woodland rides on the chalk superficials eg. Grovely Wood and bare places.

10 km² 22 (42%) 1 km² 112 (3%)   Map 339, page 254

Origanum L.

Origanum vulgare L.
Marjoram

Native. Dry grassland, often among scrub, on chalk and limestone downland and road verges.

N. In large colonies on limestone.

S. Widespread on the chalk but colonies usually small.

10 km² 39 (75%) 2 km² 253 (27%)   Map 340, page 254

Thymus L.

Thymus pulegioides L.
Large Thyme

Native. Unimproved chalk and limestone downland.

N. Abundant in a few places on bare or sparse turf on limestone. Records on the chalk unconfirmed.

S. Unimproved chalk grassland. On anthills with *T. polytrichus* on Pertwood Down where the larger size of the plant and stronger smell were immediately apparent and called for closer examination for positive identification. Grose's record near Knoyle Down Farm refound, 1991 BG. Possibly overlooked due to confusion with *T. polytrichus*.

10 km² 19 (37%) 1 km² 34 (<1%)   Map 341, page 258

Thymus polytrichus A. Kerner ex Borbás ssp. britannicus (Ronn.) Kerguélen
Thymus praecox Opiz ssp. *arcticus* (Durand) Jalas
Wild Thyme

Native. Unimproved short chalk, limestone and greensand grassland.

N. Locally abundant on dry, grazed chalk downland. Occasional on limestone near Castle Combe and along the NW county boundary. One site on Lower Greensand at Spye Park.

S. On most grazed chalk grassland, especially on active anthills.

10 km² 42 (81%) 1 km² 621 (17%)   Map 342, page 258

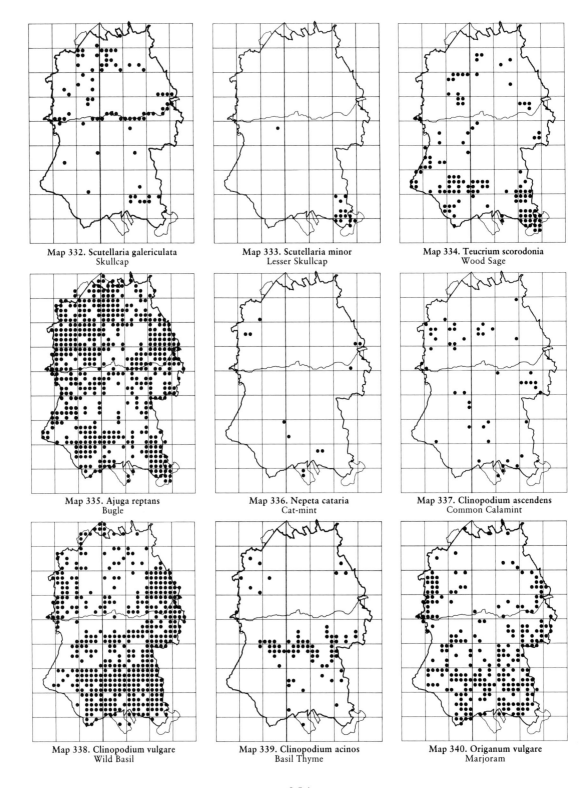

Map 332. Scutellaria galericulata
Skullcap

Map 333. Scutellaria minor
Lesser Skullcap

Map 334. Teucrium scorodonia
Wood Sage

Map 335. Ajuga reptans
Bugle

Map 336. Nepeta cataria
Cat-mint

Map 337. Clinopodium ascendens
Common Calamint

Map 338. Clinopodium vulgare
Wild Basil

Map 339. Clinopodium acinos
Basil Thyme

Map 340. Origanum vulgare
Marjoram

Lycopus L.

Lycopus europaeus L.
Gipsywort

Native. River, stream, lake, canal, pond and gravel pit edges.
N. Abundant in the main river valleys, frequent in damp ditches in the Minety area.
S. 'Follows' the K & A Canal and the rivers Avon, Wylye, Nadder and Bourne. Elsewhere occurs on pond edges.
10 km² 40 (77%) 1 km² 305 (8%)   Map 343, page 258

Mentha L.

Species of this critical genus hybridise freely and vary according to the habitat. Garden escapes that have become naturalised in the wild add to problems with identification. Careful scrutiny is required in naming species other than *M. arvensis* and *M. aquatica*.

Mentha arvensis L.
Corn Mint

Native. Arable and disturbed land, damp woodland rides. On dry chalk grassland on SPTA.
10 km² 43 (83%) 1 km² 282 (8%)   Map 344, page 258

Mentha arvensis x M. aquatica =
M. x verticillata L.
Whorled Mint

Native. Naturally occurring hybrid. In damp places and disturbed ground, the habitats of the parents, but distribution restricted. Most frequent in SE. The commonest hybrid mint in GB.
10 km² 13 (25%) 1 km² 50 (1%)   Map 345, page 258

Mentha arvensis x M. aquatica x M. spicata =
M. x smithiana R. A. Graham
Tall Mint

Probable introduction. Damp places and waste ground. Like most mints, this plant can be invasive and often escapes or is thrown out by gardeners.
S. Damp places include water-meadows: R. Avon at Britford and Downton; R. Ebble at Homington 1984 NLC & BKC; R. Wylye at Bathampton; R. Till at Berwick St James and gravel pits Steeple Langford 1987 BL. In contrasting habitat a large patch on edge of old allotment St Mark's Road, Salisbury 1985 PM.
10 km² 3 (6%)   1 km² 11 (<1%)

Mentha arvensis x M. spicata = M. x gracilis Sole
M. gentilis auct. non L.
Bushy Mint

Possibly native.
S. Bed of stream Bramshaw VC8 (Hants) 1990 RPB & JO.
10 km² 1 (2%)   1 km² 1 (<1%)

Mentha aquatica L.
Water Mint

Native. Wet habitats but not fast-flowing water.
N. A constant species in ponds and ditches on heavy clay in Braydon Forest and Malmesbury areas.
S. In wet places in river valleys, streams and wet woodland.
10 km² 50 (96%) 1 km² 684 (19%) Map 346, page 258

Mentha aquatica x M. spicata =
M. x piperita L.
Peppermint

Native. Can be found occurring naturally as a hybrid. Distribution restricted but habitat requirements difficult to determine. According to Stace 'damp ground and waste places, escape or throw-out when glabrous, usually spontaneous when pubescent.'
10 km² 15 (29%) 1 km² 32 (<1%)

Mentha spicata L.
Spear Mint

Introduction. Much cultivated. Naturalised from escapes on to waste ground and as a throw-out on rubbish dumps, landfill sites and road verges.
Five records for *M. longifolia* (four in VC7, one in VC8) are now considered pubescent variants of *M. spicata*.
10 km² 31 (60%) 1 km² 90 (3%)

Mentha spicata x M. suaveolens = M. x villosa Hudson var. **alopecuroides** (Hull) Briq.
Apple Mint

Introduction. Garden escape by means of discarded roots. Probably the most frequently planted of all mints.
10 km² 6 (12%) 1 km² 12 (<1%)

Mentha suaveolens Ehrh.
Round-leaved Mint

Introduction. Roadside banks, woodland edge, streamsides, ditches and waste ground. An escape from cultivation, naturalised to form extensive colonies. Most frequent in area around Marlborough.
10 km² 22 (42%) 1 km² 43 (1%)

Salvia L.

Salvia pratensis L.
Meadow Clary

British Red Data Book species.
Native. Calcareous grassland.
S. Surviving site for county on remote area Tenantry Down SPTA(W). First recorded 1924 Awdry. Record included in the NCC Rare Plants Survey 1986 SE & AH, 1981-91 BGH.
10 km² 1 (2%) 1 km² 1 (<1%)

Salvia verbenaca L.
Wild Clary

Native. Road verges and grassy banks.
N. Only two localities, both on unimproved limestone downland, Turleigh 1984 JP, Sherston 1985 DG.
S. Main concentration of records N and W of Salisbury. Salisbury, Stratford-sub-Castle, Wilsford 1984 PM, B3082 Berwick St James 1984 BL, A30 N of Burcombe 1987 OS, A36 South Newton 1989 BL. Elsewhere roadside bank Chirton 1986 RF.
10 km² 5 (10%)   1 km² 10 (<1%)   Map 347, page 258

CALLITRICHACEAE

Callitriche L.
Being aware of the difficulties of distinguishing between the species due to variation in form, especially leaf shape and the necessity for mature fruits for identification, a group of recorders (NLC, PMWF, AH, BL, DJW and PMW) with help from RV from Hants, persevered and returned later in the season to obtain mature fruit. Although not confirmed by an expert, we believe these records show six different species.

Callitriche hermaphroditica L.
Autumnal Water-starwort

Nationally scarce plant.
Native.
S. Single plant in pond Quar Hill 1989 DJW, (ver. AH), first VC8 record.
10 km² 1 (2%)   1 km² 1 (<1%)

Callitriche stagnalis Scop. agg.
Common Water-starwort

Native. Muddy edges of ponds, in streams, rivers, canals and gravel pits. Common in suitable habitats throughout the county. All *Callitriche* species in VC7 recorded as *C. stagnalis*.
10 km² 39 (75%) 1 km² 376 (10%) Map 348, page 258

Callitriche platycarpa Kuetz.
Various-leaved Water-starwort

Native. More often in flowing water than *C. stagnalis* with which it has some resemblances.
S. Of the nine records, seven are from R. Wylye, including slack water with *Lemna minuta*, and adjacent wet meadow and ditch from Steeple Langford S to Ditchampton 1987-1990 BL. North Pond in Bentley Wood 1991 PMW & AH, Plaitford Common 1991 RV.
10 km² 4 (8%)   1 km² 10 (<1%)

Callitriche obtusangula Le Gall
Blunt-fruited Water-starwort

Native. Rivers, streams, ditches and ponds.
S. R. Wylye: near Boyton 1987 BSBI meeting, Hanging Langford and Bathampton Estate 1987, South Newton and Wishford 1989 BL. R. Avon, Upavon PMWF (ver. AH). R. Nadder, old mill West Harnham 1987 NLC. Ditches Middle Wick, Downton 1986 and Middle Street, West Harnham 1987 NLC, stream East Grimstead PMW.
10 km² 7 (13%)   1 km² 14 (<1%)

Callitriche brutia Petagna
Pedunculate Water-starwort

Native. Very shallow water, drying to mud.
S. Furzley Common 1991 RV, (conf. C Preston), first VC8 (Hants) record.
10 km² 1 (2%)   1 km² 1 (<1%)

Callitriche hamulata Kuetz. ex Koch
Callitriche intermedia Hoffm. ssp. *hamulata* (Kuetz. ex Koch) Clapham
Intermediate Water-starwort

Native. Rivers, streams, ponds.
S. Ponds: behind surgery Whiteparish 1985 PMW not found 1986, large quantity Newhouse Lake 1990 DJW, Six Wells Bottom 1991 PMW, Tinney's

Plantation 1991 DJW, Bramshaw and Hatches 1991 RV. Rivers: R. Wylye, near Boyton 1987 BSBI meeting; R. Nadder, fairly deep, swiftly-flowing water 1988 SMP & MDT and stream Teffont Evias 1988 VH & AH; R. Avon, Upavon 1988 PMWF (ver. AH); R. Blackwater, Rix's Bridge 1991 RV.
10 km² 7 (13%)   1 km² 12 (<1%)

PLANTAGINACEAE

Plantago L.

Plantago coronopus L.
Buck's-horn Plantain

Native. Acidic sand and gravel.
N. Refind of Grose's 1952 record in turf and along tracks Spye Park 1987 DG.
S. Site of only the sixth VC8 record on old railway-line Bemerton destroyed 1985 JBH. Many plants sandy track Ash Hill, Cowesfield 1989 PMW. Remaining sites are in far SE: Nomansland and Bramshaw; Penn, Canada, Furzley and West Wellow Commons (Hants) 1991 RV, VW.
10 km² 4 (8%)   1 km² 12 (<1%)

Plantago major L.
Greater Plantain

Native. Open, disturbed and well-trampled land. Very common.
10 km² 52 (100%)2 km² 894 (94%)

Plantago media L.
Hoary Plantain

Native. Unimproved calcareous and neutral grassland. Most frequent on chalk and limestone downland. Less frequent in unimproved meadows on the clay.
10 km² 47 (90%)   1 km² 1068 (29%) Map 349, page 258

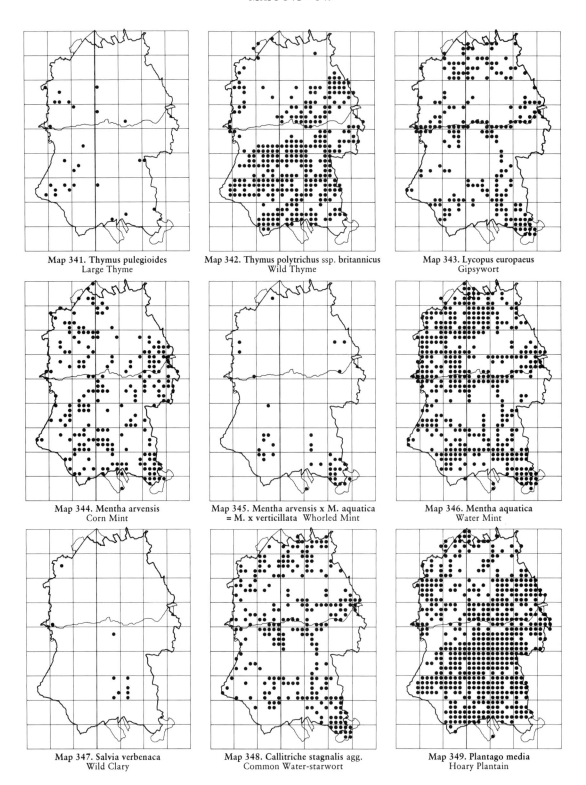

Map 341. **Thymus pulegioides**
Large Thyme

Map 342. **Thymus polytrichus** ssp. **britannicus**
Wild Thyme

Map 343. **Lycopus europaeus**
Gipsywort

Map 344. **Mentha arvensis**
Corn Mint

Map 345. **Mentha arvensis x M. aquatica**
= M. x verticillata Whorled Mint

Map 346. **Mentha aquatica**
Water Mint

Map 347. **Salvia verbenaca**
Wild Clary

Map 348. **Callitriche stagnalis** agg.
Common Water-starwort

Map 349. **Plantago media**
Hoary Plantain

Plantago lanceolata L.
Ribwort Plantain

Native. All types of grassland except on very acid soils. Very common.
10 km² 50 (96%) 2 km² 899 (95%)

BUDDLEJACEAE

Buddleja L.

Buddleja davidii Franchet
Butterfly-bush

Introduction. Recently disturbed soil, waste ground, walls, derelict buildings, railway banks and quarries.
N. Well-distributed especially on ground disturbed during building development. The dominant shrub on the Swindon railway siding.
S. Easily spread by seed. Of the few sites mentioned by Grose in *The Flora of Wiltshire*, that at the Pitton quarry persists. Now more widespread. Some planting as on the Warminster by-pass.
10 km² 39 (75%) 1 km² 150 (4%)   Map 350, page 262

OLEACEAE

Fraxinus L.

Fraxinus excelsior L.
Ash

Native. The climax woodland tree species on calcareous soils and common as standards in hedgerows. Very common and widely-distributed.
Var. **monophylla**
Single-leaved Ash
Introduction. Cultivated form. Seedlings from a planted avenue in regenerating woodland on disused army camp Chiseldon and roadside

Gypsy Lane, Swindon 1990 JEO.
10 km² 51 (98%) 2 km² 880 (93%)

Syringa L.

Syringa vulgaris L.
Lilac

Introduction. Always planted or a throw-out in hedges and on road verges. Well-distributed except in some areas of the chalk.
10 km² 37 (71%) 1 km² 166 (5%)

Ligustrum L.

Ligustrum vulgare L.
Wild Privet

Native. Woodland, hedgerows, scrub and road verges on chalk and limestone. An almost ubiquitous species of these habitats. Less common on the clays and Clays-with-flints and rare on acid soils.
10 km² 50 (96%) 1 km² 1449 (40%) Map 351, page 262

Ligustrum ovalifolium Hassk.
Garden Privet

Introduction. Always planted, most commonly for garden hedges or pheasant cover.
10 km² 41 (79%) 1 km² 248 (7%)

SCROPHULARIACEAE

Verbascum L.

Verbascum blattaria L.
Moth Mullein

Introduction. Garden escape.
N. Home Farm, Great Chalfield 1988 GY, disused railway near Moredon, Swindon 1990 JN.
10 km² 2 (4%)   1 km² 2 (<1%)

Verbascum virgatum Stokes
Twiggy Mullein

Nationally scarce plant.
Native in GB, introduction in Wilts.
N. Railway yard Swindon 1986 DG.
S. Numerous plants alongside railway track and between it and Hawkeridge Lane, Westbury 1988-90 JG & PS.
10 km² 2 (4%)   1 km² 2 (<1%)

Verbascum phlomoides L.
Orange Mullein

Introduction.
N. One plant on road verge SE of Easton Grey, plants on road verge Westbrook 1985 DG.
10 km² 2 (4%)   1 km² 2 (<1%)

Verbascum densiflorum Bertol.
Dense-flowered Mullein

Introduction.
S. Naturalised on embankment of new bypass, Bugley W of Warminster 1990 DG, first VC8 record.
10 km² 1 (2%)   1 km² 1 (<1%)

Verbascum thapsus L.
Great Mullein

Native. Disturbed calcareous and sandy soils in open situations including woodland clearings and scrub. Widely-distributed especially on disturbed soil on road verges on the chalk.
10 km² 48 (92%) 1 km² 466 (13%)   Map 352, page 262

Verbascum nigrum L.
Dark Mullein

Native. Rough grassland, road embankments and waste ground mainly on calcareous soils.
N. Rare, only 1-2 plants in some localities. Main

localities remaining as recorded by Grose at North Wraxall, Lockeridge and Mannington, some records being 100 years old.
S. Most common on road verges and rough chalk grassland around Salisbury.
10 km² 24 (46%) 1 km² 114 (3%)   Map 353, page 262

Scrophularia L.

Scrophularia nodosa L.
Common Figwort

Native. Most records are for woodland. Frequent and widely-distributed but in small numbers.
10 km² 48 (92%) 2 km² 490 (52%)   Map 354, page 262

Scrophularia auriculata L.
Water Figwort

Native. Lime-rich, wet places. Frequent and widely-distributed in these habitats.
10 km² 46 (88%) 2 km² 421 (44%)   Map 355, page 262

Scrophularia umbrosa Dumort.
Green Figwort

Nationally scarce plant.
Native. Riversides.
S. Plentiful on both sides of stream by watercress beds 'Shalbourne Stream', Wiltshire's only site, known since 1915. Reported as growing along stream for 1 km from its source to near Standen Manor 1986 CM, 1987 HJMB.
10 km² 1 (2%)   1 km² 1 (<1%)

Scrophularia vernalis L.
Yellow Figwort

Introduction.
S. Growing as a weed in a very old garden, Homington 1989 JA.
10 km² 1 (2%)   1 km² 1 (<1%)

Mimulus L.

Mimulus moschatus Douglas ex Lindley
Musk

Introduction.
N. Naturalised, growing between cobbles Roboan House, Dauntsey 1989 PD. First record since 1975.
10 km² 1 (2%)   1 km² 1 (<1%)

Mimulus guttatus DC.
Monkeyflower

Introduction. River and stream sides.
N. Long-standing records from the R. Kennet. Elsewhere, very rare.
S. Most records are from the rivers Wylye, Bourne and Till.
10 km² 19 (37%) 1 km² 62 (2%)   Map 356, page 262

Mimulus luteus L.
Blood-drop-emlets

Introduction.
S. In a ditch West Lavington 1989 RF, in the bed of a stream Cheverell Green Road 1991 BGH.
10 km² 2 (4%)   1 km² 2 (<1%)

Chaenorhinum (DC. ex Duby) Reichb.

Chaenorhinum minus (L.) Lange
Small Toadflax

Native. Open ground including arable soil and railway tracks.
Although widely-distributed in the county, this plant is usually found in small numbers. It is particularly· frequent on bare chalk on Salisbury Plain, around Aldbourne and as a garden weed.
10 km² 46 (88%) 2 km² 245 (26%)   Map 357, page 262

Misopates Raf.

Misopates orontium (L.) Raf.
Antirrhinum orontium L.
Lesser Snapdragon

Probably native. Weed of cultivated ground especially on sand.
N. Occurs only in market gardens on Lower Greensand at Bromham 1986 DG.
S. Fifty plants in one recently dug plot St Mark's Road allotments, Salisbury 1984 and allotments Quidhampton 1985 PM. On disturbed ground on railway bridge near London Road cemetery Salisbury 1990 NL. Gardens: Collingbourne Ducis 1986 JR, Whiteparish 1988 DJW. Fields: set-aside Whiteparish 1989 and maize grown for fodder Milkhills Farm, Redlynch 1990 DJW, near Hamptworth 1989 PW.
10 km² 5 (10%)   1 km² 8 (<1%)   Map 358, page 262

Asarina Miller

Asarina procumbens Miller
Trailing Snapdragon

Introduction.
S. Old Manor Hospital, Salisbury, two bushy specimens in roadside wall 1984 PM & MDT.
10 km² 1 (2%)   1 km² 1 (<1%)

Cymbalaria Hill

Cymbalaria muralis P. Gaertner, Meyer & Scherb.
Ivy-leaved Toadflax

Introduction. On old walls throughout the county. Common in the Cotswold towns and villages in NW Wilts, Swindon, Salisbury and Vale of Wardour.
10 km² 45 (87%) 2 km² 329 (35%) Map 359, page 265

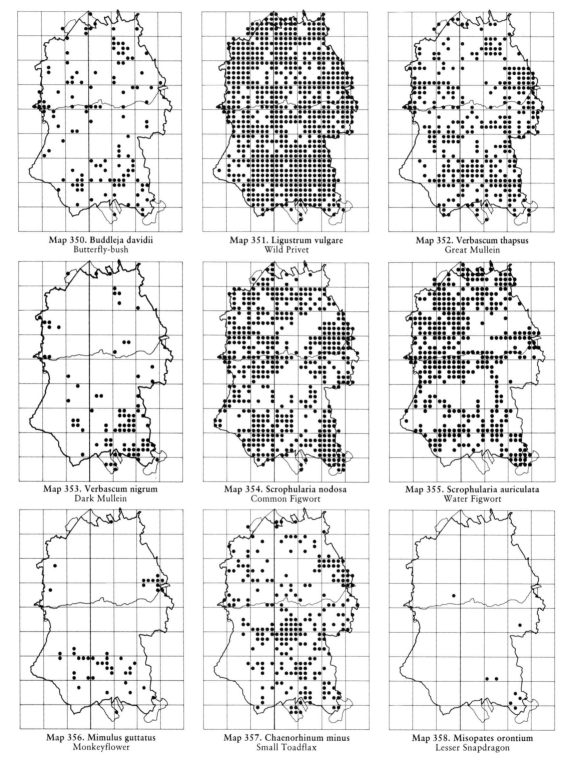

Map 350. **Buddleja davidii**
Butterfly-bush

Map 351. **Ligustrum vulgare**
Wild Privet

Map 352. **Verbascum thapsus**
Great Mullein

Map 353. **Verbascum nigrum**
Dark Mullein

Map 354. **Scrophularia nodosa**
Common Figwort

Map 355. **Scrophularia auriculata**
Water Figwort

Map 356. **Mimulus guttatus**
Monkeyflower

Map 357. **Chaenorhinum minus**
Small Toadflax

Map 358. **Misopates orontium**
Lesser Snapdragon

Kickxia Dumort.

Kickxia elatine (L.) Dumort.
Sharp-leaved Fluellin

Probably native. Arable land on calcareous soils. Uncommon, only occurring in reasonable quantity on the limestone in the NW and on chalk in SE. In decline due to the use of herbicides to create a sterile strip around headlands on arable land. Similar distribution to the next species.
10 km² 24 (46%) 1 km² 73 (2%)   Map 360, page 265

Kickxia spuria (L.) Dumort.
Round-leaved Fluellin

Probably native. Arable and waste land, only plentiful on calcareous soils.
N. Common on stony ground among cereal crops on the limestone but very rare on the chalk.
S. Occurs among cereal crops on the chalk but in decline due to the use of herbicides to create a sterile strip around the headlands. More common than *K. elatine*.
10 km² 25 (48%) 1 km² 106 (3%)   Map 361, page 265

Linaria Miller

Linaria vulgaris Miller
Common Toadflax

Native. Rough and waste ground, grassland. Locally frequent especially on railway cinder tracks and on semi-improved and rough chalk grassland.
10 km² 48 (92%) 2 km² 576 (61%)

Linaria purpurea (L.) Miller
Purple Toadflax

Introduction. A garden plant introduced from Italy in 1648. After escaping, it has shown considerable persistence colonising bare ground, railway embankments, walls and their bases,

usually near houses. Some evidence that it has been transported along the railways, but remains sparsely distributed throughout the county.
10 km² 34 (65%) 1 km² 111 (3%)   Map 362, page 265

Linaria purpurea x L. repens = L. x dominii Druce

Native.
N. First county record beside the railway at Swindon 1989 JN. Hybrid similar to *L. repens* but spur curved and more than half the length of the corolla.
10 km² 1 (2%)   1 km² 1 (<1%)

Linaria repens (L.) Miller
Pale Toadflax

Native in GB, introduction in Wilts.
N. An adventive along disused railway tracks. Main concentration around Swindon and on ballast in railway siding and embankment 1987 DG. Elsewhere at Thingley 1983 DG, near Coxhill Farm, Red Lodge 1984 MWS, known 4-5 years at base of wall East Kennet 1989 VS and Purton 1990 JW, Melksham 1990 JP and Cricklade 1991 SW.
S. Considered probably native on the chalk downs of VC8 by Grose in *The Flora of Wiltshire* but the only WFMP record was of an introduction on top of a rocky bank in lane Tisbury 1986 MM.
10 km² 7 (13%)   1 km² 11 (<1%)   Map 363, page 265

Digitalis L.

Digitalis purpurea L.
Foxglove

Native. Woodland clearings, hedges and heaths always on acid soils, including chalk superficials. Often planted and may survive in unsuitable calcareous habitat for a season or two.
N. Abundant only in very limited areas such as at

Spye Park, the Savernake Forest area and Flisteridge Wood near Minety.

S. Highest concentrations on Upper Greensand and clays in the SW and on the clays of the SE.

10 km² 41 (79%) 1 km² 456 (13%) Map 364, page 265

Digitalis lutea L.
Straw Foxglove

Introduction.

S. Roadside verge Codford St Mary 1987 BSBI meeting, Hindon. Refind of only known site comm. Mrs BG Sykes. Surviving in spite of road works on a WCC protected verge.

10 km² 1 (2%) 1 km² 1 (<1%)

Veronica L.

Veronica serpyllifolia L.
Thyme-leaved Speedwell

Native. Open woodland, neutral grassland, heaths and on leached or superficial deposits on chalk hill-tops. Common in suitable habitats.

10 km² 49 (94%) 2 km² 450 (47%) Map 365, page 265

Veronica officinalis L.
Heath Speedwell

Native. Open woodland, unimproved neutral to acidic grassland and heathland on well-drained soil. Thinly distributed due to the restriction of these habitats.

10 km² 41 (79%) 2 km² 152 (16%) Map 366, page 265

Veronica chamaedrys L.
Germander Speedwell

Native. Hedgebanks, roadside verges, unimproved neutral grassland, scrub and downland. Common and widely-distributed.

10 km² 50 (96%) 2 km² 836 (88%)

Veronica montana L.
Wood Speedwell

Native. Woodland, and lanes adjacent to woods. Indicative of ancient woodland sites but also occurs in older secondary woodland and steep-sided lanes adjacent to woods in N Wilts. Concentrations in wooded SE and Vale of Wardour in S Wilts.

10 km² 43 (83%) 1 km² 343 (9%) Map 367, page 265

Veronica scutellata L.
Marsh Speedwell

Native. Acidic bogs, marshes, borders of lakes and ponds.

N. Pond Goldborough Farm, Wootton Bassett 1986 JF.

S. In scattered localities. At Fonthill Lake 1985 VH, in a marshy meadow Stratford-sub-Castle 1985 PM, Wincombe 1987 JO and in meadow beside R. Nadder 1987 MDT, in a wet field West Grimstead 1988 IA, in drainage channels bordering wet meadows and in a bog in the Redlynch/Hamptworth area 1989 DJW & VW, 1991 AB.

10 km² 7 (13%) 1 km² 11 (<1%) Map 368, page 267

Veronica beccabunga L.
Brooklime

Native. Rivers, streams, canals, ponds and lakes where the water is lime-rich. Frequent in these habitats.

10 km² 46 (88%) 2 km² 443 (47%) Map 369, page 267

Veronica anagallis-aquatica L.
Blue Water-speedwell

Native. Running water, less commonly in gravel pits and canals. Common along the major rivers especially in lime-rich water.

10 km² 45 (87%) 1 km² 294 (8%) Map 370, page 267

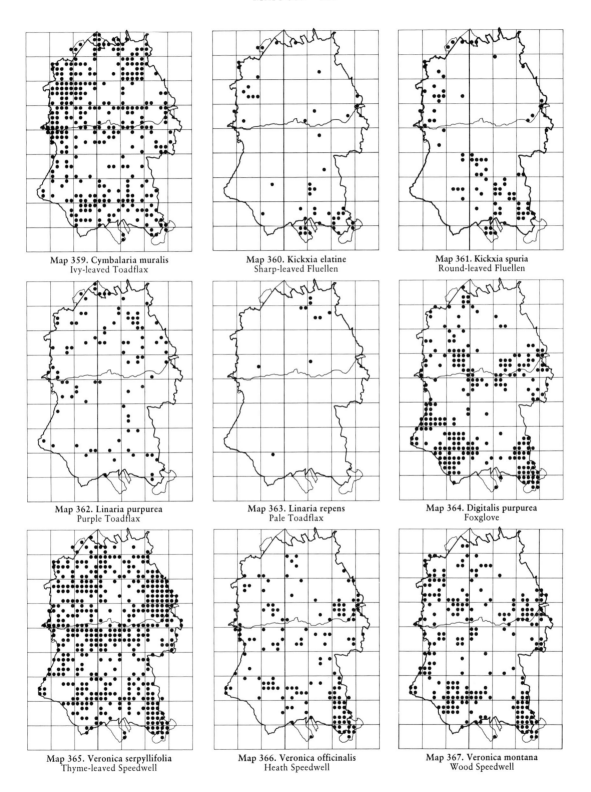

Map 359. **Cymbalaria muralis**
Ivy-leaved Toadflax

Map 360. **Kickxia elatine**
Sharp-leaved Fluellen

Map 361. **Kickxia spuria**
Round-leaved Fluellen

Map 362. **Linaria purpurea**
Purple Toadflax

Map 363. **Linaria repens**
Pale Toadflax

Map 364. **Digitalis purpurea**
Foxglove

Map 365. **Veronica serpyllifolia**
Thyme-leaved Speedwell

Map 366. **Veronica officinalis**
Heath Speedwell

Map 367. **Veronica montana**
Wood Speedwell

Veronica catenata Pennell
Pink Water-speedwell

Native. River, stream and pond mud where the water is usually slow-moving or static.
N. Abundant beside R. Kennet and upper reaches of the Bristol Avon. Occurs at the edge of the CWP lakes, the Brinkworth Brook and many ponds on the clay in the N of VC7.
S. Only four records. Semington Brook near Seend 1985 and almost dried out pond Bulkington 1990 BGH, Chilmark 1987 DF and in fast-flowing section of R. Avon centre of Pewsey 1990 JEO.
10 km² 13 (25%) 1 km² 48 (1%)   Map 371, page 267

Veronica arvensis L.
Wall Speedwell

Native. Restricted to stony ground, sparse grassland on thin soil and tops of walls. Common in these habitats.
10 km² 49 (94%) 2 km² 492 (52%)   Map 372, page 267

Veronica agrestis L.
Green Field-speedwell

Native. Cultivated ground and short turf.
N. Market garden Bromham 1986 JN & RR, church-yard Lydiard Millicent and Okus (Swindon) 1990 PA, Overton Down 1986 KP, Manton 1988 MP.
S. Bare ground by gateway to barley field Etchilhampton Hill 1984 BG.
10 km² 6 (12%)   1 km² 7 (<1%)   Map 373, page 267

Veronica polita Fries
Grey Field-speedwell

Native. Old stone walls, quarries, bare stony ground and arable land.
N. Frequent on stony cultivated land on limestone and greensand soils.
S. Most frequent around Salisbury.
10 km² 34 (65%) 1 km² 123 (3%)   Map 374, page 267

Veronica persica Poiret
Common Field-speedwell

Introduction. A common weed of cultivated land.
10 km² 51 (98%) 2 km² 788 (83%)

Veronica filiformis Smith
Slender Speedwell

Introduction. Mainly mown grass. Garden lawns, churchyards, public gardens. First Wilts record 1951. An increasing species, becoming well-established.
10 km² 47 (90%) 2 km² 297 (31%)   Map 375, page 267

Veronica hederifolia L.
Ivy-leaved Speedwell

Both ssp. *hederifolia* and ssp. *lucorum* (Klett & Richter) Hartl occur in the county but, for the WFMP, were recorded as the species.
Native. Disturbed soil. Common, often in large colonies.
10 km² 51 (98%) 2 km² 508 (54%)   Map 376, page 267

Veronica longifolia L.
Garden Speedwell

Introduction.
S. Known for 20 years at Pinecrest, Ford Down. First under hedge now at back of roadside verge 1985 PM.
10 km² 1 (2%)   1 km² 1 (<1%)

Melampyrum L.

Melampyrum arvense L.
Field Cow-wheat

British Red Data Book species.
Native. Occurs in six other sites in GB. A colony of considerable size which had appeared annually

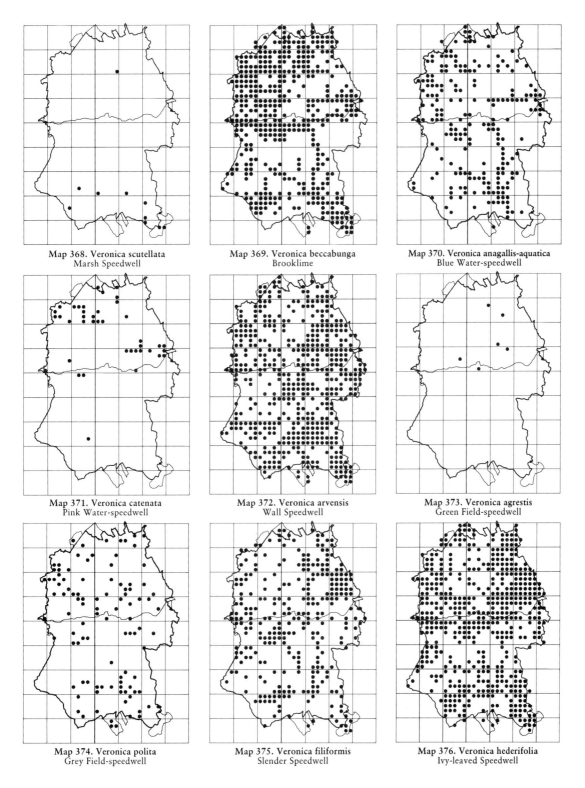

Map 368. Veronica scutellata
Marsh Speedwell

Map 369. Veronica beccabunga
Brooklime

Map 370. Veronica anagallis-aquatica
Blue Water-speedwell

Map 371. Veronica catenata
Pink Water-speedwell

Map 372. Veronica arvensis
Wall Speedwell

Map 373. Veronica agrestis
Green Field-speedwell

Map 374. Veronica polita
Grey Field-speedwell

Map 375. Veronica filiformis
Slender Speedwell

Map 376. Veronica hederifolia
Ivy-leaved Speedwell

for *c.*30 years in two garden flower-beds in N Wilts was reported to R Wright and confirmed by DG 1990. The garden is on the site of an arable field with boundary hedges on two sides of the property which were removed some years after the house was built. The colony, 175 plants in 1990, grows in well-tended weeded beds, the somewhat invasive cow-wheat itself being weeded until its value was realised. Since 1990, seed has been collected annually and sent to seedbanks for storage and distribution to new receptor sites. The host of this semi-parasitic plant in this colony has not been ascertained. Except for native *Achillea millefolium* all other plants in the beds are garden species.

10 km² 1 (2%)   1 km² 1 (<1%)

Melampyrum pratense L. ssp. **pratense**
Common Cow-wheat

Native. Woods and scrub on acid soil. Regarded as an indicator of ancient woodland.
N. Andover's Gorse, Charlton 1983 GR, trackside Puthall Park, Savernake Forest 1991 HK.
S. Common and a significant component of the ground flora of open woods in and around the New Forest. Frequent Whiteparish Common and the adjacent woodlands, in small numbers in Bentley Wood. Scattered records: from Fovant Wood 1984 MDT, Odstock and Muddyford Lane, Redlynch 1985 NLC & BKC (perhaps ssp. *commutatum*), Totterdale Farm woods, Tisbury 1987 MM, Frouds Copse, Semley 1987 and Chaddenwick Wood, Mere 1989 AH, footpath near Oakhill Farm 1988 CM, in Chase Woods and near Shermel Gate, Shire Rack 1991 JO.
Ssp. **commutatum** (Tausch ex A. Kerner) C. Britton
Native. Occurs on calcareous soils.
N. Ford near Mercombe Wood 1983 DG.
10 km² 13 (25%) 1 km² 33 (1%)   Map 377, page 271

Euphrasia L.
Owing to the difficulty of differentiating between the species of this genus all unconfirmed records have been included under *Euphrasia* agg. Dr A Silverside's help in identifying material is gratefully acknowledged.

Euphrasia L. agg.
Eyebright

Euphrasia nemorosa (Pers.) Wallr.
This is considered to be the commonest species in Wiltshire.
Native. Unimproved calcareous grassland and heathland. Very common especially in short turf on chalk downland. Less common on limestone and heathland.
10 km² 42 (81%) 1 km² 500 (14%)   Map 378, page 271

Euphrasia nemorosa x E. pseudokerneri

Native. Chalk downland.
N. Recorded only on Knap Hill 1986 KP (conf. Dr A Silverside).
10 km² 1 (2%)   1 km² 1 (<1%)

Euphrasia pseudokerneri Pugsley

Nationally scarce plant.
Native. Chalk downland.
N. Recorded only on Knap Hill 1986 KP (conf. Dr A Silverside).
10 km² 1 (2%)   1 km² 1 (<1%)

Odontites Ludwig

Odontites vernus (Bellardi) Dumort.
Red Bartsia

Native. Semi-improved and poached chalk grassland. Wasteland and woodland rides on chalk and clay, and on Clay-with-flints in Savernake Forest. Occurs in great quantity in some places especially on disturbed chalk soil.
10 km² 51 (98%) 2 km² 607 (64%)

Parentucellia Viv.

Parentucellia viscosa (L.) Caruel
Yellow Bartsia

Nationally scarce plant.
Native in GB, introduction in Wilts.
S. Three well-grown plants in rough grassland on imported soil by railway line Pewsey 1988 RD, DC, AJS & AH. An inland site for a plant usually found near the coast. Second VC8 record, first was at Manningford Abbotts about 1.5 km away 1952.
10 km² 1 (2%)   1 km² 1 (<1%)

Rhinanthus L.

Rhinanthus minor L. ssp. **minor**
Yellow-rattle

Native. Open grassland. Common in unimproved neutral lowland meadows especially in N Wilts and on chalk and limestone downland. Otherwise rare.
Ssp. **calcareus** (Wilm.) E. Warb.
Native. Late-flowering ssp. occurs only on chalk and limestone from Dorset to W Glos.
N. On limestone gravel CWP Ashton Keynes 1988 DG, in large numbers near chalk pit Morgan's Hill 1988 DG.
S. Frequent on chalk downland Bratton Castle 1990 DG.
10 km² 45 (87%) 2 km² 329 (35%) Map 379, page 271

Pedicularis L.

Pedicularis palustris L.
Marsh Lousewort

Native.
S. Growing with other wet heath plants on man-made site, an extraordinary record RAF Chilmark, Dinton 1987 PP (ver. AH).
10 km² 1 (2%)   1 km² 1 (<1%)

Pedicularis sylvatica L.
Lousewort

Native. Woodland rides, heaths and damp grassland on sandy acid soils.
N. Rare, occurring in several areas of Braydon Forest, in a sandy field corner at Compton Bassett, near Atworth and Colerne.
S. Most frequent in SE and in Nadder valley. Records show a marked decrease since 1957, though some earlier records may date from the 19th century.
10 km² 13 (25%) 1 km² 30 (<1%)   Map 380, page 271

OROBANCHACEAE

Lathraea L.

Lathraea squamaria L.
Toothwort

Native. Ancient woodland and banks of old sunken lanes through woodland. Requires moist, rich soil. Parasitic on roots of trees and shrubs especially hazel.
N. Very common in woods along the By Brook valley at Castle Combe and between Marlborough and Aldbourne. Rare elsewhere.
S. There are two main concentrations of records: in the Chute/Collingbourne and Redlynch/Tytherley areas.
The earliest recorded site (1805) at Clarendon survives.
10 km² 21 (40%) 1 km² 79 (2%)   Map 381, page 271

Lathraea clandestina L.
Purple Toothwort

Introduction. Perhaps naturalised.
S. Six patches in full flower on aspen, one of its usual hosts, after felling West Wood near Easterton 1992 JMP (ver. AH), first VC8 record.
10 km² 1 (2%)   1 km² 1 (<1%)

Orobanche L.

Orobanche elatior Sutton
Knapweed Broomrape

Native. Rank, unmanaged grassland as on banks of roads and lanes, usually on chalk soil, where the host of this root-parasite *Centaurea scabiosa* grows.
N. Very common on the chalk NE of Marlborough. On Corallian Beds at Wootton Bassett, Lyneham and Swindon. Absent from Oolite limestone where the host plant grows.
S. Very common on chalk over whole area. On Portland Limestone near Tisbury. Spikes up to 1 metre tall are a spectacle on rough grassland especially verges of old downland tracks. A large proportion of the GB population occurs in S Wilts.
10 km² 32 (62%) 1 km² 452 (12%) Map 382, page 271

Orobanche minor Smith var. **minor**
Common Broomrape

Native. Grassland and clover fields where host plants, members of Fabaceae, (mostly *Trifolium* species) and Asteraceae families grow.
N. Rare, occurring intermittently.
S. Widely-distributed but in small numbers, mainly on chalk soil.
10 km² 33 (63%) 1 km² 145 (4%)   Map 383, page 271

LENTIBULARIACEAE

Pinguicula L.

Pinguicula lusitanica L.
Pale Butterwort

Native. Bogs and wet flushes.
S. Only recorded in these habitats where associated with the New Forest and adjoining commons. Populations scattered, colonies varying from a few to 100+ plants. WTNC reserve Landford Bog 1992 PM.
10 km² 1 (2%)   1 km² 4 (<1%)

CAMPANULACEAE

Campanula L.

Campanula patula L.
Spreading Bellflower

Nationally scarce plant.
Native. In open grassy ride on Midford Sands in Westonbirt Arboretum (within the present county of Glos but botanical district VC7). Believed to be extinct but site protected by Arboretum staff after one plant was found 1985 HB; three plants and a second location found 100m away 1989 DG. Occurs in adjacent Silk Wood (VC 34 Glos) where first recorded 1939 (Jackson). Lost from all sites recorded earlier.
10 km² 1 (2%)   1 km² 1 (<1%)

Campanula glomerata L.
Clustered Bellflower

Native. Unimproved calcareous downland. Plant height varies greatly due to annual and seasonal variations in temperature, rainfall and in the grazing regime.
N. Very localised except on chalk around Aldbourne and on Pewsey Downs escarpment from Martinsell Hill W to Devizes. Sizeable colonies on limestone grassland around Castle Combe. Outlier colonies on Corallian Beds at Lyneham and around Swindon.
Form with white flowers, Danks Down 1984 DG, Truckle Hill 1985 ASk.
S. Frequent, a typical chalk grassland plant, though colonies may be thinly scattered over an area. In Nadder valley colonies occur on Portland/ Purbeck Beds.
10 km² 35 (67%) 1 km² 438 (12%) Map 384, page 271

Campanula latifolia L.
Giant Bellflower

Native in GB, introduction in Wilts.

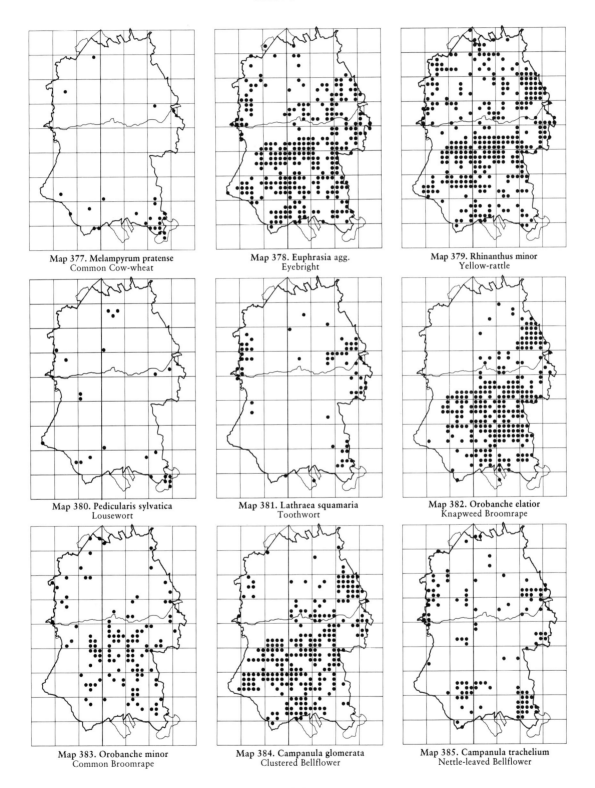

Map 377. Melampyrum pratense
Common Cow-wheat

Map 378. Euphrasia agg.
Eyebright

Map 379. Rhinanthus minor
Yellow-rattle

Map 380. Pedicularis sylvatica
Lousewort

Map 381. Lathraea squamaria
Toothwort

Map 382. Orobanche elatior
Knapweed Broomrape

Map 383. Orobanche minor
Common Broomrape

Map 384. Campanula glomerata
Clustered Bellflower

Map 385. Campanula trachelium
Nettle-leaved Bellflower

N. Near Battle Lake 1984 MWS & CS, near Lower Mill Farm CWP 1984 JS.
S. With seedlings The Pennings near Sidbury Hill 1986 BG.
10 km² 3 (6%)   1 km² 3 (<1%)

Campanula trachelium L.
Nettle-leaved Bellflower

Native. Woods, woodland rides, green lanes, hedgebanks and road verges on calcareous soils.
N. Plentiful in older woodland on the slopes of the By Brook valley from Castle Combe to Box and especially around Aldbourne. Its occurrence on road verges is always adjacent to, or within, ancient woodland or ancient hedges.
S. Most frequent in Vale of Wardour and in SE where plants are scattered along many old hedgebanks and woodland tracks. A fine colony on both sides of the Dinton/Wylye road is probably an outlier of Grovely Wood. These verges are protected.
10 km² 34 (65%) 1 km² 165 (5%)   Map 385, page 271

Campanula rotundifolia L.
Harebell

Native. Unimproved calcareous downland and dry sandy grassland.
N. Frequent on chalk downland but less common on limestone. Occurs in small quantity on sand at Bromham and Spye Park and on gravel in the CWP.
S. Widespread especially on the chalk, its range extending SE onto the acid soils of the New Forest.
10 km² 45 (87%) 1 km² 751 (21%) Map 386, page 274

Legousia Durande

Legousia hybrida (L.) Delarbre
Venus's-looking-glass

Native. Arable land on calcareous soils.
N. Restricted to a few localities on the Oolite limestone and clays. Very rare on the chalk.

S. More frequent. Records concentrated to N and S of Salisbury. See Wiltshire's Arable Weed Flora p.43.
10 km² 28 (54%) 1 km² 121 (3%)   Map 387, page 274

Wahlenbergia Schrader ex Roth

Wahlenbergia hederacea (L.) Reichb.
Ivy-leaved Bellflower

Native. Damp, acidic places.
S. Gutch Common 1987 PWa(NCC), one small patch surviving, original record 1868 (J Hussey). Cadnam Common (Hants) 1991 RV.
10 km² 2 (4%)   1 km² 2 (<1%)

Phyteuma L.

Phyteuma orbiculare L.
Phyteuma tenerum R. Schulz
Round-headed Rampion

Nationally scarce species.
Native. Unimproved chalk grassland.
N. Restricted to the chalk in four adjacent 10 km² of the downs lying N of the Vale of Pewsey between Devizes/Pewsey including Oliver's Castle, Beacon and King's Play Hills, Calstone Down, Avebury Circle and Tan, Kitchen Barrow and Walker's Hills.
S. Three widely separated locations, Martin Down, East Winterslow (first found and well-recorded) and Everleigh. See article p.81.
10 km² 7 (13%)   1 km² 29 (<1%)   Map 388, page 274

Jasione L.

Jasione montana L.
Sheep's-bit

Native. Sandy heathland.
S. Near Blenmans Farm, S of Furzley 1990 DJW.
10 km² 1 (2%)   1 km² 1 (<1%)

RUBIACEAE

Sherardia L.

Sherardia arvensis L.
Field Madder

Native. Cultivated land, disturbed soil and waste land.
N. Almost entirely on calcareous soils. Frequent on bare soil on arable field headlands, sometimes occurring in large colonies.
S. Common on SPTA on bare chalk and disturbed soil. See Wiltshire's Arable Weed Flora p.43.
10 km² 44 (85%) 1 km² 375 (10%)   Map 389, page 274

Asperula L.

Asperula cynanchica L.
Squinancywort

Native. Unimproved calcareous grassland. A typical plant of short chalk grassland, much more localised on limestone downland. This species has the ability to grow up through heaped soil on anthills and on some downland is more frequent on the mounds than in the surrounding grassland.
10 km² 36 (69%) 1 km² 419 (12%)   Map 390, page 274

Galium L.

Galium odoratum (L.) Scop.
Woodruff

Native. Woods and hedges on calcareous and base-rich soils. Common constituent of older woodlands where it is often locally abundant.
10 km² 41 (79%) 1 km² 365 (10%)   Map 391, page 274

Galium uliginosum L.
Fen Bedstraw

Native. Base-rich wet habitats. Has a more restricted distribution than that of G. *palustre* but are sometimes found growing together.
10 km² 36 (69%) 1 km² 116 (3%)   Map 392, page 274

Galium constrictum Chaub.
Galium debile Desv. non Hoffsgg. & Link
Slender Marsh-bedstraw

British Red Data Book species.
Native. Ditches and pondsides.
S. Drainage ditch margin, North Charlton water-meadows 1984 NLC (ver. JO). Approximately 30 plants in imported scalpings lining dry pond Shire Horse Centre, Teffont 1988 VH (ver. AH). First and second VC8 records (specimens from the two sites compared).
10 km² 2 (4%)   1 km² 2 (<1%)

Galium palustre L.
Common Marsh-bedstraw

Native. Wet and marshy places, including poorly drained unimproved fields, pond edges and ditches.
N. Most common on the low-lying clays N of Chippenham, in Braydon Forest area and along river valleys.
S. Most common on low-lying clays E of Trowbridge and in SE, on a variety of soils in Vale of Wardour, around Warminster and along river valleys.
10 km² 45 (87%) 1 km² 417 (11%)   Map 393, page 274

Galium verum L.
Lady's Bedstraw

Native. Unimproved and semi-improved grassland on chalk and limestone. A common species of these habitats, surviving on calcareous soils along road verges adjacent to arable land and far-removed from unimproved grassland. Less frequent on neutral and acid soils.
10 km² 48 (92%) 1 km² 1570 (43%) Map 394, page 274

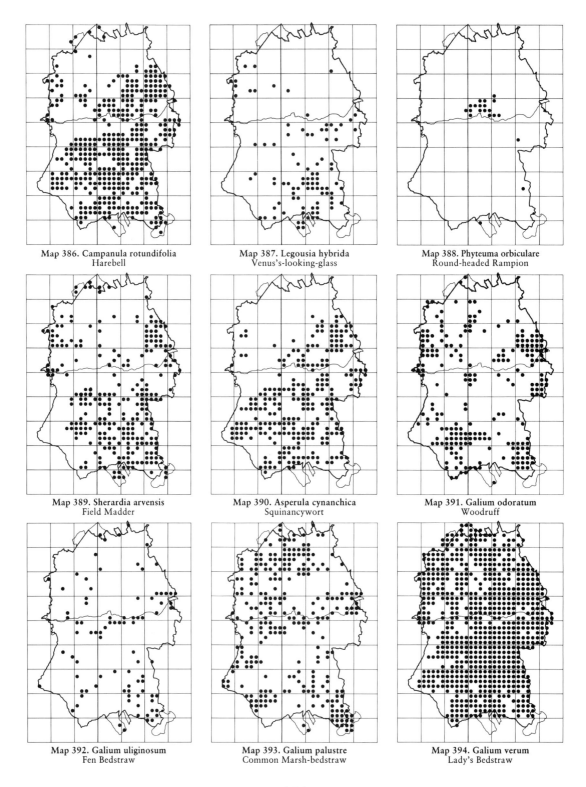

Map 386. **Campanula rotundifolia**
Harebell

Map 387. **Legousia hybrida**
Venus's-looking-glass

Map 388. **Phyteuma orbiculare**
Round-headed Rampion

Map 389. **Sherardia arvensis**
Field Madder

Map 390. **Asperula cynanchica**
Squinancywort

Map 391. **Galium odoratum**
Woodruff

Map 392. **Galium uliginosum**
Fen Bedstraw

Map 393. **Galium palustre**
Common Marsh-bedstraw

Map 394. **Galium verum**
Lady's Bedstraw

Galium mollugo L. ssp. **mollugo**
Hedge-bedstraw

Native. Hedgerows, grassy places. Widespread
and frequent.
Ssp. **erectum** Syme
Upright Hedge-bedstraw
Native. The status of this ssp. in GB is questioned
in Stace's *New Flora of the British Isles*. Side of
K & A Canal at Lower Foxhangers Farm, Devizes
1987 JEO.
10 km² 50 (94%) 2 km² 648 (68%)

Galium pumilum Murray
Slender Bedstraw

Nationally scarce plant.
Native. Dry chalk grassland.
S. Slay Down, Larkhill Ranges SPTA(C) 1986
RP (ver. M Wigginton NCC), second VC8 record.
10 km² 2 (4%)   1 km² 2 (<1%)

Galium saxatile L.
Heath Bedstraw

Native. Heaths, dry grassland and open woodland
rides on acid soils.
N. Far less frequent than the dots on the map
might suggest. Common only in the Savernake area
on superficial deposits on the chalk. Occurs locally
in Braydon Forest, on remnants of acid heath N of
Chippenham and on an area of greensand in Spye
Park undisturbed for many years.
S. Common on heaths and open woodland in SE.
Occurs in Great Ridge Wood on chalk superficials.
Elsewhere concentrations on clays and Upper
Greensand.
10 km² 31 (60%) 1 km² 154 (4%)   Map 395, page 278

Galium aparine L.
Cleavers

Native. Hedges, cultivated field and woodland

edges and open waste land. Very common.
10 km² 52 (100%)2 km² 913 (96%)

Cruciata Miller

Cruciata laevipes Opiz
Galium cruciata (L.) Scop.
Crosswort

Native. Woodland edges, hedges and rough
grassland on chalk superficials and clay.
N. Local, except N of Aldbourne where it is
common on banks and road verges.
S. Largest concentration on the superficials in
Great Ridge and Grovely Woods.
10 km² 30 (58%) 1 km² 108 (3%)   Map 396, page 278

CAPRIFOLIACEAE

Sambucus L.

Sambucus nigra L.
Elder

Native. Hedges, woodland. Very common
throughout the county.
10 km² 52 (100%)2 km² 907 (96%)

Sambucus ebulus L.
Dwarf Elder

Introduction, possibly native. Rhizomatous
perennial which spreads over large areas.
N. Roadside Ashley near Box and Slaughterford
where first recorded 1685 (John Aubrey) 1984
DG, Park Coppice, Ramsbury 1984 BP, Poole
Keynes 1985 SW, protected road verge Stowell
near Corsham 1986 DG, Fresden Farm near
Highworth 1989 MWS, W of Somerford Common
1990 PD. Known for a long time from many
locations.
S. Hundreds of bushes in unkempt hedges and in
large area near chicken farm Winterbourne Stoke

1983 JO, 1985 BG & JN, several on road verge Edington 1985 and in quantity roadside Chitterne to Codford 1989 HW, E of Codford St Mary 1991 JEO. For a species able to produce such large stands it is surprising that only three of the 12 sites in Grose's *The Flora of Wiltshire* survive.

10 km² 9 (17%)   1 km² 12 (<1%)   Map 397, page 278

Viburnum L.

Viburnum opulus L.
Guelder-rose

Native. Woodland, scrub, hedges and streambanks. Widely-distributed but often occurs singly. Found in similar habitats to those of *V. lantana*, but is more tolerant of non-calcareous soils.

10 km² 49 (94%) 1 km² 732 (20%)   Map 398, page 278

Viburnum lantana L.
Wayfaring-tree

Native. Woodland edges, scrub and hedges mainly on calcareous soils.
N. A constant species of hedges and scrub on the chalk and limestone. Very rare on more acidic soil.
S. Common in woods, scrub and hedges on calcareous soils. On clay only in the SE. Absent from large areas of SPTA.

10 km² 47 (90%) 1 km² 978 (27%)   Map 399, page 278

Symphoricarpos Duhamel

Symphoricarpos albus (L.) S. F. Blake
Symphoricarpos rivularis Suksd.
Snowberry

Introduction. Woods, hedges and scrub. Planted as hedges for ornament and pheasant cover. Strong suckering properties have led to weed status. Widely-distributed, in remote areas often indicates the site of an old cottage or farm buildings.

10 km² 47 (90%) 1 km² 419 (12%)

Lonicera L.

Lonicera nitida E. Wilson
Wilson's Honeysuckle

Introduction. A species commonly planted as cover for pheasants and found as a remnant of old cottage gardens.

10 km² 5 (10%)   1 km² 18 (<1%)

Lonicera xylosteum L.
Fly Honeysuckle

British Red Data Book species.
Native in GB, introduction in Wilts. Garden escape and planted in woods for pheasant cover.

10 km² 4 (8%)   1 km² 6 (<1%)

Lonicera periclymenum L.
Honeysuckle

Native. Woods, hedges and scrub. A good indicator of neutral and acid soil conditions where it is frequent in woodland and scrub.

10 km² 50 (96%) 1 km² 1179 (32%) Map 400, page 278

ADOXACEAE

Adoxa L.

Adoxa moschatellina L.
Moschatel

Native. Moist woodland, streambanks and the base of ancient hedges usually where high levels of humus are present.
N. Occurs in most woods but is less common on the heavy clay in the Braydon Forest area than elsewhere.
S. Widely-distributed in moist woods. Absent from the dry woods on the chalk.

10 km² 47 (90%) 1 km² 656 (18%) Map 401, page 278

VALERIANACEAE

Valerianella Miller

Valerianella locusta (L.) Laterr.
Common Cornsalad

Native. Cultivated land, walls, waste ground and bare places.
N. Uncommon, most of the records are from the base of walls and cottage gardens in the Cotswold villages in the NW and N of Aldbourne.
S. The largest concentration of records is from arable land on the chalk W of Salisbury.
10 km² 23 (44%) 1 km² 63 (2%)   Map 402, page 278

Valerianella carinata Lois.
Keeled-fruited Cornsalad

Native. Walls, cracks in paving stones. Rare.
N. On dumped soil CWP 1988 SCH, Reybridge causeway 1990 DG, Old Swindon 1991 PA.
S. High Post Hotel and Woodford Green 1984 PM, Chicksgrove quarry 1985 MM, on cleared ground Odstock Hospital 1987 JO.
10 km² 6 (12%)   1 km² 7 (<1%)

Valerianella rimosa Bast.
Broad-fruited Cornsalad

British Red Data Book species.
Native. Cornfields and rough ground.
S. Beside a hedge adjacent to Whiteparish quarry 1983-84 RC & NLC.
10 km² 1 (2%)   1 km² 1 (<1%)

Valerianella dentata (L.) Pollich
Narrow-fruited Cornsalad

Nationally scarce plant.
Native. Arable and rough ground, railway cuttings and embankments. Once frequent in cornfields.

N. Only two records, near Chippenham DG and in Savernake Forest.
S. Now only frequent around Salisbury. See Wiltshire's Arable Weed Flora p.43.
10 km² 14 (27%) 1 km² 40 (1%)   Map 403, page 278

Valeriana L.

Valeriana officinalis L.
Common Valerian

Native. Damp and dry habitats. Riverbanks, woodland glades, hedgebanks and among tall rank vegetation.
N. Widespread, especially on damp road verges in the Braydon Forest area.
S. Widespread, including woodland edge and scrub on the chalk in and around Grovely and Great Ridge Woods.
10 km² 47 (90%) 1 km² 518 (14%) Map 404, page 280

Valeriana dioica L.
Marsh Valerian

Native. Fens, bogs, marshes, wet meadows and woodland.
N. Restricted to the wettest areas, sometimes in open alder woodland. Abundant in meadows adjacent to the R. Kennet E of Marlborough and along the clay/greensand spring-line near Lacock. Elsewhere, in valley bottoms on Corallian Beds and Oolite limestone.
S. Damp meadows in the Salisbury Avon valley. In damp woods in Whiteparish/Redlynch area.
10 km² 30 (58%) 1 km² 87 (2%)   Map 405, page 280

Centranthus Necker ex Lam. & DC.

Centranthus ruber (L.) DC.
Red Valerian

Introduction. Naturalised on walls (usually stone),

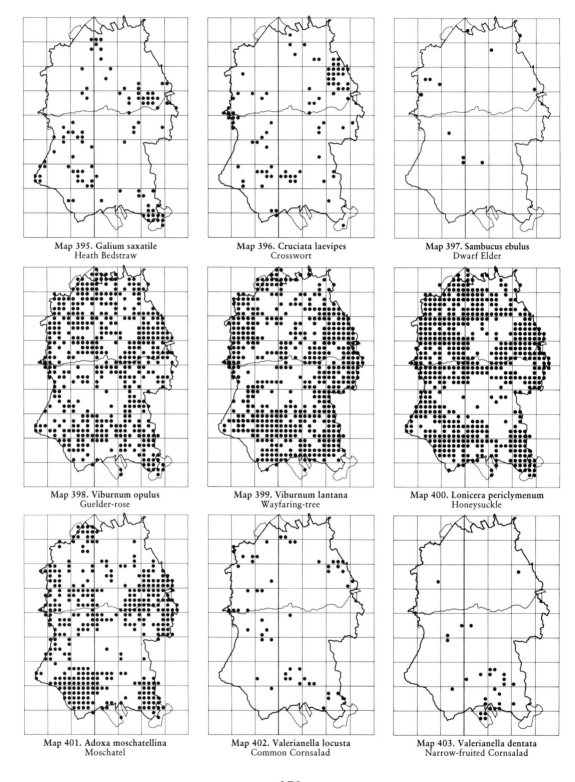

Map 395. Galium saxatile
Heath Bedstraw

Map 396. Cruciata laevipes
Crosswort

Map 397. Sambucus ebulus
Dwarf Elder

Map 398. Viburnum opulus
Guelder-rose

Map 399. Viburnum lantana
Wayfaring-tree

Map 400. Lonicera periclymenum
Honeysuckle

Map 401. Adoxa moschatellina
Moschatel

Map 402. Valerianella locusta
Common Cornsalad

Map 403. Valerianella dentata
Narrow-fruited Cornsalad

pavements, derelict buildings and waste ground. This perennial can become large and, with its efficient adaptation for wind dispersal of its seeds, it is invasive. Grown on garden walls for its showy red flowers. Form with white flowers is frequent in N.
10 km² 37 (71%) 1 km² 105 (3%)   Map 406, page 280

DIPSACACEAE

Dipsacus L.

Dipsacus fullonum L.
Dipsacus sylvestris Hudson
Teasel

Native. Marginal land between many types of habitat: field edges, road verges, stream banks, waste places, disturbed edges of woodland rides. Well-distributed. Likely to occur in the right conditions almost anywhere.
10 km² 51 (98%) 1 km² 895 (25%)   Map 407, page 280

Dipsacus pilosus L.
Small Teasel

Native. Open woodland, woodland edges, damp hedgerows, river and stream banks. Occurs along some stretches of the Bristol Avon and its tributaries, R. Frome, R. Nadder, on the Lower Greensand NW of Devizes, around Potterne and on heavy clays in NW of the county. Scattered elsewhere.
10 km² 20 (38%) 1 km² 55 (2%)   Map 408, page 280

Knautia L.

Knautia arvensis (L.) Coulter
Field Scabious

Native. Unmanaged grassland on grassy banks, field borders, track and roadside verges. Most commmon on calcareous soils, occurring sparingly elsewhere and avoiding heavy clays.
10 km² 48 (92%) 1 km² 1341 (37%) Map 409, page 280

Succisa Haller

Succisa pratensis Moench
Devils'-bit Scabious

Native. Damp and dry unimproved grassland. Neutral meadows, chalk and limestone downland, scrub, woodland rides and clearings on all but very acidic soils. Widespread and sometimes locally abundant.
10 km² 49 (94%) 2 km² 378 (40%)   Map 410, page 280

Scabiosa L.

Scabiosa columbaria L.
Small Scabious

Native. Unimproved calcareous downland.
N. Occurs widely in this habitat and rarely elsewhere.
S. Large populations on chalk grassland especially where grazed, as at Parsonage Down NNR.
10 km² 42 (81%) 1 km² 729 (20%)   Map 411, page 280

ASTERACEAE

Carlina L.

Carlina vulgaris L.
Carline Thistle

Native. Chalk and limestone downland. The distribution of this plant is localised to areas within this habitat where the soil is thin and vegetation sparse.
N. More widespread on chalk than limestone. Numerous colonies on the Pewsey Downs and in By Brook valley.
S. Colonies usually small. Old chalk quarries

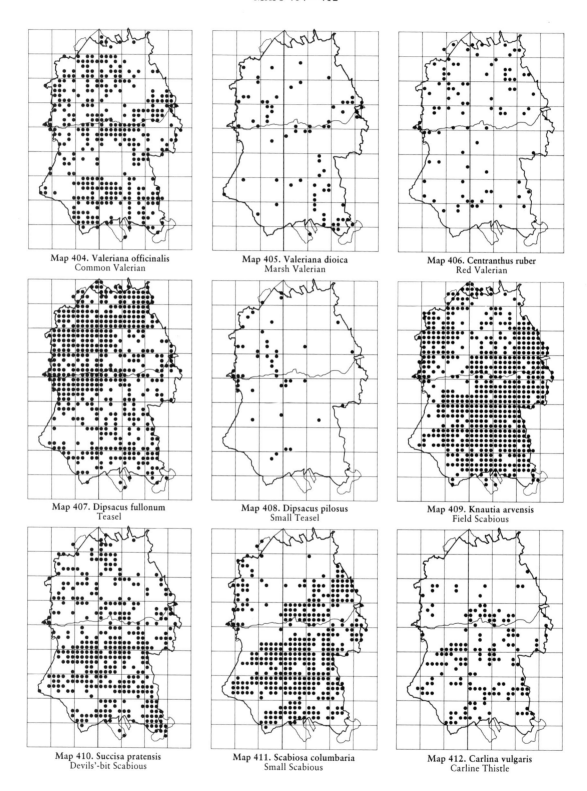

Map 404. *Valeriana officinalis*
Common Valerian

Map 405. *Valeriana dioica*
Marsh Valerian

Map 406. *Centranthus ruber*
Red Valerian

Map 407. *Dipsacus fullonum*
Teasel

Map 408. *Dipsacus pilosus*
Small Teasel

Map 409. *Knautia arvensis*
Field Scabious

Map 410. *Succisa pratensis*
Devils'-bit Scabious

Map 411. *Scabiosa columbaria*
Small Scabious

Map 412. *Carlina vulgaris*
Carline Thistle

and prehistoric man-made banks are typical sites where flowering stems remain throughout the winter.

10 km² 30 (58%) 1 km² 234 (6%)   Map 412, page 280

Arctium L.

Arctium lappa L.
Greater Burdock

Native. Road verges, hedgerows, woodland edges. Well-distributed. Most frequent on lowland clay. Some records may have been mis-identified for *A. minus* agg.

10 km² 41 (79%) 1 km² 298 (8%)   Map 413, page 284

Arctium minus (Hill) Bernh.
Lesser Burdock

Two sspp. *A. minus* ssp. *minus*, and *A. minus* ssp. *pubens* (Bab.) Arènes were recorded as an aggregate during the WFMP.
Native. Woodland, field margins, road verges, river and stream banks. Common throughout the county.

10 km² 52 (100%) 1 km² 1921 (53%)

Carduus L.

Carduus tenuiflorus Curtis
Slender Thistle

Native. A coastal rather than an inland species.
S. Large colony, 100+ specimens on banks of regularly-maintained drainage ditch Hurdcott near Ford with very large numbers of *C. vulgare* and *C. arvense* 1984. Specimens reduced to 30+, and numbers of other *Cirsium* species much reduced, the bare soil of the previous year having become covered 1985 PM. Only fifth site for county since first recorded 100 years ago.

10 km² 1 (2%)   1 km² 1 (<1%)

Carduus crispus L. ssp. multiflorus (Gaudin) Franco
Carduus acanthoides auct. non L.
Welted Thistle

Native. Hedgerows, rough ground and woodland clearings. Widely-distributed especially on clay soils. Much more frequent in N than S.

10 km² 48 (92%) 2 km² 465 (49%)   Map 414, page 284

Carduus nutans L.
Musk Thistle

Native. Rough grassland and disturbed calcareous soils. Frequent on chalk especially on the SPTA where bare soil is regularly exposed by tanks and exploding shells. Local on limestone. Rare elsewhere.

10 km² 43 (83%) 2 km² 377 (40%)   Map 415, page 284

Cirsium Miller

Cirsium eriophorum (L.) Scop.
Woolly Thistle

Native. Chalk and limestone downland, road verges, rough pasture and woodland clearings on calcareous soils.
N. Locally common. A bane to some farmers due to its large size. Occurs occasionally on calcareous clays.
S. Most frequent on SPTA where large areas of unfarmed land with localised soil disturbance provide an ideal habitat. Usually grows in small colonies.

10 km² 39 (75%) 1 km² 347 (10%)   Map 416, page 284

Cirsium vulgare (Savi) Ten.
Spear Thistle

Native. Grassland, waste and cultivated land. Very common.

10 km² 52 (100%) 2 km² 887 (93%)

Cirsium dissectum (L.) Hill
Meadow Thistle

Native. Unimproved wet grassland, on neutral to acid soils.
N. Distribution very restricted. Highest concentration is in unimproved meadows in the Minety area: Red Lodge 1984 DG, Minety Common 1985 MWS, Emmett Hill 1986 JF and Pike Corner (CWP) 1986 DH. Elsewhere near Honey Hill Copse 1986 JF and Alderton 1991 DG. Has declined (cf. Grose).
S. Its stronghold extends from neutral/acidic meadows near Whiteparish and Redlynch to peat bogs associated with the New Forest at Landford and Furzley Bogs. Elsewhere scattered: on greensand and gault clays near Stourton 1991 PMW, Dinton 1989 SMP and Chapmanslade 1991 LB, Vale of Pewsey 1984 BG & WTNC/ST, 1985 RF.
10 km² 12 (23%) 1 km² 27 (<1%)   Map 417, page 284

Cirsium tuberosum (L.) All.
Tuberous Thistle

British Red Data Book species.
Native. Unimproved chalk grassland. In GB, all but two locations for this plant are in Wilts.
N. The frequency of the hybrid C. tuberosum x C. acaule on some sites has led to a misconception that C. tuberosum is more frequent than is its real status. Records for Calstone Down (where it was not refound) and the Pewsey Downs are true-bred. All the others in the N show a degree of hybridity.
S. Majority of GB population occurs in S Wilts. Most frequent on SPTA(W) with outlying colonies to the S. See article on p.83.
10 km² 9 (17%) 1 km² 13 (<1%)

Cirsium tuberosum x C. acaule = C. x medium All.

Native. Chalk downland both grazed and ungrazed.

N. Flower spikes vary in height from 150-450 mm. Small colonies 3-40 plants Oliver's Castle, Oldbury Castle, Avebury SE, DG & VS 1983-86, Milk Hill and Knap Hill KP 1985.
S. The largest colonies are on SPTA(W) at Warden's Down and Ladywell 1986 SE. Twelve small colonies found SPTA(W) 1992 JPi. Kingston Deverill 1986 BG & AH. See article on p.83.
10 km² 5 (10%) 1 km² 14 (<1%)

Cirsium tuberosum x C. palustre = C. x semidecurrens H. Richter

S. Single plant in a different site from that recorded by Grose 1986 SE.
10 km² 1 (2%) 1 km² 1 (<1%)

Cirsium heterophyllum (L.) Hill
Cirsium helenioides auct. non (L.) Hill
Melancholy Thistle

Native in GB, introduction in Wilts.
S. Lower Coombe, Ludwell 1991 MM, refind of first county record 1984 RT.
10 km² 1 (2%) 1 km² 1 (<1%)

Cirsium acaule (L.) Scop.
Dwarf Thistle

Native. Frequent on unimproved chalk and limestone grassland. Occurs locally on base-rich meadows over gravel in CWP and on clay.
10 km² 45 (87%) 2 km² 454 (48%)   Map 418, page 284

Cirsium palustre (L.) Scop.
Marsh Thistle

Native. Damp woodland and grassland habitats. Frequent and locally abundant on damp grassland. Also occurs on dry chalk grassland on Salisbury Plain.
10 km² 49 (94%) 2 km² 553 (58%)   Map 419, page 284

Cirsium arvense (L.) Scop.
Creeping Thistle

Native. Grassland, especially where trampled by farm stock. Very common throughout the county.
10 km² 52 (100%)2 km² 908 (96%)

Onopordum L.

Onopordum acanthium L.
Cotton Thistle

Introduction. Waste land and road verges. Scattered. The unpredictable appearance of this 3 m tall biennial in its second year of growth can be dramatic.
10 km² 8 (15%)   1 km² 14 (<1%)

Silybum Adans.

Silybum marianum (L.) Gaertner
Milk Thistle

Introduction. Naturalises on rough ground.
N. Hayes Wood Farm 1989, Townsend Farm, Horton 1986 BG & JL.
S. Large patch on road verge Seend Cleeve 1990 BG, garden escape Manor Farm, Steeple Langford 1985 BL.
10 km² 4 (8%)   1 km² 4 (<1%)

Serratula L.

Serratula tinctoria L.
Saw-wort

Native. Unimproved chalk and limestone downland, damp unimproved neutral meadows and pasture, woodland edges and roadside verges on clay.
N. Most abundant in damp ridge-and-furrow pastures in Braydon Forest area where it frequently survives on field boundary hedge lines along the

edge of improved fields. Abundant on West Yatton Down on limestone. Local on the chalk.
S. Mainly on chalk grassland, especially within the Impact Area of SPTA(C). Frequent at Chickengrove Bottom (WTNC Reserve) on superficial deposits. Elsewhere, local in damp meadows and woodland clearings.
10 km² 34 (65%) 1 km² 336 (9%)   Map 420, page 284

Centaurea L.

Centaurea scabiosa L.
Greater Knapweed

Native. Rough grassland and road verges on chalk and limestone and in unimproved meadows CWP. In these habitats it is common and locally abundant. Elsewhere it occurs sparingly.
Form with white flowers, Salisbury Clump 1984 PM, Stoford 1988 BL, Wylye Down 1990 DP.
10 km² 50 (96%) 2 km² 654 (69%) Map 421, page 284

Centaurea montana L.
Perennial Cornflower

Introduction. Perennial garden throw-out persisting for many years at original site but apparently unable to regenerate from seed.
10 km² 5 (10%)   1 km² 10 (<1%)

Centaurea cyanus L.
Cornflower

Nationally scarce plant.
Native and introduction. More than half the records appear to be of traditionally naturalised plants.
N. All bird-seed introductions. No natural occurrences for many years.
S. Large numbers of plants appeared with *Agrostemma githago* after removal of a hedge Westbury recreation ground 1986 VEH. A most interesting record. 2-3 plants side of lane Edington and single plant in middle of field Marston 1986

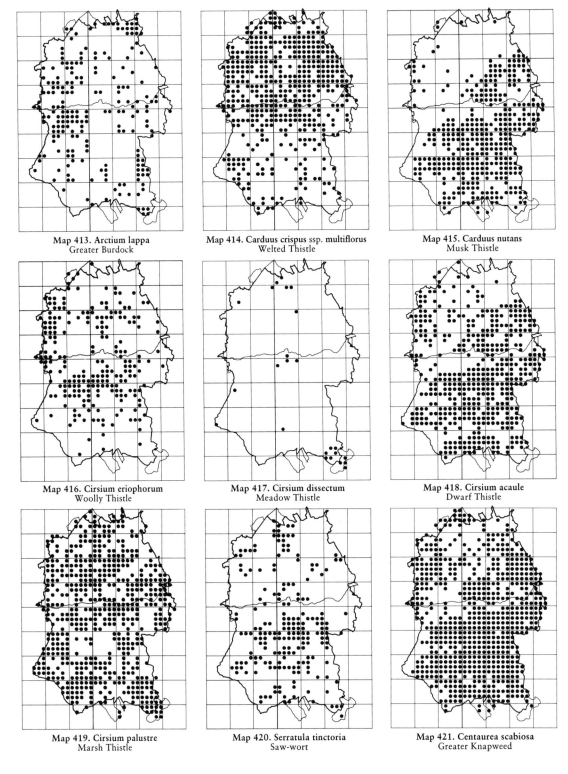

Map 413. *Arctium lappa*
Greater Burdock

Map 414. *Carduus crispus* ssp. *multiflorus*
Welted Thistle

Map 415. *Carduus nutans*
Musk Thistle

Map 416. *Cirsium eriophorum*
Woolly Thistle

Map 417. *Cirsium dissectum*
Meadow Thistle

Map 418. *Cirsium acaule*
Dwarf Thistle

Map 419. *Cirsium palustre*
Marsh Thistle

Map 420. *Serratula tinctoria*
Saw-wort

Map 421. *Centaurea scabiosa*
Greater Knapweed

BGH. In cornfield Tottenham House Park 1986 FP, two plants in hayfield Carver's Hill Farm, Shalbourne 1987 CM, Conygre Farm, Easton Royal 1988 KMM, Westcourt, Burbage 1988 WW, two plants in grassland cut for hay Fordbrook near Pewsey 1988 JEO.

10 km² 7 (13%)   1 km² 11 (<1%)   Map 422, page 290

Centaurea nigra L.
Common Knapweed

Native. Grassland, roadsides, wasteland. The *C. nigra*/*C. nemoralis* group was recorded as an aggregate during the WFMP. The level of gradation between these species is such that there is a lack of sustainable evidence to differentiate between the two. We believe that *C. nemoralis*, whatever its rank, is more common on chalk and limestone than on the heavier soils of the N.

Form with white flowers, Manor Farm, East Grimstead 1984 PAW, East Knoyle 1990 DP.

10 km² 49 (94%) 2 km² 762 (80%)

Cichorium L.

Cichorium intybus L.
Chicory

Possibly native. Waste ground, road verges, arable field margins and grassland. Exact habitat requirements are unknown. Colonies usually small but often long-lived, many are probably remnants of cultivation. Less frequent S of Salisbury Plain. Form with white flowers, Black Acre Farm, Holt 1989 TB.

10 km² 29 (56%) 1 km² 91 (3%)   Map 423, page 290

Lapsana L.

Lapsana communis L.
Nipplewort

Native. Open woodlands, hedgerows and waste ground. Locally common. Widely-distributed.

10 km² 50 (96%) 2 km² 806 (85%)

Hypochaeris L.
One of the superficially similar yellow-flowered genera of Asteraceae which presented WFMP recorders with identification problems. Assistance with identification was given at field and herbarium workshops, the importance of close examination of fruits and pappus being stressed.

Hypochaeris radicata L.
Cat's-ear

Native. Many types of grassland, lawns and churchyards. Frequent and widespread.

10 km² 49 (94%) 2 km² 555 (58%)

Leontodon L.
See remarks for *Hypochaeris*.

Leontodon autumnalis L.
Autumn Hawkbit

Native. Many grassland habitats. Frequent, especially on chalk soil.

10 km² 49 (94%) 2 km² 620 (65%)

Leontodon hispidus L.
Rough Hawkbit

Native. Calcareous and neutral grassland. Most frequent on calcareous soil.

10 km² 49 (94%) 2 km² 607 (64%)

Leontodon saxatilis Lam.
Leontodon taraxacoides (Villars) Mérat
Lesser Hawkbit

Native. Grassland mainly on calcareous and basic soils, but on neutral to acid soils around the New

Forest area. Occurs in similar habitats and flowering at the same time as *L. hispidus*. Probably under-recorded and sometimes mis-identified.

10 km² 40 (77%) 1 km² 210 (6%)   Map 424, page 290

Picris L.

See remarks for *Hypochaeris*.

Picris echioides L.
Bristly Oxtongue

Probably introduced. Waste ground and disturbed soil mainly on clay.

N. Common on the M4 verges, on agricultural land in NE and building sites at Swindon.

S. Most records are from clay soils in the Devizes, Trowbridge and Westbury areas and on London Clay near Dean Hill. Few records from the chalk.

10 km² 32 (62%) 1 km² 179 (5%)   Map 425, page 290

Picris hieracioides L.
Hawkweed Oxtongue

Native. Unimproved chalk and limestone grassland, woodland edges, road verges and quarries on calcareous soils.

N. Herb-rich, ungrazed calcareous grassland and, as a relic, on road verges and railway cuttings.

S. Unimproved chalk grassland, particularly common on SPTA.

10 km² 39 (75%) 1 km² 119 (3%)   Map 426, page 290

Tragopogon L.

Tragopogon pratensis L. ssp. minor (Miller) Wahlenb.
Goat's-beard

Native. Rough, dry grassy places particularly on calcareous soils. Widely-distributed but always in small numbers.

10 km² 49 (94%) 1 km² 1242 (34%)

Sonchus L.

Sonchus arvensis L.
Perennial Sow-thistle

Native. Arable land and hedgebanks. Widely-distributed. Less common than *S. oleraceus* and *S. asper*.

10 km² 50 (96%) 2 km² 669 (70%)

Sonchus oleraceus L.
Smooth Sow-thistle

Native. Cultivated land, especially in gardens and other disturbed habitats on all soil types. Distributed throughout the county.

10 km² 51 (98%) 1 km² 1287 (35%)

Sonchus asper (L.) Hill
Prickly Sow-thistle

Native. All types of cultivated and disturbed soil. Widespread throughout. More common than *S. arvensis* or *S. oleraceus*.

10 km² 51 (98%) 1 km² 1573 (43%)

Lactuca L.

Lactuca serriola L.
Prickly Lettuce

Probably native in GB, introduction in Wilts. Disturbed soil on road verges, tips, farmyards and grassland. One of the most successful invaders in the last 20 years. Grose had four entries in *The Flora of Wiltshire*. The completion of the M4 in 1971 provided a continuous length of bare soil along which this plant, with its wind-borne seeds, extended its range westward from London across the county. The expansion of Swindon and road widening in many areas has enabled its spread to include more rural locations.

10 km² 28 (54%) 1 km² 112 (3%)   Map 427, page 290

Lactuca virosa L.
Great Lettuce

Introduction. Apparently unable to spread as readily as *L. serriola*.
N. On waste soil CWP near Howells Barn and at Ashton Keynes 1986-87 DG.

10 km² 1 (2%)   1 km² 2 (<1%)

Cicerbita Wallr.

Cicerbita macrophylla (Willd.) Wallr.
Common Blue-sow-thistle

Introduction. A garden plant which has naturalised very successfully in rank vegetation on road verges.

10 km² 14 (27%) 1 km² 25 (<1%)

Mycelis Cass.

Mycelis muralis (L.) Dumort.
Wall Lettuce

Native. Woodland, walls and hedgerows.
N. Often abundant on walls in Cotswold towns and villages, especially at Bradford-on-Avon and Malmesbury. Scattered elsewhere.
S. Frequent in beech hangers on N edge of Salisbury Plain, in Avon valley above Salisbury and Pepperbox Hill.

10 km² 37 (71%) 1 km² 176 (5%)   Map 428, page 290

Taraxacum Wigg.
Identification of the microspecies of this very critical genus was not attempted by most WFMP recorders.

Taraxacum Wigg. agg.
Dandelions

Taraxacum sect. Ruderalia Kirschner, Oellgaard & Stepanek
Sect. *Vulgaria* Dahlst. nom. illeg.
Taraxacum officinale Wigg. group
Common Dandelion

Native. All types of grassland and waste land. Very common throughout the county.
Very few of the many species identified for GB within this aggregate group have been accurately determined in Wiltshire. With the exception of the species listed below, all non-specific *Taraxacum* records submitted for the WFMP have been included in the figures below.

10 km² 52 (100%) 2 km² 911 (96%)

Taraxacum sect. Erythrosperma (Lindb. f.) Dahlst.
Taraxacum laevigatum (Willd.) DC. group
Lesser Dandelion

Native. Chalk downland.
S. Recolonised bare chalk among rabbit-grazed downland near Shrewton Folly SPTA(C) 1984 BG. Scattered Idmiston Down OS, Middleton Down 1989 BL, with *Carex humilis* Croucheston Drove 1991 PW, one plant Knapp Down 1991 MDT.

10 km² 7 (13%)   1 km² 11 (<1%)

Taraxacum sect. Palustria (Dahlst.) Dahlst.
Taraxacum palustre (Lyons) Symons group
Marsh Dandelion

Native. Damp unimproved neutral pasture. Rare.
S. Several plants and possible hybrids with *T. sect. Ruderalia* Etchilhampton, a few plants amongst *T. sect. Ruderalia* and one hybrid Hatfield Farm. Both sites may be refinds of *The Flora of*

Wiltshire records. One plant Marden. All 1985
RF (ver. AH).
10 km² 1 (2%)   1 km² 3 (<1%)

Crepis L.
See remarks for *Hypochaeris*.

Crepis biennis L.
Rough Hawk's-beard

Introduction. Road verges, railway cuttings and
waste places.
N. Only frequent along a few stretches of railway
line especially between Hullavington and Alderton.
S. Probably mis-identified and over-recorded in
some localities. Occurs on track verge at Hare
Warren near Wilton and on disturbed grassland
Potterne.
10 km² 24 (46%) 1 km² 91 (3%)

Crepis capillaris (L.) Wallr.
Smooth Hawk's-beard

Native. Grassland and disturbed soil. Common
throughout the county.
10 km² 51 (98%) 2 km² 630 (66%)

Crepis vesicaria L.
Beaked Hawk's-beard

Introduction. Disturbed ground, road verges. Has
recently spread to lowland pastures. An increasing
species.
10 km² 44 (85%) 2 km² 362 (38%)   Map 429, page 290

Crepis setosa Haller f.
Bristly Hawk's-beard

Introduction.
N. Marlborough College grounds 1989 MH. All
previous records were from the 19th century.
10 km² 1 (2%)   1 km² 1 (<1%)

Pilosella Hill

Pilosella officinarum F. Schultz & Schultz-Bip.
Hieracium pilosella L.
Mouse-ear Hawkweed

Native. Short grassland, having good drainage,
on a wide range of soils. Widespread and often
dominant in suitable habitats, especially where
there is little competition from other species.
10 km² 50 (96%) 2 km² 446 (47%)

Pilosella praealta (Villars ex Gochnat) F. Schultz
& Schultz-Bip. **ssp. thaumasia** (Peter) Sell
Ssp. *arvorum* (Naeg. & Peter) Sell & C. West; ssp.
spraguei (Pugsley) Sell & C. West; *H. pilosella*
ssp. *thaumasium* (Peter) Sell
Tall Mouse-ear Hawkweed

Introduction.
S. In large numbers on railway siding Trowbridge
station, 1981 JP. Still present 1992. A specimen
was given to DG who visited the site in 1982 and
found a very tall (750 mm) glaucous-leaved, small-
flowered stoloniferous hawkweed. [This he
determined as *Pilosella praealta* ssp. *spraguei*. It
was finally determined by *Hieracium* expert Peter
Sell as ssp. *arvorum*.] There are very few colonies
of this plant in GB.
10 km² 1 (2%)   1 km² 1 (<1%)

Pilosella aurantiaca (L.) F. Schultz & Schultz-Bip.
Hieracium aurantiacum L.
Fox-and-cubs

Ssp. **aurantiaca**
Ssp. **carpathicola** (Naeg. & Peter) Soják
Hieracium brunneocroceum Pugsley
Introductions.
Both these ssp. occur in the county but since very
little material was forwarded to VC recorders for
accurate determination, it is not possible to map
either of them with any accuracy.
10 km² 13 (25%) 1 km² 21 (<1%)

Hieracium L.

In the early years of the WFMP it became clear that the species of this critical genus would not be recorded accurately by all recorders. The distribution map shows all records as an aggregate. The following species were identified by botanists with experience of sections within the genus and a map for *H. maculatum* is included.

Hieracium L. agg.
Hawkweeds
10 km² 42 (81%) 2 km² 250(26%)   Map 430, page 290

Hieracium sect. Sabauda F. Williams

Hieracium sabaudum L.
Hieracium perpropinquum (Zahn) Druce

Native. Woodland rides, banks and road verges on acid soils. Very local.
N. Savernake Forest, Hodson and Flisteridge Wood.
S. Most abundant on New Forest fringe including Whiteparish Common, Landford Wood, Park Water/Cowesfield and Earldoms. Elsewhere at Castle Wood near Stourton, Chicksgrove Quarry, Ridge near Chilmark and Bemerton (Salisbury).
10 km² 8 (15%)   1 km² 11 (<1%)

Hieracium rigens Jordan

Native.
S. In *Bromopsis erecta-Festuca rubra* chalk grassland. Population *c.* 100 flowering shoots, dispersed over an area of 20 m² Penning Down, SPTA(C) 1986 RP (ver. J Bevan). First VC8 record.
10 km² 1 (2%)   1 km² 1 (<1%)

Hieracium salticola (Sudre) Sell & C. West

Native.
N. First found 1979 on railway siding at Shockerwick near Box. Still present 1988 DG.
10 km² 1 (2%)   1 km² 1 (<1%)

Hieracium vagum Jordan

Native.
N. First found 1979 on railway siding at Shockerwick near Box. Still present 1988 DG.
10 km² 1 (2%)   1 km² 1 (<1%)

Hieracium sect. Tridentata F. Williams

Hieracium trichocaulon (Dahlst.) Johansson

Native.
S. Penn Common 1991 RV.
10 km² 1 (2%)   1 km² 1 (<1%)

Hieracium calcaricola (F. Hanb.) Roffey

Native.
N. Railway siding Shockerwick near Box 1979 DG, determined by the then BSBI *Hieracium* referee C Andrews. Since that date Jim Bevan, coordinator of the BSBI *Hieracium* study group has questioned all records for this localised endemic species. It is now thought that the only location is in the Stroud area of Gloucestershire. Other specimens from South Wales, previously determined as *H. calcaricola*, have now been attributed to *H. scabrisetum*, as have specimens preserved by the late Dr West, a previous BSBI *Hieracium* referee. Thus the determination of the Shockerwick record must now be in doubt. Still present 1990 DG.
10 km² 1 (2%)   1 km² 1 (<1%)

Hieracium sect. Vulgata F. Williams

Hieracium vulgatum Fries

Native in GB. Introduction in Wilts. A northern species apparently spreading S along the railways.
N. Two separate colonies adjacent to the railway near Swindon station 1991 JN.

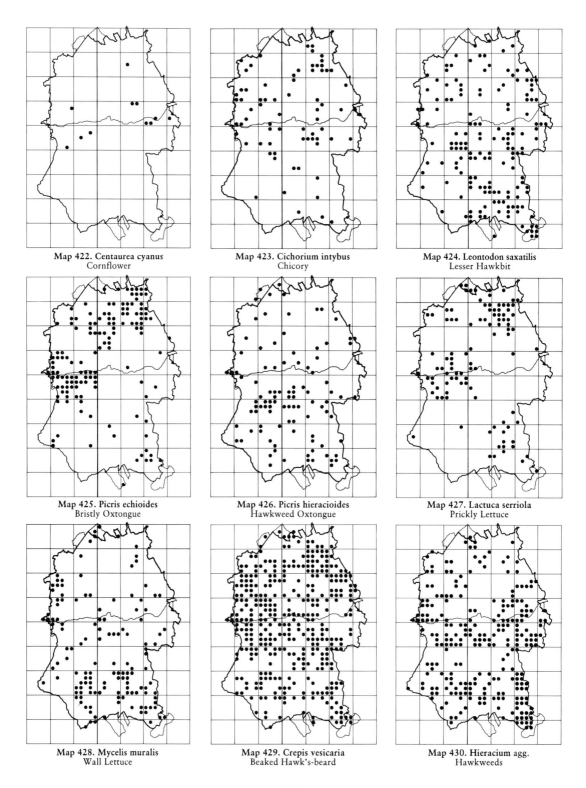

Map 422. **Centaurea cyanus**
Cornflower

Map 423. **Cichorium intybus**
Chicory

Map 424. **Leontodon saxatilis**
Lesser Hawkbit

Map 425. **Picris echioides**
Bristly Oxtongue

Map 426. **Picris hieracioides**
Hawkweed Oxtongue

Map 427. **Lactuca serriola**
Prickly Lettuce

Map 428. **Mycelis muralis**
Wall Lettuce

Map 429. **Crepis vesicaria**
Beaked Hawk's-beard

Map 430. **Hieracium agg.**
Hawkweeds

S. Colony on railway embankment stonework Limpley Stoke 1983 DG.

10 km² 2 (4%)   1 km² 3 (<1%)

Hieracium acuminatum Jordan
Hieracium strumosum (Ley ex W. R. Linton) Ley

Native. Railway lines, dry stony ground and woodland edge. Spreading along railway lines from the W of the county.

N. Abundant in some localities on quarry waste, cinder tracks and walls. Avoncliff, Box Common, Thingley, Alderton Grove, Hampton Farm and Wootton Bassett 1983-89 DG. Clearings in Great Wood and Webb's Wood 1987-88 MWS.

10 km² 6 (12%)   1 km² 10 (<1%)

Hieracium maculatum Smith
Spotted Hawkweed

Doubtful native, introduction in Wilts. Railway cuttings, embankments and sidings, walls, chalk downland and woodland.

N. Well-documented history as an aggressive invader on spoil heaps in stone quarries around Bath (Avon) from where it spread E into Wilts. Grose reported it as a frequent plant in the stone quarries of Box and Corsham, since when it has travelled extensively E along the railway system occurring on railway cuttings at Bowerhill, Luckington, Alderton, Wootton Bassett and Purton. Elsewhere on road cutting Ford and wall top St Leonards Malmesbury.

S. Naturalising on chalk downland and in woodland. Most frequent on chalk downland on SPTA(C) where it is locally abundant on Chirton Down. Elsewhere in woodland near Fonthill Bishop, under beech Great Ridge Wood, introduced in woodland ride Grovely Wood and one plant along trackside edge Bentley Wood. On stonework on garden walls Teffont Magna, railway bridge South Newton and one plant on Salisbury Cathedral Close wall.

10 km² 13 (25%)   1 km² 30 (<1%)   Map 431, page 294

Hieracium sublepistoides (Zahn) Druce

Native in GB, introduction in Wilts. A very critical and variable species, difficult to determine accurately. The records below, widely-distributed over N Wilts appear to be attributable to this species.

N. Bowood 1985 DG, refind of Grose's record. Abundant along disused railway cutting CWP 1987 DG, Alderton 1988 DG.

10 km² 3 (6%)   1 km² 3 (<1%)

Hieracium exotericum Jordan ex Boreau

Native in GB, introduction in Wilts.

N. Deep in shaded woodland and on chalk track reverting to woodland West Woods and on chalkland reverting to woodland near Lockeridge 1985 JEO. Railway cutting Alderton 1990 DG.

S. Chalk quarry, Harnham 1987 BKC & NLC.

10 km² 3 (6%)   1 km² 5 (<1%)

Filago L.

Filago vulgaris Lam.
Common Cudweed

Native. Disturbed and bare sandy soil, very rare and occurring intermittently.

N. Track across arable field Tottenham Park 1986 AJS, first county record since 1956. Edge of arable field Sandy Lane 1988 AJS.

S. Bare mud in green lane Poulshot 1987 BG.

10 km² 2 (4%)   1 km² 3 (<1%)

Gnaphalium L.

Gnaphalium sylvaticum L.
Heath Cudweed

Nationally scarce plant.
Native.

S. Great Ridge Wood 1990 CJH.

10 km² 1 (2%)   1 km² 1 (<1%)

Gnaphalium uliginosum L.
Marsh Cudweed

Native. Arable land, vehicle ruts, woodland tracks and places wet in winter. Abundant in wet areas of arable fields especially on heavier clay soils. Most frequent in SE where it also occurs as a garden weed.
10 km² 40 (77%) 1 km² 242 (7%)   Map 432, page 294

Inula L.

Inula helenium L.
Elecampane

Introduction. Garden escape. Established as a long-lived naturalised species in Wilts for many years.
N. Several patches spreading along ditches at Shaw 1985 JEO. Most of the population at Upper Woodshaw, Wootton Bassett has been built over and lost 1986 VG. Common on a road verge near Lydiard Tregoze 1990 PD.
10 km² 2 (4%)   1 km² 2 (<1%)

Inula conyzae (Griess.) Meikle
Inula conyza DC.
Ploughman's-spikenard

Native. Woods, grassland on thin soils, bare and rocky places, quarries, walls and railway cuttings on chalk, limestone, and occasionally greensand.
N. Common only on steep, eroded limestone and uncommon on the chalk except on Roundway Hill.
S. Locally distributed on chalk grassland, often near or in shelter of woodland especially on Porton Down. Occasional on rides in Bentley Wood.
10 km² 28 (54%) 1 km² 102 (3%)   Map 433, page 294

Pulicaria Gaertner

Pulicaria dysenterica (L.) Bernh.
Common Fleabane

Native. Wet and damp places by rivers, streams, canals, ditches and marshes. Well-distributed adjacent to water courses and on clay in NW and S of county.
10 km² 43 (83%) 1 km² 562 (15%)   Map 434, page 294

Solidago L.
It is known that there was confusion with identification of members of this genus during the WFMP. *Solidago virgaurea* was probably over-recorded in mistake for one of the introduced species that had been thrown-out or escaped naturally from gardens. Records of *S. canadensis* and *S. gigantea* were aggregated for the WFMP because of possible mis-identification of both species and very few specimens were forwarded for verification.

Solidago virgaurea L.
Goldenrod

Native. Open woodland, road verges, railway cuttings and heathland on acid soils.
N. Very rare. Confirmed records along railway cutting Alderton and Luckington 1987 DG, Savernake Forest 1990 AJS and Burderop JEO.
S. Rare, except in SE where frequent in open woodland and on track verges on clay in Bentley and Langley Woods, Hamptworth and Whiteparish Common but not extending further S into New Forest. In other areas probably over-recorded due to confusion with one of the introduced *Solidago* species.
10 km² 18 (35%) 1 km² 50 (1%)   Map 435, page 294

Solidago L. agg.
Canadian Goldenrod and Early Goldenrod

Introduction. Road verges, railway embankments and waste land. *Solidago canadensis* and *S. gigantea* have escaped from gardens and become naturalised forming extensive roadside colonies reproducing by both seed and rhizomatous roots. *S. canadensis* is considered to be more common.
10 km² 34 (65%) 1 km² 115 (3%)   Map 436, page 294

Aster L.

These closely related garden escapes were treated as an aggregate by all recorders except JEO. The following were reported but not confirmed.

Aster schreberi Nees
Aster macrophyllus auct. non L.
Nettle-leaved Michaelmas-daisy
Aster laevis L.
Glaucous Michaelmas-daisy
Aster laevis x A. novi-belgii = A. x versicolor Willd.
Late Michaelmas-daisy
Aster novi-belgii L.
Aster longifolius auct. non Lam.
Confused Michaelmas-daisy
Aster novi-belgii x A. lanceolatus = A. x salignus Willd.
Common Michaelmas-daisy
Aster lanceolatus Willd.
Narrow-leaved Michaelmas-daisy
10 km² 24 (46%) 1 km² 54 (2%)

Erigeron L.

Erigeron acer L.
Blue Fleabane

Native. Disturbed, shallow soil on chalk and limestone. Walls, quarries and railway embankments.
N. Localised to these habitats and abundant in some localities. Able to colonise disturbed ground rapidly as on the gravel in the CWP.
S. Most frequent on SPTA(C) where it occurs in shell craters, and in Amesbury and Porton Down.
10 km² 21 (40%) 1 km² 56 (2%)   Map 437, page 294

Conyza Less.

Conyza canadensis (L.) Cronq.
Erigeron canadensis L.
Canadian Fleabane

Introduction. Disturbed ground. Railway sidings, motorway hard-shoulders, pavements and as an arable weed on sandy soils.
N. Rapid spread in recent years. Easily visible from a train in the Swindon area and from a car along the M4 motorway.
S. Most frequent on roadsides and waste ground. First county record was in Salisbury 1931.
10 km² 26 (50%) 1 km² 64 (2%)   Map 438, page 294

Bellis L.

Bellis perennis L.
Daisy

Native. Most grassland, tolerating heavy trampling and close mowing. Very common and widely-distributed but less common on SPTA in the absence of grazing.
10 km² 51 (98%) 2 km² 886 (93%)

Tanacetum L.

Tanacetum parthenium (L.) Schultz-Bip.
Feverfew

Introduction. Naturalised on walls and waste places, usually having escaped from gardens. Distributed over much of the county, generally near habitation.
10 km² 43 (83%) 1 km² 236 (6%)   Map 439, page 294

Tanacetum vulgare L.
Tansy

Native. Marginal land including river banks, road verges and railway embankments.
N. Frequent on banks of Bristol Avon. Invasive on waste ground and railway embankments.
S. Road verges. Most frequent between Trowbridge and Devizes.
10 km² 38 (73%) 1 km² 208 (6%)   Map 440, page 298

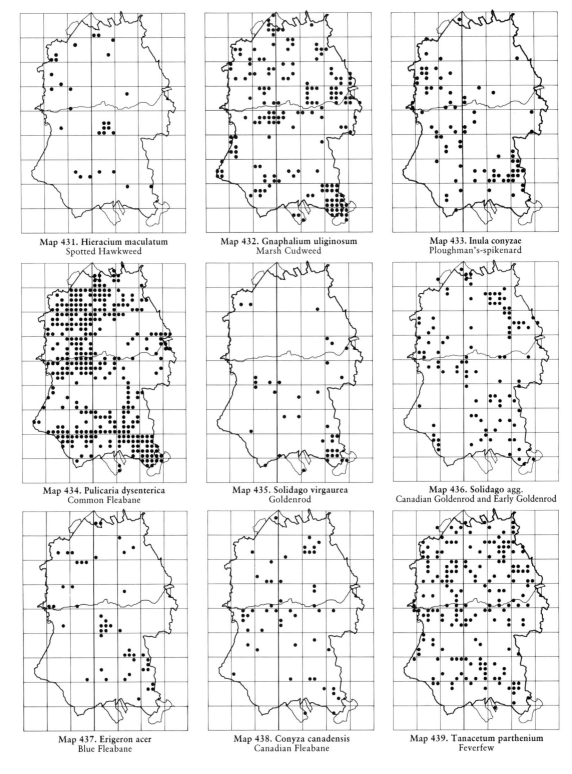

Map 431. **Hieracium maculatum**
Spotted Hawkweed

Map 432. **Gnaphalium uliginosum**
Marsh Cudweed

Map 433. **Inula conyzae**
Ploughman's-spikenard

Map 434. **Pulicaria dysenterica**
Common Fleabane

Map 435. **Solidago virgaurea**
Goldenrod

Map 436. **Solidago agg.**
Canadian Goldenrod and Early Goldenrod

Map 437. **Erigeron acer**
Blue Fleabane

Map 438. **Conyza canadensis**
Canadian Fleabane

Map 439. **Tanacetum parthenium**
Feverfew

Artemisia L.

Artemisia vulgaris L.
Mugwort

Native. Road verges, railway embankments and waste ground. Common throughout the county.
10 km² 51 (98%) 2 km² 725 (76%)

Artemisia absinthium L.
Wormwood

Introduction. Once grown as a garden herb for use as an insecticide to repel fleas and control parasitic worms. Usually occurs as a single plant near farmsteads and as a casual.
N. Survived many years at Euridge Manor, Colerne 1950 (DM Frowde) refound 1989 DG, gravel pit CWP 1985 DG, E of Kemble airfield 1985 MK, Burton 1988 JH, Widdenham/Colerne 1989 DG.
S. Ashton Common 1991 Westbury Nats. Soc.
10 km² 5 (10%)   1 km² 6 (<1%)

Achillea L.

Achillea ptarmica L.
Sneezewort

Native. Damp areas in open woodland and grassland, on road verges and banks of streams. Always on neutral to acid soils.
N. Frequent only on the heavy clays in the Braydon Forest area and on parts of the lowland near Melksham.
Form with double flowers, one record from Membury 1986 SK was probably an escape from cultivation.
S. Mostly in damp or marshy fields. Common only on Kimmeridge and London Clay in Bentley and Clarendon Woods, the New Forest fringe and on clays between Trowbridge and the Vale of Pewsey.
10 km² 26 (50%) 1 km² 128 (4%)   Map 441, page 298

Achillea millefolium L.
Yarrow

Native. Found in all types of grassland except on very acid soils. Very common.
10 km² 52 (100%)2 km² 908 (96%)

Chamaemelum Miller

Chamaemelum nobile (L.) All.
Chamomile

Native. Sandy soils on heavily grazed New Forest lawns and roadside verges.
S. Confined to extreme SE. Plaitford Common 1985 RV, Furzley area 1989 VW & AB, two sites Penn Common 1990-91 VW & RV, Bramshaw, Sturtmoor and Canada Commons 1991 RV.
10 km² 1 (2%)   1 km² 9 (<1%)

Anthemis L.
One of three genera having superficially similar species (see *Matricaria* and *Tripleurospermum*) which presented problems to WFMP recorders. Field and herbarium workshops were held to help with identification but it is considered that some mis-identification and under-recording occurred.

Anthemis arvensis L.
Corn Chamomile

Native. Arable weed on chalk soils. Rare.
S. Over-recorded for *A. cotula*. Only a few records were accepted, Newtown near Tisbury, S of Grovely Wood and around Salisbury.
10 km² 3 (6%)   1 km² 6 (<1%)

Anthemis cotula L.
Stinking Chamomile

Native. Weed of arable land, waste places and roadsides.

N. Locally abundant on heavier clays, less common on the chalk.

S. Most frequent around Salisbury.

See Wiltshire's Arable Weed Flora p.43.

10 km² 27 (52%) 1 km² 96 (3%) Map 442, page 298

Chrysanthemum L.

Chrysanthemum segetum L.
Corn Marigold

Introduction. Arable weed of mainly sandy soils.
N. A diminishing species only occurring regularly in market gardens at Bromham. Other records are of casual occurrence.

S. A common weed of arable crops and field headlands around Alderbury, Whiteparish, Hamptworth and Plaitford sometimes seeding onto road verges. Scattered populations, sometimes large but varying from year to year, occur in other parts of the S particularly on greensand. Abundant in field on chalk near Broad Chalke 1985 RW & AH.

10 km² 17 (33%) 1 km² 37 (1%) Map 443, page 298

Leucanthemum Miller

Leucanthemum vulgare Lam.
Oxeye Daisy

Native. Grassland and bare areas on roadside banks on base-rich soils. Common throughout much of the county.

10 km² 49 (94%) 2 km² 719 (75%) Map 444, page 298

Matricaria L.
See remarks for *Anthemis*.

Matricaria recutita L.
Scented Mayweed

Native. Arable land, disturbed and waste places. Occurs mainly on heavier clays and acid soils.

Uncommon on the chalk.

10 km² 35 (67%) 1 km² 132 (4%) Map 445, page 298

Matricaria discoidea DC.
Matricaria matricarioides (Less.) Porter
Pineappleweed

Introduction. Cultivated ground, gateways, roadsides and tracks. First recorded in Wilts 1915. Now occurs in most field entrances where the ground has been disturbed.

10 km² 51 (98%) 2 km² 855 (90%)

Tripleurospermum Schultz-Bip.
See remarks for *Anthemis*.

Tripleurospermum inodorum (L.) Schultz-Bip.
Scentless Mayweed

Native. Cultivated and waste land. Very common.

10 km² 51 (98%) 2 km² 784 (83%)

Senecio L.

Senecio fluviatilis Wallr.
Broad-leaved Ragwort

Introduction. River and streamsides.

S. Three large groups on bank of the Bristol Avon near Timothy Rise Farm downstream from Winsley 1985-87 JM. Large colony known for several years beside stream near Brook Lane, Westbury 1990 VEH.

10 km² 2 (4%) 1 km² 2 (<1%)

Senecio jacobaea L.
Common Ragwort

Native. Grassland and waste land. A problem weed on downland not grazed by sheep and on some set-aside land. This plant is poisonous to cattle when fresh or dry and is classified as a noxious weed which landowners are obliged to control.

10 km² 51 (98%) 2 km² 831 (88%)

Senecio aquaticus Hill
Marsh Ragwort

Native. River and streamsides and damp pastures.
N. Abundant in some river valley meadows and areas of damp grassland on the clay.
S. Distribution follows the rivers Avon, Wylye, Nadder and Bourne and areas of damp grassland.

10 km² 38 (73%) 1 km² 242 (7%)   Map 446, page 298

Senecio erucifolius L.
Hoary Ragwort

Native. Road verges, hedgebanks, rough chalk grassland, railway embankments, meadows and pastures. Most common on neutral to acid soils especially around Minety in the N and on chalk SPTA(W&C) and neutral to acid soils in the SE.
Although flowering 2-3 weeks later than S. jacobaea, confusion with that species may give rise to under-recording.

10 km² 41 (79%) 1 km² 272 (7%)   Map 447, page 298

Senecio squalidus L.
Oxford Ragwort

Introduction. Walls, waste land, railway sidings and roadsides. The history of this plant is well-documented nationally and in Wiltshire where it was first recorded at Pewsey 1863. It spread along the railway network, which is now much reduced. In 1971 the building of the M4 gave it a new man-made high-speed means of dispersal. The motorway banks were quickly invaded and the plant continues to be common there. Most common around Swindon.

10 km² 30 (58%) 1 km² 172 (5%)   Map 448, page 298

Senecio vulgaris L.
Groundsel

Native. Disturbed ground and bare soil. Very common.
Form **radiatus** Hegi
Native.
N. Roadside Ford 1983 DG, North Meadow, Cricklade 1985 KP.
S. The Butts, Salisbury 1985 PM.

10 km² 51 (98%) 2 km² 860 (91%)

Senecio sylvaticus L.
Heath Groundsel

Native. Open woodland, heaths, disturbed soil and arable land on neutral to acid soils.
N. Abundant only in and around Savernake Forest. Of infrequent occurrence in Bowood Park and a few localities in Braydon Forest area.
S. Most commonly recorded in Farley, Redlynch, Landford and Stourton areas where the soils are non-calcareous. Abundant in areas of woodland which are clear-felled and disturbed as in Bentley Wood.

10 km² 23 (44%) 1 km² 66 (2%)   Map 449, page 301

Senecio viscosus L.
Sticky Groundsel

Possibly native. Waste ground and roadsides. Particularly on railway tracks and marshalling yards.
N. Lockeridge 1985 JEO, railway siding Hullavington 1987 JH, abundant around Swindon especially disused marshalling yards 1987-91 DG & JN, disused railway line Cricklade 1991 DG & SW.
S. Pavement cracks and waste places Salisbury 1984 PM, Westbury Trading Estate 1984 EC and railway station 1990 PS. In SE, Plaitford 1985 RV, Hamptworth 1990 DW, Nomansland 1991 JW. Disused railway line Bemerton 1985 JBH, railway line Dinton and Baverstock 1988-91 SMP.

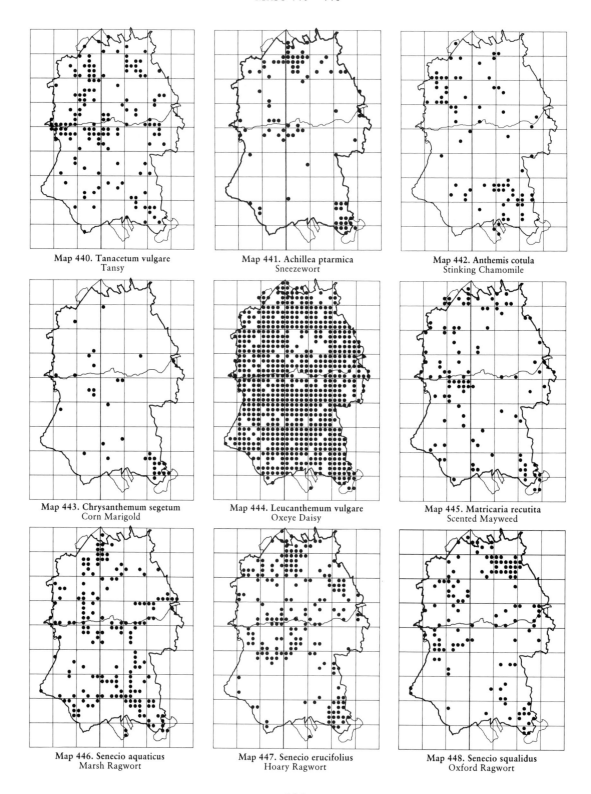

Map 440. **Tanacetum vulgare**
Tansy

Map 441. **Achillea ptarmica**
Sneezewort

Map 442. **Anthemis cotula**
Stinking Chamomile

Map 443. **Chrysanthemum segetum**
Corn Marigold

Map 444. **Leucanthemum vulgare**
Oxeye Daisy

Map 445. **Matricaria recutita**
Scented Mayweed

Map 446. **Senecio aquaticus**
Marsh Ragwort

Map 447. **Senecio erucifolius**
Hoary Ragwort

Map 448. **Senecio squalidus**
Oxford Ragwort

Pewsey Wharf and near Fordbrook, Pewsey 1960 JEO, near Semley 1987 MH & JN, abundant chalk quarry Quidhampton 1987 PM, rubbish dump South Newton 1989 BL, on introduced soil Potterne BGH, edge of wood and field track Everleigh 1990 FP.
10 km² 13 (25%) 1 km² 30 (<1%)   Map 450, page 301

Tephroseris (Reichb.) Reichb.

Tephroseris integrifolia (L.) Holub
Senecio integrifolius (L.) Clairv.
Field Fleawort

Nationally scarce plant.
Native. Unimproved chalk downland. Wiltshire has one of the largest populations in GB.
N. The colonies on the downland N of Devizes at King's Play Hill, Morgan's Hill, Cherhill Down and N of Pewsey Vale have remained constant since 1957, but those recorded at that time on the N Marlborough Downs have been lost to aerial spraying and extensive arable farming.
S. The stronghold of this plant is on the chalk downland above the Nadder and Wylye valleys and around Salisbury, as at Dean Hill. Comparison of the dots on maps 451 and 451a show losses and new records since Grose's *Flora of Wiltshire* 1957.
10 km² 18 (35%) 1 km² 54 (2%)   Map 451, page 301

Doronicum L.

Doronicum pardalianches L.
Leopard's-bane

Introduction. Garden escape or planted. Has become naturalised in woodland.
N. Battle Lake 1984 MWS, disused railway near Staverton 1986 JP, Belvedere Wood and the adjacent cemetery Devizes 1987 PC.
S. Grovely Wood 1983 MDT, Manor Woods, Lavington 1984 RF, Oddford Brook, Tisbury 1985 MM, Larkhill SPTA(C) 1989 JL.
10 km² 6 (12%) 1 km² 7 (<1%)

Tussilago L.

Tussilago farfara L.
Colt's-foot

Native. Disturbed ground, roadsides, railway banks and rubbish dumps. Frequent.
10 km² 49 (94%) 2 km² 581 (61%)

Petasites Miller

Petasites hybridus (L.) P. Gaertner, Meyer & Scherb.
Butterbur

Native. Beside rivers, streams, canals and damp road verges.
N. Locally abundant on banks of K & A Canal, in R. Kennet valley and Christian Malford area.
S. Most records are in the vicinity of rivers Avon and Wylye, Vale of Wardour and SW of Devizes.
10 km² 38 (73%) 1 km² 235 (6%)   Map 452, page 301

Petasites japonicus (Siebold & Zucc.) Maxim.
Giant Butterbur

Introduction. Planted, rather than an escape, as an ornamental garden plant for its large, impressive leaves up to 1 m in diameter.
N. Water-meadow Chilton Foliat 1984 DG.
S. The Close, Pewsey 1986 AJS.
10 km² 2 (4%)   1 km² 2 (<1%)

Petasites fragrans (Villars) C. Presl
Winter Heliotrope

Introduction. Naturalises aggressively in waste places and successfully on roadside verges where it replaces the natural vegetation. The flowers, which produce a very strong vanilla scent, are often at their best at Christmas and the New Year.

About half the records are from roadside verges. Two different types of site: dump at edge of tank-standing Grovely Wood 1987 BL and a very steep slope of old sand-pit Holloway, East Knoyle 1989 JHa. The species was originally recommended for damp shade in gardens and particularly woodland. Records from in and around ditches Whiteparish 1988 PMW and Hoggington Lane, Southwick 1991 GY and by river bank West Kington 1988 JH. Preference for greater humidity shows on the map with the westerly distribution (N and S) and in the damp conditions of the SE corner. The strong spreading by underground stems was noticed at Limpley Stoke 1987 and 1991 JM.

10 km² 16 (31%) 1 km² 35 (1%)   Map 453, page 301

Galinsoga Ruiz Lopez & Pavon

Galinsoga parviflora Cav.
Gallant Soldier

Introduction.
N. Market garden Bromham 1986 JN, railway track Chiselden 1989 JEO.

10 km² 2 (4%)   1 km² 2 (<1%)

Galinsoga quadriradiata Ruiz Lopez & Pavon
Galinsoga ciliata (Raf.) S. F. Blake
Shaggy Soldier

Introduction. Cultivated and waste land.
N. Long history in some localities. Below railway bridge Chippenham, around Lacock church 1983 and market garden weed Bromham 1985 DG.
S. First recorded c.1930, but has not increased as much as predicted in 1960s. Salisbury Corporation flower-beds, several plants between Salisbury Playhouse and Fisherton Street 1984 PM, old railway lines Bemerton (site now destroyed) 1985 JBH and Newton Tony 1989 DOG, nursery Woodborough 1988 and waste land Sharcott 1989 RG, Clay Street Whiteparish 1989 PMW,

allotments Pewsey 1989 KN and roadside Swallowcliffe 1989 JB.

10 km² 8 (15%) 1 km² 15 (<1%)   Map 454, page 301

Bidens L.

Bidens cernua L.
Nodding Bur-marigold

Native. Lakes, ponds, rivers, streams and canal in more acidic water than *B. tripartita*.
N. Very rare. Restricted to ponds in Savernake Forest and around the lake in Bowood Park 1986 DG.
S. Uncommon. Neutral to acidic ponds on the edge of the New Forest and sporadically on R. Avon and on clay between Devizes and Westbury. Sometimes growing with *B. tripartita*.

10 km² 11 (21%) 1 km² 28 (<1%)   Map 455, page 301

Bidens tripartita L.
Trifid Bur-marigold

Native. Lakes, ponds, rivers, streams and canal.
N. In heavily silted bays along the lower reaches of the Bristol Avon where winter flooding occurs. Very abundant on the banks of the Brinkworth Brook near Sherston. Only common along the K & A Canal where it runs parallel to the Bristol Avon.
S. Occurs sporadically along R. Avon, scattered elsewhere on clay. Sometimes growing with *B. cernua*.

10 km² 20 (38%) 1 km² 55 (2%)   Map 456, page 301

Eupatorium L.

Eupatorium cannabinum L.
Hemp-agrimony

Native. Damp places and dry rough ground. Frequent, especially on heavier soils.

10 km² 50 (96%) 2 km² 435 (46%) Map 457, page 304

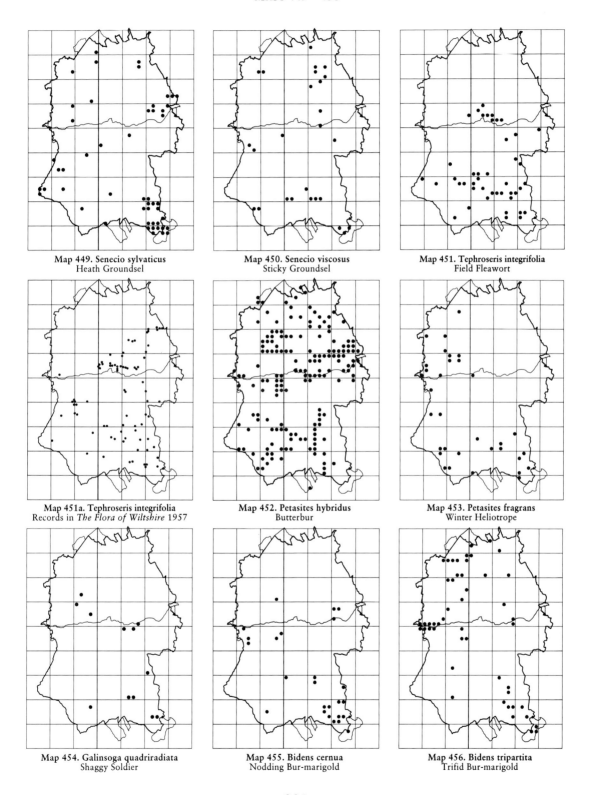

Map 449. Senecio sylvaticus
Heath Groundsel

Map 450. Senecio viscosus
Sticky Groundsel

Map 451. Tephroseris integrifolia
Field Fleawort

Map 451a. Tephroseris integrifolia
Records in *The Flora of Wiltshire* 1957

Map 452. Petasites hybridus
Butterbur

Map 453. Petasites fragrans
Winter Heliotrope

Map 454. Galinsoga quadriradiata
Shaggy Soldier

Map 455. Bidens cernua
Nodding Bur-marigold

Map 456. Bidens tripartita
Trifid Bur-marigold

BUTOMACEAE

Butomus L.

Butomus umbellatus L.
Flowering-rush

Native. Rivers and canals. Planted in lakes and ponds.
N. Swill Brook on edge of CWP, upper reaches of R.Thames, Bristol Avon downstream from Great Somerford.
S. K & A Canal: single plant Trowbridge 1984 DG, Rowde and Horton 1984-87 JL. All other records from river systems. Bristol Avon: Westwood 1989 JM. Salisbury Avon: water-meadow N Charlton 1984 NLC furthest point downstream, Scammells Bridge, Salisbury 1984 PM, Churchill Gardens, Salisbury 1986 NLC, Lake and Great Durnford 1991 PM. R.Wylye: two records, Ditchampton 1984 DS-G. R. Nadder: four plants on edge of slow-flowing drainage ditch Dinton 1989 SMP.
10 km² 12 (23%) 1 km² 20 (<1%)   Map 458, page 304

ALISMATACEAE

Sagittaria L.

Sagittaria sagittifolia L.
Arrowhead

Native. Rivers and canals. Restricted to only two river systems and K & A Canal.
N. Throughout the Bristol Avon and locally in the Brinkworth Brook. In Grose's *The Flora of Wiltshire* more common in K & A Canal than in rivers but now rare.
S. All the records are associated with Salisbury Avon. S of Salisbury from the main carrier in Alderbury Meadows, N of Charlton to Downton Borough and Mill Pool 1984 to water beside The Moot 1986, in a ditch in Churchill Gardens, Salisbury 1986 NLC & BKC. Well-established N of Salisbury where the river is rather sluggish below the cattle market 1986, The Butts, Stratford-sub-Castle, Little Durnford, Middle Woodford, occasional on silty margins of the river in the grounds of Heale House, at Great Durnford and at Wilsford Manor 1989-90 PM.
10 km² 14 (27%) 1 km² 52 (1%)   Map 459, page 304

Alisma L.

Alisma plantago-aquatica L.
Water-plantain

Native. Rivers, streams, lakes, ponds, canals and gravel pits. Abundant in many of these habitats throughout the county, but always growing away from the main current.
10 km² 39 (75%) 1 km² 259 (7%)   Map 460, page 304

Alisma lanceolatum With.
Narrow-leaved Water-plantain

Native.
N. Two records within the Bristol Avon catchment area: K & A Canal Avoncliff 1983 MW and R. Avon Waddon 1986 DG. Elsewhere Oaksey Ford Bridge CK & MK. Historically, most records were from the canal systems.
10 km² 2 (4%)   1 km² 3 (<1%)

HYDROCHARITACEAE

Stratiotes L.

Stratiotes aloides L.
Water-soldier

Nationally scarce plant.
Native in GB, introduction in Wilts.
N. Planted in roadside pond and growing abundantly, Ashley near Crudwell 1988 MK & CK.
10 km² 1 (2%)   1 km² 1 (<1%)

Elodea Michaux

Elodea canadensis Michaux
Canadian Waterweed

Introduction. Lakes, canals, gravel pits and ponds. Less often in fast-flowing water courses. Present in many types of open water. Flowering in great quantity in shallow water (<500 mm deep) 1988 in CWP.
10 km² 26 (50%) 1 km² 102 (3%)   Map 461, page 304

Elodea nuttallii (Planchon) H. St. John
Nuttall's Waterweed

Introduction.
N. First reported to NCC by Dr Halliday 1978 CWP and found there 1980 SCH. Plant has now colonised many CWP lakes and is invading the nearby R. Thames and tributaries. Occurs along the K & A Canal, abundant between Honey Street and Devizes 1988-90 JEO. Nationally there is some evidence that *E. nuttallii* may, in time, become dominant to *E. canadensis*.
S. Pond close to Salisbury Avon at Scales Bridge, Rushall 1986 PMWF.
10 km² 9 (17%) 1 km² 34 (<1%)   Map 462, page 304

Lagarosiphon Harvey

Lagarosiphon major (Ridley) Moss
Curly Waterweed

Introduction. Supposedly introduced into goldfish ponds from South Africa. First reported in GB 1944. Increasing in ponds, canals and gravel pits.
N. Becoming frequent in CWP. In ponds Box, Ashley and Burderop Hospital.
S. W of Pewsey Wharf, K & A Canal 1986 JEO, first VC8 record. In quantity in some ponds. Manor Farm, Plaitford 1990 PMW.
10 km² 7 (13%) 1 km² 10 (<1%)

JUNCAGINACEAE

Triglochin L.

Triglochin palustre L.
Marsh Arrowgrass

Native. Marshy places and wet fields preferably inundated by highly calcareous water.
N. Colonies usually very small. In the valleys of the By Brook and its tributary the Lidbrook at Colerne and Slaughterford, in marshy area in pasture on hill near Dundas Aqueduct, Bowden Hill and several places in CWP 1984-90 DG. Howe Mill on R. Kennet near Ramsbury 1984 JN, near Littlecott Farm, Lyneham 1984 WTNC/ST, North Meadow NNR, Cricklade 1986 NCC, Lydiard Millicent and Parkside Farm 1988 JF.
S. Unimproved wet meadow Etchilhampton 1985 BG, water-meadows beside R. Avon Stratford-sub-Castle 1984-85, very frequent along edge of some ditches Little Durnford 1986 and occasional in wet ditches of semi-improved water-meadow Lake 1991 PM. Marsh beside R. Nadder Netherhampton 1987 NLC & BKC. Unimproved water-meadow Porton 1987 JF. Abundant in marsh beside nature trail Jones's Mill, Pewsey 1987 AJS, one plant Semington Brook 1988 BGH, many plants in wet field The Moors, West Grimstead 1988 IA.
10 km² 13 (25%) 1 km² 19 (<1%)   Map 463, page 304

POTAMOGETONACEAE

Potamogeton L.
Although restricted within the county by the shortage of aquatic habitats it is considered that the genus *Potamogeton* and the thread-leaved species in particular were under-recorded during the WFMP.

Potamogeton natans L.
Broad-leaved Pondweed

Native. Lakes, ponds, canals and gravel pits. The

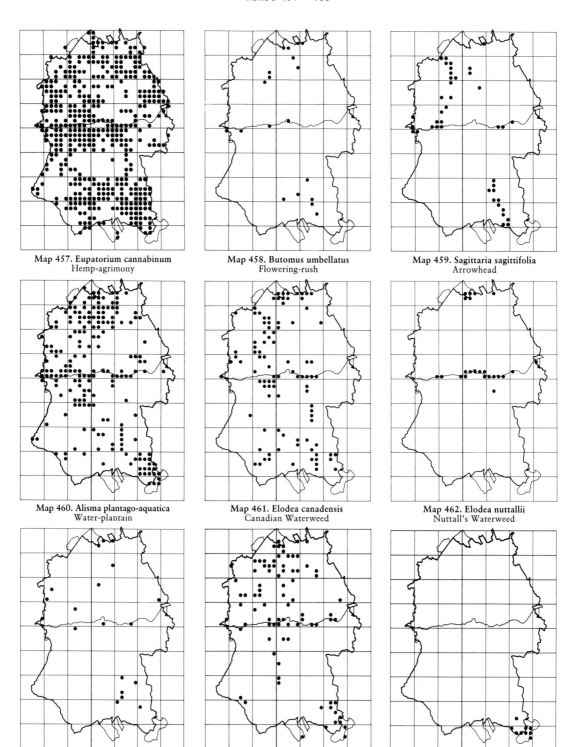

Map 457. Eupatorium cannabinum
Hemp-agrimony

Map 458. Butomus umbellatus
Flowering-rush

Map 459. Sagittaria sagittifolia
Arrowhead

Map 460. Alisma plantago-aquatica
Water-plantain

Map 461. Elodea canadensis
Canadian Waterweed

Map 462. Elodea nuttallii
Nuttall's Waterweed

Map 463. Triglochin palustre
Marsh Arrowgrass

Map 464. Potamogeton natans
Broad-leaved Pondweed

Map 465. Potamogeton polygonifolius
Bog Pondweed

most frequent of the broad-leaved *Potamogeton*.
N. Occurs prominently in lakes and ponds in the
Braydon Forest area and on low-lying clay.
S. Common in large ponds. Occurs in the few
remaining dewponds holding water on SPTA.
10 km² 29 (56%) 1 km² 98 (3%)   Map 464, page 304

Potamogeton polygonifolius Pourret
Bog Pondweed

Native. Ponds, ditches and permanently water-
logged areas of acid peat bog with still or slow-
flowing water.
S. Confined to extreme SE, mainly the New
Forest area. An outlying record to the N was
associated with standing water in a hollow within
the root system of a fallen tree 1988 DJW.
10 km² 2 (4%)   1 km² 14 (<1%)   Map 465, page 304

Potamogeton nodosus Poiret
Loddon Pondweed

British Red Data Book species.
Native. Occurs in the Bristol Avon from Staverton
downstream to the county boundary and beyond
to Saltford in Avon. Large and small colonies
throughout the river, especially below Bradford-
on-Avon bridge, at Avoncliff and Dundas
Aqueduct growing in shallow water along both
river banks throughout these stretches and in
great abundance in shallow fast-flowing stretches
often below weirs 1985-87 DG.
10 km² 2 (4%)   1 km² 5 (<1%)   Map 466, page 308

Potamogeton lucens L.
Shining Pondweed

Native. Rivers, canals and gravel pits.
N. Very local in the Bristol Avon and K & A
Canal but abundant in some of the CWP gravel
pits.
S. Most frequent S of Salisbury.
10 km² 11 (21%) 1 km² 20 (<1%)   Map 467, page 308

Potamogeton perfoliatus L.
Perfoliate Pondweed

Native. Flowing and static water.
N. Swill Brook, Ashton Keynes, several stretches
By Brook, K & A Canal at Semington 1986-88
DG, K & A Canal Burbage 1988 AJS and Oak Hill
near Froxfield 1988 CM. R. Avon near Beanacre
1989 DG.
S. Rare. R. Avon: in current of deeper water
Standlynch Mill 1984 NLC & BKC, single strand
caught in water-crowfoot, many will have drifted
from upriver Lower Woodford 1989 PM, two
sites in flowing, deepish water near Scales Bridge,
Upavon 1986 PMWF, R. Wylye at Ditchampton
1989 BL.
10 km² 10 (19%) 1 km² 14 (<1%)   Map 468, page 308

Potamogeton friesii Rupr.
Flat-stalked Pondweed

Nationally scarce plant.
Native. K & A Canal: Caen Hill locks Devizes
1986 DG, Oakhill 1988 CM.
10 km² 2 (4%)   1 km² 2 (<1%)

Potamogeton pusillus L.
Lesser Pondweed

Native.
N. Occurs in all the shallow pits in CWP where
first noted by SCH 1982. In ponds near Box
Brook, gravel pit Great Somerford 1984, pond BR
marshalling yard Swindon 1986 DG and pond
Ramsbury Meadow WTNC reserve 1990 JN.
10 km² 5 (10%) 1 km² 17 (<1%)   Map 469, page 308

Potamogeton obtusifolius Mert. & Koch
Blunt-leaved Pondweed

Native. K & A Canal near Foxhanger's Farm, Devizes
1989 JEO (det. C Jermy BM), first county record.
10 km² 1 (2%)   1 km² 1 (<1%)

Potamogeton berchtoldii Fieber
Potamogeton pusillus auct. non L.
Small Pondweed

Native. Static and slow-moving water.
N. Common in some CWP lakes and occurs in stretches of the K & A Canal.
S. Rare. Two plants Quar Hill Pond, small population among *P. natans* Loosehanger 1989 DJW (ver. AH).
10 km² 6 (12%)   1 km² 13 (<1%)   Map 470, page 308

Potamogeton trichoides Cham. & Schldl.
Hairlike Pondweed

Nationally scarce plant.
Native. This species has often been mis-identified and only records for which specimens have been confirmed by the national referee, C Jermy, have been accepted. K & A Canal at Honey Street 1986 JEO, CWP 1987 CP.
10 km² 2 (4%)   1 km² 2 (<1%)

Potamogeton crispus L.
Curled Pondweed

Native. Found in all types of water bodies. Most common where water is slow-moving or static.
N. Abundant in several stretches of the K & A Canal, the Bristol Avon upstream of Malmesbury and in the CWP.
S. Three records Nadder valley, ponds Six Wells Bottom near Stourhead and Melchet Court near Whiteparish, stream West Lavington, Nine Mile River and Britford.
10 km² 17 (33%) 1 km² 33 (<1%)   Map 471, page 308

Potamogeton pectinatus L.
Fennel Pondweed

Native. Slow-moving and static water bodies. The commonest of the thread-leaved *Potamogeton* species.

N. Present throughout much of the length of the K & A Canal and the CWP gravel pits in great quantity.
S. Most frequent in R. Avon and R. Wylye.
10 km² 16 (31%) 1 km² 44 (1%)   Map 472, page 308

Groenlandia Gay

Groenlandia densa (L.) Fourr.
Opposite-leaved Pondweed

Native. Ponds, canals, gravel pits and streams. Very local in its distribution.
N. Increasing in the CWP gravel pits and present in adjacent streams, 1984-86 DG. Other locations include farm pond Gastard 1985 RR and K & A Canal, Grafton 1986 DG, JN & RR. Possibly under-recorded.
10 km² 3 (6%)   1 km² 5 (<1%)

ZANNICHELLIACEAE

Zannichellia L.

Zannichellia palustris L.
Horned Pondweed

Native. Rivers, lakes, ponds and gravel pits.
N. Abundant in CWP gravel pit lakes and adjacent R. Thames streams. Beside R. Kennet at Knighton 1985-89 DG, along K & A Canal at Pewsey and Honey Street 1986 RR, Crofton 1986 DG and Martinslade 1987 JEO. Dewpond Milk Hill 1986 KP, pond near Hebden Farm 1990 DG, churchyard Lydiard Millicent 1990 JEO.
S. Abundant along stretches of R. Avon from Scales Bridge to West Chisenbury 1986-90 PMWF. Jones's Mill near Pewsey 1986 AJS, R. Nadder at Dinton 1988 SMP. Pond East Grimstead 1985 PMW, common in Clarendon Lake 1988 MD, locally abundant in streams Heron and Heath Bridges and Ashton Mill Farm all near Worton 1988-89 BGH.
10 km² 11 (21%) 1 km² 24 (<1%)   Map 473, page 308

ARACEAE

Acorus L.

Acorus calamus L.
Sweet-flag

Introduction. Only two extant records.
N. Bowood Lake, 1984 DG. Record of 1940 (Sandwith) refound K & A Canal 1984 BG.
10 km² 2 (4%)   1 km² 2 (<1%)

Arum L.

Arum maculatum L.
Lords-and-Ladies

Native. Hedgerow banks, woodlands. Common. Forms with spotted and unspotted leaves occur but the distribution of neither has been recorded.
10 km² 51 (98%) 2 km² 835 (88%)

Arum italicum Miller ssp. italicum
Italian Lords-and-Ladies

Nationally scarce plant.
Native in GB, introduction in Wilts. Garden escape or planted.
N. The only records are from Old Priory Gardens and parkland near R. Kennet, Marlborough 1990 JEO.
10 km² 1 (2%)   1 km² 3 (<1%)

LEMNACEAE

Spirodela Schleiden

Spirodela polyrhiza (L.) Schleiden
Lemna polyrhiza L.
Greater Duckweed

Native. Static or slow-flowing water.

N. In some years abundant through much of the length of the K & A Canal. Elsewhere, restricted to ponds in Savernake Forest, R. Kennet and a few areas in N.
S. The few records are from the rivers Avon, Ebble and Wylye.
10 km² 14 (27%) 1 km² 41 (1%)   Map 474, page 308

Lemna L.

Lemna gibba L.
Fat Duckweed

Native. Ponds and canal.
N. This plant has been known from the K & A Canal for many years but the population fluctuates in its occurrence and abundance from year to year. Only two are records away from canal: in a roadside pond at Leigh 1989 DG and in the slow-flowing R. Avon near Dodford Farm, Christian Malford 1989 JW.
S. Downton 1984 NLC & BKC.
10 km² 5 (10%)   1 km² 9 (<1%)

Lemna minor L.
Common Duckweed

Native. Static and slow-moving water. Locally abundant, sometimes covering the entire water surface.
10 km² 48 (92%) 2 km² 333 (35%) Map 475, page 311

Lemna trisulca L.
Ivy-leaved Duckweed

Native. Static and slow-flowing water and the edges of fast-flowing rivers.
N. Most common in the central section of the K & A Canal. In ponds and slack water of streams on the clay.
S. Rare. Occurs along the edge of the fast-flowing R. Wylye.
10 km² 14 (27%) 1 km² 40 (1%)   Map 476, page 311

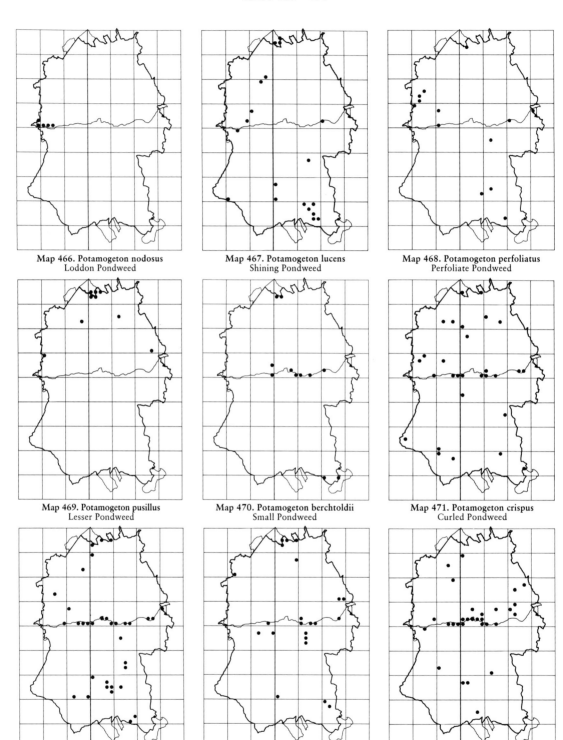

Map 466. Potamogeton nodosus
Loddon Pondweed

Map 467. Potamogeton lucens
Shining Pondweed

Map 468. Potamogeton perfoliatus
Perfoliate Pondweed

Map 469. Potamogeton pusillus
Lesser Pondweed

Map 470. Potamogeton berchtoldii
Small Pondweed

Map 471. Potamogeton crispus
Curled Pondweed

Map 472. Potamogeton pectinatus
Fennel Pondweed

Map 473. Zachinellia palustris
Horned Pondweed

Map 474. Spirodela polyrhiza
Greater Duckweed

Lemna minuta Kunth
Lemna miniscula Herter nom. illeg.
Least Duckweed

Introduction. Canal, ponds and slow-flowing water in rivers.

N. This plant spreads rapidly in some water courses, particularly the K & A Canal JEO, since it was first found in ponds at Peckingell near Chippenham 1987 DG. Elsewhere Redstocks 1988 DG, slow-flowing ditch and R. Thames/Isis, Castle Eaton 1991 JEO. See Aquatic Plants of the K & A Canal p.57.

S. R. Avon Salisbury 1989 JEO, first VC8 record. Elsewhere in pockets of still water on R. Avon at Avon Bridge, Middle Woodford, Heale House, Upper Woodford and Great Durnford; on R. Wylye S of Norton Bavant and Stapleford; on R. Bourne at Hurdcott, Winterbourne Gunner and Idmiston and abundant in farm pond Brokerswood.

10 km² 9 (17%)   1 km² 40 (1%)   Map 477, page 311

JUNCACEAE

Juncus L.

Juncus squarrosus L.
Heath Rush

Native. Wet heaths.
S. Confined to the New Forest growing on peat and alluvial soils, often adjacent to streams. Landford Bog, Plaitford, West Wellow, Cadnam Commons 1989-90 VW.

10 km² 1 (2%)   1 km² 14 (<1%)

Juncus tenuis Willd.
Slender Rush

Introduction. Bare and sparsely vegetated ground on tracks, road verges and woodland rides.
N. First VC7 record from a roadside verge Winsley JP. Flattening of the plant by farm machinery appears to aid seed dispersal.
S. Roman Road, Great Ridge Wood 1987 BL,

middle of track Quar Hill Plantation 1989 DJW, Black Lane, Hamptworth 1990 DJW, along shore Shear Water and High Wood, Longleat 1990 DG, 1991 VEH.

10 km² 4 (8%)   1 km² 7 (<1%)

Juncus compressus Jacq.
Round-fruited Rush

Native.
N. Two records. Very numerous in trodden areas of water-meadow near path, in gateways and on road verge Knighton 1984 DG, refind of Grose's 1941 record. Gaulters Mill, By Brook valley 1989 PB.

10 km² 2 (4%)   1 km² 2 (<1%)

Juncus bufonius L.
Toad Rush

Native. Damp habitats. Woodland rides, field gateways and pond margins. Frequent. Unevenly recorded.

10 km² 42 (81%)   2 km² 258 (27%)   Map 478, page 311

Juncus subnodulosus Schrank
Blunt-flowered Rush

Native. Marshy places with a flow of lime-rich water. Very localised.
N. Flaxlands, Derry Fields pit 40 CWP, near Wootton Bassett 1984-85 DG, two localities N of Swindon 1990 PD.

10 km² 3 (6%)   1 km² 4 (<1%)

Juncus articulatus L.
Jointed Rush

Native. Riverside and damp meadows and woodland rides, around springs, ponds and gravel pits. Neutral and alkaline soils. Frequent and locally abundant.

10 km² 40 (77%)   2 km² 230 (24%)   Map 479, page 311

Juncus acutiflorus Ehrh. ex Hoffm.
Sharp-flowered Rush

Native. Wet grassland, marshes and pond edges on neutral to acid soils.
N. Mainly on Oxford Clay from Melksham to Cricklade in the NE, in R. Kennet valley and in limited wet habitats in Savernake Forest.
S. Most records are from the area bordering the New Forest on London Clay.
10 km² 30 (58%) 1 km² 152 (4%)   Map 480, page 311

Juncus bulbosus L.
Juncus kochii F. Schultz
Bulbous Rush

Native. Wet and water-logged land on acid soils.
N. Near Stock Common, Savernake Forest 1983 DG & MP, Spye Park 1985 DG, pond Draycot Park 1986 DG, Webb's Wood 1986 CS & MS.
S. Aucombe Marsh, Shear Water 1991 ER. All other records confined to SE corner. Frequent on wet rides, particularly in wheel-ruts on heavy clay Barnsell Copse 1986 PMW and in a water-logged hole left by an uprooted tree Moor Copse, Whiteparish 1987 DJW. Frequent on wet heaths in the New Forest where leaves are often semi-submerged in bog pools.
10 km² 7 (13%)   1 km² 23 (<1%)   Map 481, page 311

Juncus inflexus L.
Hard Rush

Native. Wet grassland and sides of ditches on neutral, usually heavy clay soils, most common where the flow of water is restricted or where soil is poached by cattle. Frequent, locally abundant.
10 km² 48 (92%) 2 km² 467 (49%) Map 482, page 311

Juncus effusus L.
Soft-rush

Native. Wet grassland, river banks and open damp woods on acid and neutral soils. Frequent, locally abundant.
Var. subglomeratus DC.
Var. *compactus* Lej. & Courtois
Native. Wet places on acid or neutral soils.
N. Very common in Braydon Forest, Savernake Forest and Spye Park.
S. Common in wet pasture in Vale of Pewsey. Not recognised by all recorders.
10 km² 47 (90%) 2 km² 496 (52%)   Map 483, page 311

Juncus conglomeratus L.
Compact Rush

Native. Open woodland, heaths, marshes, bogs and other watery places on neutral to more acid soils.
N. Restricted by habitat to the heavy clay in the Braydon Forest and Melksham areas where it is locally frequent.
S. On acid soils in the SE and SW and on the clay between Trowbridge and Devizes.
10 km² 30 (58%) 1 km² 141 (4%)   Map 484, page 314

Luzula DC.

Luzula forsteri (Smith) DC.
Southern Wood-rush

Native. Woods, hedgebanks and road verges.
S. Unlike the other *Luzula* species *L. forsteri* is confined to southern half of county. It is locally common in the SE with outliers in the SW at Stourhead House gardens and at Park Hill to the NW of the gardens, at Himsel and Heath Wood in Grovely Wood. Scattered in clearings and by paths in Clarendon Wood and plentiful by the lake. Records from the SE at Loosehanger, Brook Golf Course and Penn Cottage Wood, Coles's Bury, near Gills Hole, Wall Copse, Lowdens Copse, The Earldoms, Broadlands Copse, Plaitford Green, Hound Wood and Chickard Wood.
10 km² 6 (12%)   1 km² 18 (<1%)   Map 485, page 314

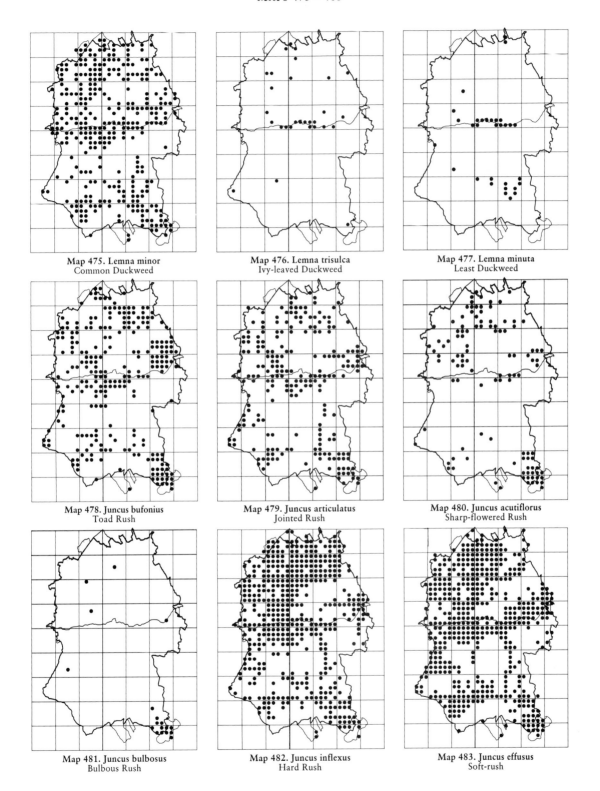

Map 475. Lemna minor
Common Duckweed

Map 476. Lemna trisulca
Ivy-leaved Duckweed

Map 477. Lemna minuta
Least Duckweed

Map 478. Juncus bufonius
Toad Rush

Map 479. Juncus articulatus
Jointed Rush

Map 480. Juncus acutiflorus
Sharp-flowered Rush

Map 481. Juncus bulbosus
Bulbous Rush

Map 482. Juncus inflexus
Hard Rush

Map 483. Juncus effusus
Soft-rush

Luzula pilosa (L.) Willd.
Hairy Wood-rush

Native. Woods, green lanes and streamsides. An ancient woodland indicator species.
This plant is restricted to permanently shaded, sometimes damp areas in old woodland where mosses are an important component of the ground flora. Concentrations occur in Savernake, Great Ridge and Grovely Woods and in the SE. There are scattered populations in many other woods and copses.
10 km² 32 (62%) 1 km² 202 (6%)   Map 486, page 314

Luzula sylvatica (Hudson) Gaudin
Great Wood-rush

Native. Woodland on acid soils.
N. Restricted to small areas in and around Savernake Forest. First record since 1951 Savernake 1989 VS. Chisbury Wood near Great Bedwyn 1990 MP and Chisbury Hill 1991 BG.
S. More widely distributed than in the N. Frequent and locally abundant in open woodland, on steep wooded slopes and in deep shade in beech woodland between Devizes and Lavington. There are scattered locations between Stourton and Warminster. It is locally abundant in Southleigh Wood, widespread in open and mixed woodland and under bracken Great Ridge Wood. It occurs on the edge of woodland rides Grovely Wood, on wooded stream and roadside banks in the R. Nadder valley and under beech and in hazel coppice in the SE.
10 km² 11 (21%) 1 km² 45 (1%)   Map 487, page 314

Luzula campestris (L.) DC.
Field Wood-rush

Native. Unimproved chalk, limestone and neutral grassland, lawns and churchyards. Frequent and widespread.
10 km² 50 (96%) 2 km² 488 (51%)   Map 488, page 314

Luzula multiflora (Ehrh.) Lej.
Heath Wood-rush

Native. Woodlands, heaths and railway cuttings on acid soils.
N. Frequent only in woodlands and acidic grassland in the Braydon Forest area. Occurs in cuttings beside M4 motorway E of junction 17 near Chippenham, railway cuttings Rodbourne and Hullavington and wood near Clench Common.
S. Main concentrations on the clays and sands in two large areas in SE, Redlynch/Brook/Whiteparish triangle and West Grimstead to Bentley Wood. Elsewhere Upper Woodford Valley 1985 PM, Black Dog Woods near Chapmanslade 1985 VEH, Stourton and Castle Wood 1991 PMW and on Clay-with-flints deposits on top of chalk downland with other plants of acid soils Great Ridge Wood 1987 PM.
Ssp. **congesta** (Thuill.) Arcang.
N. More frequent than the species. Always with it.
S. Growing with the species at some of the sites especially in SE. West Grimstead 1987 PH, nine records further S including Earldoms and opposite Chadwell Farm 1987 PMW. Elsewhere, occasional Castle Hill 1991 PMW and six plants on imported soil Wick Ball Camp, Teffont 1991 VH.
10 km² 15 (29%) 1 km² 68 (2%)   Map 489, page 314

CYPERACEAE

Eriophorum L.

Eriophorum angustifolium Honck.
Common Cottongrass

Native. Bogs and fens.
N. Very rare, refound only in water-meadows Chilton Foliat 1983 DG.
S. In three areas: Jones's Mill near Pewsey, refound 1984 DG, in the W near Sedgehill 1986 JHa, undrained bogs in the New Forest where populations vary from small, scattered clumps at Landford to quite extensive stands around Furzley.
10 km² 4 (8%)   1 km² 11 (<1%)   Map 490, page 314

Trichophorum Pers.

Trichophorum cespitosum (L.) Hartman
Scirpus cespitosus L.
Deergrass

Native. Undrained bogs and very wet commons with acid soils.
S. Scattered locally, usually in small numbers, on edge of New Forest. Appears to be associated with *Molinia*. Grazing may be detrimental to its survival. Six sites on Hamptworth Common 1986 NCC, first records for this century. Another site, footpath Hamptworth Common 1989 VW. Landford Bog VW, W edge Cadnam Common (Hants) 1990 AB & VW, abundant Plaitford Common (Hants) 1991 AB. Pleasing increase in number of sites recorded but not refound Pound Bottom.
10 km² 1 (2%)   1 km² 7 (<1%)   Map 491, page 314

Eleocharis R. Br.

Eleocharis palustris (L.) Roemer & Schultes
Common Spike-rush

Native. Ponds, rivers, marshes and canals. Frequent in these habitats, less common on acid soils.
10 km² 37 (71%) 2 km² 132 (14%) Map 492, page 314

Eleocharis uniglumis (Link) Schultes
Slender Spike-rush

Native. Wet gravel, riverside marshes inundated with water during the winter.
N. Occurring in great abundance Pike Corner (CWP). This discovery followed unconfirmed record 1982 RH, verified 1984 DG who found extensive colonies in adjacent heavily grazed unimproved pasture and drainage ditch. North Meadow NNR, Cricklade 1985 KP, pond in a cereal field Oaksey Bridge 1987 CK & MK. Gravel pit Jenning Moor (CWP) (also known as Oaksey Moor) 1987 DG, refind of earlier record (RE Sandell).

S. Marsh adjacent to Semington Brook, Seend Cleeve 1985 LW, 1989 BGH, first VC8 record, (ver. DG). S of church Plaitford 1991 RPB.
10 km² 4 (8%)   1 km² 6 (<1%)   Map 493, page 318

Eleocharis multicaulis (Smith) Desv.
Many-stalked Spike-rush

Native. Bogs and wet heathland.
S. Fairly common in appropriate habitat in New Forest and associated Commons. Hamptworth, Plaitford, West Wellow and Cadnam Commons, bog N of Furzely 1986-91 NCC, RV & VW.
10 km² 1 (2%)   1 km² 8 (<1%)

Eleocharis quinqueflora (F. Hartmann) O. Schwartz
Few-flowered Spike-rush

Native.
N. Very small colony in unimproved wet pasture CWP 1986 RH. First county record from meadow Marston 1885 (Druce). No other site was ever found for this plant within the Wiltshire part of the Thames basin for 101 years until the 1986 RH record. Until then some doubt had been cast on the reliability of Druce's record.
10 km² 1 (2%)   1 km² 1 (<1%)

Eleocharis acicularis (L.) Roemer & Schultes
Needle Spike-rush

Nationally scarce plant.
Native. A diminutive plant of waterbody silt often covered by water for many years. First county record in the canal at Marston Meysey 1885 (Druce). The canal is now dry. Reported CWP 1983 CWP/ST but not confirmed until August 1984 when the water level in the gravel pit was very low and the exposed silt held 30-40 colonies of this plant flowering in profusion DG & SCH. Material held by DG, SCH and Devizes Museum. Found in two further localities in the CWP VC7

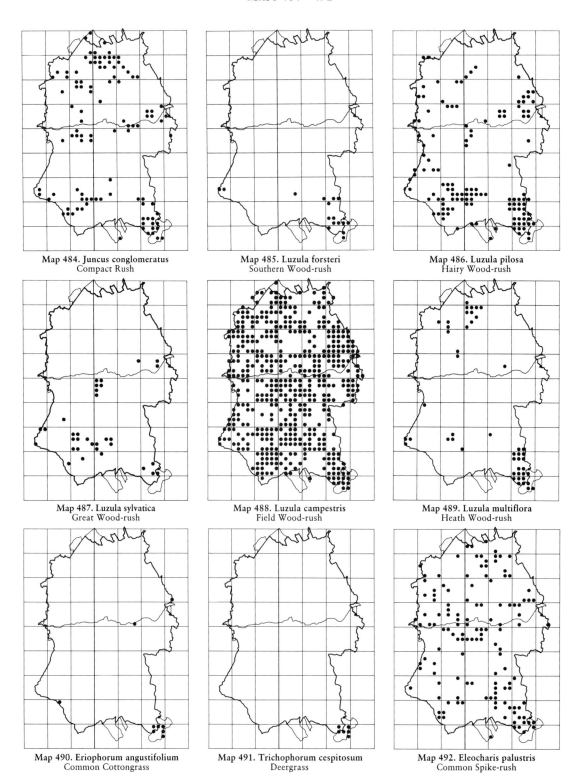

Map 484. **Juncus conglomeratus**
Compact Rush

Map 485. **Luzula forsteri**
Southern Wood-rush

Map 486. **Luzula pilosa**
Hairy Wood-rush

Map 487. **Luzula sylvatica**
Great Wood-rush

Map 488. **Luzula campestris**
Field Wood-rush

Map 489. **Luzula multiflora**
Heath Wood-rush

Map 490. **Eriophorum angustifolium**
Common Cottongrass

Map 491. **Trichophorum cespitosum**
Deergrass

Map 492. **Eleocharis palustris**
Common Spike-rush

(Glos) 1989 M Wade (conf. N Stewart) and flowering after introduction with water plants in a pond at Corston 1990 PD.

10 km² 3 (6%) 1 km² 4 (<1%)

Bolboschoenus (Asch.) Palla

Bolboschoenus maritimus (L.) Palla
Scirpus maritimus L.
Sea Club-rush

Native in GB, introduction in Wilts.
N. Possibly planted beside lake Bremhill House near Calne 1987 DH (id. FR).

10 km² 1 (2%) 1 km² 1 (<1%)

Scirpus L.

Scirpus sylvaticus L.
Wood Club-rush

Native. Shaded places in marshes and wet woods, beside ponds and rivers having lime-rich water.
N. Distribution greatly reduced since the 1950s when Grose had 30+ records in western half of VC7 alone. Occurs on the wettest ground beside streams on greensand at Spye Park and beside some tributaries of the Bristol Avon. Very rare elsewhere.
S. Where once frequent by the southern tributaries of the Bristol Avon, now only recorded from four tetrads. Grose's records at Stourton and Donhead survive. W of Landford may be a new site.

10 km² 13 (25%) 1 km² 30 (<1%)   Map 494, page 318

Schoenoplectus (Reichb.) Palla

Schoenoplectus lacustris (L.) Palla
Common Club-rush

Native. In the shallows of rivers, streams, lakes, large ponds, canals and gravel pits.

N. Most frequent along the Bristol Avon where it stretches from bank to bank in some places. Abundant in the R. Kennet E of Marlborough. Localised in still water in the K & A Canal, Braydon Pond and Coate Water.
S. Most frequent near the R. Avon S of Salisbury.

10 km² 24 (46%) 1 km² 78 (2%)   Map 495, page 318

Schoenoplectus tabernaemontani (C. Gmelin) Palla
Scirpus tabernaemontani C. Gmelin
Grey Club-rush

Native. Lime-rich still water.
N. In six gravel pits CWP 1986-89 DG, in pond N side of railway line Sodom Lane, Dauntsey 1989 DG.

10 km² 2 (4%) 1 km² 5 (<1%)   Map 496, page 318

Isolepis R. Br.

Isolepis setacea (L.) R.Br.
Scirpus setaceus L.
Bristle Club-rush

Native. Wet grassland, woodland rides, edges of ponds and gravel pits having lime-rich water.
N. Water-meadows Ramsbury 1983, several places in the By Brook valley 1984-86, damp woodland ride Spye Park 1985 DG, in profusion in damp grassland round a pond Giddea Hall 1987 DC and three sites on bare gravel CWP 1987 DG & RR.
S. There was a refind of a 1958 record in Nightwood Copse 1986 MD. The other five records were a small patch in a wet field at The Moors, West Grimstead 1988 IA, in a wet meadow Marden 1988 JMP, a scattering of plants Ford Wood, Woodborough 1989 VS, in Abbey Wood, Fonthill 1989 MM and on West Wellow Common (VC8 Hants) 1991 RV.

10 km² 9 (17%) 1 km² 13 (<1%)   Map 497, page 318

Eleogiton Link

Eleogiton fluitans (L.) Link
Scirpus fluitans L.
Floating Club-rush

Native. Bog pools and streams on acid soils.
S. Not found in any of the sites reported by Grose. Small populations occur in wetter areas of Canada, Cadnam and West Wellow Commons, (all Hants) 1990-91 RV & VW. Man-made duckpond Tinney's Plantation 1991 DJW.
10 km² 1 (2%)   1 km² 4 (<1%)

Blysmus Panzer ex Schultes

Blysmus compressus (L.) Panzer ex Link
Flat-sedge

Native. Damp unimproved meadows.
N. Throughout a large part of Doncombe Meadow at Ford 1984 DG refind of 1941 record (Frowde). Water-meadow beside R. Kennet Ramsbury 1984 DG, in large numbers Pike Corner and adjacent scraped gravel CWP 1985-86 DG & RR, damp area around pond Biddestone 1988 DC.
10 km² 3 (6%)   1 km² 4 (<1%)

Cyperus L.

Cyperus longus L.
Galingale

Nationally scarce plant.
Native in GB, introduction in Wilts. Stream and pond sides and marshes.
N. It seems likely that the records are of garden escapes or deliberate plantings of an attractive plant sold in garden centres. Beside footpath Holt 1986 EC, Parkers Bridge near Kemble 1985 CK & MK, R. Thames at Ashton Keynes 1988 DG.
S. Edges of ponds Brookmead, West Grimstead

1984 PAW, Urchfont 1989 JMP, wet meadow Donhead St Andrew 1990 MM.
10 km² 6 (12%)   1 km² 6 (<1%)

Rhynchospora Vahl

Rhynchospora alba (L.) Vahl
White Beak-sedge

Native. Wet, acid peat.
S. Confined to the New Forest where it is widespread on the wettest parts of the heaths and the colonies can be extensive. Hamptworth Common 1989 NCC/ST, Plaitford Common, bog N of Furzley, West Wellow Common 1989 VW and Cadnam Common 1990 VW.
10 km² 1 (2%)   1 km² 8 (<1%)

Rhynchospora fusca (L.) W. T. Aiton
Brown Beak-sedge

Nationally scarce plant.
Native. Wet heaths.
S. Varying numbers of plants with much *R. alba*, Plaitford Common. First county record VC8 (Hants) 1983-91 FR.
10 km² 1 (2%)   1 km² 1 (<1%)

Cladium P. Browne

Cladium mariscus (L.) Pohl
Great Fen-sedge

Native in GB, introduction in Wilts. A clump planted in the CWP 1986 DG & SCH.
10 km² 1 (2%)   1 km² 1 (<1%)

Carex L.

The genus has been well covered, although some recorders experienced problems of identification especially with the *C. spicata* group (*C. spicata*, *C. muricata* agg. and *C. divulsa*) and *C. viridula* group.

Carex paniculata L.
Greater Tussock-sedge

Native. Lakes, canals, rivers, marshes, fens and woodland on base-rich soils.
N. Found very close to water, often partly submerged, on base-rich soil where the water is lime-rich. Tussocks in the *Alnus* climax woodland in Spye Park stand at 1.5 metres and with one season's growth are taller than a man 1984 DG. K & A Canal abundant only E of Alton Barnes, R. Kennet: Froxfield 1984 WTNC/ST and from Ramsbury to the E 1985 JN. Stream-side near Coate Water (Swindon) 1984, Chittoe, Bowood Lake, woodlands at Rowde 1984-90, Littlecott and large colony The Strings valley both near Lyneham 1986 DG.
S. Once 'locally plentiful in Vale of Pewsey' (Grose). Still present in swamps and fens Jones's Mill near Pewsey 1984 AJS, Woodborough, Beechingstoke, Marden and Manor Woods, Market Lavington 1984-1985 RF. Beside R. Avon: Enford, West Chisenbury and Manningfords including wet woodland near disused mill. R. Ebble: ungrazed spring-fed marsh, isolated record in this valley Homington 1986 JT. In SE: wet ditch East Grimstead 1986 PAW, wet woodland SE of Redlynch, old wet meadows W of Chadwell Farm 1990 DJW and wet area Earldoms 1990 PMW.
10 km² 13 (25%) 1 km² 39 (1%)   Map 498, page 318

Carex otrubae Podp.
False Fox-sedge

Native. Wet places on heavy clay soils. Most frequent in Braydon Forest area, W of Devizes and on calcareous clay in the NW of the county.
10 km² 36 (69%) 2 km² 229 (24%)   Map 499, page 318

Carex spicata Hudson
Spiked Sedge

Native. Unimproved neutral grassland, hedgebanks and road verges. Locally abundant in clay meadows and hedgebanks in the N. Occurs on chalk around Aldbourne and scattered throughout VC8.
10 km² 40 (77%) 2 km² 184 (19%)   Map 500, page 318

Carex muricata L. ssp. **lamprocarpa** Celak
Carex pairii F. Schultz
Small-fruited Prickly-sedge

Native. Dry, acid soils.
N. Recorded from Lower Greensand at Bromham and Chittoe for many years, though the only record during WFMP is of a single plant on road verge Bowden Hill 1987 DG.
S. Four records all on the Wilts/Hants border at Plaitford (two) and East Wellow 1986, West Wellow 1991 RV. First records for more than 20 years.
10 km² 2 (4%)   1 km² 3 (<1%)

Carex divulsa Stokes ssp. **divulsa**
Grey Sedge

Native. Woodland edges, hedgebanks and road verges where it usually occurs at the base of the bank, almost level with the road.
N. Large populations in the Colerne area and E of Marlborough.
S. Common in the extreme S. On Clay-with-flints overlying chalk.
10 km² 30 (58%) 1 km² 184 (5%)   Map 501, page 318

Carex disticha Hudson
Brown Sedge

Native. Water-meadows, damp unimproved neutral grassland, marshes, fens, lake and pond edges.
N. Large colonies at Coate Water (Swindon) and CWP, rare North Meadow NNR at Cricklade. Common in R. Kennet valley E of Marlborough. Very local elsewhere.
S. Scarce except E of Trowbridge, adjacent to stretches of the Salisbury Avon and in SE.
10 km² 20 (38%) 1 km² 80 (2%)   Map 502, page 321

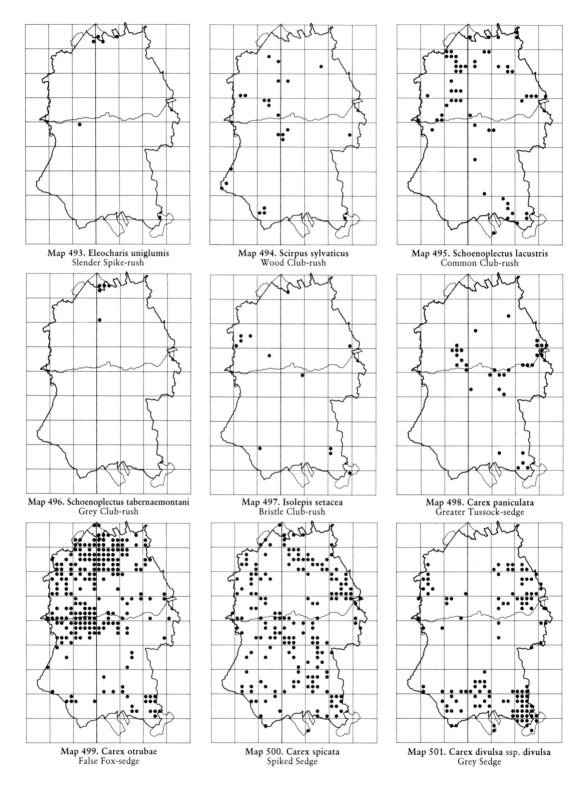

Map 493. Eleocharis uniglumis
Slender Spike-rush

Map 494. Scirpus sylvaticus
Wood Club-rush

Map 495. Schoenoplectus lacustris
Common Club-rush

Map 496. Schoenoplectus tabernaemontani
Grey Club-rush

Map 497. Isolepis setacea
Bristle Club-rush

Map 498. Carex paniculata
Greater Tussock-sedge

Map 499. Carex otrubae
False Fox-sedge

Map 500. Carex spicata
Spiked Sedge

Map 501. Carex divulsa ssp. divulsa
Grey Sedge

Carex remota L.
Remote Sedge

Native. Wet woodland, stream, pond and ditch sides.
N. Widely-distributed in these habitats on limestone and clays, often growing as an emergent species where the ground is flooded by water for most of the winter.
S. Most frequent on clays and Upper Greensand around and extending SW from Trowbridge to Stourhead, around the Donheads, in the SE and in the Vale of Pewsey.
10 km² 37 (71%) 1 km² 308 (8%)   Map 503, page 321

Carex ovalis Gooden.
Oval Sedge

Native. Unimproved and semi-improved neutral grassland, marshes and around ponds on clay.
N. Greatest concentration on stiff clays with restricted water-flow in Braydon Forest, near Melksham and at Luckington. Often the only sedge occurring in some ridge-and-furrow pastures.
S. Greatest concentration in the SE. Frequent in the Vale of Pewsey.
10 km² 22 (42%) 1 km² 107 (3%)   Map 504, page 321

Carex echinata Murray
Star Sedge

Native. Acidic wet meadows and bogs.
N. Very rare. Confined to peaty water-meadows in the R. Kennet valley at Chilton Foliat 1983 DG.
S. Frequent in neutral to acidic meadows in the extreme SE at Plaitford Common, Nomansland, Redlynch and New Forest.
10 km² 13 (25%) 1 km² 37 (1%)

Carex curta Gooden.
White Sedge

Native. Very wet bogs.

S. Plaitford Common 1990 FR, first record for VC8 (Hants).
10 km² 1 (2%)   1 km² 2 (<1%)

Carex hirta L.
Hairy Sedge

Native. Pond edges and damp places on heavy clay soils, including ground poached by cattle. Frequent in these habitats.
10 km² 42 (81%) 2 km² 306 (32%)   Map 505, page 321

Carex acutiformis Ehrh.
Lesser Pond-sedge

Native. Wet land adjacent to rivers, streams and ponds. Well-distributed, especially along the Salisbury Avon. Similar distribution to that of *C. riparia*.
10 km² 36 (69%) 1 km² 257 (7%)   Map 506, page 321

Carex riparia Curtis
Greater Pond-sedge

Native. Rivers, streams, lakes and canal.
N. Often abundant and extensive, in the river systems and K & A Canal.
S. Well-distributed in the R. Avon valley, occurs on stretches of rivers Wylye, Nadder and Bourne.
10 km² 35 (67%) 1 km² 186 (5%)   Map 507, page 321

Carex pseudocyperus L.
Cyperus Sedge

Native. Riparian habitats, particularly ponds.
N. Most frequent in the disused farm ponds on clay in the area between Clyffe Pypard and Wootton Bassett. Braydon Pond, ponds at Hullavington, Sells Green and adjacent to railway Waite Hill, gravel pits CWP 1988 DG, Wootton Bassett 1984 JF, Coate Water 1986 JN.
S. Lakeside Westbury 1985 DG.
10 km² 8 (15%) 1 km² 12 (<1%)   Map 508, page 321

Carex rostrata Stokes
Bottle Sedge

Native. Fens, ditches and pond edges.
N. Water-meadow ditch in R.Kennet valley near Knighton 1985 LW (ver. DG, retained in Devizes Museum Hb.). First VC7 record since 1874.
S. Four records: water-meadow Jones's Mill, two sites 1983 DG & RR, 1984 SH & AJS, small fen Beechingstoke 1985 RF, numerous plants on edge of pond Lower Pensworth, Redlynch 1989 DJW. The only five sites recorded since 1951.
10km² 4 (8%)   1 km² 4 (<1%)

Carex pendula Hudson
Pendulous Sedge

Native. Damp woods, stream and pond margins on clay and greensand. A dominant species of wet woods Spye Park and Longleat, luxuriant growth Stourton Woods.
10 km² 38 (73%) 2 km² 249 (26%)   Map 509, page 321

Carex sylvatica Hudson
Wood-sedge

Native. Ancient and secondary woodland especially on neutral soils. A common and constant species of these habitats.
10 km² 48 (92%) 2 km² 324 (34%)   Map 510, page 321

Carex strigosa Hudson
Thin-spiked Wood-sedge

Native. Woodland, open rides, ditches, woodland embankments and areas wet in winter where the water is alkaline.
N. Often at the lowest and wettest point in a wood. Mainly in woodlands on heavy neutral clay around West Kington 1985, Castle Combe area and on Lower Greensand especially at Bowood, Prickmoor Wood, Derry Hill Wood and Pigsty Copse 1986-90 DG. Elsewhere, Great Wood at Grittenham and in large numbers in some rides Silk Wood 1983 DG.
S. Fewer records than in N but a three-fold increase. Two new areas: Grovely Wood 1987-88 BL and two woods Redlynch and Earldoms 1986-88 PMW & MD. Potterne Wood/West Lavington/Stert 1984-85 RF including The Warren, West Lavington, a refind of Grose's 1948 record. Wet wood Heywood 1985 WTNC/ST and 50-100 plants in ditch bordering Brokerswood 1991 DG.
10 km² 9 (17%)   1 km² 33 (<1%)   Map 511, page 324

Carex flacca Schreber
Glaucous Sedge

Native. Wet and dry unimproved grassland on chalk, limestone and neutral clay. Frequent and locally abundant especially on chalk and limestone.
10 km² 51 (98%) 2 km² 535 (56%) Map 512, page 324

Carex panicea L.
Carnation Sedge

Native. Damp grassland, marshes, fens, bogs and around calcareous springs.
N. Only common in damp neutral grassland in the Braydon Forest area. This sedge has declined in recent years due to drainage of wet meadows.
S. Main concentration of records on the clays in the SE. Scattered elsewhere with a few records from the chalk.
10 km² 28 (54%) 1 km² 118 (3%)   Map 513, page 324

Carex laevigata Smith
Smooth-stalked Sedge

Native. Damp woodland.
N. Historically known only from Spye Park (T B Flower 1857). Refound at Chittoe 1984 DG and Spye Park 1985 DG & RR.
S. Found in wet woodland, rides and hedgerows and open grassland associated with woodland. Commonly occurs only as small tufts with few

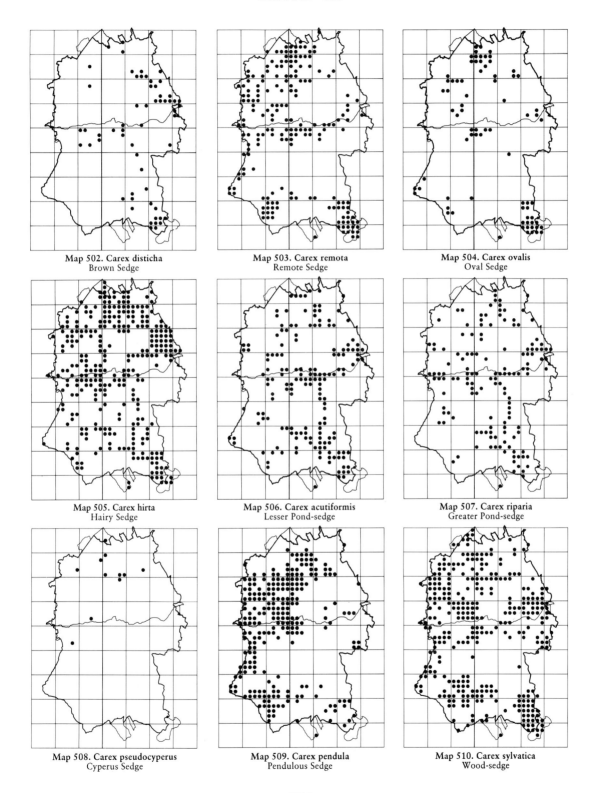

Map 502. **Carex disticha**
Brown Sedge

Map 503. **Carex remota**
Remote Sedge

Map 504. **Carex ovalis**
Oval Sedge

Map 505. **Carex hirta**
Hairy Sedge

Map 506. **Carex acutiformis**
Lesser Pond-sedge

Map 507. **Carex riparia**
Greater Pond-sedge

Map 508. **Carex pseudocyperus**
Cyperus Sedge

Map 509. **Carex pendula**
Pendulous Sedge

Map 510. **Carex sylvatica**
Wood-sedge

flowering spikes. Most frequent in the New Forest area, unusual elsewhere. Recorded from Stourton 1985 FR, Teffont 1988 VH and Clarendon 1986 MD.

10 km² 5 (10%)   1 km² 17 (<1%)

Carex binervis Smith
Green-ribbed Sedge

Native. Acid heathland and woodland clearings.
N. Repeated searches near the Column, Savernake Forest have failed to find the plant last recorded there 1968 (N E King). The habitat remains suitable.
S. Stronghold on New Forest heathland in dry, free-draining soil conditions. Populations scattered and can be conspicuous in some clear-felled areas as on the edge of Hamptworth Estate VW. Elsewhere, Longleat Park 1987 DG, Stourton area 1991 DG & PMW.

10 km² 4 (8%)   1 km² 14 (<1%)

Carex distans L.
Distant Sedge

Native. Damp grassland containing lime-rich water, usually in small numbers.
N. Pike Corner (CWP) many thousands of plants 1985, pasture near Dundas Aqueduct 1986, limestone grassland Lyneham 1985, marsh Broughton Gifford and several localities in the Lidbrook and By Brook valleys 1984-89, unimproved pasture on gravel CWP 1984-89 DG.
S. Beside Semington Brook 1988-91 BGH (conf. RW David). New site and first VC8 record since 1903.

10 km² 7 (13%)   1 km² 18 (<1%)   Map 514, page 324

Carex hostiana DC.
Tawny Sedge

Native. Fen-like conditions and seasonally flooded grassland in highly lime-rich strata.

N. Chilton Foliat water-meadow 1983, bare ground near pit 24 (CWP) and unimproved meadow Pike Corner 1986 DG.

10 km² 2 (4%)   1 km² 3 (<1%)

Carex viridula Michaux ssp. brachyrrhyncha (Celak.) B. Schmid
Carex lepidocarpa Tausch
Long-stalked Yellow-sedge

Native. Damp places on base-rich soils.
N. Pasture on hillside near Dundas Aqueduct, Lidbrook near Colerne, marshy field Hullavington, several places CWP, abundant Pike Corner growing with *C. viridula* ssp. *oedocarpa* 1984-86 DG. Material in Grose's herbarium and specimens collected by DG from Braydon Forest area were named as *C. viridula* ssp. *oedocarpa*. However, due to the amount of gradation between ssp. *brachyrrhyncha* and ssp. *oedocarpa* it is very difficult to decide to which ssp. these specimens should be attributed.
S. Abundant in main drain of unimproved water-meadow West Gomeldon Farm 1987 JF, in luxuriant masses near Damerham 1991 JO.

10 km² 6 (12%)   1 km² 7 (<1%)

Carex viridula Michaux ssp. oedocarpa (Anderson) B. Schmid
Carex demissa Hornem.
Common Yellow-sedge

Native. Bogs and very wet places in woods, woodland rides, meadows, gravel pits and heaths.
N. Localised to the Braydon Forest and Somerford Common area where it occurs in large numbers in damp and poached woodland rides. Also occurs in pure gravel at Pike Corner (CWP) a rare habitat for the species. Recorded from a fen near R. Kennet at Chilton Foliat.
S. Common in the New Forest area, decreasing further N due to the less acidic conditions. Occurs elsewhere in suitable conditions. New records

from Bentley Wood, Redlynch and Plaitford Common in the SE.
10 km² 16 (31%) 1 km² 59 (2%)   Map 515, page 324

Carex pallescens L.
Pale Sedge

Native. Woodland rides, glades, meadows and open areas on neutral to acid clay soils.
N. Somerford Common 1984 JF, Pond Plantation around Braydon Pond 1985 DG, Stanton Park Wood 1986 JH, Webb's and Braydon Woods 1986 MWS, Lower Sands Farm, Compton Basset 1987 BG, Pilpot Wood, Bowood 1988 ER.
S. Clearly associated with clays, most records are from SE corner. Bentley Wood eight sites 1984-90 IA, PMW & MD, Blackmoor Copse 1985-90 PAW & IA. Numerous plants with *C. remota*, *C. sylvatica* and *C. laevigata* Grove Copse 1989 JW & PMW. Damp hay meadows, occasional Cadley Farm 1985 RF, rare Fiddington 1986 RF.
10 km² 13 (25%) 1 km² 37 (1%)   Map 516, page 324

Carex digitata L.
Fingered Sedge

Nationally scarce plant.
Native. Shady woodland on limestone. Occurs in two localities on steep woodland banks in the Slaughterford/Colerne Park areas of the By Brook valley. The number of plants per colony fluctuates annually: from 52 (1983) to 46 (1991) at one site and 23 (1983) to 18 (1991) at another DG.
Historical records: Colerne 1834 (Davis), three sites Colerne 1858 (SH Bicpham), Lucknam 1861 (Mrs Torrence), Box 1869 (TB Flower), Slaughterford 1869 (R Withers), wood near Slaughterford 1869 (WA Clark), between Ford/Slaughterford 1837 (NY Sandwith), Colerne 1976 (RW David).
10 km² 1 (2%)   1 km² 2 (<1%)

Carex humilis Leysser
Dwarf Sedge

Nationally scarce plant.
Native. Unimproved chalk downland.
N. The only colony near Bishops Cannings has been lost due to agricultural improvement of the downland grass.
S. A speciality of unimproved downland on Salisbury Plain, between the rivers Wylye/Nadder and between Salisbury and Cranborne Chase. Frequent and locally abundant forming dense swathes. One hundred sites include Parsonage Down 1984 BG and Wylye Down 1985 BL both NNR's, Prescombe Down 1988 PT, Deptford Down 1986-91 BL, Tytherington Down 1991 VH, Throope Down 1991 PW, Middleton Down WTNC reserve. Small scattered colonies persist among long ungrazed grass SPTA(C) mainly on steep banks, ditches and tumuli. Most northerly colony on W-facing slope Water Dean Bottom near Casterley Camp. See article on p.91.
10 km² 11 (21%) 1 km² 78 (2%)   Map 517, page 324

Carex caryophyllea Latour.
Spring-sedge

Native. Calcareous and unimproved neutral grassland. Occurs more frequently on unimproved chalk and limestone grassland but is easily overlooked after flowering.
10 km² 38 (73%) 1 km² 278 (8%)   Map 518, page 324

Carex filiformis L.
Carex tomentosa L.
Downy-fruited Sedge

British Red Data Book species.
Native. Damp meadows.
N. Historically recorded only from the extreme N, now the CWP area. First British locality Marston Meysey (Teesdale 1799) was visited by 19th and early 20th century botanists, the last sighting by Lousley 1936 described in a letter

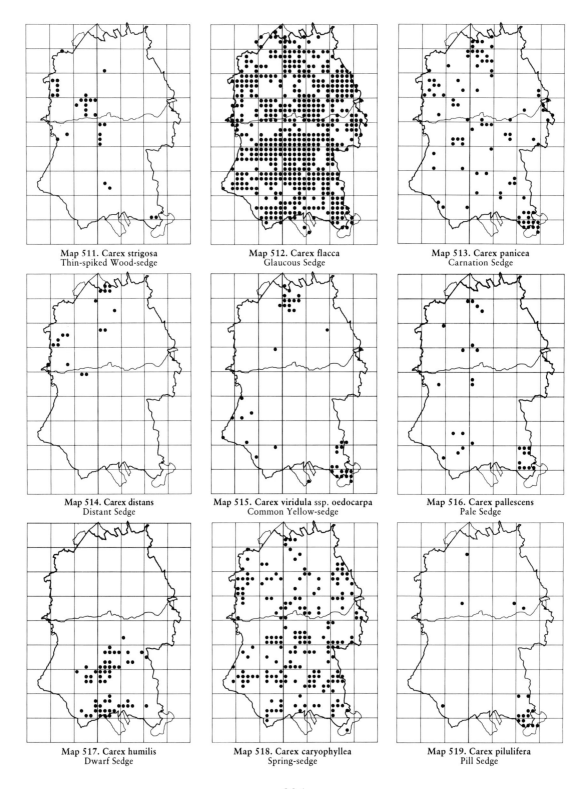

Map 511. Carex strigosa
Thin-spiked Wood-sedge

Map 512. Carex flacca
Glaucous Sedge

Map 513. Carex panicea
Carnation Sedge

Map 514. Carex distans
Distant Sedge

Map 515. Carex viridula ssp. oedocarpa
Common Yellow-sedge

Map 516. Carex pallescens
Pale Sedge

Map 517. Carex humilis
Dwarf Sedge

Map 518. Carex caryophyllea
Spring-sedge

Map 519. Carex pilulifera
Pill Sedge

(dated 1937) to D Grose as being mainly in the furrows in a water-meadow S of the canal near the Round House S of Marston Meysey. 1985 DG found the field to be a flat wheat field. Recorded in old hay meadow 1969 DW where the plant still occurs (NCC). Ridge-and-furrow pasture Minety parish 1988 LW. See article on p.91.
10 km² 1 (2%)   1 km² 2 (<1%)

Carex pilulifera L.
Pill Sedge

Native. Open acidic woodland and heaths on sand and clay.
N. On greensand in Spye Park 1985 DG, Pond Plantation in Braydon Forest 1985 DG & LW, several localities in Savernake Forest.
S. Most commonly found on damp, clay soils in open woodland. Small, scattered populations growing among grass species. One record from Semley Hill 1987 JO, BSBI meeting, all others from SE corner.
10 km² 7 (13%)   1 km² 22 (<1%)   Map 519, page 324

Carex acuta L.
Slender Tufted-sedge

Native. Rivers, streams, lakes and ponds.
N. Usually occurs in isolated clumps. First recent record in a ditch North Meadow, Cricklade 1982 SCH. Growing in the adjacent meadow 1984 DG. Continues growing in large quantity Braydon Pond 1985 DG. Other localities: Gauze Brook near Rodbourne 1984 DC, Coate Water new lake 1984 DG, Bradford-on-Avon and Tedcroft near Malmesbury 1987 DG.
10 km² 5 (10%)   1 km² 7 (<1%)   Map 520, page 327

Carex nigra (L.) Reichard
Common Sedge

Native. Marshes, damp grassland, river, stream, lake and pond margins and wet woodland on neutral and acid soils.

N. Only frequent on the heavier clays in the Braydon Forest and Melksham areas, at Coate Water near Swindon, beside the R. Kennet and in ponds in the Savernake area.
S. Largest number of records from the Vale of Pewsey, parts of the Salisbury Avon and in the SE.
10 km² 38 (73%) 1 km² 163 (5%)   Map 521, page 327

Carex pulicaris L.
Flea Sedge

Native. A species of very different habitats in Wilts, mesotrophic to eutrophic, silty soil in wet meadows and dry chalk grassland.
N. Recorded in two areas of chalk grassland within 2 km of one another: Morgan's Hill 1987 JN, Calstone Down 1989 BG. Water-meadow Chilton Foliat 1983 DG, on heavy clay in woodland ride Somerford Common 1985 RR.
S. Four records, all from damp/wet meadows. Two sites Jones's Mill, Pewsey 1984 AJS, wet meadow Chadwell, Whiteparish 1988 and damp meadow near Quar Hill Plantation 1990 DJW.
10 km² 7 (13%)   1 km² 7 (<1%)   Map 522, page 327

POACEAE

The coverage by recorders is shown in Figure 12 on p.115. Generally the coverage is good, though some species of the following genera caused identification problems and in so doing may have been under-recorded or over-recorded: *Festuca*, *Poa*, *Glyceria*, *Agrostis* and *Bromus*. Some species were only accepted if identified by an experienced botanist.

Nardus L.

Nardus stricta L.
Mat-grass

Native. Acid soil.
N. Heathland turf St Catherine's churchyard 1984 MP and 1 km NE of Column 1990 DG, both in Savernake Forest.
S. Mainly on edge of New Forest: Furzley 1989 VW

& AB, Penn, Plaitford and Canada Commons 1991
RV. Elsewhere on superficials Weather Hill SPTA(E)
1988 BG.
10 km² 3 (6%)   1 km² 9 (<1%)

Milium L.

Milium effusum L.
Wood Millet

Native. A grass of ancient and older woodland
especially on calcareous soil. Especially frequent
around Marlborough and common in Great Ridge
and Grovely Woods.
10 km² 42 (81%) 1 km² 303 (8%)   Map 523, page 327

Festuca L.

Festuca pratensis Hudson
Meadow Fescue

Native. Unimproved and rough grassland on
neutral to calcareous soils.
N. A consistent constituent of the unimproved
neutral meadows, less frequent on dry chalk.
S. Occurs in damp meadows and rough chalk
grassland.
10 km² 45 (87%) 1 km² 488 (13%)   Map 524, page 327

Festuca arundinacea Schreber
Tall Fescue

Native. Woodland rides, road verges and many types
of grassland. Widely-distributed. A coarse grass,
can become dominant in grassland. An increasing
species, more widespread than in the 1950s.
10 km² 46 (88%) 1 km² 560 (15%)   Map 525, page 327

Festuca gigantea (L.) Villars
Giant Fescue

Native. Hedgerows and woodland in semi-shade.

Frequent on heavier soils.
10 km² 45 (87%) 2 km² 445 (47%)   Map 526, page 327

Festuca heterophylla Lam.
Various-leaved Fescue

Introduction with other agricultural grass-seed
mixtures.
S. Naturalised in a dozen sites Grovely Wood.
Old, planted-up downland Middle Hills 1985.
Tare Coat 1987, six records 1988 and four 1989
mainly on edges of rides and paths BL. Margin
between grassland and hedgebank, Wick Down
1987 NLC.
10 km² 2 (4%)   1 km² 8 (<1%)   Map 527, page 327

Festuca rubra L. agg.
Red Fescue

Native. All types of grassland. Forms dense
mattresses on some areas of flat, ungrazed chalk
grassland. Common and widely-distributed.
10 km² 48 (92%) 2 km² 675 (71%)

Festuca ovina L. agg.
Sheep's-fescue

Native. Short turf mainly on chalk and limestone
grassland. Frequency difficult to determine where
it grows with *F. rubra*.
10 km² 44 (85%) 2 km² 371 (39%)   Map 528, page 327

Festuca filiformis Pourret
Festuca tenuifolia Sibth.
Fine-leaved Sheep's-fescue

Native.
S. West Wellow Common 1988 RV and along the
edge of woodland rides Hamptworth 1990 DJW
(ver. AH), Furzley Common and Penn Common
1991 RV.
10 km² 1 (2%)   1 km² 4 (<1%)

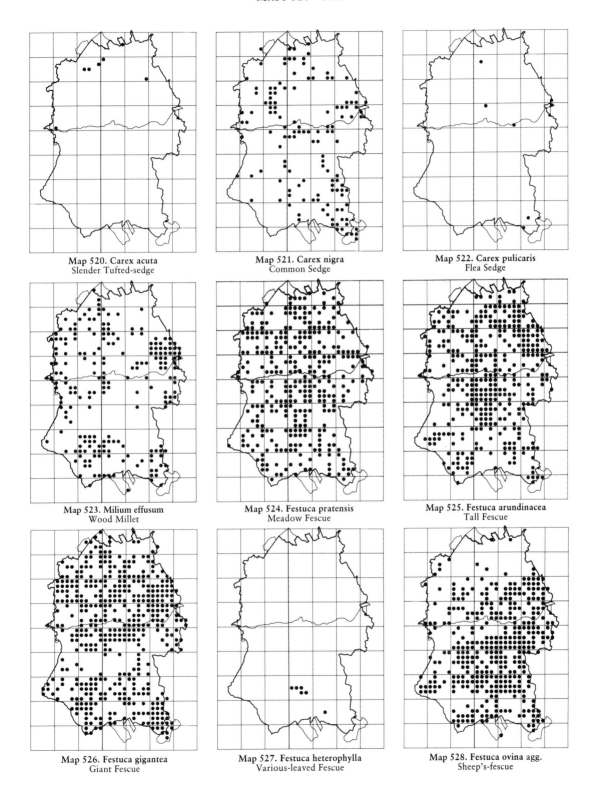

Map 520. Carex acuta
Slender Tufted-sedge

Map 521. Carex nigra
Common Sedge

Map 522. Carex pulicaris
Flea Sedge

Map 523. Milium effusum
Wood Millet

Map 524. Festuca pratensis
Meadow Fescue

Map 525. Festuca arundinacea
Tall Fescue

Map 526. Festuca gigantea
Giant Fescue

Map 527. Festuca heterophylla
Various-leaved Fescue

Map 528. Festuca ovina agg.
Sheep's-fescue

X Festulolium Asch. & Graebner

Festuca pratensis x Lolium perenne =
X Festulolium loliaceum (Hudson) P. Fourn.
Hybrid Fescue

Sterile intergeneric hybrid.
Native. Old grassland, usually on rich, heavy soils. Local. The reseeding of much grassland with *Lolium perenne* has created the opportunity for the natural hybridisation to occur with *Festuca pratensis*. High concentrations of this hybrid are likely to occur where traditional pastures and meadows are found adjacent to areas of reseeded *Lolium perenne*.
10 km² 35 (67%) 1 km² 110 (3%)   Map 529, page 331

Lolium L.

Lolium perenne L.
Perennial Rye-grass

Native. All types of grassland. The commonest grass species sown for silage and pasture crops. A common escape from cultivation.
10 km² 52 (100%)2 km² 851 (90%)

Lolium perenne x L. multiflorum =
L. x boucheanum Kunth

Introduction and occasionally native. This hybrid appears to be the commonest *Lolium* planted by farmers. However it was not recorded during WFMP due to the difficulty of separating it from its parents.

Lolium multiflorum Lam.
Italian Rye-grass

Introduction and occurs as a relic of cultivation on field margins, road verges and arable land. Sown in hay and silage mixtures. Under-recorded.
10 km² 45 (87%) 1 km² 322 (9%)

Lolium temulentum L.
Darnel

Introduction. Formerly common in corn crops but now occurs only as a casual in waste places. Infamous as the bearer of the poisonous ergot fungus which developed in the seed. This killed many who ate bread from infected grain in the Middle Ages, death being preceded by convulsions and gangrene.
S. Seend Head 1990 BGH.
10 km² 1 (2%)   1 km² 1 (<1%)

Vulpia C. Gmelin

Vulpia bromoides (L.) Gray
Squirreltail Fescue

Native. Waste places including railway tracks and stations on open, free-draining soils.
N. Known in its natural acidic turf habitat only in Spye Park and in sand pits Compton Bassett and Sandridge 1989 DG. Elsewhere at Bradford-on-Avon 1987 SY, near Great Wood, Grittenham and on railway Rodbourne 1985-90 DG, waste ground and along railway tracks Swindon 1990-91 JN.
S. Most records from SE corner where it grows on heathy tracks including residential driveway 1990-91 RV, JW & PMW. Elsewhere, grassy ride Grovely Wood 1987 BL, waste ground Market Lavington 1990 JMP, common among gorse Summerslade Down, Brixton Deverill 1991 BG.
10 km² 11 (21%) 1 km² 19 (<1%)   Map 530, page 331

Vulpia myuros (L.) C. Gmelin
Rat's-tail Fescue

Probably native. Rough ground, especially in association with railway lines and apparently always in man-made habitats.
N. Large colonies on some railway lines. Studley, pits 54/55 CWP, Semington, Seend station and railway Shockerwick 1984-90 DG, Hullavington goods yard 1986 JH, disused railway Martinslade 1988 BG, Kemble station and near railway

Severalls Copse 1988 MK & CK, churchyard Lydiard Millicent, near R. Avon S of Malmesbury, on concrete anti-tank pill-boxes near R. Avon SE of Malmesbury 1989 JEO.

S. Old railway line, site later destroyed, Bemerton 1985 JBH, Semley 1987 BSBI meeting, path by railway Patney 1988 JMP.

10 km² 13 (25%) 1 km² 17 (<1%)   Map 531, page 331

Cynosurus L.

Cynosurus cristatus L.
Crested Dog's-tail

Native. Unimproved and semi-improved grassland. Common and widespread especially on calcareous soil.

10 km² 50 (96%) 2 km² 656 (69%)   Map 532, page 331

Briza L.

Briza media L.
Quaking-grass

Native. Frequent on unimproved chalk and limestone downland. Very local in neutral meadows but occurs in quantity in some in the N.

10 km² 48 (92%) 2 km² 491 (52%)   Map 533, page 331

Poa L.

Poa annua L.
Annual Meadow-grass

Native. Waste ground, paths, lawns and short-cut turf. Common.

10 km² 52 (100%) 2 km² 839 (88%)

Poa trivialis L.
Rough Meadow-grass

Native. Unimproved, semi-improved and improved grassland, partial shade in woodland, cultivated and waste ground. Common and widely-distributed.

10 km² 49 (94%) 2 km² 754 (79%)

Poa humilis Ehrh. ex Hoffm.
Poa subcaerulea Smith
Spreading Meadow-grass

Native. More common further N in GB in wet grassland, coastal dunes and hill pastures.

N. On thin bare chalk soil with little competition from other grasses Walker's Hill, Pewsey Downs NNR 1983 DG (conf. Kew). Second county record.

S. All records on edge of New Forest, roadside Furzley 1989 VW & AB, roadside on edge of Deazle Wood 1991 VW and Plaitford Common 1991 AB.

10 km² 2 (4%)   1 km² 4 (<1%)

Poa pratensis L.
Smooth Meadow-grass

Native. Dry grassland and rough ground. Common and widespread. Flowers earlier than *P. trivialis*.

10 km² 49 (94%) 2 km² 658 (69%)   Map 534, page 331

Poa angustifolia L.
Narrow-leaved Meadow-grass

Native. Well-drained grassy banks on calcareous soils.

N. Road cutting adjacent to A420 at Ford and West Yatton Down on limestone 1983 DG.

S. Lane Knighton near Broad Chalke 1986 BGa, near rabbit warren Porton Range 1986 OS. Probably under-recorded, especially as this plant usually grows with *Bromopsis erecta* and is difficult to see.

10 km² 3 (6%)   1 km² 4 (<1%)

Poa compressa L.
Flattened Meadow-grass

Native. Limestone walls, bare calcareous ground and gravel.

N. Nowhere frequent but quite widely-distributed especially on the oldest walls in the Cotswold villages where mortar is crumbling. Occurs on boundary walls of churches and manor houses, walls at Turleigh, Lacock, Biddestone, Holt and Malmesbury, a rocky outcrop in railway cutting Hullavington, gravel banks at three sites CWP, woodland clearing Hussey Hill Wood in By Brook valley.
S. Wall West Ashton 1987 DG and grounds Chisenbury Priory 1988 PMWF.
10 km² 9 (17%)   1 km² 18 (<1%)   Map 535, page 331

Poa nemoralis L.
Wood Meadow-grass

Native. In the shade of trees in woods, on woodland banks and in lanes. Well-distributed.
N. Often local in occurrence, therefore liable to be overlooked in large woods. In many of the older woods, particularly common at Sandy Lane and in Savernake Forest.
S. Most frequent in SW, in Vale of Pewsey and in SE.
10 km² 40 (77%) 1 km² 180 (5%)   Map 536, page 331

Dactylis L.

Dactylis glomerata L.
Cock's-foot

Native. Grassland and cultivated ground on all except acid soils. Very common, forming dense tussocks on damp ground.
10 km² 52 (100%)2 km² 898 (95%)

Catabrosa P. Beauv.

Catabrosa aquatica (L.) P. Beauv.
Whorl-grass

Native. Ponds, rivers and very wet places. Described by Grose as rare, the plant is now very rare.

N. Floating on a pond Flaxland 1984 DG, Boggs Meadow, Surrendall 1986 JH.
S. Standlynch Mill, R. Avon 1985 PMW, Chadwell, Whiteparish 1986 PMW.
10 km² 4 (8%)   1 km² 4 (<1%)

Catapodium Link

Catapodium rigidum (L.) C. E. Hubb.
Desmazeria rigida (L.) Tutin
Fern-grass

Native. Walls, bare ground, quarries and railway tracks. Occurs more often on walls than on chalk grassland in Wilts compared with other counties. Most records are from walls in the Cotswolds and bare gravel in the CWP, walls around Wilton and Salisbury and bare ground Porton Down.
10 km² 19 (37%) 1 km² 46 (1%)   Map 537, page 331

Glyceria R. Br.

Glyceria maxima (Hartman) O. Holmb.
Reed Sweet-grass

Native. Wet places.
Occurs along the silted edges of most rivers and streams. Common in ditches in the Malmesbury area and in stretches of the K & A Canal. The distribution map clearly marks its occurrence along the rivers. Sometimes described as 'aggressive' where it forms large patches.
10 km² 41 (79%) 1 km² 343 (9%)   Map 538, page 334

Glyceria fluitans (L.) R. Br.
Floating Sweet-grass

Native. Ponds, ditches, shallow water and mud. Common and widely-distributed in these habitats.
10 km² 45 (87%) 2 km² 344 (36%) Map 539, page 334

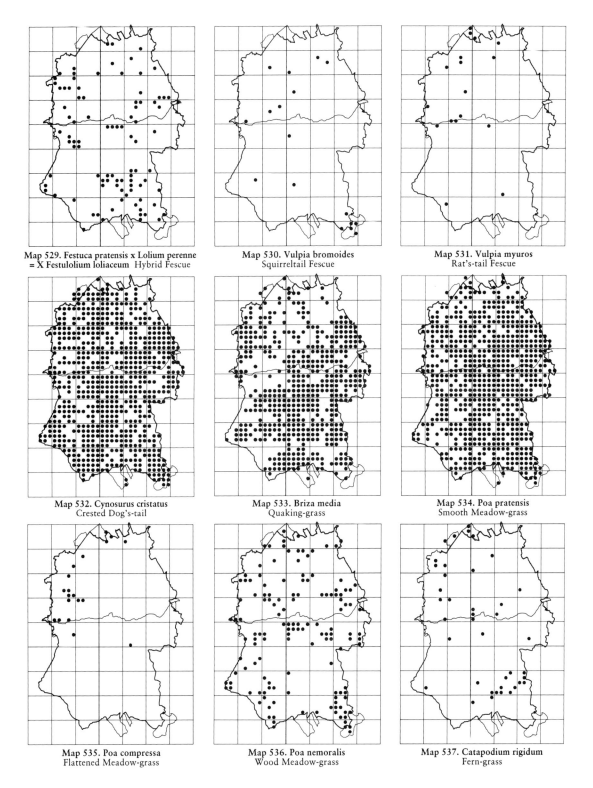

Map 529. Festuca pratensis x Lolium perenne
= X Festulolium loliaceum Hybrid Fescue

Map 530. Vulpia bromoides
Squirreltail Fescue

Map 531. Vulpia myuros
Rat's-tail Fescue

Map 532. Cynosurus cristatus
Crested Dog's-tail

Map 533. Briza media
Quaking-grass

Map 534. Poa pratensis
Smooth Meadow-grass

Map 535. Poa compressa
Flattened Meadow-grass

Map 536. Poa nemoralis
Wood Meadow-grass

Map 537. Catapodium rigidum
Fern-grass

Glyceria fluitans x G. notata = G. x pedicellata
F. Towns.
Hybrid Sweet-grass

Native. Streams, ponds, ditches, wet meadows. Probably more frequent than indicated by the available records. Occurs in the absence of either parent.
N. Berhills Farm, Sells Green 1988 DG, in two ponds near Alderton 1990 DG.
S. Damp, unimproved corner of a meadow Etchilhampton 1984 BG.
10 km² 3 (6%)   1 km² 4 (<1%)

Glyceria declinata Bréb.
Small Sweet-grass

Native. Ponds, depressions in pastures and tracks wet in winter, on a variety of soils.
N. Mainly in the S of the VC including dewponds on top of Pewsey Downs, on Jurassic Clay in the Melksham area, in acidic ponds in Savernake Forest. On gravel in CWP.
S. More than half the records from clay in SE: Loosehanger, Bramshaw, Plaitford, Furzley and Cadnam Commons, Earldoms, Whiteparish, Redlynch. Elsewhere, marshy dyke The Butts, Salisbury, meadows beside R. Nadder S of Dinton, Marston and Dewey's Water near Littleton Pannell, Stanton St Bernard, Buttermere Pond, E of Bessy Copse and Hook Copse, damp ditch Great Ridge Wood.
10 km² 15 (29%) 1 km² 37 (1%)   Map 540, page 334

Glyceria notata Chevall.
Glyceria plicata (Fries) Fries
Plicate Sweet-grass

Native. Wet ground including streamsides and ponds.
N. Most frequent on Jurassic clays on ponds that hold water only in winter. Rare elsewhere.
S. Most frequent on clay soil E of Trowbridge and in the Vale of Pewsey. Dewpond on

Urchfont Hill.
The similarity of this species to *G. fluitans*, with which it hybridises and with which it can be confused, has probably resulted in it being under-recorded.
10 km² 28 (54%) 1 km² 103 (3%)   Map 541, page 334

Melica L.

Melica uniflora Retz.
Wood Melick

Native. Woodland and shaded hedgebanks. Common. Most frequent on the limestone in NW where it is an indicator species of ancient woodland sites, around Aldbourne, Vale of Wardour and Grovely Wood and in SE.
10 km² 41 (79%) 2 km² 215 (23%)   Map 542, page 334

Helictotrichon Besser ex Schultes & Schultes f.

Helictotrichon pubescens (Hudson) Pilger
Avenula pubescens (Hudson) Dumort.
Downy Oat-grass

Native. Dry, unimproved calcareous grassland, especially on the chalk. Occurs in some neutral pastures and meadows. Locally abundant. Similar distribution to that of *H. pratense* but the two do not always grow together.
10 km² 41 (79%) 1 km² 547 (15%) Map 543, page 334

Helictotrichon pratense (L.) Besser
Avenula pratensis (L.) Dumort.
Meadow Oat-grass

Native. Dry, unimproved grassland, almost exclusively on chalk. Occurs as scattered plants, not as a dominant grass species on much of the chalk grassland. Most frequent on SPTA. A plant with easily recognisable leaves.
10 km² 38 (73%) 1 km² 524 (14%) Map 544, page 334

Arrhenatherum P. Beauv.

Arrhenatherum elatius (L.) P. Beauv. ex J. S. &
C. Presl
False Oat-grass

Native. Areas of coarse grass, road verges and
hedgerows where it is often dominant, except on
acid soils. Very common and widely-distributed.
Var. **bulbosum** (Willd.)
Onion Couch
Native. Invades arable land, especially on chalk.
N. Arable field near the monument in Savernake
Forest 1987 DG.
S. Shrewton 1990 TCGR.
True national distribution not known.
10 km² 50 (96%) 2 km² 821 (87%)

Avena L.

Avena fatua L.
Wild-oat

Introduction. Arable and waste ground. A frequent
weed of cereal crops.
10 km² 49 (94%) 2 km² 561 (59%)

Avena sterilis L. ssp. **ludoviciana** (Durieu) Gillet
& Magne
Winter Wild-oat

Introduction. A weed of arable land almost
certainly under-recorded by WFMP recorders.
10 km² 4 (8%) 1 km² 5 (<1%)

Avena sativa L.
Oat

Introduction. Where it has been grown as a crop, it
appears as a weed in alternative crops in subsequent
years. Not recognised as a 'weed' by many WFMP
recorders.
10 km² 3 (6%) 1 km² 4 (<1%)

Gaudinia P. Beauv.

Gaudinia fragilis (L.) P. Beauv.
French Oat-grass

Introduction. Meadows and pastures.
N. Recorded as a casual in Sandridge area 1951-
57. Found in three damp, grazed meadows near
Melksham 1978 (J Swanborough). Since then DG
has found plant in nine adjacent fields and a
further 11 sites in the county: Bird's Marsh,
Bewley Common, Colerne, W of Chippenham,
between Frogditch/Daisybrook, W of Melksham,
Sandridge, near Spye Park, Thingley 1984-90 DG
and Bowden Hill 1986 DG & 1990 BG. Of these
20 fields nine are recent leys, 11 unimproved or
semi-improved grassland, 13 lie on heavy Jurassic
clay, six on its junction with Lower Greensand
and one on Oolite limestone. Grows well where
soil is thin or poor. Unable to sustain itself against
more vigorous grasses such as *Arrhenatherum
elatius*. After the hay cut in July, a second flowering
of some of the plants occurs at end of August.
10 km² 3 (6%) 1 km² 10 (<1%) Map 545, page 334

Trisetum Pers.

Trisetum flavescens (L.) P. Beauv.
Yellow Oat-grass

Native. Dry calcareous and neutral grassland.
Common in these habitats especially on the chalk.
10 km² 48 (92%) 1 km² 733 (20%) Map 546, page 334

Koeleria Pers.

Koeleria macrantha (Ledeb.) Schultes
Koeleria cristata auct. non (L.) Pers.
Crested Hair-grass

Native. Unimproved chalk and limestone
grassland. More frequent on the chalk where it is
commonly found on active anthills and dry, steep
slopes where the soil is thin and the sward sparse.

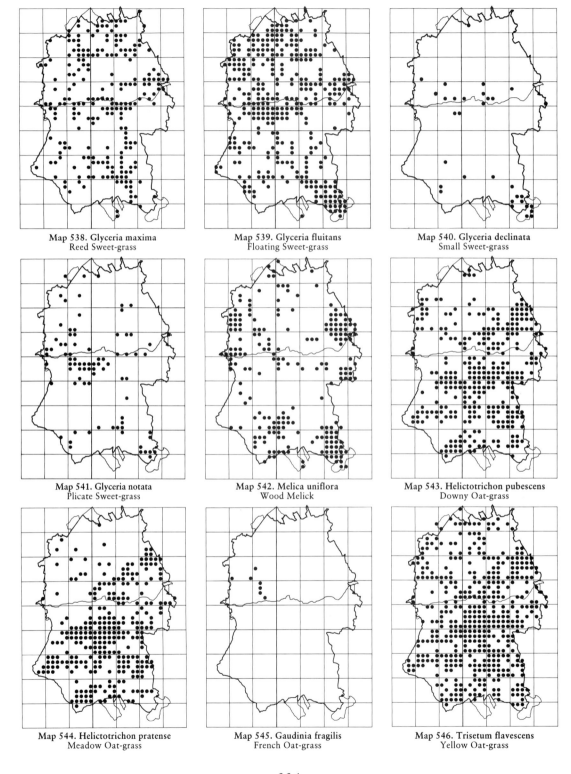

Map 538. Glyceria maxima
Reed Sweet-grass

Map 539. Glyceria fluitans
Floating Sweet-grass

Map 540. Glyceria declinata
Small Sweet-grass

Map 541. Glyceria notata
Plicate Sweet-grass

Map 542. Melica uniflora
Wood Melick

Map 543. Helictotrichon pubescens
Downy Oat-grass

Map 544. Helictotrichon pratense
Meadow Oat-grass

Map 545. Gaudinia fragilis
French Oat-grass

Map 546. Trisetum flavescens
Yellow Oat-grass

A few records from old pasture in CWP.
10 km² 37 (71%) 1 km² 454 (12%)   Map 547, page 337

Deschampsia P. Beauv.

Deschampsia cespitosa (L.) P. Beauv.
Tufted Hair-grass

Native. Damp grassland, ditches and woodland on heavier soils. Frequent and widespread. Sometimes dominant in wet and occasionally dry woodland after clear-felling. Common in the furrows of ridge-and-furrow pasture in Braydon Forest area.
10 km² 50 (96%) 2 km² 634 (67%)

Deschampsia flexuosa (L.) Trin.
Wavy Hair-grass

Native. Open woods and heaths on acid soils.
N. Occurs on Clay-with-flints in Savernake Forest and West Woods under old beech trees.
S. Most records are from Stourton and Great Bradley Woods, Great Ridge Wood, Vale of Wardour and from woods and heaths associated with the New Forest area.
10 km² 14 (27%) 1 km² 58 (2%)   Map 548, page 337

Holcus L.

Holcus lanatus L.
Yorkshire-fog

Native. Rough grassland, waste ground and open woodland. Common and widely-distributed. Very common on heavy clay.
10 km² 51 (98%) 2 km² 838 (88%)

Holcus mollis L.
Creeping Soft-grass

Native. Open woodland, scrub, ungrazed

grassland and arable land nearly always on sandy or other acid soils.
N. Occurs mainly on sand, clay and Clay-with-flints. Only common in Savernake Forest.
S. Mainly in woodland on clay, greensand or sand and gravels. Most frequent in SE.
10 km² 40 (77%) 1 km² 353 (10%)   Map 549, page 337

Aira L.

Aira caryophyllea L.
Silver Hair-grass

Native. Dry, bare places such as railway cuttings and embankments or areas of short turf on acid soils including leached soil on the chalk. Very local and usually occurring in small quantity.
10 km² 8 (15%)   1 km² 13 (<1%)   Map 550, page 337

Aira praecox L.
Early Hair-grass

Native. Grazed acidic grassland on sand, Clay-with-flints and leached chalk soils.
N. Abundant in short grassland on greensand in Spye Park, among sarsen stones on unimproved leached chalk grassland on Fyfield Down NNR, on Clay-with-flints Pewsey Downs NNR and around The Monument in Savernake Forest.
S. Free-draining sandy soil, particularly on old woodbanks adjacent to New Forest heathland and in a small area of Bentley Wood. On inactive anthill on leached chalk grassland Brixton Deverill.
10 km² 7 (13%)   1 km² 21 (<1%)   Map 551, page 337

Anthoxanthum L.

Anthoxanthum odoratum L.
Sweet Vernal-grass

Native. Grassland on all soil types. Frequent in unimproved grassland.
10 km² 51 (98%) 2 km² 596 (63%) Map 552, page 337

Phalaris L.

Phalaris arundinacea L.
Reed Canary-grass

Native. Wet places, especially along the silted edges of rivers, lakes and in deep ditches, frequent throughout the county.
Form with variegated leaves: naturalised garden throw-out on road verge, Braydon 1990 JW.
10 km² 48 (92%) 1 km² 604 (17%) Map 553, page 337

Phalaris aquatica L.
Phalaris bulbosa L.
Bulbous Canary-grass

Introduction. Sown as a fodder crop for pheasants on field headlands.
N. New plantation, Ufcott 1986 VS, Wroughton aerodrome and Hackpen Hill 1986 JEO. First VC7 records.
10 km² 1 (2%)   1 km² 2 (<1%)

Phalaris canariensis L.
Canary-grass

Introduction. Common in bird-seed mixtures. Not persistent.
10 km² 10 (19%) 1 km² 15 (<1%)

Phalaris paradoxa L.
Awned Canary-grass

Introduction.
N. Many thousands large plants, many over 1 m tall, in cereal crop Ditteridge 1983 Mr Roberts.
10 km² 1 (2%)   1 km² 1 (<1%)

Phalaris paradoxa L. ssp. praemorsa Coss & Dur.

N. Common weed Lower Sands Farm, Calne

1980-81 RH (det. KM Goodway, conf. Kew 1980), first county record. On dumped soil Kilma Farm, Lacock 1987 DG.
10 km² 2 (4%)   1 km² 2 (<1%)

Agrostis L.

Agrostis capillaris L.
Common Bent

Native. All types of grassland, particularly on neutral to acid soils. Frequent and widespread.
10 km² 46 (88%) 2 km² 413 (44%) Map 554, page 337

Agrostis gigantea Roth
Black Bent

Native. Cultivated and waste ground and in the shade along the edges of woods and fields, occasionally in pasture. Locally a serious weed of arable crops. Unevenly recorded.
10 km² 27 (52%) 1 km² 126 (3%)   Map 555, page 337

Agrostis stolonifera L.
Creeping Bent

Native. Damp and wet ground in all habitats. Common. The dominant grass species of damp ground and closely-grazed improved chalk grassland. Often crowds out other species at the edge of paths and ponds.
10 km² 50 (96%) 2 km² 710 (75%)

Agrostis curtisii Kerguélen
Agrostis setacea Curtis non Villars
Bristle Bent

Native. Heathland, especially along path edges on light acid soils.
S. Common grass of the New Forest and associated commons. Relic populations on woodbanks surrounding reclaimed heathland. The

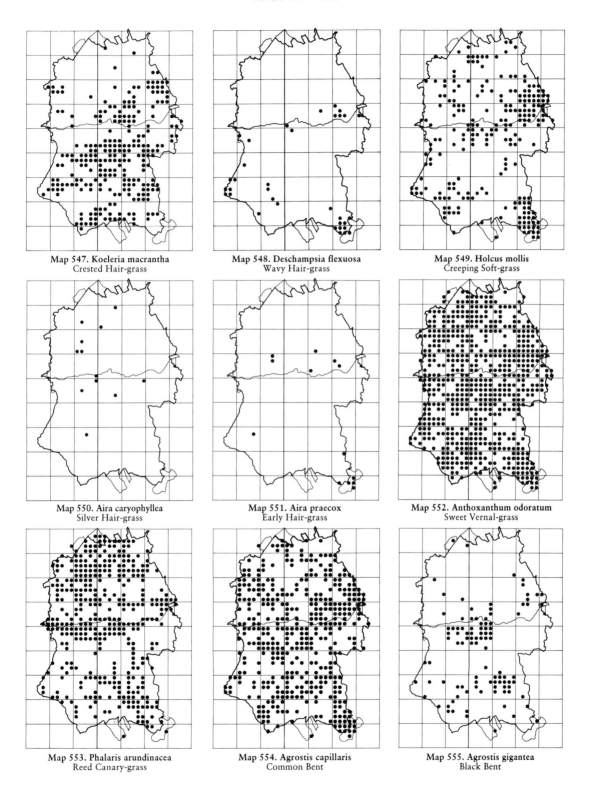

Map 547. **Koeleria macrantha**
Crested Hair-grass

Map 548. **Deschampsia flexuosa**
Wavy Hair-grass

Map 549. **Holcus mollis**
Creeping Soft-grass

Map 550. Aira caryophyllea
Silver Hair-grass

Map 551. **Aira praecox**
Early Hair-grass

Map 552. **Anthoxanthum odoratum**
Sweet Vernal-grass

Map 553. **Phalaris arundinacea**
Reed Canary-grass

Map 554. **Agrostis capillaris**
Common Bent

Map 555. **Agrostis gigantea**
Black Bent

record for Salisbury was in a railway cutting, the seed probably having been introduced in sand and gravel with that of *Plantago coronopus* found 1985 JH (ver. AH). The site was later destroyed.

10 km² 2 (4%)   1 km² 14 (<1%)   Map 556, page 340

Agrostis canina L.
Velvet Bent

Native. Acidic habitats.
N. Usually occurs on undisturbed areas, especially those associated with the remnants of old heathland N of Chippenham.
S. Widespread on acid soil in the SE, in Vale of Wardour, in the SW, around Trowbridge and in Vale of Pewsey.
Possibly mis-identified with other *Agrostis* species. Only accepted records shown on the map.

10 km² 36 (69%) 2 km² 181 (19%) Map 557, page 340

Calamagrostis Adans.

Calamagrostis epigejos (L.) Roth
Wood Small-reed

Native. Open damp woodland, road verges, railway embankments and cuttings.
N. Mainly on clay soils. Spreads mat-like, forming large colonies along the verges of the Foss Way Roman road E of Alderton. Silkwood, Oaksey, Minety Common, Somerford Common, Coombes Wood at Bowood, road verge A4 Calne, railway embankments Chippenham and Alderton, Rowde, Savernake and Little Withy Wood near Bewley Common.
S. Two areas Longdean Bottom, Great Ridge Wood, common small area Wick Farm near Potterne, wet verge and ditch Urchfont, The Plantation and small area of ancient woodland in conifer plantation Great Netley Copse, both at Clarendon. Becoming a problem grass in woodland reserves at Bentley Wood and Blackmoor Copse where it spreads into cleared

areas and becomes the dominant ground flora.
10 km² 10 (19%) 1 km² 26 (<1%)   Map 558, page 340

Apera Adans.

Apera spica-venti (L.) P. Beauv.
Loose Silky-bent

Nationally scarce plant.
Native in GB, introduction in Wilts. A cornfield weed in E England.
N. Barley field, established and spreading Netherstreet Farm 1987 DG, first VC7 record. W of Lacock, near Durlett and Biddestone 1987-88 DG.
S. Barley field Shortengrove, Grovely Wood 1984 DS-G, Fiddington Sands 1984 RF, first VC8 records, followed by Ansty 1987 MM and further sites near Grovely Wood BL.
10 km² 5 (10%)   1 km² 11 (<1%)   Map 559, page 340

Alopecurus L.

Alopecurus pratensis L.
Meadow Foxtail

Native. Improved and unimproved neutral meadows and road verges. Frequent in these habitats.
10 km² 50 (96%) 2 km² 661 (70%)

Alopecurus geniculatus L.
Marsh Foxtail

Native. Permanently or seasonally wet grassland, springs and wet wheel ruts. Frequent in these habitats.
10 km² 39 (75%) 2 km² 258 (27%) Map 560, page 340

Alopecurus myosuroides Hudson
Black-grass

Native. Arable and disturbed waste land. A

pernicious agricultural weed throughout the county, most frequent on arable land on the chalk in the N of the county.

10 km² 46 (88%) 1 km² 599 (16%)   Map 561, page 340

Phleum L.

Phleum pratense L.
Timothy

Native. Grassland on all soil types. A common component of sown grass mixtures.

10 km² 51 (98%) 2 km² 811 (85%)

Phleum bertolonii DC.
Phleum pratense L. ssp. *bertolonii* (DC.) Bornm.
Smaller Cat's-tail

Native. Common on semi-improved and unimproved calcareous grassland and downland. Local on clay.

10 km² 48 (92%) 2 km² 470 (50%)   Map 562, page 340

Bromus L.

Bromus commutatus Schrader
Meadow Brome

Native. Unimproved and semi-improved neutral meadows and pasture. Locally abundant on the heavy clays in the N. More frequent in pasture than meadows. Less frequent on limestone grassland and almost unknown on the chalk.

10 km² 15 (29%) 1 km² 43 (1%)   Map 563, page 340

Bromus racemosus L.
Smooth Brome

Native. Unimproved and semi-improved neutral meadows and pasture. This plant occurs more frequently in pasture than in meadows. The records

indicate that it is less frequent than *B. commutatus* which flowers approximately two weeks later and grows in very similar locations.

10 km² 10 (19%) 1 km² 26 (<1%)   Map 564, page 340

Bromus hordeaceus L.
Soft-brome

Native. Grassland, rough ground. Common and widespread.

10 km² 50 (96%) 2 km² 605 (64%)

Bromus hordeaceus x B. lepidus =
B. x pseudothominei P. M. Smith
Bromus thominei auct. non Hardouin
Lesser Soft-brome

Probably native.
N. Tan Hill (Pewsey Downs NNR) 1985 KP, first VC7 record. Fyfield Down NNR and Clatford Down 1985-86 KP, near Red Lodge 1985 CS & MWS. All records conf. PTO Trist (BSBI *Bromus* referee).
S. Stratford Tony Down 1990 PW.

10 km² 5 (10%) 1 km² 6 (<1%)

Bromus lepidus O. Holmb.
Slender Soft-brome

Probable introduction.
S. Warden's Down, SPTA(W) 1987 BGH (conf. F Perring).

10 km² 1 (2%) 1 km² 1 (<1%)

Bromus secalinus L.
Rye Brome

Introduction.
N. One plant Water Eaton Farm, near Cricklade 1991 PW.

10 km² 1 (2%) 1 km² 1 (<1%)

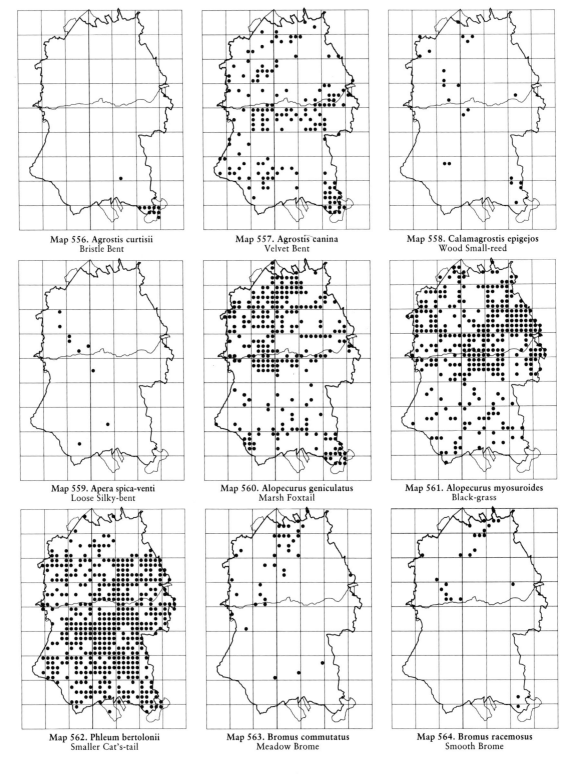

Map 556. **Agrostis curtisii**
Bristle Bent

Map 557. **Agrostis canina**
Velvet Bent

Map 558. **Calamagrostis epigejos**
Wood Small-reed

Map 559. **Apera spica-venti**
Loose Silky-bent

Map 560. **Alopecurus geniculatus**
Marsh Foxtail

Map 561. **Alopecurus myosuroides**
Black-grass

Map 562. **Phleum bertolonii**
Smaller Cat's-tail

Map 563. **Bromus commutatus**
Meadow Brome

Map 564. **Bromus racemosus**
Smooth Brome

Bromopsis (Dumort.) Fourr.

Bromopsis ramosa (Hudson) Holub
Bromus ramosus Hudson
Hairy-brome

Native. Woodland and hedgerows. Frequent and widely-distributed.
10 km² 50 (96%) 2 km² 491 (52%) Map 565, page 343

Bromopsis erecta (Hudson) Fourr.
Bromus erectus Hudson
Upright Brome

Native. Chalk and limestone downland, unimproved neutral grassland, and road verges. Abundant and widespread on chalk and limestone. Very local elsewhere.
Var. **villosus**
S. Old Sarum, Bishopdown (Salisbury), Little Down near Great Durnford and Figsbury Ring 1989 PM, Ashcombe Lane near Berwick St. John 1991 MM & PM.
10 km² 47 (90%) 2 km² 484 (51%) Map 566, page 343

Bromopsis inermis (Leysser) Holub ssp. **inermis**
Bromus inermis Leysser
Hungarian Brome

Introduction. Apparently able to naturalise fully. Large stands formed by stolons.
N. Along railway cuttings Luckington, Alderton and Hullavington 1984-85 DG. Road verges Ford 1983 and Lacock 1987 DG, M4 exit 17 1987 JH.
10 km² 5 (10%) 1 km² 7 (<1%)

Anisantha K. Koch

Anisantha sterilis (L.) Nevski
Bromus sterilis L.
Barren Brome

Native. Cultivated land, grassland, hedgerows and waste ground. Common and widespread.
10 km² 51 (98%) 2 km² 754 (79%)

Ceratochloa DC. & P. Beauv.

Ceratochloa carinata (Hook. & Arn.) Tutin
Bromus carinatus Hook. & Arn.
California Brome

Introduction. Seed contaminant.
S. Appeared on bare chalk following digging footings for new farm buildings Cherry Lodge Farm, Shrewton 1984 BG (conf. KP), second VC8 record. Frequent on waste ground and tracks in and N and E of Salisbury 1985 PM. Waysides Nunton 1985, Charlton and near A354 Coombe Bissett 1987 NLC & BKC.
10 km² 3 (6%) 1 km² 11 (<1%) Map 567, page 343

Brachypodium P. Beauv.

Brachypodium pinnatum (L.) P. Beauv.
Tor-grass

Native. Chalk and limestone downland, road verges and unimproved neutral grassland. An invasive grass that dominates some areas of downland, spreading in ever-widening circles eliminating less aggressive species.
N. A serious problem on the Marlborough Downs around Aldbourne, and on limestone grassland at Castle Combe.
S. Less frequent than in the N. Widely-distributed on SPTA, in small patches only.
10 km² 42 (81%) 1 km² 249 (7%) Map 568, page 343

Brachypodium sylvaticum (Hudson) P. Beauv.
False Brome

Native. Woodland and hedgerows. Invasive among chalk grassland scrub. Frequent and widespread.
10 km² 51 (98%) 2 km² 644 (68%)

Elymus L.

Elymus caninus (L.) L.
Agropyron caninum (L.) P. Beauv.
Bearded Couch

Native. Hedgebanks and verges of green lanes. Locally distributed.
10 km² 43 (83%) 2 km² 243 (26%)   Map 569, page 343

Elytrigia Desv.

Elytrigia repens (L.) Desv. ex Nevski ssp. repens
Elymus repens (L.) Gould
Common Couch

Native. Rough, cultivated ground and gardens. Common and invasive.
Var. aristatum
Native. The awned form of common couch is known to be fairly common especially in SU05, but was not recorded systematically during the WFMP. No accurate distribution map is available.
10 km² 51 (98%) 2 km² 721 (76%)

Hordeum L.

Hordeum murinum L.
Wall Barley

Native. Walls, roadsides and disturbed soils. Occurs locally throughout the county but usually in small numbers.
10 km² 37 (71%) 2 km² 209 (22%)   Map 570, page 343

Hordeum secalinum Schreber
Meadow Barley

Native. Improved and unimproved grassland on clay soils.
N. Well-distributed in these habitats where it is locally abundant in some unimproved meadows.
Very local on chalk.
S. Restricted to the clay and greensand between Devizes and Trowbridge and to river valleys in the chalk country.
10 km² 31 (60%) 1 km² 246 (7%)   Map 571, page 343

Danthonia DC.

Danthonia decumbens (L.) DC.
Heath-grass

Native. Heaths, unimproved grassland on leached superficials on the chalk, open woodland and pasture on neutral to acid soils.
N. Occurs locally in unimproved neutral pasture in the Braydon Forest/CWP area and on Pewsey Downs. Abundant in parts of Savernake Forest.
S. Several new records from the chalk since 1950s including Parsonage and Wylye Down NNRs and on SPTA.
10 km² 25 (48%) 1 km² 70 (2%)   Map 572, page 343

Molinia Schrank

Molinia caerulea (L.) Moench
Purple Moor-grass

Native. Bogs, heaths and open woodland on acid soils.
N. Very localised. Occurs in any number only in restricted areas of Savernake Forest and Spye Park 1986-89 DG. Grows in most unusual habitat in unimproved meadow adjacent to pit 40 CWP with calcifuges *Anagallis tenella* and *Menyanthes trifoliata*, and calcicoles *Bromopsis erecta* and *Ononis spinosa*.
S. Abundant on New Forest heaths growing with *Erica tetralix* and *Calluna vulgaris*, small populations in pasture Moor Copse, Milkhills and Chadwell N of the Forest 1989-90 DJW. Elsewhere in grazed meadow Lydeway 1984 WTNC/ST, unexpectedly N of nursery Netherhampton 1987 NLC & BKC and two sites

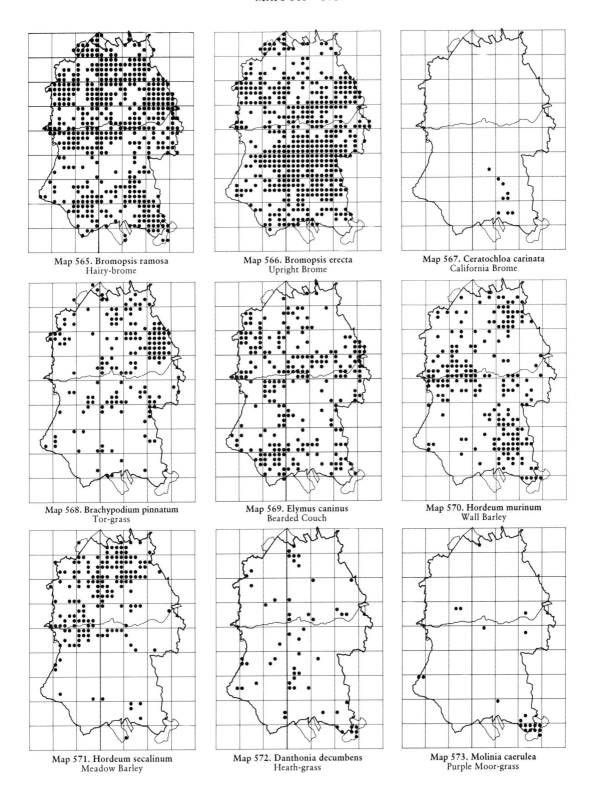

Map 565. Bromopsis ramosa
Hairy-brome

Map 566. Bromopsis erecta
Upright Brome

Map 567. Ceratochloa carinata
California Brome

Map 568. Brachypodium pinnatum
Tor-grass

Map 569. Elymus caninus
Bearded Couch

Map 570. Hordeum murinum
Wall Barley

Map 571. Hordeum secalinum
Meadow Barley

Map 572. Danthonia decumbens
Heath-grass

Map 573. Molinia caerulea
Purple Moor-grass

in woods, Maiden Bradley 1991 DLH.
10 km² 9 (17%)   1 km² 29 (<1%)   Map 573, page 343

Phragmites Adans.

Phragmites australis (Cav.) Trin. ex Steudel
Phragmites communis Trin.
Common Reed

Native. River, stream, canal, gravel pit, pond and ditch margins.
N. Common along the rivers and ditches on the clay. Scattered in small colonies beside the K & A Canal.
S. Mainly by the rivers, the distribution map clearly marking the Salisbury Avon and R. Wylye.
10 km² 37 (71%)   1 km² 235 (6%)   Map 574, page 347

Echinochloa P. Beauv.

Echinochloa crusgalli (L.) P. Beauv.
Cockspur

Introduction. Garden weed from bird-seed.
N. Marlborough 1984 DG, Hullavington 1989 JH.
S. Great Thornham Farm, Seend 1990 BG.
10 km² 3 (6%)   1 km² 4 (<1%)

Setaria P. Beauv.

Setaria pumila (Poiret) Roemer & Schultes
Setaria lutescens Hubb.
Yellow Bristle-grass

Introduction. Common in bird-seed mixtures.
N. Dauntsey vicarage and Marlborough 1984 DG, garden Winsley 1991 JP.
S. Garden Trowbridge 1989 EC (conf. RM Payne BSBI referee), St. John's churchyard Devizes 1989 SN, set-aside land near Whiteparish 1989 DJW (ver. AH), rubbish tip Westbury 1992 JG & EC (ver. AH). First VC8 records.
10 km² 6 (12%)   1 km² 7 (<1%)

SPARGANIACEAE

Sparganium L.

Sparganium erectum L.
Branched Bur-reed

Native. Rivers, streams, canals and ponds. Common in most water habitats including the surviving dewponds on SPTA.
10 km² 42 (81%)   1 km² 364 (10%)   Map 575, page 347

Sparganium emersum Rehmann
Unbranched Bur-reed

Native. Slow-flowing rivers and static water.
N. Abundant along parts of the K & A Canal, common in the Bristol Avon tributary running through Tetbury, but localised elsewhere on R. Avon, R. Kennet E of Marlborough and the R. Thames.
S. Only recorded from R. Avon and R. Nadder.
10 km² 16 (31%)   1 km² 52 (1%)   Map 576, page 347

TYPHACEAE

Typha L.

Typha latifolia L.
Bulrush

Native. Rivers, streams, canals, lakes, ponds, ditches and gravel pits. More common in static and slow-flowing water.
N. Abundant in ditches, silted-up ponds and backwaters on the clay.
S. Beside the rivers Avon, Nadder and Wylye and on lowland clay.
10 km² 42 (81%)   1 km² 342 (9%)   Map 577, page 347

Typha augustifolia L.
Lesser Bulrush

Native. Static water. This plant may have been

introduced at some of the locations.

N. Lake near Lyneham 1984, three CWP lakes 1984-87, gravel pits Inwood near Beanacre 1988 DG.

S. Pond Brookmead, East Grimstead 1984 PAW. Pond Cowesfield Manor where understood not to have been introduced 1986 PMW.

10 km² 4 (8%)   1 km² 5 (<1%)

LILIACEAE

Narthecium Hudson

Narthecium ossifragum (L.) Hudson
Bog Asphodel

Native. Acid peat bogs.

S. Confined to the New Forest where it is widespread, forming extensive patches in favourable conditions. The specific name was given to the plant because it was believed that cattle eating it developed brittle bones. It is now realised that the plant grows in nutrient-poor conditions and that this is responsible for the condition of livestock.

10 km² 1 (2%)   1 km² 10 (<1%)   Map 578, page 347

Colchicum L.

Colchicum autumnale L.
Meadow Saffron

Native. Woodland rides and clearings, road verges, neutral meadows.

N. Distribution almost entirely restricted to ancient and older woodlands usually on calcareous soils, occurring in very large numbers in some places including Silk Wood near Westonbirt VC7 (Glos). Predominantly a plant of meadows in adjacent counties but no longer the case in Wilts. Due to it being poisonous to cattle it was dug up and almost eradicated from this habitat. Only recorded from two meadows during the WFMP. Form with white flowers, Silk Wood near Westonbirt.

S. Great Bradley, Great Ridge, Grovely, Bentley, Everleigh and Collingbourne Woods. Form with white flowers, colony at Great Ridge Wood.

10 km² 22 (42%)   1 km² 67 (2%)   Map 579, page 347

Gagea Salisb.

Gagea lutea (L.) Ker Gawler
Yellow Star-of-Bethlehem

Nationally scarce plant.

Native. One very small colony in woodland in the Bristol Avon valley known for many years (comm. RR) but flowers seen only once in the mid-1980s. Several ash trees in its immediate vicinity were blown down in 1987 and carefully removed by BTCV in 1988, since when the single patch has increased to 10-12 colonies spread over an area of 20 m². The immature leaves of the newly developing bulbs have not yet grown sufficiently to produce flowering plants. The only extant site.

10 km² 1 (2%)   1 km² 1 (<1%)

Tulipa L.

Tulipa sylvestris L.
Wild Tulip

Introduction. Naturalised in woodland, hedgerows.

S. Known for many years 1984 EC, recently in a second area Erlestoke Wood 1986 CQ-R. Verge and bank Redlynch, known for 50 years, in flower 1983-84 NLC & BKC and 1988 BKC. Wild garden adjacent to water-meadows West Chisenbury 1986 SW-B and wood N of Syrencot House 1986 AJS.

10 km² 3 (6%)   1 km² 3 (<1%)

Fritillaria L.

Fritillaria meleagris L.
Fritillary

Nationally scarce plant.
Native. Unimproved low-lying alluvial meadows.

N. Native locations restricted to the upper Thames water-meadows where it is known at ten sites, some containing only a handful to a few dozen plants. Four have in excess of 100,000 flowering annually and are protected by SSSI status and/or by management agreements. One is owned by WTNC. At the 50 ha site at Oaksey noted by Flower in 1872, sadly now only a memory, plants were still plentiful in one field 1977 but, following fertiliser application, only five found 1989. Another historical meadow, now agriculturally improved, was visited in 1989 (DG & SW) in search for possible surviving plants along the margins and hedgerows. Two small boys overheard the botanists' conversation which lead to a searching question-and-answer session which revealed that across a large arable field and through an almost impenetrable hedge was a 4 ha semi-improved meadow containing at least 100,000 flowering plants! There is no evidence that this large colony was previously known by any conservation organisation. The two locations in W Wiltshire are introductions. See article on p.95.

10 km² 6 (12%)   1 km² 16 (<1%)   Map 580, page 347

Lilium L.

Lilium martagon L.
Martagon Lily

Introduction. Nowhere has this plant become fully naturalised as it has in neighbouring Glos. Most records are of obvious plantings.
N. Battle Lake 1984 MWS, Belvedere Wood and adjacent cemetery Devizes 1985 PC, Easton Grey 1988 JWi.
S. Shrub Down 1990 JM.
10 km² 4 (8%)   1 km² 5 (<1%)

Convallaria L.

Convallaria majalis L.
Lily-of-the-valley

Native. Dry ancient woodland on calcareous soils.

N. Very localised, still occurring in woods beside By Brook and tributaries. Colonies at most sites very small and scattered within the woods. First county record (1837 Prior) Collett's Bottom Wood refound 1983 DG. Outwood, Colerne Park, Sewell Wood. Appeared in large numbers in several places and flowered profusely following block-felling North Wood 1985 DG. Other records refer to garden throw-outs.
S. Some colonies in Grose's *The Flora of Wiltshire*, particularly in large woods, not refound but in Southleigh Wood seems to be spreading 1984 JM, 1989 VEH & MHS. Coles's Bury near Battscroft 1984 DJW, widespread in N of Hound Wood 1986 WTNC/ST & VW, two areas Smokeways Copse, Bentley Wood 1987-88 VW, Dinton 1988 SMP, another large flowering colony Bentley Wood 1989 IA. Introduced but may become naturalised Whiteparish Common 1985 PMW. Introduced Slittems Wood 1986 JM and probably Manor Woods, Market Lavington 1984 RF.
10 km² 9 (17%)   1 km² 17 (<1%)   Map 581, page 347

Polygonatum Miller

Polygonatum multiflorum (L.) All.
Solomon's-seal

Native. Ancient and secondary woodlands, most frequent on calcareous soils, rarely on acid soils.
N. Usually one small colony within a wood. Three main concentrations: woods E of Marlborough, the Bowood area and the wooded hillsides of the By Brook and its tributaries around Castle Combe.
S. More widespread than in the N occurring in nearly all main woodland areas especially Great Ridge and Grovely Woods, in the SE (but not extending into New Forest), Stype Wood, woods on the Berks border W of Hungerford, Great and Little Perham Copse, Collingbourne Wood and two small woods to the north.
10 km² 30 (58%) 1 km² 161 (4%)   Map 582, page 347

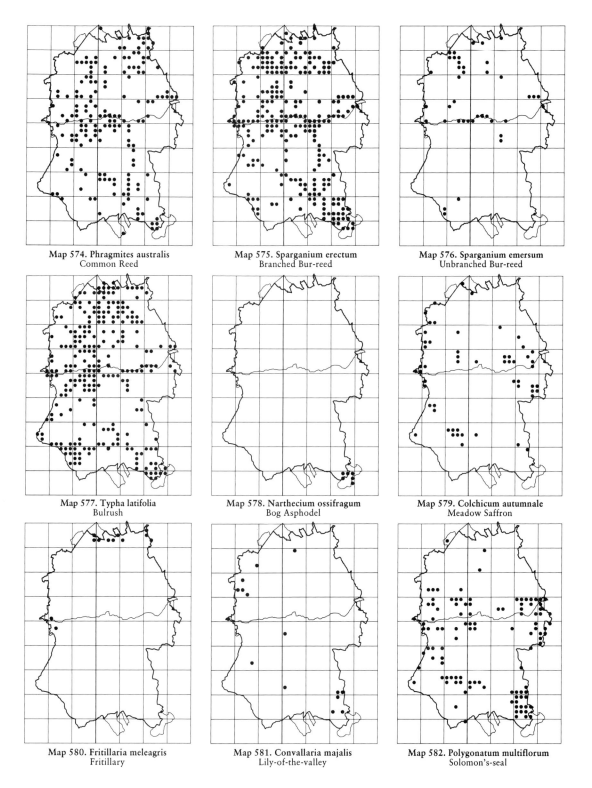

Map 574. *Phragmites australis*
Common Reed

Map 575. *Sparganium erectum*
Branched Bur-reed

Map 576. *Sparganium emersum*
Unbranched Bur-reed

Map 577. **Typha latifolia**
Bulrush

Map 578. *Narthecium ossifragum*
Bog Asphodel

Map 579. **Colchicum autumnale**
Meadow Saffron

Map 580. **Fritillaria meleagris**
Fritillary

Map 581. **Convallaria majalis**
Lily-of-the-valley

Map 582. **Polygonatum multiflorum**
Solomon's-seal

Polygonatum multiflorum x P. odoratum =
P. x hybridum Bruegger
Garden Solomon's-seal

Native. Stace describes this plant as an introduction and grown in gardens. In Wilts, this hybrid occurs naturally.
N. Wood on limestone overlooking the By Brook near Castle Combe where both parents occur. First found Colerne Park 1939 (Miss GA Peters). No plants seen until 1954 (Miss DM Frowde) when the colony was large and flourishing. DG visited DMF 1984 but she was unable to recall the spot. Twenty plants in two adjacent areas amongst brambles in area of ash climax woodland 1984 DG (conf. AL Grenfell). The colony has again disappeared though suitable sites remain within the wood. Truckle Wood (an historical site for the hybrid) has been searched to confirm a report but only *P. odoratum* was found.
10 km² 2 (4%)   1 km² 2 (<1%)

Polygonatum odoratum (Miller) Druce
Angular Solomon's-seal

Nationally scarce plant.
Native. Woodland on limestone.
N. The only known sites are in ancient woodlands on limestone in the By Brook valley at Wraxhall Park Wood, Colerne Park and wood W of Truckle Hill 1985 DG, all refinds of Grose's records. In two of these the population is restricted to 1-2 m²; in the third many thousands of flowering spikes found in one section of the wooded hillside.
10 km² 1 (2%)   1 km² 3 (<1%)

Paris L.

Paris quadrifolia L.
Herb-Paris

Native. Damp areas in ancient and secondary woodlands on calcareous soils.
N. Many records, but the plant usually occurs in small numbers and, having leaves the same colour as those of *Mercurialis perennis* with which it invariably grows, it is never easy to find. Woodland on limestone from Bradford-on-Avon N to beyond Castle Combe, on the ridge of Corallian Beds around Lyneham, scattered on the Marlborough Downs and the edges of West Woods and Savernake Forest.
S. Most colonies small, but five large ones and five-leaved plants seen twice. Slittems Wood 1986-88, very locally abundant Avoncliff 1989 JM. Greatest concentration of records in NE: in woods on Clay-with-flints Collingbourne Ducis/Upper Chute and Rag Copse 1984 FP, Shaw Bottom, hundreds of flowers in a small patch Coldridge Wood 1986 JS, two patches Cleves Copse 1984 & 1987 ER, Botley Hill Wood, Oxenwood 1988 JR. Further N, clump of about 40 flowers in cleared area of Stype Wood 1984 MN, Catmore Copse 1987 DC, group Kingsley Copse, Bagshot 1989 CM. Elsewhere, Standlych Down 1984 RC, Dirtley Wood 1984 VEH, Coulston Hill Wood 1985 JPi, on a very steep bank Ansty Down 1986 MM, Tottenham Wood (there is an old record) 1987, hillside wood Baynton 1987 BGH and Bentley Wood.
10 km² 24 (46%) 1 km² 57 (2%)   Map 583, page 352

Ornithogalum L.

Ornithogalum pyrenaicum L.
Spiked Star-of-Bethlehem

Nationally scarce plant.
Native. Woodland, streamsides, green lanes, unimproved and semi-improved grassland on calcareous soils. National distribution restricted, greatest concentration being on Wilts/Avon county boundary near Bath where it is known locally as Bath asparagus. Locally abundant.
N. Main distribution throughout the Box to Bradford-on-Avon area, extending E to Broughton Gifford with small scattered colonies in By Brook valley. In the N on chalk at Wroughton and Clouts Wood. Small colony Lockeridge.

S. In NW: widespread at Westwood and Rowdenham 1989 JM, Druce's Farm roadbank 1985 LB (not seen in two previous years), single plant Clanger Wood 1990 EC. Devizes area: greenlanes Roundway, Stert and Potterne Field and scattered throughout Potterne Wood 1985 RF, BG & BGH. Elsewhere large colony Farley Copse and nearby well-known protected verges 1987 MD. Sometimes frequent in far E in three copses Catmore, Frith and Trindledown near Shalbourne 1984 LW, 1987 DGC, 1988 CM. See article p.99.

10 km² 11 (21%) 1 km² 44 (<1%)   Map 584, page 352

Ornithogalum angustifolium Boreau
Ornithogalum umbellatum auct. non L.
Star-of-Bethlehem

Native and introduction. Open woodland, more frequently roadside verges, semi-improved grassland and hedges. Planted in churchyards.
N. Most colonies are small, few appear to be native.
S. One-third of the sites occur on MOD land (SPTA and Porton Ranges) on open, ungrazed semi-improved grassland and appear to be native.

10 km² 25 (48%) 1 km² 59 (2%)   Map 585, page 352

Ornithogalum nutans L.
Drooping Star-of-Bethlehem

Introduction.
N. Inglesham churchyard 1990 MWS.

10 km² 1 (2%)   1 km² 1 (<1%)

Hyacinthoides Heister ex Fabr.

Hyacinthoides non-scripta (L.) Chouard ex Rothm.
Bluebell

Native. Woodlands, hedgerows and open pasture. Most frequent on greensand and neutral to acid soils. Absent from many woodlands on the chalk but occurs on superficial deposits over chalk, as in Savernake Forest and in woods on limestone. The garden hybrid is sometimes mis-identified for the native.
Form with white flowers found in many populations. Form with pink flowers, Briary Wood 1987 SK.

10 km² 51 (98%) 2 km² 639 (67%)   Map 586, page 352

Hyacinthoides non-scripta x H. hispanica

Introduction. Stace considers this to be the plant most commonly grown in gardens.
S. Two accepted records: The Butts, Salisbury 1985 and Little Durnford 1991 PM.

10 km² 1 (2%)   1 km² 2 (<1%)

Hyacinthoides hispanica (Miller) Rothm.
Spanish Bluebell

Introduction. Planted in ornamental woodlands and found as a garden throw-out. Pink and white colour forms occur.

10 km² 10 (19%) 1 km² 28 (<1%)

Muscari Miller

Muscari neglectum Guss. ex Ten.
Grape-hyacinth

Native in GB, introduction in Wilts. Rarely naturalises as near Wilton 1985 AH where recorded for 60 years. Some records may have been of *M. armeniacum* Garden Grape-hyacinth.

10 km² 7 (13%)   1 km² 9 (<1%)

Muscari botryoides (L.) Miller
Compact Grape-hyacinth

Introduction. Garden throw-out.

10 km² 1 (2%)   1 km² 6 (<1%)

Allium L.

Allium paradoxum (M. Bieb.) Don
Few-flowered Leek

Introduction. Long-lasting and therefore likely to spread.
N. Clyffe Pypard 1984 DG, first VC7 record.
S. A large colony and scattered individuals at Bradshaw, Potterne 1988 and Poulshot Common 1991 BGH.
10 km² 2 (4%)   1 km² 3 (<1%)

Allium ursinum L.
Ramsons

Native. Woods, hedge bottoms, beside streams, usually in shade but occasionally on field edges. Most frequent in the damper parts of woodland on the Oolite limestone, on the Lower Greensand at Bowood and on Upper Greensand and clays in the Nadder valley. Sometimes covers large areas of woodland floor, often shading out all other herbs.
10 km² 44 (85%) 1 km² 365 (10%)   Map 587, page 352

Allium oleraceum L.
Field Garlic

Nationally scarce plant.
Native. Unimproved calcareous grassland banks. Very rare.
N. On chalk along base of hill Oliver's Castle 1987 PC (ver. 1988 DG). Only known site.
10 km² 1 (2%)   1 km² 1 (<1%)

Allium vineale L.
Wild Onion

Native. Rough grass, grassy banks and road verges. Widely-distributed, usually in small colonies.
10 km² 47 (90%) 2 km² 475 (50%)   Map 588, page 352

Leucojum L.

Leucojum aestivum L.
Summer Snowflake

British Red Data Book species.
Native and introduction. Very wet conditions shaded by tall vegetation after the flowers have gone over.
N. Two localities for ssp. *aestivum* in the R. Kennet valley: a single clump in a slight hollow filled with *Carex riparia* known for many years 1984 DG, and the rediscovery of the first county record 1887 (Richardson) of a colony upstream in a more typical stream edge habitat dominated by riparian species 1984 JN. Elsewhere planted by pond and under willows Winterbourne Bassett 1991 JEO and garden throw-out Yatton Keynell 1989 DG.
S. The ssp. *aestivum* was identified at Woodford Green and Middle Woodford 1984-91 PM. Elsewhere two clumps along the edge of a field by a stream at Urchfont 1984 RF, 1991 BG. Fourteen plants near the bank of the R. Avon, The Butts, Salisbury 1991 KM. A colony at Win Green 1991 JJe was probably ssp. *pulchellum* (Salisb.) Briq.
See article on p.101.
10 km² 7 (13%)   1 km² 9 (<1%)

Leucojum vernum L.
Spring Snowflake

British Red Data Book species.
Possibly native in S Somerset and Dorset. Introduction in Wiltshire where it has probably been planted.
S. Boggy ground near pond after scrub clearance following some 30 years of neglect, Britford Green 1991 MMk & DPES. About 100 years previously there was a record for Britford. Interesting horticulturally if same site. The county's only record.
10 km² 1 (2%) 1 km² 1 (<1%)

Galanthus L.

Galanthus nivalis L.
Snowdrop

Introduction. Woods, roadside, hedge and streambanks.
N. Localised but widely-distributed. All colonies are considered to be of introduced origin. Some are extensive.
S. Most plants are the double-flowered form which blooms earlier than the single form which occurs in the withy bed at Quidhampton. Most probably this is B. Welch's copse referred to in *The Flora of Wiltshire* (K. Billinghurst). Known for 150 years Trafalgar plantations 1845 (Smith).
10 km² 47 (90%) 1 km² 564 (15%) Map 589, page 352

Narcissus L.

Narcissus poeticus L. ssp. poeticus
Pheasant's-eye Daffodil

Introduction. Garden escape, sometimes planted in countryside.
10 km² 5 (10%) 1 km² 5 (<1%)

Narcissus poeticus x N. pseudonarcissus = N. x incomparabilis Miller
Nonesuch Daffodil

Introduction. Naturalised in Wilts on lane verges and rubbish dumps, often near villages. Apparently more restricted in its distribution than *N. pseudonarcissus* ssp. *major* but probably not considered 'wild' and therefore ignored by some WFMP recorders.
10 km² 5 (10%) 1 km² 13 (<1%)

Narcissus pseudonarcissus L. ssp. pseudonarcissus
Wild Daffodil

Native and introduction. Woodland.

N. Colonies are extensive in some woods. Native at Pentico Wood and Bottom Coppice, Froxfield 1985-90 JN, near Foxbury Wood and Balaams Wood 1986-87 SK, many colonies in West Woods 1989-90 VS & JEO, and Gopher Wood 1990 JEO. Naturalised at Tockenham Wick 1986 DG and Puthall Park 1990 AJS.
S. Probably native in the SE. Found in old coppiced woodland in Mean Wood 1986 PMW only 5 km away from a known native site in Hants just across the county border. Plants extending over a large area, possibly naturalised, in Glazier's Copse 1986 PMW. In the SW, extensive patches Park Hill 1991 PMW but introduced to Stourhead Gardens 1991 PS. Known for a long time in Oyster's Coppice WTNC reserve. Probably planted, but long-established in Manor Woods, Market Lavington 1984 RF.
Introductions on road and trackside verges not included on map.
10 km² 17 (33%) 1 km² 40 (1%) Map 590, page 352

Narcissus pseudonarcissus L. ssp. major (Curtis) Baker
Spanish Daffodil

Introduction. The most widely naturalised of the *Narcissus* species in the county occurring on lane verges and rubbish dumps, often near villages. It was probably not considered 'wild' and was therefore ignored by most WFMP recorders.
10 km² 2 (4%) 1 km² 37 (1%)

Asparagus L.

Asparagus officinalis L. ssp. officinalis
Garden Asparagus

Introduction. An escape from allotments and a garden throw-out.
10 km² 3 (6%) 1 km² 4 (<1%)

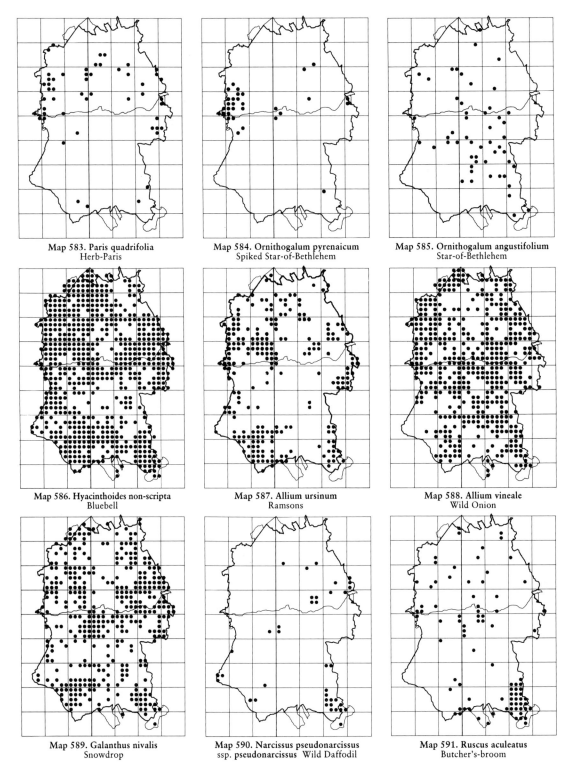

Map 583. Paris quadrifolia
Herb-Paris

Map 584. Ornithogalum pyrenaicum
Spiked Star-of-Bethlehem

Map 585. Ornithogalum angustifolium
Star-of-Bethlehem

Map 586. Hyacinthoides non-scripta
Bluebell

Map 587. Allium ursinum
Ramsons

Map 588. Allium vineale
Wild Onion

Map 589. Galanthus nivalis
Snowdrop

Map 590. Narcissus pseudonarcissus
ssp. pseudonarcissus Wild Daffodil

Map 591. Ruscus aculeatus
Butcher's-broom

Ruscus L.

Ruscus aculeatus L.
Butcher's-broom

Native and introduction. Woods, hedges and road verges.
N. Always planted. Ornamental woodland and churchyards.
S. Native in SE and probably in Cranborne Chase near the Dorset border.
10 km² 32 (62%) 1 km² 136 (4%)   Map 591, page 352

IRIDACEAE

Sisyrinchium L.

Sisyrinchium bermudiana L.
Blue-eyed-grass

Probable native in GB, introduction in Wilts.
N. M4 cutting, W-bound, near Draycot Park 1986 DG.
10 km² 1 (2%)   1 km² 1 (<1%)

Iris L.

Iris pseudacorus L.
Yellow Iris

Native. Beside streams, rivers, canals, lakes, ponds and gravel pits. In wet meadows and ditches. Occurs widely along the county's watercourses.
10 km² 46 (88%) 1 km² 477 (13%)   Map 592, page 356

Iris foetidissima L.
Stinking Iris

Native. Woods and hedges.
N. Frequent only in woods in the valleys of the Bristol Avon and By Brook, where it occurs in large numbers in some places, and W of Highworth.
S. Records are most widespread in Grovely Wood

and in woods to the E of Salisbury at Clarendon and Bentley where it is very localised. Planted along a hedge running S from Broad Chalke.
10 km² 35 (67%) 1 km² 99 (3%)   Map 593, page 356

DIOSCOREACEAE

Tamus L.

Tamus communis L.
Black Bryony

Native. Woodland edges, hedges and scrub. Well-distributed, except on Salisbury Plain where there is a lack of suitable habitat.
10 km² 51 (98%) 1 km² 1225 (34%) Map 594, page 356

ORCHIDACEAE

Cephalanthera Rich.

Cephalanthera damasonium (Miller) Druce
White Helleborine

Native. In shade, usually under beech trees with little ground cover and on wooded banks on dry chalk and limestone soils.
N. Very localised. On limestone along the valleys of R. Avon and By Brook. Murhill House and farm 1983-85 JM, Box Hill quarry 1984 RR, Lidbrook 1984 DG. On chalk, West Down and Knoll Down near Beckhampton and two sites Roundway Hill 1985 BG, Hanging Wood near Clyffe Pypard 1989 DB and near Aldbourne 1991 JN.
S. Bare chalk banks leading to Pepperbox car park (NT) off A36, Gatmore Copse 1985 MD and Pearl Wood, Beacon Hill SPTA(E) 1985 AJS. Number of plants 1-2, 8-14, 20-30. Higher numbers Short River, Westbury 1985-88, 1990 JEB, Little Durnford WTNC reserve 1984 PM, common beech/pine woods on chalk The Warren, West Lavington 1984 RF, 100+ Windmill Hill SPTA(E) 1984, 1989 AJS.
10 km² 21 (40%) 1 km² 42 (1%)   Map 595, page 356

Epipactis Zinn

Epipactis palustris (L.) Crantz
Marsh Helleborine

Native.
Known for a long time in vegetated old chalk quarry on downland in N Wilts where nine orchid species grow, including *Ophrys apifera*, *O. insectifera*, *Dactylorhiza fuchsii*, *Gymnadenia conopsea* and *Anacamptis pyramidalis*. The number of plants has increased from 20 in 1960 to 300 in 1992 BG. A second colony of 100+ plants 50 m higher up the hill located 1988 DG, may have been overlooked in previous years or earlier recorders may have found one of the two colonies but not both. The first record was in a marsh on Kingsdown (Flower 1839). All other sites referred to by Grose have been eradicated by agricultural 'improvement' or drainage.
10 km² 1 (2%)   1 km² 1 (<1%)

Epipactis purpurata Smith
Violet Helleborine

Native. Ancient woods on heavy clays and superficials over chalk.
N. The main strongholds are in the Braydon Forest and Savernake Forest areas where many of the historic sites still have colonies. At other apparently suitable old sites the plant seems to have disappeared. Four sites in Savernake Forest 1983 (D Osbourne), in Oaksey parish 1984 RFG, CK & MK, extensive colonies Silkwood VC7 (Glos) 1985 HB. On greensand at Long Copse, Lacock 1983-85 DG & JMP and Derry Hill 1987 GG & ASk.
10 km² 8 (15%)   1 km² 17 (<1%)   Map 596, page 356

Epipactis purpurata Smith var. chlorotica

N. A colony of 17 plants in a secondary woodland 1982 (D Osbourne). Number of plants fluctuates annually. This variety contains no chlorophyll, hence its pink/purple colour.
10 km² 1 (2%)   1 km² 1 (<1%)

Epipactis helleborine (L.) Crantz
Broad-leaved Helleborine

Native. Woodland, woodland rides, scrub and old green lanes in at least partial shade, mainly on calcareous soils but also on clay and chalk superficials. Sparsely distributed throughout the county, most frequent in woodland SE of Salisbury.
10 km² 27 (52%) 1 km² 63 (2%)   Map 597, page 356

Epipactis leptochila (Godfery) Godfery
Narrow-lipped Helleborine

Nationally scarce plant.
Native. In heavy shade on chalk soil.
S. Hound Wood, Farley 1984 MT & RPB. Only the second record for the county but not refound in late 1980s PMW.
10 km² 1 (2%)   1 km² 2 (<1%)

Epipactis phyllanthes G. E. Smith
E. cambrensis C. Thomas; *E. vectensis* (Stephenson & T. A. Stephenson) Brooke & F. Rose; *E. pendula* C. Thomas non A. A. Eaton; *E. confusa* D. P. Young
Green-flowered Helleborine

Nationally scarce plant.
Native. Mostly under mature beech with understorey.
N. Recorded from six 1 km² Savernake Forest, more frequently under shade of saplings rather than the large old beech trees. First found 1960 (A Sheppard) but not refound until 1983 (D Osbourne), shown to DG and 30 spikes counted.
S. Footpath between West Harnham and Lower Bemerton (Salisbury), colony known for nearly 30 years and visited regularly. Appears to have moved across path 1985 JBH. Two areas Hindon Terrace 1986 LW, VH & AH. Twenty-two spikes on edge of gravel pit lake Steeple Langford 1991 RB & BL.

The above four synonyms and other taxa are probably best recognised as vars. according to Stace in the *New Flora of the British Isles*. Of these, only one was identified but not confirmed.
Var. vectensis
Berwick St James 1982 AH, 1985 BL, South Coulston Hollow 1986 BGH, and small colony under beech with large colony of *Cephalanthera damasonium* Little Durnford Down WTNC reserve 1988 NB & AH, 1989 PM.
10 km² 7 (13)%   1 km² 8 (<1%)

Neottia Guett.

Neottia nidus-avis (L.) Rich.
Bird's-nest Orchid

Native. Saprophyte growing primarily under dense beech, less often under ash and hawthorn, mainly on dry calcareous soils. It may not flower every year but dead flower spikes persist into the next flowering season.
N. Near Dundas Aqueduct, Lidbrook valley Colerne, Combe Wood, Home Wood at Compton Bassett 1984-90 DG, roadside woodland edge near Atworth 1987 RWo, Savernake Forest 1988 AJS. On damp clay Ravensroost Wood DG, Stanton Wood 1991 OM.
S. Pinchpenny Clump 1984 VH. SPTA(E): 100 spikes Windmill Hill, Ludgershall 1984, Pearl Wood, Bulford 1985, Chalk Pit Hill, North Tidworth 1986 AJS and Coldridge Wood, Ludgershall 1986 KW. SPTA(W): 50+ spikes Grant's Wood 1986 RT, 12 1988 BGH. Stockton Wood and Chilmark Down 1988 PM, well-known site Hindon Terraces 1989 PCh, two sites one under yew but on beech litter Porton Ranges 1989 OS & DOG. On non-calcareous soil: Oakfrith Wood 1984 RF, several sites in Bentley Wood including Picked Copse 1987 and Smokeways Copse 1988 VH, further S in woodland and ride edges with numerous spikes amongst birch, hawthorn and oak Coalpits Copse and Howe Copse East 1989 PMW.
10 km² 14 (27%)   1 km² 22 (<1%)   Map 598, page 356

Listera R. Br.

Listera ovata (L.) R. Br.
Common Twayblade

Native. Woodland, scrub and less frequently, on unimproved grassland mainly on calcareous soils. Abundant in some woodlands, especially on the limestone escarpment of the Bristol Avon valley and around Aldbourne. The second most frequent orchid species.
10 km² 45 (87%)   1 km² 396 (11%)   Map 599, page 356

Spiranthes Rich.

Spiranthes spiralis (L.) Chevall.
Autumn Lady's-tresses

Native. Short unimproved chalk and limestone downland. Number of flower-spikes fluctuate from year to year varying from large spreading colonies one year to a single spike the following year. Due to fast development of spikes in the right conditions and the short flowering period in hot weather the plant is prone to not being recorded.
N. On limestone at Gilling Grove and near Gatcombe Hill 1985 ASk, West Yatton Down 1986 HB. On chalk downland King's Play, Milk and Walker's Hills 1984 KP, earthwork embankment Avebury 1984 DG, down NW of Lodge Lower Barn Aldbourne 1988 JN.
S. Known for 100+ years in areas of shorter turf Pepperbox Hill 1985, 40+ spikes 1987 but an increase in the following years PMW. Some of the newly-recorded sites: several hundred S-facing and single N-facing slope Church Bottom, Middle Woodford and St. Birinius churchyard, Morgan's Vale 1990 JO. WTNC reserves: Grovely Down 1987 AH, Great Cheverell Hill 1987 BGH, Middleton Down 1989 BL. Prescombe Down NCC/ST, Longcombe Bottom 1987 BGH and E of Great Cheverell Hill 1989 BG, both SPTA(W), Upper Farm Down, Little Langford 1987, hundreds of spikes Deptford 1990 BL, Brimsdown 1991 ER.
10 km² 13 (25%)   1 km² 20 (<1%)   Map 600, page 356

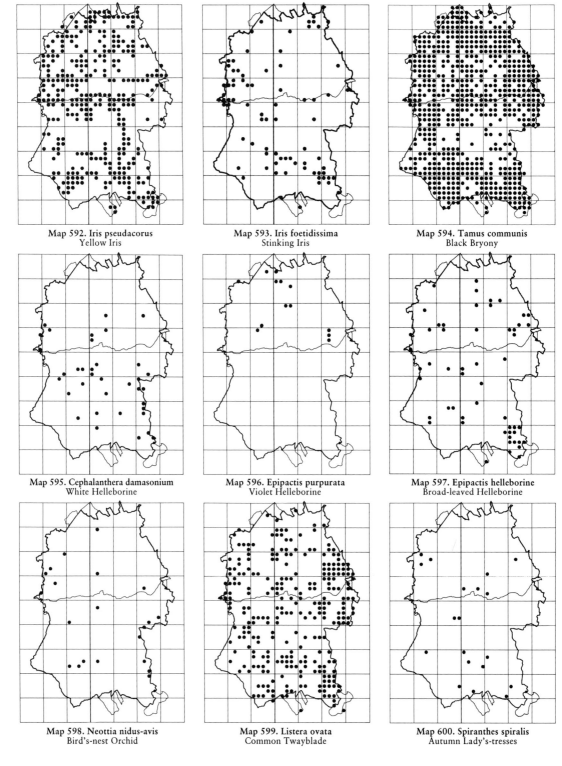

Map 592. Iris pseudacorus
Yellow Iris

Map 593. Iris foetidissima
Stinking Iris

Map 594. Tamus communis
Black Bryony

Map 595. Cephalanthera damasonium
White Helleborine

Map 596. Epipactis purpurata
Violet Helleborine

Map 597. Epipactis helleborine
Broad-leaved Helleborine

Map 598. Neottia nidus-avis
Bird's-nest Orchid

Map 599. Listera ovata
Common Twayblade

Map 600. Spiranthes spiralis
Autumn Lady's-tresses

Herminium L.

Herminium monorchis (L.) R. Br.
Musk Orchid

Nationally scarce plant.
Native. Short turf on steep chalk downland. Rare.
N. Very small colony Morgan's Hill, known for many years but not found every year, 1985 BG. The only site in VC7.
S. Above-average erratic behaviour in flowering and resting even for an orchid. In spite of its ability to reproduce both sexually, and vegetatively by means of long rhizomes, this orchid has become rarer nationally, especially in Wiltshire since 1957. Not quite as rare as in Dorset but certainly rarer than in Hants. As with frog orchids, once one spike has been focused on by an observer more should then be found. Height usually 50-100 mm but taller at the best-known site at Ham Hill where its persistence in flowering makes this WTNC reserve the most reliable area in the county and it was one of Donald Grose's favourite places. Several hundred flowering spikes seen there 1986 JR and *c.*12 near the path in a very limited area BGH. See Plate 2. In the S it was first recorded beside the track to Trow Down in 1964 but has not been seen since the early 1980s. On the same downland ridge, near East Combe Wood, BF discovered a colony in 1958 (which was visited by D Grose) and found six spikes in the mid-1980s. The musk orchid flowers from the end of June to the third week in July but flowering period reduced in very hot summers. The pale yellowish flowers aid recognition and the scent of honey is a bonus.
10 km² 3 (6%)   1 km² 6 (<1%)

Platanthera Rich.

Platanthera chlorantha (Custer) Reichb.
Greater Butterfly-orchid

Native. Woods and occasionally on unimproved chalk grassland.
N. Sparsely distributed and nowhere frequent.

Main concentrations in the Braydon Forest area and on limestone in NW on the edge of the Cotswolds.
S. A conspicuous orchid usually occurring in very small numbers, 50+ in a clearing Great Ridge Wood 1990 VH exceptional. Main areas, Great Ridge, Grovely and Bentley Woods. Ride and tracksides on grassland Bayton Wood, 40+ downland near Fernicombe SPTA(W) BG and Everleigh Ashes AJS.
10 km² 23 (44%) 1 km² 81 (2%)   Map 601, page 360

Platanthera bifolia (L.) Rich.
Lesser Butterfly-orchid

Native. Open unimproved chalk downland.
N. Large numbers occur only on steep downland slopes spread over a wide area making accurate counting difficult. Roundway Hill, Oliver's Castle, Beacon Hill, King's Play Hill, Morgan's Hill, Oldbury Castle, Kitchen Barrow, Tan and Milk Hills. N of Marlborough on farm track Baydon Manor, Spring Hill near Ramsbury, Sound Bottom and around Aldbourne.
S. Noted by only five recorders, counts of 10-20. Most frequent on N edge of SPTA(W), a well-documented area: Coulston Hill, Great Cheverell Hill, near Rook Tree Farm and single plant with hundreds of *Dactylorhiza fuchsii* White Hill 1984-91 EC, BG & BGH. Elsewhere, near Tidcombe 1987 PP and in clearing with *P. chlorantha* Coalpits Copse, Bentley Wood 1991 PMW.
10 km² 7 (13%)   1 km² 29 (<1%)   Map 602, page 360

Anacamptis Rich.

Anacamptis pyramidalis (L.) Rich.
Pyramidal Orchid

Native. Grazed and ungrazed unimproved calcareous downland, railway embankments and cuttings, road verges and rarely on bare gravel.
N. Restricted to calcareous grassland where it occurs in large colonies in some places.
S. The main concentrations of records are from

ungrazed chalk grassland on SPTA where there are large areas in which this species is common. In one area, the grass is sometimes cut for hay and plants number thousands. Elsewhere, colonies are not large.

10 km² 35 (67%) 1 km² 269 (7%)   Map 603, page 360

Gymnadenia R. Br.

Gymnadenia conopsea (L.) R. Br.
Fragrant Orchid

Native. Unimproved chalk downland, very rarely on limestone.
N. Most records are from steep slopes on the Pewsey and Marlborough Downs. Two colonies on limestone at West Yatton Down, near Castle Combe.
S. All records are from chalk downland. Colonies of c. 200 flowering spikes occur and nearly always more than 20. Form with white flowers, Cockey Down 1985 PM.

10 km² 28 (54%) 1 km² 226 (6%)   Map 604, page 360

X Dactylodenia Garay & H. Sweet

Gymnadenia conopsea x Dactylorhiza fuchsii = X Dactylodenia st-quintinii (Godfery) J. Duvign.

Native.
N. First recorded Morgan's Hill (Timperley 1953), refound 1987 JH.
S. Two specimens Great Durnford 1984 PM.

10 km² 2 (4%)   1 km² 2 (<1%)

Coeloglossum Hartman

Coeloglossum viride (L.) Hartman
Frog Orchid

Native. Short springy turf on unimproved chalk downland. Number of spikes fluctuate dramatically from year to year.

N. On most sites the grassland is species-rich, Morgan's Hill 1984 PRM, Knoll Down 1985 BG, Foxhill 1985 MWS, Bailey Hill, Hodd's Hill and downs above Lower Lodge, all near Aldbourne 1986 JN, Tan, Milk, Walker's and Knap Hills 1986 KP.
S. Records for 1-10 spikes at a surprising number of sites during WFMP. Much higher counts: several hundred Figsbury Ring (NT) 1984-1985, high counts Cockey Down 1987 and High Post Golf Course 1988 PM, Dean Hill Wood 1988 DJW, 90 spikes on level strip of dry grass Bulford Ranges SPTA(E) AJS, widespread Parsonage Down NNR 1984 BG. Low numbers on S-facing slope of superb springy turf Clearbury Down 1985 NLC & BKC.

10 km² 17 (33%) 1 km² 46 (1%)   Map 605, page 360

Dactylorhiza Necker ex Nevski

Dactylorhiza fuchsii (Druce) Soó
Common Spotted-orchid

Native. Unimproved calcareous downland, both grazed and ungrazed, unimproved neutral grassland, woodland and marshes.
N. Widespread on chalk and limestone grassland and in woodland rides.
S. The most frequent orchid, recorded from nearly 50% of tetrads, though very rare on some grazed downland as at Parsonage Down NNR. Occurs in marshy areas, but more commonly on calcareous grassland and in woods.

10 km² 47 (90%) 1 km² 728 (20%) Map 606, page 360

Dactylorhiza fuchsii x D. praetermissa = D. x grandis (Druce) P. Hunt

Native. Occurs with or without both parents. Large colonies occur some distance from either parent.
N. Derryfields, CWP and Draycot Park 1986 DG, Sutton Benger 1986 RA, Widdenham and Colerne 1989 DG.

S. Three water-meadows Stratford-sub-Castle and one Winterbourne Gunner, chalk grassland Great Durnford and Figsbury Ring 1985-86 PM. Railway bank Barford Down, Downton 1985 NLC, chalk quarry West Harnham, Salisbury 1987 NLC, track Lower Pertwood 1987 VW, water-meadows Pewsey 1987 JEO, Ashdod, Whiteparish 1987 DJW, Semington Brook 1988 BGH, Milkhills, Redlynch 1989 DJW, Frogmore near Whiteparish 1989 PMW.

10 km² 9 (17%)   1 km² 18 (<1%)   Map 607, page 360

Dactylorhiza maculata (L.) Soó ssp. ericetorum (E. F. Linton) P. Hunt & Summerh.
Heath Spotted-orchid

Native. Unimproved neutral to acidic grassland.
N. Locally abundant. Colonies of considerable size in unimproved meadows and open woodland rides in the Braydon Forest area at Emmett Hill, Derryfield Farm, Cotmarsh Farm, Distillery Farm, Ravensroost Wood and Webb's Wood. Also at Grittenham, Surrendel, Wootton Bassett, Alderton, Luckington and small colonies or a single plant at other locations.
S. Mainly on heavy clays in the New Forest area. Widespread Chadwell 1987-88 DJW & PMW, Loosehanger and Milkhills 1989 DJW. Smaller populations outside this area Potterne Park Farm and Lydeway 1985 RF, Dinton 1987 PP, 1991 SMP, Stourton 1991 PMW.

10 km² 15 (29%) 1 km² 39 (1%)   Map 608, page 360

Dactylorhiza incarnata (L.) Soó
Early Marsh-orchid

Native. Marshy places and wet unimproved base-rich grassland.
N. Locations decreasing. North Meadow NNR Cricklade, 200 plants in damp grassland By Brook valley 1983 DG, marsh near Avon 1984 DG & RR later planted with trees, old water-meadows R. Kennet Chilton Foliat and Ramsbury 1983-84 DG & JN, wet valley near Lyneham 1985 DG.

S. As with D. praetermissa, which flowers later, the highest number of sites, some new, occurs in SU13 bordering the rivers Avon and Bourne. Plants in three meadows numbered 23 plants, seven in an overgrown meadow and one in fruit Stratford-sub-Castle 1985 PM. Eight plants in flower in fine water-meadow Little Durnford 1987 PM, Kingfisher Mill Great Durnford 1989 BL. Two sites on R. Bourne: Porton 1987 JF and Winterbourne Gunner PM, AH 1986. R. Wylye: Stockton 1985 AS, Smallbrook Meadow 1986 (WTNC) and Bathampton Meadow Wylye 1987 BL. Meadow Netheravon 1989 AJS.

10 km² 11 (21%) 1 km² 18 (<1%)   Map 609, page 360

Dactylorhiza praetermissa (Druce) Soó
Dactylorhiza majalis (Reichb.) P. Hunt & Summerh. ssp. praetermissa (Druce) David Moore & Soó; Orchis pardalina Pugsley
Southern Marsh-orchid

Native. Sites with restricted water-flow. Marshes, damp unimproved meadows, wet woodland and open alder carr. Occasionally on chalk.
N. Thinly distributed, some sites with very few plants. Three sites in By Brook valley, unimproved meadow Sutton Benger, pond near Charlton, Webb's Wood, CWP area, R. Kennet valley from Ramsbury to Chilton Foliat and meadow Froxfield.
S. Records from dry situations include: bank of old army moving target railway, known for 5 years Little Folly SPTA(C) 1984 AW, grassy patch, top of bank Barford Down 1985 NLC, one plant steep scarp slope near river growing with D. fuchsii Great Durnford 1985 PM, numerous colonies in chalk quarry West Harnham 1987 NLC, one near several greater butterfly-orchids on trackside Bentley Wood 1987 PMW, one downland Stockton 1988 PM, one plant Grovely Down 1989 BL, one on orchid-rich N-facing down Middle Woodford 1989 PM. Large colonies can be found in damp meadows: 300 in 1984 and 200 in 1985 in fine water-meadow Stratford-sub-

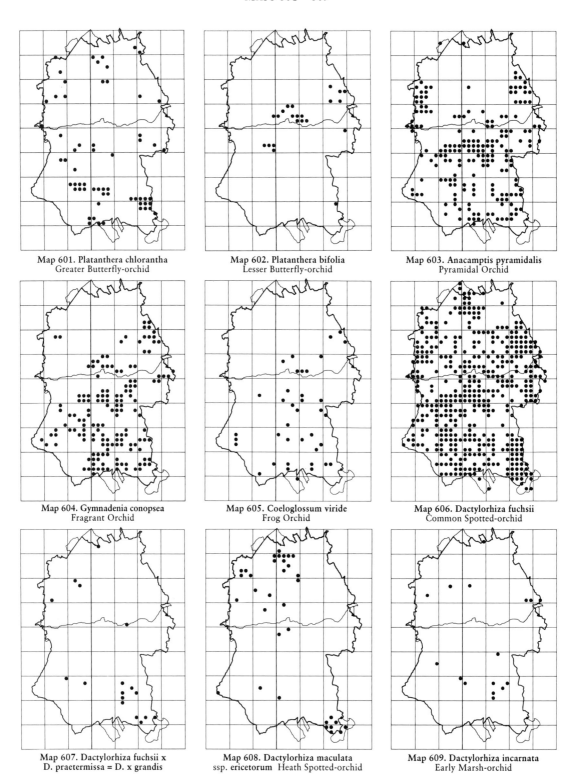

Map 601. *Platanthera chlorantha*
Greater Butterfly-orchid

Map 602. *Platanthera bifolia*
Lesser Butterfly-orchid

Map 603. *Anacamptis pyramidalis*
Pyramidal Orchid

Map 604. *Gymnadenia conopsea*
Fragrant Orchid

Map 605. *Coeloglossum viride*
Frog Orchid

Map 606. *Dactylorhiza fuchsii*
Common Spotted-orchid

Map 607. *Dactylorhiza fuchsii* x
D. praetermissa = D. x grandis

Map 608. *Dactylorhiza maculata*
ssp. *ericetorum* Heath Spotted-orchid

Map 609. *Dactylorhiza incarnata*
Early Marsh-orchid

Castle PM, 50 beside R. Till, Berwick St James 1987 BL.

10 km² 27 (52%) 1 km² 72 (2%)   Map 610, page 363

Orchis L.

Orchis mascula (L.) L.
Early-purple Orchid

Native. Ancient and old secondary woodland and unimproved downland. It occurs and is more common in most areas of ancient and old secondary woodland where plants can be 400 mm tall when growing with bluebells. Locally common on chalk and limestone downland at Roundway Hill and in the By Brook valley. Colonies often very small but some have 100+ flowering spikes. The third most frequent orchid species.

10 km² 43 (83%) 1 km² 349 (10%)   Map 611, page 363

Orchis morio L.
Green-winged Orchid

Nationally scarce plant.
Native. Unimproved neutral and calcareous grassland.
N. This plant has suffered more than any other orchid species from agricultural improvement in the last 40 years. Spraying or reseeding of lowland meadows where O. morio once grew produced grass monocultures. In 1981, only three colonies were known since when WFMP recorders have found an unexpected number of damp unimproved meadows containing colonies. Most frequent in valley of the By Brook and its tributaries in Castle Combe area and on low-lying clay in the NW. In railway cutting Hullavington. On greensand Bowood.
S. Occurs on short unimproved chalk grassland and occasionally damp clay meadows. Colour variation from pale pink to deep purple. Good colonies 70+ spikes Whiteparish over period of 10 years, Deptford Down 1985, E of Halmoor Copse

1985, Cockey Down WTNC reserve number increased 1985-88, Netheravon Down. Two spikes on site of previously demolished railway sheds Salisbury.

10 km² 26 (50%) 1 km² 58 (2%)   Map 612, page 363

Orchis ustulata L.
Burnt Orchid

Nationally scarce plant.
Native. Short turf on unimproved chalk grassland, rarely on unimproved lowland grassland and occasionally on calcareous gravels.
One of the county's treasures. Wiltshire, especially VC8, has the highest concentration of sites for this species in GB. There is more grazed and unfragmented unimproved chalk downland in Wilts than elsewhere in GB. A short orchid (150-200 mm) in GB but may be 300 mm tall on the continent. An attractive orchid having numerous small flowers and with a general similarity to a mini-Lady Orchid. The buds are dark purple giving the flower spike a burnt tip. Sepals and petals converge to give a rounded hood of a deep colour on the outside. The contrasting lip is white with a few red spots. Unlike other British orchids the rhizome grows annually, associated with a fungus, for 10 years or more before the first normal roots and green leaves appear. The mycorrhizomes are replaced by tubers, swollen roots which can resist drought. Of particular interest is the number of very small colonies (1-2 spikes) and several WFMP records from newly-recorded sites were of this nature. The majority of colonies flower from end of May to beginning of June but some, which flower in July, are now recognised as a subspecies. In some places these colonies overlap. During the 8 years of recording it was realised that it was possible to miss the orchid. Cattle and sheep could devour the flowers overnight and in hot weather the flowering period could be short. We learnt to appreciate our sites more.
N. Sites are concentrated along the Pewsey Downs escarpment, near Cherhill and N of Aldbourne. Some sites have been lost since Grose's day, notably

the Bishopstone Downs SE of Swindon which were aerially sprayed in 1970s. In N of VC7 a site has been reported from unimproved pasture on calcareous gravels.

S. Most frequent on downland overlooking the Wylye valley and on the N-facing escarpment of the Ebble valley. Thinly scattered on SPTA, mainly on SPTA(E) and eleswhere in NE of VC8. It had been considered that the species grows best on N-facing, even steep slopes, but the truth may be more complicated. Of two of our superb colonies one faces S on a slope and another is of 150 ha of undulating ground with the orchid scattered over the whole area.

10 km² 17 (33%) 1 km² 37 (1%)   Map 613, page 363

Aceras R. Br.

Aceras anthropophorum (L.) W. T. Aiton
Man Orchid

Nationally scarce plant.
Native.
S. Chalk grassland PT comm. GD Fields 1983 and RPB 1989. First and second VC8 (Hants) records, and for county.
10 km² 1 (2%)   1 km² 1 (<1%)

Ophrys L.

Ophrys insectifera L.
Fly Orchid

Native. Grassland, wood and scrub edges and old quarries on calcareous soils. Rare and difficult to find, the tall stems and beautiful flowers mimicking flies merging into the background. Colony size may fluctuate from year to year. Flowers in mid-May, 2-3 weeks earlier than *O. apifera*.
N. On chalk, known for a long time Morgan's Hill and Walker's Hill. On limestone, woodland edge Kingsdown 1984 LW, Lidbrook Valley, Colerne 1988 DG.
S. Decreasing, making the finding more

rewarding. All records are on chalk, four are of 1-2 plants: Heytesbury Plantation 1984 JWH & KH, embankment Barford Down 1985 NLC, near Westwood Quarry 1986 GY, South Down, Ebbesbourne Wake 1987 MM, Compton Down 1990 MDT, Pear Tree Hill above Cheverell 1990/91 BGH, Grovely Wood 1991 SMP and Bentley Wood OS.

10 km² 12 (23%) 1 km² 12 (<1%)   Map 614, page 363

Ophrys sphegodes Miller
Early Spider-orchid

British Red Data Book species.
Native.
S. One plant, with four florets *c.* 230 mm tall near Witherington Down 1988 FR. Sterile rosette 1989. No reports 1990-92.
10 km² 1 (2%)   1 km² 1 (<1%)

Ophrys apifera Hudson
Bee Orchid

Native. Unimproved calcareous grassland, old chalk quarries, disused gravel workings, railway embankments, woodland rides and glades.
N. Small colonies in a variety of these habitats usually in areas previously disturbed by man where the soil is thin or stony. On limestone near the Bristol Avon and By Brook, on bare gravel in CWP and on chalk downland.
S. Almost all records from chalk grassland. Colonies of 3-30 flowering spikes. Good number of records from N part of SPTA(W), the Salisbury area including Pepperbox Hill (NT) and the chalk downland W of Salisbury including Middleton Down (WTNC).
Var. **chlorantha** (Hegetschw.) Richter
Observed for 8 years West Grimstead 1988 IA.
Var. **friburgensis** Freh.
Ssp. *jurana* Ruppert
Edge of track, Bidcombe Hill 1984-85, site destroyed 1985-86 RL.
10 km² 29 (56%) 1 km² 95 (3%)   Map 615, page 363

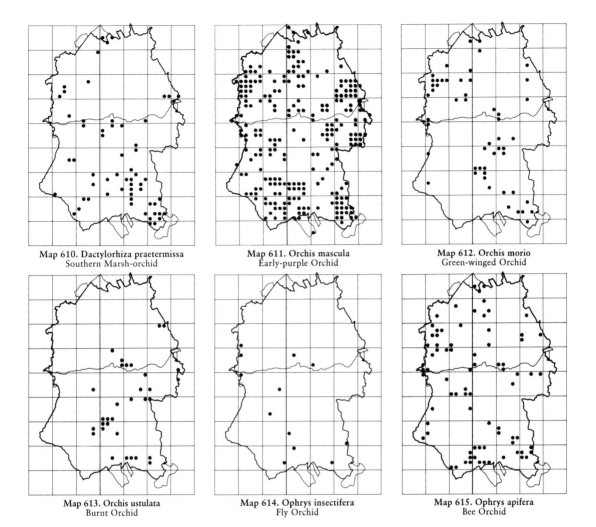

Map 610. *Dactylorhiza praetermissa*
Southern Marsh-orchid

Map 611. *Orchis mascula*
Early-purple Orchid

Map 612. *Orchis morio*
Green-winged Orchid

Map 613. *Orchis ustulata*
Burnt Orchid

Map 614. *Ophrys insectifera*
Fly Orchid

Map 615. *Ophrys apifera*
Bee Orchid

APPENDIX I

Non-native plants of infrequent occurrence in Wiltshire

Each species has been listed in only one of four defined categories although some may be considered to fall within more than one. The number of tetrads in which the species was recorded and the number of records for each species follow the English name.

Planted trees and shrubs species which have been recorded in semi-natural habitats.

		Tetrads	Records
Aesculus carnea Zeyher	Red Horse-chestnut	2	3
Chamaecyparis lawsoniana (A. Murray) Parl.	Lawson's Cypress	5	5
Cornus mas L.	Cornelian-cherry	2	2
Cornus sericea L.	Red-osier Dogwood	1	2
Kerria japonica (L.) DC.	Kerria	1	1
Laburnum anagyroides Medikus	Laburnum	6	7
Picea sitchensis (Bong.) Carrière	Sitka Spruce	2	2
Pinus nigra Arnold ssp. nigra	Austrian Pine	4	4
Platanus x hispanica Miller ex Muenchh.	London Plane	1	1
Prunus cerasus L.	Dwarf Cherry	1	1
Prunus lusitanica L.	Portugal Laurel	3	4
Pseudotsuga menziesii (Mirbel) Franco	Douglas Fir	13	14
Quercus ilex L.	Evergreen Oak	10	10
Quercus rubra L.	Red Oak	1	1
Rhododendron luteum Sweet	Yellow Azalea	1	1
Robinia pseudoacacia L.	False-acacia	10	12
Rosa rugosa Thunb. ex Murray	Japanese Rose	6	6
Spiraea x billardii Hérincq	Billard's Bridewort	1	1
Spiraea douglasii Hook.	Steeplebush	1	1
Spiraea salicifolia L.	Bridewort	3	4
Thuja plicata Donn ex D. Don	Western Red-cedar	6	7
Tsuga heterophylla (Raf.) Sarg.	Western Hemlock-spruce	1	1

Species of exotic origin and infrequent occurrence recorded in semi-natural habitats but which have, in all probability, escaped from or been thrown out of gardens.

		Tetrads	Records
Ageratum houstonianum Miller	Flossflower	1	1
Allium schoenoprasum L.	Chives	3	3
Anaphalis margaritacea (L.) Benth.	Pearly Everlasting	1	1
Anemone blanda Schott & Kotschy	Grecian Windflower	2	2
Anthemis tinctoria L.	Yellow Chamomile	1	1
Antirrhinum majus L.	Snapdragon	13	14
Aristolochia clematitis L.	Birthwort	1	1
Atriplex hortensis L.	Garden Orache	1	1
Aubrieta deltoidea (L.) DC.	Aubretia	3	3
Bambusoideae spp.	Bamboo	1	1
Borago officinalis L.	Borage	14	17
Calendula arvensis L.	Field Marigold	1	1

		Tetrads	Records
Calendula officinalis L.	Pot Marigold	4	4
Campanula persicifolia L.	Peach-leaved Bellflower	3	3
Campanula poscharskyana Degen	Trailing Bellflower	1	1
Campanula rapunculoides L.	Creeping Bellflower	2	2
Cerastium tomentosum L.	Snow-in-Summer	10	11
Clematis x jackmanii Moore	Clematis	1	1
Corydalis solida (L.) Clairv.	Bird-in-a-bush	1	3
Cotoneaster franchetii Bois	Franchet's Cotoneaster	1	1
Cotoneaster frigidus Wallich ex Lindley	Tree Cotoneaster	1	1
Crocosmia x crocosmiiflora			
(Lemoine ex Burb. & Dean) N. E. Br.	Montbretia	10	12
Crocus flavus Weston	Yellow Crocus	1	1
Crocus nudiflorus Smith	Autumn Crocus	1	1
Cyclamen hederifolium Aiton.	Cyclamen, Sowbread	1	1
Cyclamen repandum Sibth. & Smith	Cyclamen, Sowbread	1	1
Delphinium spp. L.	Garden Delphinium	1	1
Echinops sphaerocephalus L.	Glandular Globe-thistle	3	3
Erigeron karvinskianus DC.	Mexican Fleabane	2	2
Erinus alpinus L.	Fairy Foxglove	2	2
Euphorbia esula L.	Leafy Spurge	2	2
Fragaria x ananassa			
(Weston) Lois., Vilm., Nois & J. J. Deville	Garden Strawberry	4	6
Galanthus plicatus M. Bieb.	Pleated Snowdrop	1	1
Galega officinalis L.	Goat's-rue	1	1
Geranium endressii Gay	French Crane's-bill	4	5
Geranium phaeum L.	Dusky Crane's-bill	1	1
Geranium versicolor L.	Pencilled Crane's-bill	2	2
Hedera helix L. ssp. hibernica (Kirchner) D. McClint.	Atlantic Ivy	2	2
Helianthus annuus L.	Sunflower	5	5
Helianthus spp. L.	Sunflower	1	1
Hypericum hircinum L.	Stinking Tutsan	1	1
Hypericum x inodorum Miller	Tall Tutsan	2	2
Lavatera arborea L.	Tree-mallow	1	1
Leucanthemum x superbum			
(Bergmans ex J. Ingram) D. H. Kent	Shasta Daisy	4	4
Leycesteria formosa Wallich	Himalayan Honeysuckle	1	1
Lobelia erinus L.	Garden Lobelia	1	1
Lobularia maritima (L.) Desv.	Sweet Alison	2	2
Lonicera caprifolium L.	Perfoliate Honeysuckle	1	1
Lysimachia punctata L.	Dotted Loosestrife	3	3
Nigella damascena L.	Love-in-a-mist	4	4
Omphalodes verna Moench	Blue-eyed-Mary	2	2
Oxalis corniculata L.	Procumbent Yellow-sorrel	14	20
Oxalis latifolia Kunth	Garden Pink-sorrel	2	4
Oxalis stricta L.	Upright Yellow-sorrel	2	2
Paeonia spp. L.	Peony	1	1
Papaver atlanticum (Ball) Cosson	Atlas Poppy	1	2
Papaver orientale L.	Oriental Poppy	4	4
Parthenocissus quinquefolia (L.) Planchon	Virginia-creeper	1	1
Persicaria amplexicaulis (D. Don) Ronse Decraene	Red Bistort	2	2
Petroselinum crispum (Miller) Nyman ex A. W. Hill	Garden Parsley	3	4
Philadelphus coronarius L.	Mock-orange	2	2
Physocarpus opulifolius (L.) Maxim.	Ninebark	1	1
Ribes sanguineum Pursh	Flowering Currant	1	1
Salvia officinalis L.	Sage	1	1
Schizostylis coccinea Backh. & Harvey ex Hook. f.	Kaffir Lily	1	1

		Tetrads	Records
Sedum spurium M. Bieb.	Caucasian Stonecrop	1	1
Sidalcea malvaeflora (DC.) A. Gray ex Benth.	Greek Mallow	1	1
Stachys byzantina K. Koch	Lamb's-ear	1	1
Staphylea pinnata L.	Bladdernut	1	1
Tragopogon porrifolius L.	Salsify	2	2
Tropaeolum majus L.	Nasturtium	2	2

Introduced species of infrequent occurrence which are unlikely to regenerate. For example, those of bird-seed origin.

		Tetrads	Records
Abutilon theophrasti Medikus	Velvetleaf	2	2
Alcea rosea L.	Hollyhock	2	2
Allium aflatunense B. Sedtschenku	Flowering Garlic	1	1
Allium carinatum L.	Keeled Garlic	1	1
Althaea hirsuta L.	Rough Marsh-mallow	2	2
Ammi majus L.	Bullwort	2	2
Bupleurum subovatum Link ex Sprengel	False Thorow-wax	1	1
Cicerbita bourgaei (Boiss.) Beauverd	Pontic Blue-sow-thistle	1	1
Cyperus eragrostis Lam.	Pale Galingale	1	1
Descurainia sophia (L.) Webb ex Prantl	Flixweed	2	2
Digitaria sanguinalis (L.) Scop.	Hairy Finger-grass	1	1
Guizotia abyssinica (L.f.) Cass.	Niger	3	3
Hordeum jubatum L.	Foxtail Barley	2	3
Lagurus ovatus L.	Hare's-tail	1	1
Melilotus indicus (L.) All.	Small Melilot	1	1
Nicandra physalodes (L.) Gaertner	Apple-of-Peru	1	1
Panicum miliaceum L.	Common Millet	2	2
Phacelia tanacetifolia Benth.	Phacelia	1	1
Setaria viridis (L.) P. Beauv.	Green Bristle-grass	1	1
Sisymbrium altissimum L.	Tall Rocket	1	1
Sisymbrium orientale L.	Eastern Rocket	1	1
Solanum rostratum Dunal	Buffalo-bur	1	1
Sorghum bicolor (L.) Moench	Great Millet	1	1
Sorghum halepense (L.) Pers.	Johnson-grass	1	1

Relic crop species.

		Tetrads	Records
Beta vulgaris L.	Beet	2	2
Hordeum distichon L.	Two-rowed Barley	21	24
Hordeum vulgare L.	Four and Six-rowed Barley	3	3
Secale cereale L.	Rye	2	2
Solanum tuberosum L.	Potato	1	1
Triticum aestivum L.	Bread Wheat	29	45

APPENDIX II

British Red Data Book and nationally scarce species recorded during the Wiltshire Flora Mapping Project

RDB = British Red Data Book species   ! = nationally scarce species   ∗ = non-native species

+ = species native in Great Britain but an introduction to Wiltshire

!		Aceras anthropophorum	!		Fumaria parviflora
!	+	Aconitum napellus	!		Gagea lutea
		ssp. napellus	!		Galeopsis angustifolia
!	+	Adiantum capillus-veneris	RDB		Galium constrictum
RDB	∗	Agrostemma githago	!		Galium pumilum
!		Allium oleraceum	!		Gentianella anglica
RDB	∗	Althaea hirsuta	!		Gnaphalium sylvaticum
!	+	Apera spica-venti	!		Helleborus foetidus
!		Arabis glabra	!		Herminium monorchis
!	+	Arum italicum ssp. italicum	!	+	Hippophae rhamnoides
!		Callitriche hermaphroditica	!		Hyoscyamus niger
!		Campanula patula	!		Iberis amara
!	+	Cardamine bulbifera	!		Lathyrus aphaca
!		Carex digitata	!	+	Lepidium latifolium
RDB		Carex filiformis	RDB		Leucojum aestivum
!		Carex humilis	RDB	+	Leucojum vernum
!	+	Centaurea cyanus	RDB	+	Lonicera xylosteum
!		Cerastium pumilum	!	+	Meconopsis cambrica
RDB		Cirsium tuberosum	RDB		Melampyrum arvense
!		Cuscuta europaea	!		Melittis melissophyllum
!	+	Cyperus longus	!		Minuartia hybrida
!	+	Daphne mezereum	!		Moenchia erecta
!	+	Dianthus deltoides	!		Myosurus minimus
!		Draba muralis	!	+	Nymphoides peltata
!		Eleocharis acicularis	!		Oenanthe fluviatilis
!	+	Epilobium lanceolatum	!		Oenanthe pimpinelloides
!		Epipactis leptochila	RDB		Ophrys sphegodes
!		Epipactis phyllanthes	!		Orchis morio
!		Euphorbia platyphyllos	!		Orchis ustulata
RDB	+	Euphorbia serrulata	!		Ornithogalum pyrenaicum
!		Euphrasia pseudokerneri	!		Papaver argemone
!		Fritillaria meleagris	!		Papaver hybridum
!		Fumaria densiflora	!	+	Parentucellia viscosa

!		Persicaria minor
!		Phyteuma orbiculare
RDB	+	Polemonium caeruleum
!		Polygala calcarea
!		Polygonatum odoratum
!		Polygonum rurivagum
!		Potamogeton friesii
RDB		Potamogeton nodosus
!		Potamogeton trichoides
!	+	Potentilla argentea
RDB		Pulsatilla vulgaris
!		Ranunculus arvensis
!		Rhynchospora fusca
RDB	∗	Rorippa austriaca
!		Rumex maritimus
RDB		Salvia pratensis
!	∗	Scandix pecten-veneris
!		Scrophularia umbrosa
!	+	Sedum forsteranum
!		Silene gallica
!		Silene noctiflora
!	+	Stratiotes aloides
!		Tephroseris integrifolia
!		Thesium humifusum
!	∗	Torilis arvensis
!		Trifolium ornithopodioides
!		Ulex minor
!		Valerianella dentata
RDB		Valerianella rimosa
!	+	Verbascum virgatum
!	+	Vicia lutea
!		Vicia parviflora

APPENDIX III

Species for which the first Wiltshire record was made during the Wiltshire Flora Mapping Project

✶ non-native species   + species native in Great Britain but an introduction in Wiltshire

First records in VC7

- ✶ Allium paradoxum
- + Apera spica-venti
- + Bolboschoenus maritimus
- ✶ Bromus secalinus
- Bromus x pseudothominei
- Ceratocapnos claviculata
- Chenopodium ficifolium
- + Cladium mariscus
- ✶ Cotoneaster horizontalis
- ✶ Cotoneaster simonsii
- ✶ Crassula helmsii
- + Cyperus longus
- Draba muralis
- ✶ Elodea nuttallii
- Euphrasia nemorosa x pseudokerneri
- Fumaria muralis ssp. boraei
- ✶ Gaudinia fragilis
- Hieracium calcaricola
- Hieracium vagum
- Hieracium vulgatum
- ✶ Hirschfeldia incana
- Juncus tenuis
- Lactuca virosa
- Lemna minuta
- ✶ Linaria x dominii
- ✶ Myriophyllum aquaticum
- ✶ Petasites japonicus
- ✶ Phalaris aquatica
- ✶ Phalaris paradoxa ssp. praemorsa
- Poa humilis
- Potamogeton obtusifolius
- ✶ Rorippa austriaca
- Rubus norvicensis
- + Sisyrinchium bermudiana
- ✶ Symphytum grandiflorum
- Symphytum tuberosum

First records in VC8

- Aceras anthropophorum
- + Apera spica-venti
- ✶ Acorus calamus
- ✶ Alnus incana
- + Althaea hirsuta
- Callitriche brutia
- Callitriche hermaphroditica
- Carex curta
- Descurainia sophia
- ✶ Elodea nuttallii
- Galium constrictum
- Hieracium rigens
- Hieracium vulgatum
- + Hippophae rhamnoides
- ✶ Lagarosiphon major
- + Lathraea clandestina
- Lemna minuta
- Lepidium heterophyllum
- Medicago sativa ssp. varia
- ✶ Mimulus luteus
- Myriophyllum alternifolium
- ✶ Myriophyllum aquaticum
- Potamogeton obtusifolius
- Pulsatilla vulgaris
- Rubus confertiflorus
- Rubus leucandriformis
- Rubus nemorosus
- Rubus subintegribasis
- ✶ Setaria pumila
- ✶ Symphytum grandiflorum
- Symphytum tuberosum
- Tilia cordata
- Trifolium ornithopodioides
- ✶ Verbascum densiflorum

APPENDIX IV

Species included in *The Flora of Wiltshire* (1957) and the *Supplement to the Flora of Wiltshire* (1975) but not refound during the Wiltshire Flora Mapping Project

The names given for each species is that accorded by Stace in the *New Flora of the British Isles*, 1991. Names used in earlier works have been updated.

✳ species not included in Stace's flora and which therefore cannot be updated.
Rubus species are omitted and are listed on pp.191 and 192.

Native Species

Agrostis canina x capillaris
Ajuga chamaepitys
Alopecurus aequalis
Althaea officinalis
Anagallis minima
Antennaria dioica
Baldellia ranunculoides
Cardamine impatiens
✳ Carduus acanthoides x nutans
Carduus x dubius
Carex diandra
Carex divulsa ssp. leersii
Carex vesicaria
Carex vulpina
Carex x elytroides
Carex x fulva
Carex x pseudaxillaris
✳ Centaurea jacea x nemoralis x nigra
Centaurea x moncktonii
Centaurium tenuiflorum
Cephalanthera longifolia
Ceratophyllum submersum
Chenopodium glaucum
Cicuta virosa
Cirsium x celakovskianum
Cirsium x grandiflorum
Cirsium x woodwardii
Clinopodium calamintha
Coincya monensis
Crassula tillaea
Cyperus fuscus
Dactylorhiza x hallii
Dactylorhiza x transiens
Dactylorhiza x wintoni
Echium plantagineum
Eleocharis parvula
Epilobium x aggregatum
Epilobium x mutabile
Epilobium x rivulare
Epilobium x subhirsutum
Equisetum hyemale

Equisetum x litorale
Eriophorum latifolium
Eriophorum vaginatum
Erodium moschatum
Festuca ovina ssp. hirtula
Filago minima
Fumaria bastardii
Fumaria vaillantii
Galium palustre ssp. elongatum
Galium x pomeranicum
✳ Gentianella campestris
Gentianella germanica
Gentianella x pamplinii
Gymnocarpium robertianum
Himantoglossum hircinum
Hippuris vulgaris
Hottonia palustris
Huperzia selago
Hydrocharis morsus-ranae
Hypericum montanum
Hypochaeris glabra
Juncus gerardii
Juncus x diffusus
Leymus arenarius
Limosella aquatica
Littorella uniflora
Luzula x borreri
Lycopodiella inundata
Lysimachia thysiflora
Marrubium vulgare
Medicago polymorpha
Melampyrum cristatum
Melampyrum sylvaticum
Mespilus germanica
Mibora minima
Oenanthe silaifolia
Orchis x morioides
Orobanche hederae
Orobanche rapum-genistae
Papaver x hungaricum
Parnassia palustris
Persicaria laxiflora
Phegopteris connectilis

Pilularia globulifera
Pinguicula vulgaris
Polypogon monspeliensis
Potamogeton alpinus
Potamogeton x salicifolius
Potentilla neumanniana
Potentilla palustris
Potentilla x suberecta
Prunella x intermedia
Puccinellia distans
Puccinellia rupestris
Pulicaria vulgaris
Pyrus cordata
Ranunculus parviflorus
Ranunculus tripartitus
Ranunculus x novae-forestae
Rorippa x sterilis
Rosa agrestis
Rosa caesia ssp. caesia
Rosa caesia ssp. glauca
Rosa pimpinellifolia
Rumex x dufftii
Rumex x mixtus
Sagina apetala ssp. apetala
Sagina subulata
Salix x alopecuroides
Salix x capreola
Salix x dichroa
Salix x multinervis
Salix x pontederiana
Salix x rubens
Salix x rubra
Saxifraga hypnoides
Senecio x ostenfeldii
Silene conica
Silene nutans
Sium latifolium
Sonchus oleraceus x asper
Stachys germanica
Stellaria palustris
Teesdalia nudicaulis
Teucrium botrys
Thelypteris palustris

Thlaspi perfoliatum
Trifolium scabrum
Trinia glauca
Typha x glauca
Ulmus angustifolia x procera
Ulmus glabra x minor
Ulmus minor ssp. angustifolia
Ulmus minor ssp. minor
Ulmus plotii
Ulmus x elegantissima
Utricularia minor
Utricularia vulgaris
Verbascum lychnitis
Verbascum pulverulentum
Verbascum x semialbum
Vicia bithynica
Vicia lathyroides
Viola hirta ssp. calcarea
Viola lactea
Viola riviniana x lactea
Viola x bavarica
Viola x contempta
Viola x militaris
Wolffia arrhiza
X Dactyloglossum mixtum
X Gymnaglossum jacksonii

Non-native Species

Allium roseum
Allium triquetrum
∗ Alyssum argenteum
Amaranthus graecizans
Ambrosia artemisiifolia
∗ Ambrosia elatior
Ambrosia psilostachya
Anchusa azurea
Anemone apennina
∗ Anemone mexicana
∗ Anthemis wiedemanniana
Anthriscus cerefolium
Aponogeton distachyos
Argemone mexicana
Artemisia biennis
Asperugo procumbens
Asperula arvensis
Astrantia major
Avena strigosa
Axyris amaranthoides
Barbarea verna
Brassica juncea
Bunias orientalis
Camelina sativa
∗ Campanula garganica
Cannabis sativa
Carthamus tinctorius

Caucalis platycarpos
Centaurea jacea
Centaurea solstitialis
Chenopodium capitatum
Chenopodium opulifolium
Chenopodium urbicum
∗ Cichorium pumilum
Colutea arborescens
Conringia orientalis
Consolida orientalis
Coriandrum sativum
Cotoneaster prostrata
Crataegus persimilis
Crataegus submollis
Crepis vesicaria ssp. haenseleri
Crocus vernus
Cuscuta epilinum
∗ Cuscuta suaveolens
Cynodon dactylon
Cynosurus echinatus
Darmera peltata
Dianthus barbatus
Doronicum plantagineum
Dracunculus vulgaris
Elodea callitrichoides
Epilobium pedunculare
Eschscholzia californica
Fagopyrum tataricum
Falcaria vulgaris
Fragaria muricata
Galium tricornutum
Gaultheria shallon
Genista hispanica
Gentiana asclepiadea
Gentianella baltica
Geraniun collinum
Geranium nodosum
Helianthus x laetiflorus
Hemizonia pungens
Hyacinthus orientalis
Isatis tinctoria
Lactuca sativa
Lappula echinata
Lathyrus vernus
∗ Lavatera thuringiaca
Leonurus cardiaca
Lepidium perfoliatum
Linaria dalmatica
Linaria maroccana
Lupinus arboreus
Luzula luzuloides
∗ Lythrum graefferi
Madia capitata
Malva parviflora
Malva pusilla
Malva verticillata
∗ Medicago denticulata

Molucella laevis
Muscari comosum
Myrrhis odorata
∗ Narcissus x medioluteus
Neslia paniculata
∗ Oenothera laciniata
Ononis baetica
Orobanche ramosa
Oxalis debilis
∗ Oxalis martiana
∗ Oxalis valdiviensis
Panicum capillare
Panicum virgatum
∗ Phacelia ciliata
Physalis alkekengi
Pisum sativum
Plantago afra
Poa chaixii
Poa palustris
Potentilla inclinata
Potentilla norvegica
Pyracantha coccinea
Raphanus raphanistrum ssp. landra
Raphanus sativus
Reseda alba
∗ Ribes rubrum x sativum
∗ Ribes sativum
∗ Salsola pestifer
Saxifraga umbrosa
∗ Scilla italica
Scolymus hispanicus
Scorpiurus muricatus
Scorzonera hispanica
Sedum sexangulare
Sempervivum tectorum
Setaria verticillata
Sicyos angulatus
Silene armeria
∗ Silene dichotoma
Sisymbrium irio
Solanum sisymbriifolium
∗ Spiraea hypericifolia
Stachys annua
Tordylium maximum
Trifolium resupinatum
Turgenia latifolia
Vaccaria hispanica
Valerianella eriocarpa
Verbascum pyramidatum
Verbascum speciosum
Veronica peregrina
Vicia hybrida
Vicia villosa
Xanthium spinosum

BIBLIOGRAPHY

* Field Guide

Barron, R S (1976). *The Geology of Wiltshire.* Moonraker Press, Bradford-on-Avon.

Clapham, A R, Tutin, T G and Moore, D M (1987). *Flora of the British Isles.* Cambridge University Press, Cambridge.

Clapham, A R, Tutin, T G and Warburg, E F (1959). *Flora of the British Isles,* 2nd ed. 1968. Cambridge University Press, Cambridge.

Dandy, J E (1958). *List of British Vascular Plants.* British Museum, London.

Dandy, J E (1969). *Watsonian Vice-counties of Great Britain.* Ray Society, London.

Davies, P, Davies, J and Huxley, A (1983). *Wild Orchids of Britain and Europe.* Chatto & Windus, London.

Dony, J G, Jury, S L and Perring, F H (1986). *English Names of Wild Flowers,* 2nd ed. Botanical Society of the British Isles, London.

Edees, E S and Newton, A N (1988). *Brambles of the British Isles.* Ray Society, London.

Foley, M J Y (1990). The current distribution and abundance of *Orchis ustulata* L. in southern England. *Watsonia,* 18: 37-48.

Goriup, P D (1978). *Aquatic Macrophyte Atlas for Rivers and Streams.* Nature Conservancy Council.

Greenwood, W J (1914). *The Flora of Cirencester and its Neighbourhood.* Cirencester Naturalist and Archaeological Club, Cirencester.

Grigson, G (1987). *The Englishman's Flora.* J M Dent, London.

Grose, D (1957). *The Flora of Wiltshire.* Wiltshire Archaeological and Natural History Society, Devizes.

Holland, S C (1992). *The Black Poplar (Populus nigra) in Gloucestershire.* FWAG.

Holland, S C, Caddick, H M and Dudley-Smith, S S (1985). *Supplement to the Flora of Gloucestershire.* Grenfell Publications, Bristol.

*Holmes, N T H (1979). *A Guide to Identification of Batrachium Ranunculus Species of Great Britain.* Nature Conservancy Council.

*Hubbard, C E (1984). *Grasses,* 3rd ed. Penguin Books, Harmondsworth.

*Hyde, H A, Wade, A E and Harrison, S G (1969). *Welsh Ferns, Club Mosses, Quillworts and Horsetails,* 5th ed. National Museum of Wales, Cardiff.

*Hyde, H A, Wade, A E and Harrison, S G (1978). *Welsh Ferns.* National Museum of Wales, Cardiff.

Jenkinson, M (1991). *Wild Orchids of Dorset.* Orchid Sundries Ltd., Gillingham, Dorset.

Jermy, A C, Arnold, H R, Farrell, L and Perring, F H (1978). *Atlas of Ferns of the British Isles.* Botanical Society of the British Isles, London.

*Jermy, A C and Camus, J (1991). *The Illustrated Field Guide to Ferns and Allied Plants of the British Isles.* Natural History Museum Publications, London.

*Jermy, A C, Chater, A O and David, R W (1982). *Sedges of the British Isles.* BSBI Handbook No. 1. Botanical Society of the British Isles, London.

Kent, D H (1992). *List of Vascular Plants of the British Isles.* Botanical Society of the British Isles, London.

Laurence, R L (1986). *Ophrys apifera* Hudson ssp. *jurana* Ruppert found in Britain. *Watsonia*, **16**: 177-178.

Lewis, G (1982). *Ancient Woodlands Survey Stage Six*. Field Survey in Wiltshire during 1981. Nature Conservancy Council.

Lousley, J E (1950). *Wild Flowers of Chalk and Limestone*. Collins, London.

*Lousley, J E and Kent, D H (1981). *Docks and Knotweeds of the British Isles*. BSBI Handbook No. 3. Botanical Society of the British Isles, London.

Marsden-Jones, E M and Turnbull, W B (1954). *British Knapweeds*. Ray Society, London.

Maton, G (1843). *The Natural History of a Part of the County of Wilts*.

McSweeney, P (1991). *Botanical Survey and Assessment of Chalk Grassland in Wiltshire outside Ministry of Defence Areas 1989-90*. Nature Conservancy Council.

*Meikle, R D (1980). *Willows and Poplars of Great Britain and Ireland*. BSBI Handbook No. 4. Botanical Society of the British Isles, London.

*Mitchell A, (1982). *A Field Guide to the Trees of Britain and Northern Europe*. Collins, London.

Page, C N (1982). *The Ferns of Britain and Ireland*. Cambridge University Press, Cambridge.

Perring, F H (1968). *Critical Supplement to the Atlas of the British Flora*. Botanical Society of the British Isles, London.

Perring, F H and Farrell, L (1983). *British Red Data Books 1. Vascular Plants*, 2nd ed. Royal Society for Nature Conservation, Lincoln.

Perring, F H and Walters, S M (1962). *Atlas of the British Flora*. Botanical Society of the British Isles. E P Publishing Ltd., Wakefield.

*Phillips, R (1980). *Grasses, Ferns, Mosses and Lichens of Great Britain and Ireland*. Pan Books, London.

Preston, J A (1988). *The Flowering Plants of Wilts*. Wiltshire Archaeological and Natural History Society, Devizes.

Proceedings of the BSBI Hieracium Society 1981-85.

Pugsley, H W (1948). *A Prodromus of British Hieracia*, Vol. 54. The Linnean Society, London.

Rackham, O (1986). *The History of the Countryside*. J M Dent, London.

*Rich, T C G (1991). *Crucifers of Great Britain and Ireland*. BSBI Handbook No. 6. Botanical Society of the British Isles, London.

Rich, T G and Rich, M D B (1988). *Plant Crib*. Botanical Society of the British Isles, London.

Riddelsdell, H J, Hedley, G W and Price, W R (1948). *Flora of Gloucestershire*. Chalford House Press, Bristol.

Rodwell, J S (1991/92). *British Plant Communities*, Vols. 1-3. Cambridge University Press, Cambridge.

Roe, R G B (1981). *The Flora of Somerset*. Somerset Archaeological and Natural History Society, Taunton.

Ross-Craig, S (1954). *Drawings of British Plants*. Bell, London.

Salisbury, Sir E (1952). *Downs and Dunes*. Bell, London.

Salisbury, Sir E (1964). *Weeds and Aliens*, 2nd ed. Collins, London.

*Sinker, C A (1975). *A Lateral Key to Common Grasses*. Shropshire Conservation Trust.

Skinner, A and Wild, L (1986). *Botanical Survey of Ancient Woodland in Wiltshire 1984-85*. Nature Conservancy Council/Wiltshire Trust for Nature Conservation.

Stace, C A (1975). *Hybridization and the Flora of the British Isles*. Academic Press, London.

Stace, C A (1991). *New Flora of the British Isles*. Cambridge University Press, Cambridge.

Stearn, L F (1975). *Supplement to the Flora of Wiltshire*. Wiltshire Archaeological and Natural History Society, Devizes.

Summerhayes, V S (1968). *Wild Orchids of Britain*, 2nd ed. Collins, London.

*Tutin, T G (1980). *Umbellifers of the British Isles*. BSBI Handbook No. 2. Botanical Society of the British Isles, London.

*Wiggington, N J and Graham, G G (1981). *Guide to the Identification of Some Difficult Plant Groups*. Nature Conservancy Council.

*Wild Flower Society (1990). *A Guide to Some Difficult Plants*. Wild Flower Society.

Wolley-Dod, A H (1931). A revision of the British roses. *Journal of Botany*.

INDEX OF SPECIES

Page numbers in heavy type refer to species descriptions in Part Three, italics colour plates.

381